**Peter R. March &
Howard J. Curtis**

Ian Allan
PUBLISHING

Contents

Photographs by Peter R. March (PRM) unless otherwise credited

This twenty-fourth edition published 2003

ISBN 0 7110 2937 7

Published by Ian Allan Publishing

an imprint of Ian Allan Publishing Ltd, Hersham, Surrey KT12 4RG.
Printed by Ian Allan Printing Ltd, Hersham, Surrey KT12 4RG
Code: 0303/F

Front cover: A trio of Eurofighter Typhoons - all black ZH588 (DA2), two-seat ZH590 (DA4) along
with EADS Manching's 98+29. *BAE Systems*

Back cover: General Dynamics F-16A J-016 in service with the Royal Netherlands Air Force's
Teamwork display team. *PRM*

This twenty-fourth annual edition of the *abc Military Aircraft Markings*, jointly edited by Peter R. March and Howard J Curtis, lists in alphabetical and numerical order all of the aircraft that carry a United Kingdom military serial, and **which are based, or might be seen, in the UK**. It also includes airworthy and current RAF/RN/Army aircraft that are based permanently or temporarily overseas. The term *aircraft* used here covers powered, manned aeroplanes, helicopters, airships and gliders. Included are all the current Royal Air Force, Royal Navy, Army Air Corps, Defence Procurement Agency, QinetiQ operated, manufacturers' test aircraft and civilian-owned aircraft with military markings.

Aircraft withdrawn from operational use but which are retained in the UK for ground training purposes or otherwise preserved by the Services and in the numerous museums and collections are listed. The serials of some incomplete aircraft have been included, such as the cockpit sections of machines displayed by the RAF, aircraft used by airfield fire sections and for service battle damage repair training (BDRT), together with significant parts of aircraft held by preservation groups and societies. Where only part of the aircraft fuselage remains the abbreviation <ff> for front fuselage/cockpit section or <rf> for rear fuselage is shown after the type. Many of these aircraft are allocated, and sometimes wear, a secondary identity, such as an RAF 'M' maintenance number. These numbers are listed against those aircraft to which they have been allocated.

A serial 'missing' from a sequence is either because it has never issued as it formed part of a 'blackout block' or because the aircraft is written off, scrapped, sold abroad or allocated an alternative marking. Aircraft used as targets on MoD ranges to which access is restricted, and un-manned target drones, are generally omitted, as are UK military aircraft that have been permanently grounded and are based overseas and unlikely to return to Britain.

In the main, the serials listed are those markings presently displayed on the aircraft. Where an aircraft carries a false serial it is quoted in *italic type*. Very often these serials are carried by replicas, that are denoted by <R> after the type. The manufacturer and aircraft type are given, together with recent alternative, previous, secondary or civil identity shown in round brackets. Complete records of multiple previous identities are only included where space permits. The operating unit and its based location, along with any known unit and base code markings in square brackets, are given as accurately as possible. The unit markings are normally carried boldly on the sides of the fuselage or on the aircraft's fin. In the case of RAF and AAC machines currently in service, they are usually one or two letters or numbers, while the RN continues to use a well-established system of three-figure codes between 000 and 999 together with a fin letter code denoting the aircraft's operational base. RN squadrons, units and bases are allocated blocks of numbers from which individual aircraft codes are issued. To help identification of RN bases and landing platforms on ships, a list of tail-letter codes with their appropriate name, helicopter code number, ship pennant number and type of vessel, is included; as is a helicopter code number/ships' tail-letter code grid cross-reference.

Codes change, for example when aircraft move between units, and therefore the markings currently painted on a particular aircraft might not be those shown in this edition because of subsequent events. Aircraft currently under manufacture or not yet delivered to the Service, such as Westland WAH-64 Apaches at Yeovil and Eurofighter Typhoons etc are listed under their allocated serial number. Likewise there are a number of newly built aircraft for overseas air arms that carry British serials for their UK and delivery flights. The four C-17 Globemasters leased from the US government unusually carry out-of-sequence serials ZZ171-ZZ174. Those airframes which may not appear in the next edition because of sale, accident, etc, have their fates, where known, given in italic type in the *locations* column.

The Irish Army Air Corps fleet is listed, together with the serials of other overseas air arms whose aircraft might be seen visiting the UK from time to time. The serial numbers are as usually presented on the individual machine or as they are normally identified. Where possible, the aircraft's base and operating unit have been shown.

USAF, US Army and US Navy aircraft based in the UK and in Western Europe, and types that regularly visit the UK from the USA, are each listed in separate sections by aircraft type. The serial number actually displayed on the aircraft is shown in full, with additional Fiscal Year (FY) or full serial information also provided. Where appropriate, details of the operating wing, squadron allocation and base are added. The USAF is, like the RAF, in a continuing period of change, resulting in the adoption of new unit titles, squadron and equipment changes and the closure of bases. Only details that concern changes effected by January 2003 are shown.

Veteran and vintage aircraft which carry overseas military markings but which are based in the UK or regularly visit from mainland Europe, have been separately listed showing their principal means of identification. The growing list of aircraft in government or military service, often under contract to private operating companies, that carry civil registrations has again been included, but in this edition at the end of the respective country.

With the use of the Internet now very well established as a rich source of information, the section listing a selection of military aviation 'world wide web' sites, has again been expanded and up-dated this year. Although only a few of these provide details of aircraft serials and markings, they do give interesting insights into air arms and their operating units, aircraft, museums and a broad range of associated topics.

Information shown is believed to be correct at 31 January 2003, and significant changes can be monitored through the monthly 'Military Markings' and 'Vintage Serials' columns in *Aircraft Illustrated* and for Internet up-dates the 'Airnet' column.

Acknowledgements

The compilers wish to thank the many people who have taken trouble to send comments, additions, deletions and other useful information following the publication of the previous edition of *abc Military Aircraft Markings*. In particular the following individuals: Dave Albrecht, Alan Allen, Bob Archer, Mark Ayton, Allan Barley, Gordon Bartley, Mick Boulanger, Peter Budden, Damien Burke, Chris Busby, Phil Butler, John Caie, Glyn Coney, Duncan Curtis, John Curtis, Mike Draper, Bob Dunn, Ben Dunnell, Wal Gandy, Dave Haines, John Heard, Peter Holzer, Geoff Hooper, Lee Howard, Stephen Huckvale, Tim Jones, Peter Kesselaar, Paul Kirby, Iain Logan, Dan March, Andy Marden, Bernard Martin, Rod Martins, Tom McGhee, Vincent van der Meer, Tom Meikle, Julian Moody, Coert Munk, Andrew Nottage, Robyn Polderman, Martin Pole, Doug Pritchard, Mark Ray, Brian C. Rogers, Kev Slade, Kev Storer, David Stretton, Steve Sutcliffe, Martyn Swann, Mervyn Thomas, Andy Thomson, Chris Wagstaff, Lee Weston, Alan Wright, Ian Woodcock, Marc Young.

This compilation has also relied heavily on the publications and aviation groups and societies as follows: Aerodata Quantum+, Air-Britain Information Exchange, Air-Britain Digest, Air-Britain News, Graham Gaff/East London Aviation Society, Military Aviation Review, Military Spotter's Forum, NAMAR e-mail Group, P-3 Orion Research Group, St Athan Aviation Group, SAAB Viggen E-mail group, Scramble, Touchdown Tours E-mail group, Wolverhampton Aviation Group and the World Wide Web.

PRM & HJC   **January 2003**

An original RAF SE5a, F938 is on display at the RAF Museum. *PRM*

Abbreviations

AAC	Army Air Corps
AACS	Airborne Air Control Squadron
AACTS	Airborne Air Control Training Squadron
AAS	Aeromedical Airlift Squadron
ABS	Air Base Squadron
ACC	Air Combat Command
ACCGS	Air Cadets Central Gliding School
ACCS	Airborne Command and Control Squadron
ACW	Air Control Wing
AD&StA	Aberdeen, Dundee & St Andrews
AEF	Air Experience Flight
AESS	Air Engineering & Survival School
AEW	Airborne Early Warning
AF	Arméflyget (Army Air Battalion)
AFB	Air Force Base
AFD	Air Fleet Department
AFRC	Air Force Reserve Command
AFSC	Air Force Systems Command
AFSK	Armeflygskolan (Army Flying School)
AFWF	Advanced Fixed Wing Flight
AG	Airlift Group
AGA	Academia General del Aire (General Air Academy)
AkG	Aufklärüngsgeschwader (Reconnaissance Wing)
AMC	Air Mobility Command
AMD-BA	Avions Marcel Dassault-Breguet Aviation
AMF	Aircraft Maintenance Flight
AMG	Aircraft Maintenance Group
AMIF	Aircraft Maintenance Instruction Flight
AMS	Air Movements School
AMW	Air Mobility Wing
ANG	Air National Guard
APS	Aircraft Preservation Society
ARS	Air Refuelling Squadron
ARW	Air Refuelling Wing
ARWS	Advanced Rotary Wing Squadron
AS	Airlift Squadron/Air Squadron
ASCW	Airborne Surveillance Control Wing
ASF	Aircraft Servicing Flight
AS&RU	Aircraft Salvage and Repair Unit
ATC	Air Training Corps
ATCC	Air Traffic Control Centre
AVDEF	Aviation Defence Service
Avn	Aviation
Avn Co	Aviation Company
AW	Airlift Wing/Armstrong Whitworth Aircraft
AWC	Air Warfare Centre
BAC	British Aircraft Corporation
BAe	British Aerospace PLC
BAPC	British Aviation Preservation Council
BATSUB	British Army Training Support Unit Belize
BATUS	British Army Training Unit Suffield
BBMF	Battle of Britain Memorial Flight
BDRF	Battle Damage Repair Flight
BDRT	Battle Damage Repair Training
Be	Beech
Bf	Bayerische Flugzeugwerke
BFWF	Basic Fixed Wing Flight
BG	Bomber Group
BGA	British Gliding & Soaring Association
bk	black (squadron colours and markings)
bl	blue (squadron colours and markings)
BNFL	British Nuclear Fuels Ltd
BnHAtk	Helicopter Attack Battalion
BnHLn	Liaison Battalion
BP	Boulton & Paul
br	brown (squadron colours and markings)
BS	Bomber Squadron
B-V	Boeing-Vertol
BW	Bomber Wing
CAARP	Co-operative des Ateliers Air de la Région Parisienne
CAC	Commonwealth Aircraft Corporation
CAM	College of Aviation Medicine
CARG	Cotswold Aircraft Restoration Group

CASA	Construcciones Aeronauticas SA
Cav	Cavalry
CC	County Council
CCF	Combined Cadet Force/Canadian Car & Foundry Company
CDE	Chemical Defence Establishment
CEAM	Centre d'Expérimentation Aériennes Militaires (Military Air Experimental Centre)
CEPA	Centre d'Expérimentation Pratique de l'Aéronautique Navale
CEV	Centre d'Essais en Vol (Flight Test Centre)
CFS	Central Flying School
CGMF	Central Glider Maintenance Flight
CIFAS	Centre d'Instruction des Forces Aériennes Stratégiques (Air Strategic Training Centre)
CinC	Commander in Chief
CinCLANT	Commander in Chief Atlantic
CITac	Centre d'Instruction Tactique (Tactical Training Centre)
Co	Company
Comp	Composite with
CT	College of Technology
CTE	Central Training Establishment
CV	Chance-Vought
D-BA	Daimler-Benz Aerospace
D-BD	Dassault-Breguet Dornier
D&G	Dumfries and Galloway
DARA	Defence Aviation Repair Agency
DEODS	Defence Explosives Ordnance Disposal School
DERA	Defence Evaluation and Research Agency
Det	Detachment
DH	de Havilland
DHC	de Havilland Canada
DHFS	Defence Helicopter Flying School
DLMW	Dywizjon Lotniczy Marynarki Wojennej
dlt	dopravni letka (Transport Squadron)
DPA	Defence Procurement Agency
DS&TL	Defence Science & Technology Laboratory
DTI	Department of Trade and Industry
EA	Escadron Aérien (Air Squadron)
EAAT	Escadrille Avions de l'Armée de Terre
EAC	Ecole de l'Aviation de Chasse (Fighter Aviation School)
EAP	European Aircraft Project
EAT	Ecole de l'Aviation de Transport (Transport Aviation School)
EC	Escadre de Chasse (Fighter Wing)
ECM	Electronic Counter Measures
ECS	Electronic Countermeasures Squadron
EDA	Escadre de Detection Aéroportée (Air Detection Wing)
EdC	Escadron de Convoyage
EDCA	Escadron de Détection et de Control Aéroportée (Airborne Detection & Control Sqn)
EE	English Electric/Escadrille Electronique
EET	Escadron Electronique Tactique (Tactical Electronics Flight)
EH	Escadron d'Helicoptères (Helicopter Flight)
EHI	European Helicopter Industries
EKW	Eidgenössiches Konstruktionswerkstätte
EL	Escadre de Liaison (Liaison Wing)
ELT	Eskadra Lotnictwa Taktycznego (Tactical Air Squadron)
ELTR	Eskadra Lotnictwa Transportowego (Air Transport Squadron)
EMA	East Midlands Airport
EMVO	Elementaire Militaire Vlieg Opleiding (Elementary Flying Training)
ENOSA	Ecole des Navigateurs Operationales Systemes d'Armees (Navigation School)
EoN	Elliot's of Newbury
EPAA	Ecole de Pilotage Elementaire de l'Armée de l'Air (Air Force Elementary Flying School)

EPE	Ecole de Pilotage Elementaire (Elementary Flying School)
EPNER	Ecole du Personnel Navigant d'Essais et de Reception
EPTT	Exhibition, Production & Transportation Team
ER	Escadre de Reconnaissance (Reconnaissance Wing)
ERS	Escadron de Reconnaissance Stratégique (Strategic Reconnaissance Squadron)
ERV	Escadre de Ravitaillement en Vol (Air Refuelling Wing)
ES	Escadrille de Servitude
Esc	Escuadron (Squadron)
Esk	Eskadrille (Squadron)
Eslla	Escuadrilla (Squadron)
Esq	Esquadra (Squadron)
ET	Escadre de Transport (Transport Squadron)
ETE	Escadron de Transport et Entrainment (Transport Training Squadron)
ETEC	Escadron de Transport d'Entrainement et de Calibration (Transport Training & Calibration Sqn)
ETL	Escadron de Transport Légère (Light Transport Squadron)
ETO	Escadron de Transition Operationnelle
ETOM	Escadron de Transport Outre Mer (Overseas Transport Squadron)
ETPS	Empire Test Pilots' School
ETS	Engineering Training School
FAA	Fleet Air Arm/Federal Aviation Administration
FACF	Forward Air Control Flight
FBS	Flugbereitschaftstaffel
FBW	Fly by wire
FC	Forskokcentralen (Flight Centre)
FE	Further Education
FETC	Fire and Emergency Training Centre
ff	Front fuselage
FG	Fighter Group
FH	Fairchild-Hiller
FI	Falkland Islands
FISt	Flieger Staffel (Flight Squadron)
Flt	Flight
FMA	Fabrica Militar de Aviones
FMT	Flotila Militara de Transport (Transport Regiment)
FMV	Forsvarets Materielwerk
FOMA	Flag Officer Maritime Aviation
FRADU	Fleet Requirements and Air Direction Unit
FRA	FR Aviation
FS	Fighter Squadron
FSAIU	Flight Safety & Accident Investigation Unit
FSCTE	Fire Services Central Training Establishment
FTS	Flying Training School
FTW	Flying Training Wing
Fw	Focke Wulf
FW	Fighter Wing/Foster Wickner
FWTS	Fixed Wing Test Squadron
FY	Fiscal Year
F3 OCU	Tornado F3 Operational Conversion Unit
GAF	Government Aircraft Factory
GAL	General Aircraft Ltd
GAM	Groupe Aerien Mixte (Composite Air Group)
gd	gold (squadron colours and markings)
GD	General Dynamics
GHL	Groupe d'Helicopteres Legeres (Light Helicopter Group)
GI	Ground Instruction/Groupement d'Instruction (Instructional Group)
gn	green (squadron colours and markings)
GRD	Gruppe fur Rustunggdienste (Group for Service Preparation)
GT	Grupo de Transporte (Transport Wing)
GTT	Grupo de Transporte de Tropos (Troop Carrier Wing)
gy	grey (squadron colours and markings)
H&W	Hereford and Worcester
HAF	Historic Aircraft Flight
HC	Helicopter Combat Support Squadron
HCS	Hunting Contract Services
HF	Historic Flying Ltd
HFR	Heeresfliegerregiment (Army Air Regiment)
HFS	Heeresfliegerverbindungs-und Aufklärungsstaffel
HFVS	Heeresfliegerversuchstaffel
HFWS	Heeresflieger Waffenschule (Army Air Weapons School)
Hkp.Bat	Helikopter Bataljon (Helicopter Battalion)
HMA	Helicopter Maritime Attack
HMF	Harrier Maintenance Flight/Helicopter Maintenance Flight
HMS	Her Majesty's Ship
HOCU	Harrier OCU
HP	Handley-Page
HQ	Headquarters
HRO	Harcàszati Repülö Ezred
HS	Hawker Siddeley
HSF	Harrier Servicing Flight
IAF	Israeli Air Force
INTA	Instituto Nacional de Tecnica Aerospacial
IOW	Isle Of Wight
IWM	Imperial War Museum
JATE	Joint Air Transport Establishment
JbG	Jagdbombergeschwader (Fighter Bomber Wing)
JEFTS	Joint Elementary Flying Training School
JFACSTU	Joint Forward Air Control Students Training Unit
JG	Jagdgeschwader (Fighter Wing)
Kridlo	Wing
Letka	Squadron
ltBVr	letka Bitevnich Vrtulníkù (Attack Helicopter Squadron)
LTG	Lufttransportgeschwader (Air Transport Wing)
LTV	Ling-Temco-Vought
LVG	Luftwaffen Versorgungs Geschwader (Air Force Maintenance Wing)/Luft Verkehrs Gesellschaft
LZO	Letecky Zku ební Odbor (Aviation Test Department)
m	multi-coloured (squadron colours and markings)
MAPK	Mira Anachestisis Pantos Kerou (All Weather Interception Sqn)
MARPAT	Maritime Patrouillegroep (Maritime Patrol Group)
MASU	Mobile Aircraft Support Unit
MBB	Messerschmitt Bolkow-Blohm
MCAS	Marine Corps Air Station
McD	McDonnell Douglas
Med	Medical
MFG	Marine Flieger Geschwader (Naval Air Wing)
MH	Max Holste
MIB	Military Intelligence Battalion
MiG	Mikoyan – Gurevich
Mod	Modified
MR	Maritime Reconnaissance
MRF	Meteorological Research Flight
MS	Morane-Saulnier
MTM	Mira Taktikis Metaforon (Tactical Transport Sqn)
MU	Maintenance Unit
Mus'm	Museum
NA	North American
NACDS	Naval Air Command Driving School
NAEWF	NATO Airborne Early Warning Force
NAF	Naval Air Facility
NAS	Naval Air Station
NASU	Naval Air Support Unit
NATO	North Atlantic Treaty Organisation
NAWC	Naval Air Warfare Center
NAWC-AD	Naval Air Warfare Center Aircraft Division
NBC	Nuclear, Biological and Chemical
NE	North-East
NFATS	Naval Force Aircraft Test Squadron
NI	Northern Ireland
NMSU	Nimrod Major Servicing Unit
NYARC	North Yorks Aircraft Restoration Centre
OCU	Operational Conversion Unit
OEU	Operation Evaluation Unit

OFMC	Old Flying Machine Company
OGMA	Oficinas Gerais de Material Aeronautico
or	orange (squadron colours and markings)
OSAC	Operational Support Airlift Command
OVH Kmp	Observations-Helicopter Kompagni
PASF	Puma Aircraft Servicing Flight
PAT	Priority Air Transport Detachment
PBN	Pilatus Britten-Norman
PLM	Pulk Lotnictwa Mysliwskiego (Fighter Regiment)
pr	purple (squadron colours and markings)
PRU	Photographic Reconnaissance Unit
PVH Kmp	Panservaerns-Helicopter Kompagni
pzdlt	průzkumná dopravni letka (Reconnaissance & Transport Squadron)
r	red (squadron colours and markings)
R	Replica
RAeS	Royal Aeronautical Society
RAF	Royal Aircraft Factory/Royal Air Force
RAFC	Royal Air Force College
RAFM	Royal Air Force Museum
RAFGSA	Royal Air Force Gliding and Soaring Association
RCAF	Royal Canadian Air Force
RE	Royal Engineers
Regt	Regiment
REME	Royal Electrical & Mechanical Engineers
rf	Rear fuselage
RFA	Royal Fleet Auxiliary
RJAF	Royal Jordanian Air Force
RM	Royal Marines
RMB	Royal Marines Base
RMC of S	Royal Military College of Science
RN	Royal Navy
RNAS	Royal Naval Air Station
RNAW	Royal Naval Aircraft Workshop
RNAY	Royal Naval Aircraft Yard
RNGSA	Royal Navy Gliding and Soaring Association
ROF	Royal Ordnance Factory
RQS	Rescue Squadron
R-R	Rolls-Royce
RS	Reid & Sigrist/Reconnaissance Squadron
RSV	Reparto Sperimentale Volo (Experimental Flight School)
RW	Reconnaissance Wing
SA	Scottish Aviation
SAAB	Svenska Aeroplan Aktieboleg
SAH	School of Air Handling
SAL	Scottish Aviation Limited
SAOEU	Strike/Attack Operational Evaluation Unit
SAR	Search and Rescue
Saro	Saunders-Roe
SARTU	Search and Rescue Training Unit
SBoLK	Stíhacie Bombardovacie Letecké Kridlo (Fighter Bomber Air Wing)
SCW	Strategic Communications Wing
SEAE	School of Electrical & Aeronautical Engineering
SEPECAT	Société Européenne de Production de l'avion Ecole de Combat et d'Appui Tactique
SFDO	School of Flight Deck Operations
SHAPE	Supreme Headquarters Allied Forces Europe
si	silver (squadron colours and markings)
SIET	Section d'Instruction et d'Etude du Tir
SKTU	Sea King Training Unit
Skv	Skvadron (Squadron)
SLK	Stíhacie Letecké Kridlo (Fighter Air Wing)
slt	stíhací letka (Fighter Squadron)
SLV	School Licht Vliegwezen (Flying School)
Sm	Smaldeel (Squadron)
SNCAN	Société Nationale de Constructions Aéronautiques du Nord
SOES	Station Operations & Engineering Squadron
SOG	Special Operations Group
SOS	Special Operations Squadron
SoTT	School of Technical Training
SOW	Special Operations Wing
SPAD	Société Pour les Appareils Deperdussin
SPP	Strojirny Prvni Petilesky
Sqn	Squadron
SSF	Station Servicing Flight
SWWAPS	Second World War Aircraft Preservation Society
TA	Territorial Army
TAP	Transporten Avio Polk (Air Transport Regiment)
T&EE	Test & Evaluation Establishment
TFC	The Fighter Collection
TGp	Test Groep
TIARA	Tornado Integrated Avionics Research Aircraft
tlt	taktická letka (Tactical Squadron)
TMF	Tornado Maintenance Flight
TMTS	Trade Management Training School
tpzlt	taktická a průzkumná letka (Tactical & Reconnaissance Squadron)
TS	Test Squadron
TsAGI	Tsentral'ny Aerogidrodinamicheski Instut (Central Aero & Hydrodynamics Institute)
TsLw	Technische Schule der Luftwaffe (Luftwaffe Technical School)
TSW	Tactical Supply Wing
TW	Test Wing
UAS	University Air Squadron
Uberwg	Uberwachunggeschwader (Surveillance Wing)
UK	United Kingdom
UKAEA	United Kingdom Atomic Energy Authority
UNFICYP	United Nations' Forces in Cyprus
US	United States
USAF	United States Air Force
USAFE	United States Air Forces in Europe
USAREUR	US Army Europe
USCGS	US Coast Guard Station
USEUCOM	United States European Command
USMC	United States Marine Corps
USN	United States Navy
USNWTSPM	United States Navy Test Pilots School
VAAC	Vectored thrust Advanced Aircraft flight Control
VFW	Vereinigte Flugtechnische Werke
VGS	Volunteer Gliding School
vlt	vycviková letka (Training Squadron)
VMGR	Marine Aerial Refuelling/Transport Squadron
VMGRT	Marine Aerial Refuelling/Transport Training Squadron
VQ	Fleet Air Reconnaissance Squadron
VR	Fleet Logistic Support Squadron
VS	Vickers-Supermarine
VSD	Vegyes Szàllitorepülő Dandàr (Aircraft Transport Brigade)
VSL	Vycvikové Stredisko Letectva (Flying Training Centre)
w	white (squadron colours and markings)
Wg	Wing
WHL	Westland Helicopters Ltd
WLT	Weapons Loading Training
WRS	Weather Reconnaissance Squadron
WS	Westland
WSK	Wytwornia Sprzetu Kominikacyjnego
WTD	Wehrtechnische Dienstelle (Technical Support Unit)
WW2	World War II
y	yellow (squadron colours and markings)
zDL	základna Dopravnìho Letectva (Air Transport Base)
ZmDK	Zmie any Dopravny Kridlo (Mixed Transport Wing)
zSL	základna Speciálního Letectva (Training Air Base)
zTL	základna Taktického Letectva (Tactical Air Base)
zVrL	základna Vrtulníkového Letectva (Helicopter Air Base)

A Guide to the Location of Operational Military Bases in the UK

This section is to assist the reader to locate the places in the United Kingdom where operational military aircraft are based. The term *aircraft* also includes helicopters and gliders.

The alphabetical order listing gives each location in relation to its county and to its nearest classified road(s) (*by* means adjoining; *of* means proximate to), together with its approximate direction and mileage from the centre of a nearby major town or city. Some civil airports are included where active military units are also based, but **excluded** are MoD sites with non-operational aircraft (eg *gate guardians*), the bases of privately-owned civil aircraft that wear military markings and museums.

User	Base name	County/Region	Location	Distance/direction from (town)
QinetiQ	Aberporth	Dyfed	N of A487	6m ENE of Cardigan
Army	Abingdon	Oxfordshire	W by B4017, W of A34	5m SSW of Oxford
RAF	Aldergrove/Belfast Airport	Co Antrim	W by A26	13m W of Belfast
RM	Arbroath	Angus	E of A933	2m NW of Arbroath
RAF/HCS	Barkston Heath	Lincolnshire	W by B6404, S of A153	5m NNE of Grantham
RAF	Benson	Oxfordshire	E by A423	1m NE of Wallingford
QinetiQ/ RAF	Boscombe Down	Wiltshire	S by A303, W of A338	6m N of Salisbury
RAF	Boulmer	Northumberland	E of B1339	4m E of Alnwick
RAF	Brize Norton	Oxfordshire	W of A4095	5m SW of Witney
Marshall	Cambridge Airport/ Teversham	Cambridgeshire	S by A1303	2m E of Cambridge
RM/RAF	Chivenor	Devon	S of A361	4m WNW of Barnstaple
RAF	Church Fenton	Yorkshire North	S of B1223	7m WNW of Selby
RAF	Colerne	Wiltshire	S of A420, E of Fosse Way	5m NE of Bath
RAF	Coltishall	Norfolk	W of B1150	9m NNE of Norwich
RAF	Coningsby	Lincolnshire	S of A153, W by B1192	10m NW of Boston
RAF	Cosford	Shropshire	W of A41, N of A464	9m WNW of Wolverhampton
RAF	Cottesmore	Rutland	W of A1, N of B668	9m NW of Stamford
RAF	Cranwell	Lincolnshire	N by A17, S by B1429	5m WNW of Sleaford
RN	Culdrose	Cornwall	E by A3083	1m SE of Helston
Army	Dishforth	Yorkshire North	E by A1	4m E of Ripon
USAF	Fairford	Gloucestershire	S of A417	9m ESE of Cirencester
RN	Fleetlands	Hampshire	E by A32	2m SE of Fareham
RAF	Glasgow Airport	Strathclyde	N by M8 jn 28	7m W of city
RAF	Halton	Buckinghamshire	N of A4011, S of B4544	4m ESE of Aylesbury
RAF	Henlow	Bedfordshire	E of A600, W of A6001	1m SW of Henlow
RAF	Honington	Suffolk	E of A134, W of A1088	6m S of Thetford
Army	Hullavington	Wiltshire	W of A429	1m N of M4 jn 17
RAF	Kenley	Greater London	W of A22	1m W of Warlingham
RAF	Kinloss	Grampian	E of B9011, N of B9089	3m NE of Forres
RAF	Kirknewton	Lothian	E by B7031, N by A70	8m SW of Edinburgh
USAF	Lakenheath	Suffolk	W by A1065	8m W of Thetford
RAF	Leeming	Yorkshire North	E by A1	5m SW of Northallerton
RAF	Leuchars	Fife	E of A919	7m SE of Dundee
RAF	Linton-on-Ouse	Yorkshire North	E of B6265	10m NW of York
QinetiQ	Llanbedr	Gwynedd	W of A496	7m NNW of Barmouth
RAF	Lossiemouth	Grampian	W of B9135, S of B9040	4m N of Elgin
RAF	Lyneham	Wiltshire	W of A3102, S of A420	10m WSW of Swindon
RAF	Marham	Norfolk	N by A1122	6m W of Swaffham
Army	Middle Wallop	Hampshire	S by A343	6m SW of Andover
USAF	Mildenhall	Suffolk	S by A1101	9m NNE of Newmarket
RAF	Northolt	Greater London	N by A40	3m E of M40 jn 1
RAF	Odiham	Hampshire	E of A32	2m S of M3 jn 5
RN	Predannack	Cornwall	W by A3083	7m S of Helston
RAF	St Athan	South Glamorgan	N of B4265	13m WSW of Cardiff
RAF	St Mawgan/Newquay	Cornwall	N of A3059	4m ENE of Newquay
RAF	Scampton	Lincolnshire	W by A15	6m N of Lincoln
RAF	Sealand	Flint	W by A550	6m WNW of Chester
RAF	Shawbury	Shropshire	W of B5063	7m NNE of Shrewsbury
RAF	Syerston	Nottinghamshire	W by A46	5m SW of Newark
RAF	Ternhill	Shropshire	SW by A41	3m SW of Market Drayton

User	Base name	County/Region	Location	Distance/direction from (town)
RAF/ Army	Topcliffe	Yorkshire North	E of A167, W of A168	3m SW of Thirsk
RAF	Valley	Gwynedd	S of A5 on Anglesey	5m SE of Holyhead
RAF	Waddington	Lincolnshire	E by A607, W by A15	5m S of Lincoln
Army/ RAF	Wattisham	Suffolk	N of B1078	5m SSW of Stowmarket
RAF	Weston-on-the-Green	Oxfordshire	E by A43	9m N of Oxford
RAF	Wittering	Cambridgeshire	W by A1, N of A47	3m S of Stamford
RAF	Woodvale	Merseyside	W by A565	5m SSW of Southport
RAF	Wyton	Cambridgeshire	E of A141, N of B1090	3m NE of Huntingdon
RN	Yeovilton	Somerset	S by B3151, S of A303	5m N of Yeovil

Returned after loan to Spain, the Avro Rota K4232 is back at the RAFM, Hendon. *PRM*

This Fairey Swordfish II W5856 is flown by the RN Historic Flight from Yeovilton. *PRM*

British Military Aircraft Serials

The Committee of Imperial Defence through its Air Committee introduced a standardised system of numbering aircraft in November 1912. The Air Department of the Admiralty was allocated the first batch 1-200 and used these to cover aircraft already in use and those on order. The Army was issued with the next block from 201-800, which included the number 304 which was given to the Cody Biplane now preserved in the Science Museum. By the outbreak of World War 1 the Royal Navy was on its second batch of serials 801-1600 and this system continued with alternating allocations between the Army and Navy until 1916 when number 10000, a Royal Flying Corps BE2C, was reached.

It was decided not to continue with five digit numbers but instead to start again from 1, prefixing RFC aircraft with the letter A and RNAS aircraft with the prefix N. The RFC allocations commenced with A1 an FE2D and before the end of the year had reached A9999 an Armstrong Whitworth FK8. The next group commenced with B1 and continued in logical sequence through the C, D, E and F prefixes. G was used on a limited basis to identify captured German aircraft, while H was the last block of wartime-ordered aircraft. To avoid confusion I was not used, so the new postwar machines were allocated serials in the J range. A further minor change was made in the serial numbering system in August 1929 when it was decided to maintain four numerals after the prefix letter, thus omitting numbers 1 to 999. The new K series therefore commenced at K1000, which was allocated to an AW Atlas.

The Naval N prefix was not used in such a logical way. Blocks of numbers were allocated for specific types of aircraft such as seaplanes or flying-boats. By the late 1920s the sequence had largely been used up and a new series using the prefix S was commenced. In 1930 separate naval allocations were stopped and subsequent serials were issued in the 'military' range which had by this time reached the K series. A further change in the pattern of allocations came in the L range. Commencing with L7272 numbers were issued in blocks with smaller blocks of serials between not used. These were known as blackout blocks. As M had already been used as a suffix for Maintenance Command instructional airframes it was not used as a prefix. Although N had previously been used for naval aircraft it was used again for serials allocated from 1937.

With the build-up to World War 2 the rate of allocations quickly accelerated and the prefix R was being used when war was declared. The letters O and Q were not allotted, and nor was S which had been used up to S1865 for naval aircraft before integration into the RAF series. By 1940 the serial Z9999 had been reached, as part of a blackout block, with the letters U and Y not used to avoid confusion. The option to recommence serial allocation at A1000 was not taken up; instead it was decided to use an alphabetical two-letter prefix with three numerals running from 100 to 999. Thus AA100 was allocated to a Blenheim IV.

This two-letter, three-numeral serial system which started in 1940 continues today. The letters C, I, O, Q, U and Y were, with the exception of NC, not used. For various reasons the following letter combinations were not issued: DA, DB, DH, EA, GA to GZ, HA, HT, JE, JH, JJ, KR to KT, MR, NW, NZ, SA to SK, SV, TN, TR and VE. The first postwar serials issued were in the VP range while the end of the WZs had been reached by the Korean War. The current new issues are in the latter part of the ZJ range and there are now no blackout blocks of unallocated serials. This being so, and at the current rate of issue, the Z range will last for many years. Occasionally an 'out-of-sequence' serial is issued to a manufacturer's prototype or development aircraft viz ZK101 and ZT800. However, a break in the established sequence has come with the four Boeing C-17 Globemasters leased from Boeing, that carry the serials ZZ171-ZZ174.

Note: Whilst every effort has been made to ensure the accuracy of this publication, no part of the contents has been obtained from official sources. The compilers will be pleased to receive comments, corrections and further information for inclusion in subsequent editions of *Military Aircraft Markings* and the monthly up-date of additions and amendments that is published in *Aircraft Illustrated*. Please send your information to Military Aircraft Markings, PO Box 46, Westbury-on-Trym, Bristol BS9 1TF; fax to 0117 968 3928 or e-mail to HJCurtis@ntlworld.com

British Military Aircraft Markings

A serial in *italics* denotes that it is not the genuine marking for that airframe.

Serial	Type (other identity) [code]	Owner/operator, location or fate	Notes
168	Sopwith Tabloid Scout <R> (G-BFDE)	RAF Museum, Hendon	
304	Cody Biplane (BAPC 62)	Science Museum, South Kensington	
687	RAF BE2b <R> (BAPC 181)	RAF Museum, Hendon	
1701	RAF BE2c <R> (BAPC 117)	Privately owned, Orpington	
2345	Vickers FB5 Gunbus <R> (G-ATVP)	RAF Museum, Hendon	
2699	RAF BE2c	Imperial War Museum, Lambeth	
3066	Caudron GIII (G-AETA/9203M)	RAF Museum, Hendon	
5964	DH2 <R> (BAPC 112)	Privately owned, Stretton on Dunsmore	
5964	DH2 <R> (G-BFVH)	Privately owned, Withybush	
6232	RAF BE2c <R> (BAPC 41)	Yorkshire Air Museum, stored Elvington	
8359	Short 184 <ff>	FAA Museum, RNAS Yeovilton	
A301	Morane BB (frame)	RAF Museum Restoration Centre, Cosford	
A1325	RAF BE2e (G-BVGR)	Privately owned, Milden	
A1742	Bristol Scout D <R> (BAPC 38)	Privately owned, Solihull	
A4850	RAF SE5a <R> (BAPC 176)	Bygone Times Antique Warehouse, Ecclestone, Lancs	
A7317	Sopwith Pup <R> (BAPC 179)	Midland Air Museum, Coventry	
A8226	Sopwith 1½ Strutter <R> (G-BIDW)	RAF Museum, Hendon	
B895	RAF SE5a <R> (G-BUOD) [W]	Privately owned, Kemble	
B1807	Sopwith Pup (G-EAVX) [A7]	Privately owned, Keynsham, Avon	
B2458	Sopwith 1F.1 Camel <R> (G-BPOB/*F542*) [R]	Privately owned, Booker	
B3459	Nieuport Scout 17/23 <R> (G-BWMJ) [21]	Privately owned, Fairoaks	
B5539	Sopwith 1F.1 Camel <R>	Privately owned, Booker	
B6401	Sopwith 1F.1 Camel <R> (G-AWYY/C1701)	FAA Museum, RNAS Yeovilton	
B7270	Sopwith 1F.1 Camel <R> (G-BFCZ)	Brooklands Museum, Weybridge	
C1904	RAF SE5a <R> (G-PFAP) [Z]	Privately owned, Syerston	
C3011	Phoenix Currie Super Wot (G-SWOT) [S]	The Real Aeroplane Company, Breighton	
C4451	Avro 504J <R> (BAPC 210)	Southampton Hall of Aviation	
C4918	Bristol M1C <R> (G-BWJM)	The Shuttleworth Collection, Old Warden	
C4940	Bristol M1C <R>	*Currently not known*	
C4994	Bristol M1C <R> (G-BLWM)	RAF Museum, Hendon	
C9533	RAF SE5a <R> (G-BUWE) [M]	Privately owned, Boscombe Down	
D276	RAF SE5a <R> (BAPC 208) [A] Farnborough	Prince's Mead Shopping Centre,	
D3419	Sopwith 1F.1 Camel <R> (*F1921*/BAPC 59)	RAF Museum, Cosford	
D5329	Sopwith 5F.1 Dolphin	RAF Museum Restoration Centre, Cosford	
D5649	Airco DH9	Aero Vintage, Hatch	
D7560	Avro 504K	Science Museum, South Kensington	
D7889	Bristol F2b Fighter (G-AANM/BAPC 166)	Privately owned, Old Warden	
D8084	Bristol F2b Fighter (G-ACAA/F4516) [S]	The Fighter Collection, Duxford	
D8096	Bristol F2b Fighter (G-AEPH) [D]	The Shuttleworth Collection, Old Warden	
D8781	Avro 504K <R> (G-ECKE)	*Sold to New Zealand, September 2002*	
E373	Avro 504K <R> (BAPC 178)	Privately owned,	
E449	Avro 504K (G-EBJE/9205M)	RAF Museum, Hendon	
E2466	Bristol F2b Fighter (BAPC 165) [I]	RAF Museum, Hendon	
E2581	Bristol F2b Fighter [13]	Imperial War Museum, Duxford	
F141	RAF SE5a <R> (G-SEVA) [G]	Privately owned, Boscombe Down	
F235	RAF SE5a <R> (G-BMDB) [B]	Privately owned, Boscombe Down	
F904	RAF SE5a (G-EBIA)	The Shuttleworth Collection, Old Warden	

F938 – L1710

Notes	Serial	Type (other identity) [code]	Owner/operator, location or fate
	F938	RAF SE5a (G-EBIC/9208M)	RAF Museum, Hendon
	F943	RAF SE5a <R> (G-BIHF) [S]	Museum of Army Flying, Middle Wallop
	F943	RAF SE5a <R> (G-BKDT)	Yorkshire Air Museum, Elvington
	F1010	Airco DH9A [C]	RAF Museum, Hendon
	F3556	RAF RE8	Imperial War Museum, Duxford
	F5447	RAF SE5a <R> (G-BKER) [N]	Privately owned, Cumbernauld
	F5459	RAF SE5a <R> (G-INNY) [Y]	Privately owned, Goodwood
	F5475	RAF SE5a <R> (BAPC 250)	Brooklands Museum, Weybridge
	F6314	Sopwith 1F.1 Camel (9206M) [B]	RAF Museum, Hendon
	F8010	RAF SE5a <R> (G-BDWJ) [Z]	Privately owned, Graveley
	F8614	Vickers FB27A Vimy IV <R> (G-AWAU)	RAF Museum, Hendon
	H1968	Avro 504K <R> (BAPC 42)	Yorkshire Air Museum, stored Elvington
	H2311	Avro 504K (G-ABAA)	Gr Manchester Mus of Science & Industry
	H3426	Hawker Hurricane <R> (BAPC 68)	NW Aviation Heritage Group, Hooton Park
	H5199	Avro 504K (BK892/3118M/ G-ACNB/G-ADEV)	The Shuttleworth Collection, Old Warden
	J7326	DH53 Humming Bird (G-EBQP)	Privately owned, Audley End
	J8067	Westland Pterodactyl 1a	Science Museum, South Kensington
	J9941	Hawker Hart 2 (G-ABMR)	RAF Museum, Hendon
	K1786	Hawker Tomtit (G-AFTA)	The Shuttleworth Collection, Old Warden
	K1930	Hawker Fury <R> (G-BKBB/ OO-HFU)	Privately owned, Old Warden
	K2050	Isaacs Fury II (G-ASCM)	Privately owned, Brize Norton
	K2059	Isaacs Fury II (G-PFAR)	Privately owned, Dunkeswell
	K2060	Isaacs Fury II (G-BKZM)	Privately owned, Haverfordwest
	K2075	Isaacs Fury II (G-BEER)	Privately owned,
	K2227	Bristol 105 Bulldog IIA (G-ABBB)	RAF Museum, Hendon
	K2567	DH82A Tiger Moth (DE306/ 7035M/G-MOTH)	Privately owned, Tadlow
	K2572	DH82A Tiger Moth (NM129/ G-AOZH)	Privately owned, Redhill
	K2572	DH82A Tiger Moth <R>	The Aircraft Restoration Company, Duxford
	K2587	DH82A Tiger Moth <R> (G-BJAP)	Privately owned, Shobdon
	K3215	Avro 621 Tutor (G-AHSA)	The Shuttleworth Collection, Old Warden
	K3661	Hawker Nimrod II (G-BURZ)	Aero Vintage, St Leonards-on-Sea
	K3731	Isaacs Fury <R> (G-RODI)	Privately owned, Hailsham
	K4232	Avro 671 Rota I (SE-AZB)	RAF Museum, Hendon
	K4259	DH82A Tiger Moth (G-ANMO) [71]	Privately owned, White Waltham
	K4972	Hawker Hart Trainer IIA (1764M)	RAF Museum, Hendon
	K5054	Supermarine Spitfire <R> (BAPC 190/EN398)	Privately owned, Sevenoaks, Kent
	K5054	Supermarine Spitfire <R> (BAPC 214)	Tangmere Military Aviation Museum
	K5054	Supermarine Spitfire <R> (G-BRDV)	Southampton Hall of Aviation
	K5054	Supermarine Spitfire <R>	Kent Battle of Britain Museum, Hawkinge
	K5414	Hawker Hind (G-AENP/BAPC 78) [XV]	The Shuttleworth Collection, Old Warden
	K5600	Hawker Audax I (2015M/G-BVVI)	Aero Vintage, St Leonards-on-Sea
	K5673	Isaacs Fury II (G-BZAS)	Bournemouth Aviation Museum
	K5673	Hawker Fury I <R> (BAPC 249)	Brooklands Museum, Weybridge
	K6035	Westland Wallace II (2361M)	RAF Museum, Hendon
	K7271	Hawker Fury II <R> (BAPC 148)	Shropshire Wartime Aircraft Recovery Grp Mus, Sleap
	K8042	Gloster Gladiator II (8372M)	RAF Museum, Hendon
	K8203	Hawker Demon I (G-BTVE/2292M)	Demon Displays, Hatch
	K8303	Isaacs Fury II (G-BWWN) [D]	Privately owned, Lower Upham
	K9926	VS300 Spitfire I <R> (BAPC 217) [JH-C]	RAF Bentley Priory, on display
	K9942	VS300 Spitfire I (8383M) [SD-D]	RAF Museum Restoration Centre, Cosford
	K9962	VS300 Spitfire I <R> [JH-C]	Privately owned,
	L1070	VS300 Spitfire I <R> (BAPC 227) [XT-A]	Edinburgh airport, on display
	L1592	Hawker Hurricane I [KW-Z]	Science Museum, South Kensington
	L1679	Hawker Hurricane I <R> (BAPC 241) [JX-G]	Tangmere Military Aviation Museum
	L1710	Hawker Hurricane I <R> (BAPC 219) [AL-D]	RAF Biggin Hill, on display

Serial	Type (other identity) [code]	Owner/operator, location or fate	Notes
L2301	VS Walrus I (G-AIZG)	FAA Museum, RNAS Yeovilton	
L2940	Blackburn Skua I	FAA Museum, RNAS Yeovilton	
L5343	Fairey Battle I [VO-S]	RAF Museum, Hendon	
L6906	Miles M14A Magister I (G-AKKY/ T9841/BAPC 44)	Museum of Berkshire Aviation, Woodley	
L7005	Boulton Paul P82 Defiant I <R> [PS-B]	Boulton Paul Association, Wolverhampton	
L7181	Hawker Hind (G-CBLK)	Aero Vintage, Hatch	
L8756	Bristol 149 Bolingbroke IVT (RCAF 10001) [XD-E]	RAF Museum, Hendon	
N248	Supermarine S6A (S1596)	Southampton Hall of Aviation	
N500	Sopwith LC-1T Triplane <R> (G-PENY/G-BWRA)	Privately owned, Dunkeswell/RNAS Yeovilton	
N546	Wright Quadruplane 1 <R> (BAPC 164)	Southampton Hall of Aviation	
N1671	Boulton Paul P82 Defiant I (8370M) [EW-D]	RAF Museum, Hendon	
N1854	Fairey Fulmar II (G-AIBE)	FAA Museum, RNAS Yeovilton	
N2078	Sopwith Baby (8214/8215)	FAA Museum, RNAS Yeovilton	
N2532	Hawker Hurricane I <R> (BAPC 272) [GZ-H]	Kent Battle of Britain Museum, Hawkinge	
N2980	Vickers Wellington IA [R]	Brooklands Museum, Weybridge	
N3177	RAF BE2e <R>	Barton Aviation Heritage Society, Barton	
N3194	VS300 Spitfire I <R> (BAPC 220) [GR-Z]	RAF Biggin Hill, on display	
N3289	VS300 Spitfire I <R> (BAPC 65) [DW-K]	Kent Battle of Britain Museum, Hawkinge	
N3313	VS300 Spitfire I <R> (MH314/ BAPC 69) [KL-B]	Kent Battle of Britain Museum, Hawkinge	
N3317	VS361 Spitfire IX <R> (BAPC 268)	Privately owned, St Mawgan	
N3320	VS361 Spitfire IX <R>	Privately owned, Wellesbourne Mountford	
N3378	Boulton Paul P82 Defiant I	Boulton Paul Association, Wolverhampton	
N4389	Fairey Albacore (N4172) [4M]	FAA Museum, RNAS Yeovilton	
N4877	Avro 652A Anson I (G-AMDA) [VX-F]	Imperial War Museum, Duxford	
N5177	Sopwith 1_ Strutter <R>	Botany Bay Village, Chorley, Lancs	
N5182	Sopwith Pup <R> (G-APUP/ 9213M)	RAF Museum, Hendon	
N5195	Sopwith Pup (G-ABOX)	Museum of Army Flying, Middle Wallop	
N5492	Sopwith Triplane <R> (BAPC 111)	FAA Museum, RNAS Yeovilton	
N5518	Gloster Sea Gladiator	FAA Museum, RNAS Yeovilton	
N5628	Gloster Gladiator II	RAF Museum, Hendon	
N5719	Gloster Gladiator II (G-CBHO)	Privately owned, Glos	
N5903	Gloster Gladiator II (N2276/ G-GLAD) [H]	The Fighter Collection, Duxford	
N5912	Sopwith Triplane (8385M)	RAF Museum, Hendon	
N6181	Sopwith Pup (G-EBKY/N5180)	The Shuttleworth Collection, Old Warden	
N6290	Sopwith Triplane <R> (G-BOCK)	The Shuttleworth Collection, Old Warden	
N6452	Sopwith Pup <R> (G-BIAU)	FAA Museum, RNAS Yeovilton	
N6466	DH82A Tiger Moth (G-ANKZ)	Privately owned, Durley, Hants	
N6537	DH82A Tiger Moth (G-AOHY)	AAC Historic Aircraft Flt, Middle Wallop	
N6720	DH82A Tiger Moth (G-BYTN/ 7014M) [RUO-B]	Privately owned, Hatch	
N6797	DH82A Tiger Moth (G-ANEH)	Privately owned, Goodwood	
N6812	Sopwith 2F.1 Camel	Imperial War Museum, Lambeth	
N6847	DH82A Tiger Moth (G-APAL)	Privately owned, Little Gransden	
N6965	DH82A Tiger Moth (G-AJTW) [FL-J] (wreck)	Privately owned, Tibenham	
N7033	Noorduyn AT-16 Harvard IIB (FX442)	Kent Battle of Britain Museum, Hawkinge	
N9191	DH82A Tiger Moth (G-ALND)	Privately owned, Abergavenny	
N9192	DH82A Tiger Moth (G-DHZF) [RCO-N]	Privately owned, Sywell	
N9389	DH82A Tiger Moth (G-ANJA)	Privately owned, Seething	
N9899	Supermarine Southampton I (fuselage)	RAF Museum, Hendon	
P1344	HP52 Hampden I (9175M) [PL-K]	RAF Museum Restoration Centre, Cosford	
P1344	HP52 Hampden I <rf> (parts Hereford L6012)	RAF Museum, Hendon	
P2617	Hawker Hurricane I (8373M) [AF-A]	RAF Museum, Hendon	

Notes	Serial	Type (other identity) [code]	Owner/operator, location or fate
	P2793	Hawker Hurricane I <R> (BAPC 236) [SD-M]	Eden Camp Theme Park, Malton, North Yorkshire
	P2902	Hawker Hurricane I (G-ROBT)	Privately owned, Milden
	P2921	Hawker Hurricane I <R> (BAPC 273) [GZ-L]	Kent Battle of Britain Museum, Hawkinge
	P3059	Hawker Hurricane I <R> (BAPC 64) [SD-N]	Privately owned, Bassingbourn
	P3175	Hawker Hurricane I (wreck)	RAF Museum, Hendon
	P3208	Hawker Hurricane I <R> (BAPC 63/*L1592*) [SD-T]	Kent Battle of Britain Museum, Hawkinge
	P3386	Hawker Hurricane I <R> (BAPC 218) [FT-A]	RAF Bentley Priory, on display
	P3395	Hawker Hurricane IV (KX829) [JX-B]	Millennium Discovery Centre, Birmingham
	P3554	Hawker Hurricane I (composite)	The Air Defence Collection, Salisbury
	P3679	Hawker Hurricane I <R> (BAPC 278) [GZ-K]	Kent Battle of Britain Museum, Hawkinge
	P3717	Hawker Hurricane I (composite) (DR348)	Privately owned, Hinckley, Leics
	P3873	Hawker Hurricane I <R> (BAPC 265) [YO-H]	Yorkshire Air Museum, Elvington
	P4139	Fairey Swordfish II (HS618) [5H]	FAA Museum, RNAS Yeovilton
	P6382	Miles M14A Hawk Trainer 3 (G-AJRS) [C]	The Shuttleworth Collection, Old Warden
	P7350	VS329 Spitfire IIA (G-AWIJ) [XT-D]	RAF BBMF, Coningsby
	P7540	VS329 Spitfire IIA [DU-W]	Dumfries & Galloway Avn Mus, Dumfries
	P7966	VS329 Spitfire II <R> [D-B]	Manx Aviation & Military Museum, Ronaldsway
	P8140	VS329 Spitfire II <R> (*P9390*/ BAPC 71) [ZF-K]	Norfolk & Suffolk Avn Museum, Flixton
	P8448	VS329 Spitfire II <R> (BAPC 225) [UM-D]	RAF Cranwell, on display
	P9374	VS300 Spitfire IA (G-MKIA)	Privately owned, Braintree
	P9444	VS300 Spitfire IA [RN-D]	Science Museum, South Kensington
	R1914	Miles M14A Magister (G-AHUJ)	Privately owned, Strathallan
	R3821	Bristol 149 Bolingbroke IVT (G-BPIV/*Z5722*) [UX-N]	The Aircraft Restoration Company, Duxford
	R4115	Hawker Hurricane I <R> (BAPC 267) [LE-X]	Imperial War Museum, Duxford
	R4118	Hawker Hurricane I (G-HUPW)	Privately owned, Sutton Courtenay
	R4922	DH82A Tiger Moth II (G-APAO)	Privately owned, Duxford
	R4959	DH82A Tiger Moth II (G-ARAZ) [59]	Privately owned, Temple Bruer
	R5136	DH82A Tiger Moth II (G-APAP)	The Aircraft Restoration Co, Duxford
	R5172	DH82A Tiger Moth II (G-AOIS) [FIJ-E]	Privately owned, Sherburn-in-Elmet
	R5250	DH82A Tiger Moth II (G-AODT)	Privately owned, Tibenham
	R5868	Avro 683 Lancaster I (7325M) [PO-S]	RAF Museum, Hendon
	R6690	VS300 Spitfire I <R> (BAPC 254) [PR-A]	Yorkshire Air Museum, Elvington
	R6915	VS300 Spitfire I	Imperial War Museum, Lambeth
	R9125	Westland Lysander III (8377M) [LX-L]	RAF Museum, Hendon
	R9371	HP59 Halifax II <ff>	Cotswold Aircraft Rest'n Grp, Innsworth
	S1287	Fairey Flycatcher <R> (G-BEYB)	FAA Museum, RNAS Yeovilton
	S1579	Hawker Nimrod I <R> (G-BBVO) [571]	Privately owned, Basingstoke
	S1581	Hawker Nimrod I (G-BWWK) [573]	The Fighter Collection, Duxford
	S1595	Supermarine S6B	Science Museum, South Kensington
	T5298	Bristol 156 Beaufighter I (4552M) <ff>	Midland Air Museum, Coventry
	T5424	DH82A Tiger Moth II (G-AJOA)	Privately owned, Chiseldon
	T5672	DH82A Tiger Moth II (G-ALRI)	Privately owned, Chalmington
	T5854	DH82A Tiger Moth II (G-ANKR)	Privately owned, Baxterley
	T5879	DH82A Tiger Moth II (G-AXBW) [RUC-W]	Privately owned, Frensham
	T6296	DH82A Tiger Moth II (8387M)	RAF Museum, Hendon
	T6313	DH82A Tiger Moth II (G-AHVU)	Privately owned, Liphook
	T6562	DH82A Tiger Moth II (G-ANTE)	Privately owned, Sywell

Serial	Type (other identity) [code]	Owner/operator, location or fate	Notes
T6818	DH82A Tiger Moth II (G-ANKT) [91]	The Shuttleworth Collection, Old Warden	
T6953	DH82A Tiger Moth II (G-ANNI)	Privately owned, Little Gransden	
T6991	DH82A Tiger Moth II (G-ANOR/ DE694)	Privately owned, Paddock Wood	
T7230	DH82A Tiger Moth II (G-AFVE)	Privately owned, stored Booker	
T7281	DH82A Tiger Moth II (G-ARTL)	Privately owned, Egton, nr Whitby	
T7404	DH82A Tiger Moth II (G-ANMV) [04]	Privately owned, stored Booker	
T7793	DH82A Tiger Moth II (G-ANKV)	Privately owned, Croydon, on display	
T7842	DH82A Tiger Moth II (G-AMTF)	Privately owned, Boughton, Suffolk	
T7909	DH82A Tiger Moth II (G-ANON)	Privately owned, Sherburn-in-Elmet	
T7997	DH82A Tiger Moth II (NL750/ G-AHUF)	Privately owned, Edburton	
T8191	DH82A Tiger Moth II (G-BWMK)	Privately owned, Welshpool	
T9707	Miles M14A Magister I (G-AKKR/ 8378M/T9708)	Museum of Army Flying, Middle Wallop	
T9738	Miles M14A Magister I (G-AKAT)	Privately owned, Breighton	
V1075	Miles M14A Magister I (G-AKPF)	Privately owned, Old Warden	
V3388	Airspeed AS10 Oxford I (G-AHTW)	Imperial War Museum, Duxford	
V6028	Bristol 149 Bolingbroke IVT (G-MKIV) [GB-D] <rf>	The Aircraft Restoration Co, stored Duxford	
V6799	Hawker Hurricane I <R> (BAPC 72/ V7767) [SD-X]	Gloucestershire Avn Coll, stored Gloucester	
V7350	Hawker Hurricane I (fuselage)	Brenzett Aeronautical Museum	
V7467	Hawker Hurricane I <R> (BAPC 223) [LE-D]	RAF Coltishall, on display	
V7467	Hawker Hurricane I <R> [LE-D]	Wonderland Pleasure Park, Farnsfield, Notts	
V7497	Hawker Hurricane I (G-HRLI)	Hawker Restorations, Milden	
V9367	Westland Lysander IIIA (G-AZWT) [MA-B]	The Shuttleworth Collection, Old Warden	
V9673	Westland Lysander IIIA (V9300/ G-LIZY) [MA-J]	Imperial War Museum, Duxford	
V9723	Westland Lysander IIIA (2442/ OO-SOT) [MA-D]	SABENA Old Timers, Brussels, Belgium	
W1048	HP59 Halifax II (8465M) [TL-S]	RAF Museum, Hendon	
W2068	Avro 652A Anson I (VH-ASM) [68]	RAF Museum, Hendon	
W2718	VS Walrus I (G-RNLI)	Dick Melton Aviation, Great Yarmouth	
W4041	Gloster E28/39 [G]	Science Museum, South Kensington	
W4050	DH98 Mosquito	Mosquito Aircraft Museum, London Colney	
W5856	Fairey Swordfish II (G-BMGC) [A2A]	RN Historic Flight, Yeovilton	
W9385	DH87B Hornet Moth (G-ADND) [YG-L,3]	The Shuttleworth Collection, Old Warden	
X4590	VS300 Spitfire I (8384M) [PR-F]	RAF Museum, Hendon	
X7688	Bristol 156 Beaufighter I (3858M/ G-DINT)	Privately owned, Hatch	
Z1206	Vickers Wellington IV (fuselage)	Midland Warplane Museum, Baxterley	
Z2033	Fairey Firefly I (G-ASTL) [275]	FAA Museum, stored RNAS Yeovilton	
Z2315	Hawker Hurricane IIA [JU-E]	Imperial War Museum, Duxford	
Z2389	Hawker Hurricane IIA	Brooklands Museum, Weybridge	
Z5052	Hawker Hurricane IIA	Privately owned, Milden	
Z5207	Hawker Hurricane IIB (G-BYDL)	Privately owned, Dursley, Glos	
Z5252	Hawker Hurricane IIB (G-BWHA/ Z5053) [GO-B]	Privately owned, Dursley, Glos	
Z7015	Hawker Sea Hurricane IB (G-BKTH) [7-L]	The Shuttleworth Collection, Old Warden	
Z7197	Percival P30 Proctor III (G-AKZN/ 8380M)	RAF Museum, Hendon	
Z7258	DH89A Dragon Rapide (NR786/ G-AHGD)	Privately owned, Membury (wreck)	
Z7381	Hawker Hurricane XIIA (G-HURI) [XR-T]	Historic Aircraft Collection, Duxford	
AA550	VS349 Spitfire VB <R> (BAPC 230/AA908) [GE-P]	Eden Camp Theme Park, Malton, North Yorkshire	
AB130	VS349 Spitfire VA (parts)	Privately owned,	
AB910	VS349 Spitfire VB (G-AISU) [ZD-C]	RAF BBMF, Coningsby	
AD540	VS349 Spitfire VB (wreck)	Kennet Aviation, North Weald	

Notes	Serial	Type (other identity) [code]	Owner/operator, location or fate
	AE436	HP52 Hampden I [PL-J] (parts)	Lincolnshire Avn Heritage Centre, E Kirkby
	AL246	Grumman Martlet I	FAA Museum, RNAS Yeovilton
	AM561	Lockheed Hudson V (parts)	Cornwall Aero Park, Helston
	AP506	Cierva C30A (G-ACWM)	The Helicopter Museum, Weston-super-Mare
	AP507	Cierva C30A (G-ACWP) [KX-P]	Science Museum, South Kensington
	AR213	VS300 Spitfire IA (K9853/G-AIST) [PR-D]	Privately owned, Booker
	AR501	VS349 Spitfire LF VC (G-AWII/ AR4474) [NN-A]	The Shuttleworth Collection, Old Warden
	BB807	DH82A Tiger Moth (G-ADWO)	Southampton Hall of Aviation
	BE417	Hawker Hurricane XIIB (G-HURR) [LK-A]	The Real Aeroplane Company, Breighton
	BE421	Hawker Hurricane IIC <R> (BAPC 205) [XP-G]	RAF Museum, Hendon
	BL614	VS349 Spitfire VB (4354M) [ZD-F]	RAF Museum, Hendon
	BL655	VS349 Spitfire VB (wreck)	Lincolnshire Avn Heritage Centre, East Kirkby
	BL924	VS349 Spitfire VB <R> (BAPC 242) [AZ-G]	Tangmere Military Aviation Museum
	BM361	VS349 Spitfire VB <R> [XR-C]	RAF Lakenheath, on display
	BM597	VS349 Spitfire LF VB (5718M/ G-MKVB) [JH-C]	Historic Aircraft Collection, Duxford
	BN230	Hawker Hurricane IIC (LF751/ 5466M) [FT-A]	RAF Manston, Memorial Pavilion
	BR600	VS361 Spitfire IX <R> (BAPC 222) [SH-V]	RAF Uxbridge, on display
	BR600	VS361 Spitfire IX <R> (fuselage)	Privately owned
	BW881	Hawker Hurricane XIIA (G-KAMM)	Privately owned, Milden
	CB733	SA122 Bulldog (G-BCUV/G-112)	Privately owned, Old Sarum
	DD931	Bristol 152 Beaufort VIII (9131M) [L]	RAF Museum, Hendon
	DE208	DH82A Tiger Moth II (G-AGYU)	Privately owned, Ronaldsway
	DE470	DH82A Tiger Moth II (G-ANMY)	Privately owned,
	DE623	DH82A Tiger Moth II (G-ANFI)	Privately owned, Withybush
	DE673	DH82A Tiger Moth II (6948M/ G-ADNZ)	Privately owned, Old Buckenham
	DE992	DH82A Tiger Moth II (G-AXXV)	Privately owned, Upavon
	DE998	DH82A Tiger Moth (comp G-APAO & G-APAP) [RCU-T]	Imperial War Museum, Duxford
	DF112	DH82A Tiger Moth II (G-ANRM)	Privately owned, Clacton
	DF128	DH82A Tiger Moth II (G-AOJJ) [RCO-U]	Privately owned, White Waltham
	DF155	DH82A Tiger Moth II (G-ANFV)	Privately owned, Chilbolton
	DF198	DH82A Tiger Moth II (G-BBRB)	Privately owned, Biggin Hill
	DG202	Gloster F9/40 (5758M) [G]	RAF Museum, Cosford
	DG590	Miles M2H Hawk Major (8379M/ G-ADMW)	RAF Museum Restoration Centre, Cosford
	DP872	Fairey Barracuda II (fuselage)	FAA Museum, stored Yeovilton
	DR613	Foster-Wikner GM1 Wicko (G-AFJB)	Privately owned, Southampton
	DV372	Avro 683 Lancaster I <ff>	Imperial War Museum, Lambeth
	EE416	Gloster Meteor F3 <ff>	Martin Baker Aircraft, Chalgrove
	EE425	Gloster Meteor F3 <ff>	Gloucestershire Avn Coll, stored Gloucester
	EE531	Gloster Meteor F4 (7090M)	Midland Air Museum, Coventry
	EE549	Gloster Meteor F4 (7008M) [A]	Tangmere Military Aviation Museum
	EF545	VS349 Spitfire VC <ff>	Privately owned, High Wycombe
	EJ693	Hawker Tempest V (N7027E) [SA-J]	Privately owned, Booker
	EJ922	Hawker Typhoon IB <ff>	Privately owned, Hawkinge
	EM720	DH82A Tiger Moth II (G-AXAN)	Privately owned, Little Gransden
	EM727	DH82A Tiger Moth II (G-AOXN)	Privately owned, Yeovil
	EN224	VS366 Spitfire F XII (G-FXII)	Privately owned, Newport Pagnell
	EN343	VS365 Spitfire PR XI <R> (BAPC 226)	RAF Benson, on display
	EN398	VS361 Spitfire F IX <R> (BAPC 184) [WO-A]	Shropshire Wartime Aircraft Recovery Grp Mus, Sleap

Serial	Type (other identity) [code]	Owner/operator, location or fate	Notes
EP120	VS349 Spitfire LF VB (5377M/ 8070M/G-LFVB) [AE-A]	The Fighter Collection, Duxford	
EX976	NA AT-6D Harvard III (FAP.1657)	FAA Museum, RNAS Yeovilton	
EZ259	NA AT-6D Harvard III (G-BMJW) <ff>	*Moved to Belgium*	
FB226	Bonsall Mustang <R> (G-BDWM) [MT-A]	Privately owned, Gamston	
FE695	Noorduyn AT-16 Harvard IIB (G-BTXI) [94]	The Fighter Collection, Duxford	
FE905	Noorduyn AT-16 Harvard IIB (LN-BNM)	RAF Museum, Hendon	
FE992	Noorduyn AT-16 Harvard IIB (G-BDAM) [K-T]	Privately owned, Duxford	
FH153	Noorduyn AT-16 Harvard IIB (G-BBHK) [GW-A]	*Repainted as G-BBHK*	
FJ992	Boeing-Stearman PT-17 Kaydet (OO-JEH) [44]	Privately owned, Wevelgem, Belgium	
FL586	Douglas C-47A Dakota C3 (G-DAKS) [D]	Privately owned, North Weald	
FM118	Avro 683 Lancaster B X <ff>	Privately owned, Lee-on-Solent, Hants	
FR886	Piper L-4J Cub (G-BDMS)	Privately owned, Old Sarum	
FR887	Piper J-3C Cub 85 (G-BWEZ)	Privately owned, Cumbernauld	
FS628	Fairchild Argus 2 (43-14601/ G-AIZE)	RAF Museum, Cosford	
FS668	Noorduyn AT-16 Harvard IIB (PH-TBR)	Privately owned, The Netherlands	
FS728	Noorduyn AT-16 Harvard IIB (HB-RCP)	Privately owned, Gelnhausen, Germany	
FT323	NA AT-6D Harvard III (FAP 1513)	Air Engineering Services, Swansea	
FT391	Noorduyn AT-16 Harvard IIB (G-AZBN)	Privately owned, Goodwood	
FX301	NA AT-6D Harvard III (EX915/ G-JUDI) [FD-NQ]	Privately owned, Bryngwyn Bach, Clwyd	
FX360	Noorduyn AT-16 Harvard IIB (KF435)	Booker Aircraft Museum	
FX442	Noorduyn AT-16 Harvard IIB	*Repainted as N7033*	
FX760	Curtiss P-40N Kittyhawk IV (9150M) [GA-?]	RAF Museum, Hendon	
FZ626	Douglas Dakota III (KN566/ G-AMPO) [YS-DH]	RAF Lyneham, on display	
HB275	Beech C-45 Expeditor II (G-BKGM)	Privately owned, North Weald	
HB751	Fairchild Argus III (G-BCBL)	Privately owned, Little Gransden	
HH268	GAL48 Hotspur II (HH379/ BAPC 261) [H]	Museum of Army Flying, AAC Middle Wallop	
HJ711	DH98 Mosquito NF II [VI-C]	Night-Fighter Preservation Tm, Elvington	
HM354	Percival P34 Proctor III (G-ANPP)	Privately owned, Stansted	
HM503	Miles M12 Mohawk (G-AEKW)	RAF Museum Restoration Centre, Cosford	
HM580	Cierva C-30A (G-ACUU) [KX-K]	Imperial War Museum, Duxford	
HS503	Fairey Swordfish IV (BAPC 108)	RAF Museum Restoration Centre, Cosford	
JG891	VS349 Spitfire LF VC (A58-178/ G-LFVC)	Historic Flying Ltd, Audley End	
JR505	Hawker Typhoon IB <ff>	Midland Air Museum, Coventry	
JV482	Grumman Wildcat V	Ulster Aviation Society, Langford Lodge	
JV579	Grumman FM-2 Wildcat (N4845V/ G-RUMW) [F]	The Fighter Collection, Duxford	
JV928	Consolidated PBY-5A Catalina (N423RS) [Y]	Super Catalina Restoration, Lee-on-Solent	
KB889	Avro 683 Lancaster B X (G-LANC) [NA-I]	Imperial War Museum, Duxford	
KB976	Avro 683 Lancaster B X (G-BCOH) (fuselage)	Privately owned, Sandtoft	
KB994	Avro 683 Lancaster B X (G-BVBP) <ff>	Privately owned, North Weald	
KD345	Goodyear FG-1D Corsair (88297/ G-FGID) [130-A]	The Fighter Collection, Duxford	
KD431	CV Corsair IV [E2-M]	FAA Museum, RNAS Yeovilton	
KE209	Grumman Hellcat II	FAA Museum, RNAS Yeovilton	
KE418	Hawker Tempest <rf>	RAF Museum Restoration Centre, Cosford	
KF183	Noorduyn AT-16 Harvard IIB [3]	DPA/AFD/QinetiQ, Boscombe Down	

KF435 – ML796

Notes	Serial	Type (other identity) [code]	Owner/operator, location or fate
	KF435	Noorduyn AT-16 Harvard IIB <ff>	Privately owned, Swindon
	KF487	Noorduyn AT-16 Harvard IIB	Broken up for spares
	KF488	Noorduyn AT-16 Harvard IIB <ff>	Bournemouth Aviation Museum
	KF532	Noorduyn AT-16 Harvard IIB <ff>	Newark Air Museum, Winthorpe
	KF584	CCF T-6J Texan (FT239/G-BIWX/ G-RAIX) [RAI-X]	Privately owned, North Weald
	KG374	Douglas Dakota IV (KN645/ 8355M) [YS]	RAF Museum, Cosford
	KJ351	Airspeed AS58 Horsa II (TL659/ BAPC 80) [23]	Museum of Army Flying, Middle Wallop
	KK995	Sikorsky Hoverfly I [E]	RAF Museum, Hendon
	KL216	Republic P-47D Thunderbolt (45-49295/9212M) [RS-L]	RAF Museum, Cosford
	KN442	Douglas Dakota C4 (G-AMPZ)	Atlantic Airlines, Coventry
	KN448	Douglas Dakota C4 <ff>	Science Museum, South Kensington
	KN751	Consolidated Liberator C VI (IAF HE807) [F]	RAF Museum, Cosford
	KP208	Douglas Dakota IV [YS]	Airborne Forces Museum, Aldershot
	KZ191	Hawker Hurricane IV (frame only)	Privately owned, North Weald
	KZ321	Hawker Hurricane IV (G-HURY)	The Fighter Collection, Milden
	LA198	VS356 Spitfire F21 (7118M) [RAI-G]	Royal Scottish Mus'm of Flight, E Fortune
	LA226	VS356 Spitfire F21 (7119M)	RAF Museum Restoration Centre, Cosford
	LA255	VS356 Spitfire F21 (6490M) [JX-U]	RAF No 1 Sqn, Cottesmore (preserved)
	LB264	Taylorcraft Plus D (G-AIXA)	RAF Museum Restoration Centre, Cosford
	LB294	Taylorcraft Plus D (G-AHWJ)	Museum of Army Flying, Whitchurch, Hants
	LB312	Taylorcraft Plus D (HH982/ G-AHXE)	Privately owned, Netheravon
	LB367	Taylorcraft Plus D (G-AHGZ)	Privately owned, Duxford
	LB375	Taylorcraft Plus D (G-AHGW)	Privately owned, Edge Hill
	LF363	Hawker Hurricane IIC [US-C]	RAF BBMF, Coningsby
	LF738	Hawker Hurricane IIC (5405M) [UH-A]	RAF Museum, Cosford
	LF789	DH82 Queen Bee (K3584/ BAPC 186) [R2-K]	Mosquito Aircraft Museum, London Colney
	LF858	DH82 Queen Bee (G-BLUZ)	Privately owned, Rush Green
	LS326	Fairey Swordfish II (G-AJVH) [L2]	RN Historic Flight, Yeovilton
	LV907	HP59 Halifax III (HR792) [NP-F]	Yorkshire Air Museum, Elvington
	LZ551	DH100 Vampire	FAA Museum, RNAS Yeovilton
	LZ766	Percival P34 Proctor III (G-ALCK)	Imperial War Museum, Duxford
	MF628	Vickers Wellington T10 (9210M)	RAF Museum, Hendon
	MH434	VS361 Spitfire LF IXB (G-ASJV) [ZD-B]	The Old Flying Machine Company, Duxford
	MH486	VS361 Spitfire LF IX <R> (BAPC 206) [FF-A]	RAF Museum, Hendon
	MH777	VS361 Spitfire IX <R> (BAPC 221) [RF-N]	RAF Northolt, on display
	MJ147	VS361 Spitfire LF IX	Privately owned, Kent
	MJ627	VS509 Spitfire T9 (G-BMSB) [9G-P]	Privately owned, Coventry
	MJ751	VS361 Spitfire IX <R> (BAPC 209) [DU-V]	D-Day Museum, Shoreham Airport
	MJ832	VS361 Spitfire IX <R> (L1096/ BAPC 229) [DN-Y]	RAF Digby, on display
	MK178	VS361 Spitfire LF XVIE (TE311/ X4474/7241M) [LZ-V]	RAF BBMF, stored Coningsby
	MK356	VS361 Spitfire LF IXC (5690M) [2I-V]	RAF BBMF, Coningsby
	MK356	VS361 Spitfire LF IXC <R> [2I-V]	Kent Battle of Britain Museum, Hawkinge
	MK673	VS361 Spitfire LF XVIE (TB382/ X4277/7244M) [SK-E]	RAF BBMF, stored Coningsby
	MK805	VS361 Spitfire LF IX <R> [SH-B]	Privately owned, Lowestoft
	MK912	VS361 Spitfire LF IXE (G-BRRA) [SH-L]	Silver Victory Collection, Duxford
	ML407	VS509 Spitfire T9 (G-LFIX) [OU-V]	Privately owned, Duxford
	ML411	VS361 Spitfire LF IXE (G-CBNU)	Privately owned, Kent
	ML417	VS361 Spitfire LF IXE (G-BJSG) [2I-T]	To the US as N2TF, 2002
	ML427	VS361 Spitfire IX (6457M) [HK-A]	Millennium Discovery Centre, Birmingham
	ML796	Short S25 Sunderland V	Imperial War Museum, Duxford

Serial	Type (other identity) [code]	Owner/operator, location or fate	Notes
ML824	Short S25 Sunderland V [NS-Z]	RAF Museum, Hendon	
MN235	Hawker Typhoon IB	RAF Museum, Hendon	
MP425	Airspeed AS10 Oxford I (G-AITB) [G]	RAF Museum, Hendon	
MS902	Miles M25 Martinet TT1 (TF-SHC)	Museum of Berkshire Aviation, Woodley	
MT197	Auster IV (G-ANHS)	Privately owned, Spanhoe	
MT438	Auster III (G-AREI)	Privately owned, Petersfield	
MT847	VS379 Spitfire FR XIVE (6960M) [AX-H]	Gr Manchester Mus of Science & Industry	
MT928	VS359 Spitfire HF VIIIC (G-BKMI/ MV154/AR654) [ZX-M]	Privately owned, East Garston, Bucks	
MV262	VS379 Spitfire FR XIV (G-CCVV)	Privately owned, Booker	
MV268	VS379 Spitfire FR XIVE (MV293/ G-SPIT) [JE-J]	The Fighter Collection, Duxford	
MW401	Hawker Tempest II (IAF HA604/ G-PEST)	Privately owned, Hemswell, Lincs	
MW404	Hawker Tempest II (IAF HA557)	Privately owned	
MW758	Hawker Tempest II (IAF HA580)	Privately owned	
MW763	Hawker Tempest II (IAF HA586/ G-TEMT) [HF-A]	Privately owned, Hibaldstow, Lincs	
MW810	Hawker Tempest II (IAF HA591)	Privately owned, Hibaldstow, Lincs	
NF370	Fairey Swordfish III	Imperial War Museum, Duxford	
NF389	Fairey Swordfish III [D]	RN Historic Flight, Yeovilton	
NJ673	Auster 5D (G-AOCR)	Privately owned, Canterbury	
NJ695	Auster 4 (G-AJXV)	Privately owned, Newark	
NJ703	Auster 5 (G-AKPI)	Privately owned, Croft, Lincs	
NJ719	Auster 5 (TW385/G-ANFU)	Privately owned, Newcastle	
NL750	DH82A Tiger Moth II (T7997/ G-AOBH)	Privately owned, Thruxton	
NL846	DH82A Tiger Moth II (F-BGEQ)	Brooklands Museum, Hungerford (under restoration)	
NL985	DH82A Tiger Moth I (7015M/ G-BWIK)	Privately owned, Sywell	
NM181	DH82A Tiger Moth I (G-AZGZ)	Privately owned, Dunkeswell	
NP294	Percival P31 Proctor IV [TB-M]	Lincolnshire Avn Heritage Centre, E Kirkby	
NP303	Percival P31 Proctor IV (G-ANZJ)	Privately owned, Byfleet, Surrey	
NV778	Hawker Tempest TT5 (8386M)	RAF Museum Restoration Centre, Cosford	
NX534	Auster III (G-BUDL)	Privately owned, Netheravon	
NX611	Avro 683 Lancaster B VII (8375M/ G-ASXX) [DE-C,LE-C]	Lincolnshire Avn Heritage Centre, E Kirkby	
PA474	Avro 683 Lancaster B I [QR-M]	RAF BBMF, Coningsby	
PF179	HS Gnat T1 (XR541/8602M)	Global Aviation, Humberside	
PK624	VS356 Spitfire F22 (8072M) [RAU-T]	The Fighter Collection, Duxford	
PK664	VS356 Spitfire F22 (7759M) [V6-B]	RAF Museum Restoration Centre, Cosford	
PK683	VS356 Spitfire F24 (7150M)	Southampton Hall of Aviation	
PK724	VS356 Spitfire F24 (7288M)	RAF Museum, Hendon	
PM631	VS390 Spitfire PR XIX	RAF BBMF, Coningsby	
PM651	VS390 Spitfire PR XIX (7758M) [X]	RAF Museum Restoration Centre, Cosford	
PN323	HP Halifax VII <ff>	Imperial War Museum, Lambeth	
PP972	VS358 Seafire LF IIIC (G-BUAR)	Flying A Services, Earls Colne	
PR536	Hawker Tempest II (IAF HA457) [OQ-H]	RAF Museum, Hendon	
PS853	VS390 Spitfire PR XIX (G-MXIX/ G-RRGN) [C]	Rolls-Royce, Filton	
PS915	VS390 Spitfire PR XIX (7548M/ 7711M) [UM-G]	RAF BBMF, Coningsby	
PT462	VS509 Spitfire T9 (G-CTIX/ N462JC) [SW-A]	Privately owned, Caernarfon/Duxford	
PV202	VS509 Spitfire T9 (G-TRIX) [5R-Q]	Being rebuilt as IAAC161	
PZ865	Hawker Hurricane IIC (G-AMAU) [Q]	RAF BBMF, Coningsby	
RA848	Slingsby Cadet TX1	The Aeroplane Collection, stored Wigan	
RA854	Slingsby Cadet TX1	Privately owned, Wigan	
RA897	Slingsby Cadet TX1	Newark Air Museum, Winthorpe	
RD220	Bristol 156 Beaufighter TF X	Royal Scottish Mus'm of Flight, E Fortune	
RD253	Bristol 156 Beaufighter TF X (7931M)	RAF Museum, Hendon	
RF342	Avro 694 Lincoln B II (G-29-1/ G-APRJ)	Privately owned, stored Sandtoft	
RF398	Avro 694 Lincoln B II (8376M)	RAF Museum, Cosford	

Notes	Serial	Type (other identity) [code]	Owner/operator, location or fate
	RG333	Miles M38 Messenger IIA (G-AIEK)	Privately owned, Felton, Bristol
	RH377	Miles M38 Messenger 4A (G-ALAH)	Privately owned, Stretton, Cheshire
	RH746	Bristol 164 Brigand TF1 (fuselage)	Bristol Aero Collection, Kemble
	RL962	DH89A Dominie II (G-AHED)	RAF Museum Restoration Centre, Cosford
	RM221	Percival P31 Proctor IV (G-ANXR)	Privately owned, Biggin Hill
	RM689	VS379 Spitfire F XIV (G-ALGT)	Rolls-Royce, Filton
	RM694	VS379 Spitfire F XIV (6640M)	Privately owned, High Wycombe
	RM927	VS379 Spitfire F XIV	Privately owned, High Wycombe
	RN201	VS379 Spitfire FR XIV (SG-31/ SG-3/G-BSKP)	Historic Flying Ltd, Duxford
	RN218	Isaacs Spitfire <R> (G-BBJI) [N]	Privately owned, Langham
	RR232	VS361 Spitfire HF IXC (G-BRSF)	Privately owned, Exeter
	RT486	Auster 5 (G-AJGJ) [PF-A]	Bournemouth Aviation Museum
	RT520	Auster 5 (G-ALYB)	Aeroventure, Doncaster
	RT610	Auster 5A-160 (G-AKWS)	Privately owned, Crowfield
	RW388	VS361 Spitfire LF XVIE (6946M) [U4-U]	Stoke-on-Trent City Museum, Hanley
	RW393	VS361 Spitfire LF XVIE (7293M) [XT-A]	RAF Museum, Cosford
	RX168	VS358 Seafire L IIIC (IAC 157/ G-BWEM)	Privately owned, Exeter
	SL611	VS361 Spitfire LF XVIE	Supermarine Aero Engineering, Stoke-on-Trent
	SL674	VS361 Spitfire LF IX (8392M) [RAS-H]	RAF Museum Restoration Centre, Cosford
	SM520	VS361 Spitfire LF IX (G-ILDA/ G-BXHZ)	Privately owned, Ramsbottom
	SM832	VS379 Spitfire F XIVE (G-WWII) [YB-A]	The Fighter Collection, Duxford
	SM845	VS394 Spitfire FR XVIII (G-BUOS) [GZ-J]	Silver Victory Collection, Duxford
	SX137	VS384 Seafire F XVII	FAA Museum, RNAS Yeovilton
	SX336	VS384 Seafire F XVII (G-BRMG)	Kennet Aviation, North Weald
	TA122	DH98 Mosquito FB VI [UP-G]	Mosquito Aircraft Museum, London Colney
	TA634	DH98 Mosquito TT35 (G-AWJV) [8K-K]	Mosquito Aircraft Museum, London Colney
	TA639	DH98 Mosquito TT35 (7806M) [AZ-E]	RAF Museum, Cosford
	TA719	DH98 Mosquito TT35 (G-ASKC)	Imperial War Museum, Duxford
	TA805	VS361 Spitfire HF IX (G-PMNF)	Privately owned, Sandown
	TB252	VS361 Spitfire LF XVIE (G-XVIE) [GW-H]	Historic Flying Ltd, Audley End
	TB752	VS361 Spitfire LF XVIE (8086M) [KH-Z]	RAF Manston, Memorial Pavilion
	TD248	VS361 Spitfire LF XVIE (7246M/ G-OXVI) [D]	Silver Victory Collection, Duxford
	TD248	VS361 Spitfire LF XVIE <R> [8Q-T]	Norfolk & Suffolk Avn Mus'm, Flixton
	TD314	VS361 Spitfire LF IX (N601DA)	Privately owned, Norwich
	TE462	VS361 Spitfire LF XVIE (7243M)	Royal Scottish Mus'm of Flight, E Fortune
	TE517	VS361 Spitfire LF IXE (G-CCIX) [HL-K]	Privately owned, stored Booker
	TG263	Saro SR A1 (G-12-1)	Southampton Hall of Aviation
	TG511	HP67 Hastings C1 (8554M)	RAF Museum, Cosford
	TG517	HP67 Hastings T5	Newark Air Museum, Winthorpe
	TG528	HP67 Hastings C1A	Imperial War Museum, Duxford
	TJ118	DH98 Mosquito TT35 <ff>	Mosquito Aircraft Museum, stored London Colney
	TJ138	DH98 Mosquito B35 (7607M) [VO-L]	RAF Museum, Hendon
	TJ324	Auster 5 (G-APAH)	Repainted as G-APAH by June 2002
	TJ343	Auster 5 (G-AJXC)	Privately owned, stored Hook
	TJ398	Auster AOP6 (BAPC 70)	Aircraft Pres'n Soc of Scotland, E Fortune
	TJ534	Auster 5 (G-AKSY)	Privately owned, Breighton
	TJ569	Auster 5 (G-AKOW)	Museum of Army Flying, Middle Wallop
	TJ652	Auster 5 (G-AMVD)	Privately owned, Hardwick, Norfolk
	TJ672	Auster 5D (G-ANIJ) [TS-D]	Privately owned, Whitchurch, Hants
	TJ704	Beagle A61 Terrier 2 (VW993/ G-ASCD) [JA]	Yorkshire Air Museum, Elvington
	TK718	GAL59 Hamilcar I	National Tank Museum, Bovington
	TK777	GAL59 Hamilcar I (fuselage)	Museum of Army Flying, Middle Wallop

Serial	Type (other identity) [code]	Owner/operator, location or fate	Notes
TL615	Airspeed AS58 Horsa II	Robertsbridge Aviation Society, Mayfield	
TS291	Slingsby Cadet TX1 (BGA852)	Royal Scottish Mus'm of Flight, E Fortune	
TS798	Avro 685 York C1 (G-AGNV)	RAF Museum, Cosford	
TV959	DH98 Mosquito T III [AF-V]	The Fighter Collection, stored Duxford	
TV959	DH98 Mosquito T III <R>	Privately owned, Heald Green, Cheshire	
TW439	Auster 5 (G-ANRP)	The Real Aeroplane Company, Breighton	
TW467	Auster 5 (G-ANIE)	Privately owned, Bassingbourn	
TW511	Auster 5 (G-APAF)	Privately owned, Henstridge	
TW533	Beagle A61 Terrier 2 (G-ASAX)	*Repainted as G-ASAX*	
TW536	Auster AOP6 (7704M/G-BNGE) [TS-V]	Privately owned, Netheravon	
TW591	Auster 6A (G-ARIH) [N]	Privately owned, Abbots Bromley	
TW641	Beagle A61 Terrier 2 (G-ATDN)	Privately owned, Biggin Hill	
TX213	Avro 652A Anson C19 (G-AWRS)	North-East Aircraft Museum, Usworth	
TX214	Avro 652A Anson C19 (7817M)	RAF Museum, Cosford	
TX226	Avro 652A Anson C19 (7865M)	Air Atlantique Historic Flight, Coventry	
TX235	Avro 652A Anson C19	Air Atlantique Historic Flight, Coventry	
VF301	DH100 Vampire F1 (7060M) [RAL-G]	Midland Air Museum, Coventry	
VF512	Auster 6A (G-ARRX) [PF-M]	Privately owned, White Waltham	
VF516	Beagle A61 Terrier 2 (G-ASMZ) [T]	Privately owned, Eggesford	
VF526	Auster 6A (G-ARXU) [T]	Privately owned, Netheravon	
VF548	Beagle A61 Terrier 1 (G-ASEG)	Privately owned, Dunkeswell	
VF560	Auster 6A (frame)	Aeroventure, Doncaster	
VF581	Beagle A61 Terrier 1 (G-ARSL)	Privately owned, Dunkeswell	
VF611	Beagle A61 Terrier 2 (G-ATBU)	*Repainted as G-ATBU*	
VH127	Fairey Firefly TT4 [200/R]	FAA Museum, RNAS Yeovilton	
VL348	Avro 652A Anson C19 (G-AVVO)	Newark Air Museum, Winthorpe	
VL349	Avro 652A Anson C19 (G-AWSA) [V7-Q]	Norfolk & Suffolk Avn Mus'm, Flixton	
VM325	Avro 652A Anson C19	Privately owned, stored Gloucester	
VM360	Avro 652A Anson C19 (G-APHV)	Royal Scottish Mus'm of Flight, E Fortune	
VM791	Slingsby Cadet TX3 (XA312/8876M)	RAF Manston History Museum	
VN148	Grunau Baby IIb (BAPC 33/BGA2400)	Privately owned, North Wales	
VN485	VS356 Spitfire F24 (7326M)	Imperial War Museum, Duxford	
VN799	EE Canberra T4 (WJ874)	RAF No 39(1 PRU) Sqn, Marham	
VP293	Avro 696 Shackleton T4 [A] <ff>	Avro Aircraft Heritage Society, Coventry	
VP519	Avro 652A Anson C19 (G-AVVR) <ff>	Privately owned, Wolverhampton	
VP952	DH104 Devon C2 (8820M)	RAF Museum, Cosford	
VP955	DH104 Devon C2 (G-DVON)	Privately owned, Kemble	
VP957	DH104 Devon C2 (8822M) <ff>	No 1137 Sqn ATC, Belfast	
VP975	DH104 Devon C2 [M]	Science Museum, Wroughton	
VP981	DH104 Devon C2 (G-DHDV)	Air Atlantique Historic Flight, Coventry	
VR137	Westland Wyvern TF1	FAA Museum, RNAS Yeovilton	
VR192	Pervical P40 Prentice T1 (G-APIT)	SWWAPS, Lasham	
VR249	Percival P40 Prentice T1 (G-APIY) [FA-EL]	Newark Air Museum, Winthorpe	
VR259	Percival P40 Prentice T1 (G-APJB) [M]	Air Atlantique Historic Flight, Coventry	
VR930	Hawker Sea Fury FB11 (8382M) [110/O]	RN Historic Flight, Yeovilton	
VS356	Percival P40 Prentice T1 (G-AOLU)	Privately owned, Montrose	
VS562	Avro 652A Anson T21 (8012M)	Maes Artro Craft Village, Llanbedr	
VS610	Percival P40 Prentice T1 (G-AOKL)[K-L]	The Shuttleworth Collection, Old Warden	
VS623	Percival P40 Prentice T1 (G-AOKZ)[KQ-F]	Midland Air Museum, Coventry	
VT409	Fairey Firefly AS5 <rf>	North-East Aircraft Museum, stored Usworth	
VT812	DH100 Vampire F3 (7200M) [N]	RAF Museum Restoration Centre, Cosford	
VT871	DH100 Vampire FB6 (J-1173/LZ551/G-DHXX) [G]	Source Classic Jet Flight, Bournemouth	
VT935	Boulton Paul P111A (VT769)	Midland Air Museum, Coventry	
VT987	Auster AOP6 (G-BKXP)	Aerobuild Ltd, Little Gransden, Cambs	
VV106	Supermarine 510 (7175M)	FAA Museum, stored RNAS Yeovilton	
VV217	DH100 Vampire FB5 (7323M)	North-East Aircraft Museum, stored Usworth	
VV612	DH112 Venom FB50 (J-1523/WE402/G-VENI)	Source Classic Jet Flight, Bournemouth	

Notes	Serial	Type (other identity) [code]	Owner/operator, location or fate
	VV901	Avro 652A Anson T21	Yorkshire Air Museum, Elvington
	VW453	Gloster Meteor T7 (8703M) [Z]	RAF Innsworth, on display
	VW985	Auster AOP6 (G-ASEF)	Privately owned, Upper Arncott, Oxon
	VX118	Auster AOP6 (G-ASNB)	Vliegend Museum, Seppe, The Netherlands
	VX147	Alon A2 Aircoupe (G-AVIL)	Privately owned, Monewden
	VX185	EE Canberra B(I)8 (7631M) <ff>	Royal Scottish Mus'm of Flight, E Fortune
	VX250	DH103 Sea Hornet 21 [48] <rf>	Mosquito Aircraft Museum, London Colney
	VX272	Hawker P.1052 (7174M)	FAA Museum, stored RNAS Yeovilton
	VX275	Slingsby T21B Sedbergh TX1 (8884M/BGA 572)	RAF Museum Restoration Centre, Cosford
	VX461	DH100 Vampire FB5 (7646M)	RAF Museum Restoration Centre, Cosford
	VX573	Vickers Valetta C2 (8389M)	RAF Museum, stored Cosford
	VX580	Vickers Valetta C2	Norfolk & Suffolk Avn Museum, Flixton
	VX595	WS51 Dragonfly HR1	FAA Museum, stored RNAS Yeovilton
	VX665	Hawker Sea Fury FB11 <rf>	RN Historic Flight, at BAE Systems Brough
	VX926	Auster T7 (G-ASKJ)	Privately owned, Little Gransden
	VZ345	Hawker Sea Fury T20S	RN Historic Flight, stored Yeovilton
	VZ477	Gloster Meteor F8 (7741M) <ff>	Midland Air Museum, Coventry
	VZ608	Gloster Meteor FR9	Newark Air Museum, Winthorpe
	VZ634	Gloster Meteor T7 (8657M)	Newark Air Museum, Winthorpe
	VZ638	Gloster Meteor T7 (G-JETM) [HF]	Gatwick Aviation Museum, Charlwood, Surrey
	VZ728	RS4 Desford Trainer (G-AGOS)	Snibston Discovery Park, stored Coalville
	VZ962	WS51 Dragonfly HR1 [904]	The Helicopter Museum, Weston-super-Mare
	WA473	VS Attacker F1 [102/J]	FAA Museum, RNAS Yeovilton
	WA576	Bristol 171 Sycamore 3 (7900M/ G-ALSS)	Dumfries & Galloway Avn Mus, Dumfries
	WA577	Bristol 171 Sycamore 3 (7718M/ G-ALST)	North-East Aircraft Museum, Usworth
	WA591	Gloster Meteor T7 (7917M/ G-BWMF) [W]	Meteor Flight, Yatesbury
	WA630	Gloster Meteor T7 [69] <ff>	Robertsbridge Aviation Society, Newhaven
	WA634	Gloster Meteor T7/8	RAF Museum, Cosford
	WA638	Gloster Meteor T7(mod)	Martin Baker Aircraft, Chalgrove
	WA662	Gloster Meteor T7	Aeroventure, Doncaster
	WA829	Gloster Meteor F8 (WA984) [A]	Tangmere Military Aviation Museum
	WB188	Hawker Hunter F3 (7154M)	Tangmere Military Aviation Museum
	WB188	Hawker Hunter GA11 (WV256/ G-BZPB)	Hunter Flying Club, Exeter (duck egg green)
	WB188	Hawker Hunter GA11 (XF300/ G-BZPC)	Hunter Flying Club, Exeter (red)
	WB271	Fairey Firefly AS5 [204/R]	RN Historic Flight, RNAS Yeovilton
	WB440	Fairey Firefly AS6 <ff>	Privately owned, Newton-le-Willows
	WB491	Avro 706 Ashton 2 (TS897/ G-AJJW) <ff>	Avro Aircraft Heritage Society, BAE Systems Woodford
	WB556	DHC1 Chipmunk T10	RAFGSA, Bicester
	WB560	DHC1 Chipmunk T10 (comp WG403)	Aeroventure, stored Doncaster
	WB565	DHC1 Chipmunk T10 (G-PVET) [X]	Privately owned, Kemble
	WB569	DHC1 Chipmunk T10 (G-BYSJ) [R]	Privately owned, Duxford
	WB584	DHC1 Chipmunk T10 (7706M) <ff>	Royal Scottish Mus'm of Flight, E Fortune
	WB585	DHC1 Chipmunk T10 (G-AOSY) [M]	Privately owned, Blackbushe
	WB588	DHC1 Chipmunk T10 (G-AOTD) [D]	Privately owned, Biggin Hill
	WB615	DHC1 Chipmunk T10 (G-BXIA) [E]	Privately owned, Blackpool
	WB624	DHC1 Chipmunk T10 <ff>	Newark Air Museum, Winthorpe
	WB626	DHC1 Chipmunk T10 <ff>	Privately owned, Aylesbury
	WB627	DHC1 Chipmunk T10 (9248M) [N]	Dulwich College CCF
	WB645	DHC1 Chipmunk T10 (8218M)	RAFGSA, Bicester, spares use
	WB652	DHC1 Chipmunk T10 (G-CHPY) [V]	Privately owned, Staverton
	WB654	DHC1 Chipmunk T10 (G-BXGO) [U]	Privately owned, Booker
	WB657	DHC1 Chipmunk T10 [908]	RN Historic Flight, Yeovilton
	WB660	DHC1 Chipmunk T10 (G-ARMB)	Privately owned, East Winch
	WB670	DHC1 Chipmunk T10 (8361M) <ff>	Privately owned, Currie, Lothian
	WB671	DHC1 Chipmunk T10 (G-BWTG) [910]	Privately owned, Epse, The Netherlands

Serial	Type (other identity) [code]	Owner/operator, location or fate	Notes
WB685	DHC1 Chipmunk T10 <rf>	North-East Aircraft Museum, stored Usworth	
WB697	DHC1 Chipmunk T10 (G-BXCT) [95]	Privately owned, Wickenby	
WB702	DHC1 Chipmunk T10 (G-AOFE)	Privately owned, Goodwood	
WB703	DHC1 Chipmunk T10 (G-ARMC)	Privately owned, White Waltham	
WB711	DHC1 Chipmunk T10 (G-APPM)	Privately owned, Crowfield	
WB726	DHC1 Chipmunk T10 (G-AOSK) [E]	Privately owned, Audley End	
WB733	DHC1 Chipmunk T10 (comp WG422)	Aeroventure, Doncaster	
WB758	DHC1 Chipmunk T10 (7729M) [P]	Privately owned, Torbay	
WB763	DHC1 Chipmunk T10 (G-BBMR) [14]	Privately owned, Camberley, Surrey	
WB922	Slingsby T21B Sedbergh TX1 (BGA 4366)	Privately owned, Gallows Hill, Dorset	
WB924	Slingsby T21B Sedbergh TX1 (BGA 3901)	Privately owned, Dunstable	
WB938	Slingsby T21B Sedbergh TX1	Privately owned, Halton	
WB943	Slingsby T21B Sedbergh TX1 (BGA 2941)	Privately owned, Rufforth	
WB969	Slingsby T21B Sedbergh TX1	Aeroventure, Doncaster	
WB971	Slingsby T21B Sedbergh TX1 (BGA 3324)	Privately owned, Tibenham	
WB975	Slingsby T21B Sedbergh TX1 (BGA 3288)	Privately owned, Drumshade, Fife	
WB981	Slingsby T21B Sedbergh TX1 (BGA 1218)	Privately owned, Keevil	
WD286	DHC1 Chipmunk T10 (G-BBND)	Privately owned, Little Gransden	
WD288	DHC1 Chipmunk T10 (G-AOSO) [38]	Privately owned, Charlton Park, Wilts	
WD292	DHC1 Chipmunk T10 (G-BCRX)	Privately owned, White Waltham	
WD293	DHC1 Chipmunk T10 (7645M) <ff>	No 210 Sqn ATC, Newport, Gwent	
WD305	DHC1 Chipmunk T10 (G-ARGG)	Privately owned, Meppershall	
WD310	DHC1 Chipmunk T10 (G-BWUN) [B]	Privately owned, Booker	
WD318	DHC1 Chipmunk T10 (8207M) <ff>	No 145 Sqn ATC, Timperley, Gr Manchester	
WD325	DHC1 Chipmunk T10 [N]	AAC Historic Aircraft Flight, Middle Wallop	
WD331	DHC1 Chipmunk T10 (G-BXDH) [J]	Privately owned, Enstone	
WD347	DHC1 Chipmunk T10 (G-BBRV)	Privately owned, Liverpool	
WD355	DHC1 Chipmunk T10 (WD335/ G-CBAJ)	Privately owned, Wellesbourne Mountford	
WD363	DHC1 Chipmunk T10 (G-BCIH) [5]	Privately owned, North Weald	
WD370	DHC1 Chipmunk T10 <ff>	No 225 Sqn ATC, Brighton	
WD373	DHC1 Chipmunk T10 (G-BXDI) [12]	Privately owned, Staverton	
WD377	DHC1 Chipmunk T10 <ff>	RAF Millom Museum, Haverigg	
WD379	DHC1 Chipmunk T10 (WB696/ G-APLO) [K]	Privately owned, Jersey	
WD386	DHC1 Chipmunk T10 (comp WD377)	Dumfries & Galloway Avn Mus, Prestwick	
WD390	DHC1 Chipmunk T10 (G-BWNK) [68]	Privately owned, Breighton	
WD413	Avro 652A Anson T21 (7881M/ G-VROE)	Air Atlantique Historic Flight, Coventry	
WD615	Gloster Meteor TT20 (WD646/ 8189M) [R]	RAF Manston History Museum	
WD686	Gloster Meteor NF11	Muckleburgh Collection, Weybourne	
WD790	Gloster Meteor NF11 (8743M)<ff>	North-East Aircraft Museum, Usworth	
WD889	Fairey Firefly AS5 <ff>	North-East Aircraft Museum, Usworth	
WD931	EE Canberra B2 <ff>	RAF Museum, stored Cosford	
WD935	EE Canberra B2 (8440M) <ff>	Privately owned, Stroud, Glos	
WD954	EE Canberra B2 <ff>	Privately owned, Golders Green	
WE113	EE Canberra B2 <ff>	Privately owned, Woodhurst, Cambridgeshire	
WE122	EE Canberra TT18 [845] <ff>	Blyth Valley Aviation Collection, Walpole, Suffolk	
WE139	EE Canberra PR3 (8369M)	RAF Museum, Hendon	
WE168	EE Canberra PR3 (8049M) <ff>	Privately owned, Colchester	
WE173	EE Canberra PR3 (8740M) <ff>	Robertsbridge Aviation Society, Mayfield	
WE188	EE Canberra T4	Solway Aviation Society, Carlisle	

Notes	Serial	Type (other identity) [code]	Owner/operator, location or fate
	WE192	EE Canberra T4 <ff>	Blyth Valley Aviation Collection, Walpole, Suffolk
	WE275	DH112 Venom FB50 (J-1601/ G-VIDI)	BAE Systems Hawarden, Fire Section
	WE569	Auster T7 (G-ASAJ)	Privately owned, Bassingbourn
	WE591	Auster T7 (G-ASAK) [Y]	Privately owned, Biggin Hill
	WE600	Auster T7 Antarctic (7602M)	RAF Museum, Cosford
	WE724	Hawker Sea Fury FB11 (VX653/ G-BUCM) [062]	The Fighter Collection, Duxford
	WE925	Gloster Meteor F8	*Sold to Australia, 2002*
	WE982	Slingsby T30B Prefect TX1 (8781M)	RAF Museum, stored Cosford
	WE990	Slingsby T30B Prefect TX1 (BGA 2583)	Privately owned, stored Beds
	WF118	Percival P57 Sea Prince T1 (G-DACA)	Gatwick Aviation Museum, Charlwood, Surrey
	WF122	Percival P57 Sea Prince T1 [575/CU]	Privately owned, Gloucestershire
	WF128	Percival P57 Sea Prince T1 (8611M)	Norfolk & Suffolk Avn Museum, Flixton
	WF137	Percival P57 Sea Prince C1	SWWAPS, Lasham
	WF145	Hawker Sea Hawk F1 <ff>	Privately owned, Ingatestone, Essex
	WF225	Hawker Sea Hawk F1 [CU]	RNAS Culdrose, at main gate
	WF259	Hawker Sea Hawk F2 [171/A]	Royal Scottish Mus'm of Flight,E Fortune
	WF369	Vickers Varsity T1 [F]	Newark Air Museum, Winthorpe
	WF372	Vickers Varsity T1 [A]	Brooklands Museum, Weybridge
	WF376	Vickers Varsity T1	Bristol Airport Fire Section
	WF408	Vickers Varsity T1 (8395M)	Privately owned, East Grinstead
	WF410	Vickers Varsity T1 [F]	Brunel Technical College, Lulsgate
	WF643	Gloster Meteor F8 [X]	Norfolk & Suffolk Avn Museum, Flixton
	WF714	Gloster Meteor F8 (WK914)	Privately owned, stored Scampton
	WF784	Gloster Meteor T7 (7895M)	Gloucestershire Avn Coll, stored Gloucester
	WF825	Gloster Meteor T7 (8359M) [A]	Meteor Flight, Yatesbury
	WF877	Gloster Meteor T7 (G-BPOA)	Privately owned, Washington, W Sussex
	WF911	EE Canberra B2 [CO] <ff>	The Griffin Trust, Hooton Park, Cheshire
	WF922	EE Canberra PR3	Midland Air Museum, Coventry
	WG300	DHC1 Chipmunk T10 <ff>	RAFGSA, Bicester
	WG303	DHC1 Chipmunk T10 (8208M) <ff>	RAFGSA, Bicester
	WG307	DHC1 Chipmunk T10 (G-BCYJ)	*Repainted as G-BCYJ by September 2002*
	WG308	DHC1 Chipmunk T10 (G-BYHL) [71]	Privately owned, Newton
	WG316	DHC1 Chipmunk T10 (G-BCAH)	Privately owned, Shoreham
	WG321	DHC1 Chipmunk T10 (G-DHCC)	Privately owned, Wevelgem, Belgium
	WG348	DHC1 Chipmunk T10 (G-BBMV)	Privately owned, Sywell
	WG350	DHC1 Chipmunk T10 (G-BPAL)	Privately owned, Thruxton
	WG362	DHC1 Chipmunk T10 (8437M/ 8630M/*WX643*) <ff>	No 1094 Sqn ATC, Ely
	WG407	DHC1 Chipmunk T10 (G-BWMX)	Privately owned, Croydon, Cambs
	WG418	DHC1 Chipmunk T10 (8209M/ G-ATDY) <ff>	No 1940 Sqn ATC, Levenshulme, Gr Manchester
	WG419	DHC1 Chipmunk T10 (8206M) <ff>	No 1053 Sqn ATC, Armthorpe
	WG422	DHC1 Chipmunk T10 (8394M/ G-BFAX) [116]	Privately owned, Strathaven
	WG432	DHC1 Chipmunk T10 [L]	Museum of Army Flying, Middle Wallop
	WG465	DHC1 Chipmunk T10 (G-BCEY)	Privately owned, White Waltham
	WG469	DHC1 Chipmunk T10 (G-BWJY) [72]	Privately owned, Newtownards
	WG471	DHC1 Chipmunk T10 (8210M) <ff>	Thameside Aviation Museum, East Tilbury
	WG472	DHC1 Chipmunk T10 (G-AOTY)	Privately owned, Bryngwyn Bach, Clwyd
	WG477	DHC1 Chipmunk T10 (8362M/ G-ATDP) <ff>	No 281 Sqn ATC, Birkdale, Merseyside
	WG482	DHC1 Chipmunk T10 (VH-ZOT) [01]	Privately owned, Duxford
	WG483	DHC1 Chipmunk T10 (WG393/ VH-ZIT)	Privately owned, Duxford
	WG486	DHC1 Chipmunk T10 [G]	RAF BBMF, Coningsby
	WG498	Slingsby T21B Sedbergh TX1 (BGA 3245)	Privately owned, Aston Down
	WG511	Avro 696 Shackleton T4 (fuselage)	Flambards Village Theme Park, Helston
	WG718	WS51 Dragonfly HR3 [934]	Privately owned, Elvington

Serial	Type (other identity) [code]	Owner/operator, location or fate	Notes
WG719	WS51 Dragonfly HR5 (G-BRMA)	The Helicopter Museum, Weston-super-Mare	
WG724	WS51 Dragonfly HR5 [932]	North-East Aircraft Museum, Usworth	
WG751	WS51 Dragonfly HR5 [710/GJ]	World Naval Base, Chatham	
WG760	EE P1A (7755M)	RAF Museum, Cosford	
WG763	EE P1A (7816M)	Gr Manchester Mus of Science & Industry	
WG768	Short SB5 (8005M)	RAF Museum, Cosford	
WG774	BAC 221	Science Museum, at FAA Museum, RNAS Yeovilton	
WG777	Fairey FD2 (7986M)	RAF Museum, Cosford	
WG789	EE Canberra B2/6 <ff>	Norfolk & Suffolk Avn Museum, Flixton	
WH132	Gloster Meteor T7 (7906M) [J]	No 276 Sqn ATC, Chelmsford	
WH166	Gloster Meteor T7 (8052M) [A]	Privately owned, Birlingham, Worcs	
WH291	Gloster Meteor F8	SWWAPS, Lasham	
WH301	Gloster Meteor F8 (7930M) [T]	RAF Museum, Hendon	
WH364	Gloster Meteor F8 (8169M)	Meteor Flight, Yatesbury	
WH453	Gloster Meteor D16 [L]	DPA/QinetiQ, stored Llanbedr	
WH646	EE Canberra T17A <ff>	Midland Air Museum, Coventry	
WH657	EE Canberra B2	Brenzett Aeronautical Museum	
WH665	EE Canberra T17 (8763M) [J]	BAE Systems Filton, Fire Section	
WH701	EE Canberra B2 (7659M) <ff>	*Scrapped at St Athan, September 2002*	
WH725	EE Canberra B2	Imperial War Museum, Duxford	
WH734	EE Canberra B2(mod)	DPA/QinetiQ, Llanbedr	
WH739	EE Canberra B2 <ff>	No 2475 Sqn ATC, Ammanford, Dyfed	
WH740	EE Canberra T17 (8762M) [K]	East Midlands Airport Aeropark	
WH773	EE Canberra PR7 (8696M)	Gatwick Aviation Museum, Charlwood, Surrey	
WH775	EE Canberra PR7 (8128M/8868M) <ff>	Privately owned, Welshpool	
WH779	EE Canberra PR7 <ff>	QinetiQ Farnborough	
WH779	EE Canberra PR7 [BP] <rf>	RAF, stored Shawbury	
WH791	EE Canberra PR7 (8165M/8176M/8187M)	Newark Air Museum, Winthorpe	
WH803	EE Canberra T22 <ff>	Privately owned,	
WH840	EE Canberra T4 (8350M)	Privately owned, Flixton	
WH846	EE Canberra T4	Yorkshire Air Museum, Elvington	
WH849	EE Canberra T4	RAF, stored Shawbury	
WH850	EE Canberra T4 <ff>	Aeroventure, Doncaster	
WH863	EE Canberra T17 (8693M) [CP] <ff>	Newark Air Museum, Winthorpe	
WH876	EE Canberra B2(mod) <ff>	Boscombe Down Museum	
WH887	EE Canberra TT18 [847]	DPA/QinteiQ, stored Llanbedr	
WH903	EE Canberra B2 <ff>	Yorkshire Air Museum, Elvington	
WH904	EE Canberra T19	Newark Air Museum, Winthorpe	
WH946	EE Canberra B6(mod) (8185M) <ff>	Privately owned, Tetney, Grimsby	
WH953	EE Canberra B6(mod) <ff>	Blyth Valley Aviation Collection, Walpole, Suffolk	
WH957	EE Canberra E15 (8869M) <ff>	Lincolnshire Avn Heritage Centre, East Kirkby	
WH960	EE Canberra B15 (8344M) <ff>	Rolls-Royce Heritage Trust, Derby	
WH964	EE Canberra E15 (8870M) <ff>	Privately owned, Southampton	
WH984	EE Canberra B15 (8101M) <ff>	RAF Sealand	
WH991	WS51 Dragonfly HR3	Yorkshire Helicopter Preservation Group, Elvington	
WJ231	Hawker Sea Fury FB11 (*WE726*) [115/O]	FAA Museum, Yeovilton	
WJ358	Auster AOP6 (G-ARYD)	Museum of Army Flying, Middle Wallop	
WJ565	EE Canberra T17 (8871M) <ff>	Covert Forces Museum, Harrington, Northants	
WJ567	EE Canberra B2 <ff>	Privately owned, Houghton, Cambs	
WJ576	EE Canberra T17 <ff>	Boulton Paul Association, Wolverhampton	
WJ581	EE Canberra PR7 <ff>	Privately owned, Canterbury	
WJ630	EE Canberra T17 [ED]	*Scrapped at RAF Wyton*	
WJ633	EE Canberra T17 [EF] <ff>	RAF Wyton	
WJ639	EE Canberra TT18 [39]	North-East Aircraft Museum, Usworth	
WJ640	EE Canberra B2 (8722M) <ff>	Pinewood Studios, Bucks	
WJ676	EE Canberra B2 (7796M) <ff>	North-West Aviation Heritage, Hooton Park, Cheshire	
WJ677	EE Canberra B2 <ff>	Privately owned, Redruth	
WJ680	EE Canberra TT18 (G-BURM) [CT]	*Sold to Australia, May 2002*	
WJ717	EE Canberra TT18 (9052M) <ff>	RAF St Athan, Fire Section	

WJ721 – WK864

Notes	Serial	Type (other identity) [code]	Owner/operator, location or fate
	WJ721	EE Canberra TT18 [21] <ff>	Privately owned, Oban
	WJ731	EE Canberra B2T [BK] <ff>	Privately owned, Dunstable
	WJ821	EE Canberra PR7 (8668M)	Army, Bassingbourn, on display
	WJ863	EE Canberra T4 <ff>	Cambridge Airport Fire Section
	WJ865	EE Canberra T4	Privately owned, Bromsgrove
	WJ866	EE Canberra T4 [AV]	RAF No 39(1 PRU) Sqn, Marham
	WJ872	EE Canberra T4 (8492M) <ff>	*Scrapped at Kilmarnock, November 2002*
	WJ880	EE Canberra T4 (8491M) <ff>	Dumfries & Galloway Avn Mus, Dumfries
	WJ903	Vickers Varsity T1 <ff>	Aeroventure, Doncaster
	WJ945	Vickers Varsity T1 (G-BEDV) [21]	Imperial War Museum, Duxford
	WJ975	EE Canberra T19 [S]	Bomber County Aviation Museum, Hemswell
	WJ992	EE Canberra T4	Bournemouth Airport, Fire Section
	WK102	EE Canberra T17 (8780M) <ff>	Privately owned, Welshpool
	WK118	EE Canberra TT18 <ff>	Privately owned, Worcester
	WK122	EE Canberra TT18 <ff>	Phoenix Aviation, Bruntingthorpe
	WK124	EE Canberra TT18 (9093M) [CR]	MoD FSCTE, Manston
	WK126	EE Canberra TT18 (N2138J) [843]	Gloucestershire Avn Coll, stored Gloucester
	WK127	EE Canberra TT18 (8985M) <ff>	No 2484 Sqn ATC, Bassingbourn
	WK128	EE Canberra B2	DPA/QinetiQ, Llanbedr
	WK146	EE Canberra B2 <ff>	Gatwick Aviation Museum, Charlwood, Surrey
	WK163	EE Canberra B2/6 (G-BVWC)	Air Atlantique Historic Flight, Coventry
	WK198	VS Swift F4 (7428M) (fuselage)	North-East Aircraft Museum, Usworth
	WK275	VS Swift F4	Privately owned, Upper Hill, nr Leominster
	WK277	VS Swift FR5 (7719M) [N]	Newark Air Museum, Winthorpe
	WK281	VS Swift FR5 (7712M) [S]	Tangmere Military Aviation Museum
	WK393	DH112 Venom FB1 <ff>	Aeroventure, Doncaster
	WK436	DH112 Venom FB50 (J-1614/ G-VENOM)	Kennet Aviation, North Weald
	WK511	DHC1 Chipmunk T10 (G-BVBT) [905]	*Sold as ZK-SKH, August 2002*
	WK512	DHC1 Chipmunk T10 (G-BXIM) [A]	Privately owned, Brize Norton
	WK514	DHC1 Chipmunk T10 (G-BBMO)	Privately owned, Wellesbourne Mountford
	WK517	DHC1 Chipmunk T10 (G-ULAS) [84]	Privately owned, Denham
	WK518	DHC1 Chipmunk T10 [K]	RAF BBMF, Coningsby
	WK522	DHC1 Chipmunk T10 (G-BCOU)	Privately owned, Duxford
	WK549	DHC1 Chipmunk T10 (G-BTWF)	Privately owned, Breighton
	WK570	DHC1 Chipmunk T10 (8211M) <ff>	No 424 Sqn ATC, Southampton Hall of Aviation
	WK576	DHC1 Chipmunk T10 (8357M) <ff>	No 1206 Sqn ATC, Lichfield
	WK584	DHC1 Chipmunk T10 (7556M) <ff>	No 2008 Sqn ATC, Bawtry
	WK585	DHC1 Chipmunk T10 (G-BZGA)	The Aircraft Restoration Co, Duxford
	WK586	DHC1 Chipmunk T10 (G-BXGX) [V]	Privately owned, Slinfold
	WK590	DHC1 Chipmunk T10 (G-BWVZ) [69]	Privately owned, Spanhoe
	WK608	DHC1 Chipmunk T10 [906]	RN Historic Flight, Yeovilton
	WK609	DHC1 Chipmunk T10 (G-BXDN) [B]	Privately owned, Booker
	WK611	DHC1 Chipmunk T10 (G-ARWB)	Privately owned, Thruxton
	WK613	DHC1 Chipmunk T10 [P]	
	WK620	DHC1 Chipmunk T10 [T] (fuselage)	Privately owned, Twyford, Bucks
	WK622	DHC1 Chipmunk T10 (G-BCZH)	Privately owned, Horsford
	WK624	DHC1 Chipmunk T10 (G-BWHI)	Privately owned, Hawarden
	WK626	DHC1 Chipmunk T10 (8213M) <ff>	Aeroventure, stored Doncaster
	WK628	DHC1 Chipmunk T10 (G-BBMW)	Privately owned, Goodwood
	WK630	DHC1 Chipmunk T10 (G-BXDG) [11]	Privately owned, Swanton Morley
	WK633	DHC1 Chipmunk T10 (G-BXEC) [A]	Privately owned, Gamston
	WK640	DHC1 Chipmunk T10 (G-BWUV) [C]	Privately owned, Wombleton
	WK642	DHC1 Chipmunk T10 (G-BXDP) [94]	Privately owned, Kilrush, Eire
	WK654	Gloster Meteor F8 (8092M) [B]	City of Norwich Aviation Museum
	WK800	Gloster Meteor D16 [Z]	DPA/QinetiQ, Llanbedr
	WK864	Gloster Meteor F8 (WL168/7750M) [C]	Yorkshire Air Museum, Elvington

Serial	Type (other identity) [code]	Owner/operator, location or fate	Notes
WK935	Gloster Meteor Prone Pilot (7869M)	RAF Museum, Cosford	
WK991	Gloster Meteor F8 (7825M)	Imperial War Museum, Duxford	
WL131	Gloster Meteor F8 (7751M) <ff>	Aeroventure, Doncaster	
WL181	Gloster Meteor F8 [X]	North-East Aircraft Museum, Usworth	
WL332	Gloster Meteor T7 [888]	Privately owned, Long Marston	
WL345	Gloster Meteor T7	St Leonard's Motors, Hollington, E Sussex	
WL349	Gloster Meteor T7 [Z]	Gloucestershire Airport, Staverton, on display	
WL360	Gloster Meteor T7 (7920M) [G]	Meteor Flight, Yatesbury	
WL375	Gloster Meteor T7(mod)	Dumfries & Galloway Avn Mus, Dumfries	
WL405	Gloster Meteor T7	Meteor Flight, Yatesbury	
WL419	Gloster Meteor T7	Martin Baker Aircraft, Chalgrove	
WL505	DH100 Vampire FB9 (7705M/ G-FBIX)	De Havilland Aviation, Bridgend	
WL505	DH100 Vampire FB6 (J-1167/ VZ304/G-MKVI)	De Havilland Aviation, Swansea	
WL626	Vickers Varsity T1 (G-BHDD) [P]	East Midlands Airport Aeropark	
WL627	Vickers Varsity T1 (8488M) [D] <ff>	Privately owned, Preston, E Yorkshire	
WL679	Vickers Varsity T1 (9155M)	RAF Museum, Cosford	
WL732	BP P108 Sea Balliol T21	RAF Museum, Cosford	
WL790	Avro 696 Shackleton AEW2 (N790WL)	Atlantic Group, Coventry	
WL795	Avro 696 Shackleton MR2C (8753M) [T]	RAF St Mawgan, on display	
WL798	Avro 696 Shackleton MR2C (8114M) <ff>	Privately owned, Elgin	
WL925	Slingsby T31B Cadet TX3 (WV925) <ff>	RAF No 633 VGS, Cosford	
WM145	AW Meteor NF11 <ff>	N Yorks Aircraft Recovery Centre, Chop Gate	
WM167	AW Meteor NF11 (G-LOSM)	Privately owned, Bournemouth	
WM267	Gloster Meteor NF11 <ff>	Blyth Valley Aviation Collection, Walpole, Suffolk	
WM292	AW Meteor TT20 [841]	FAA Museum, stored RNAS Yeovilton	
WM311	AW Meteor TT20 (WM224/8177M)	Privately owned, North Weald	
WM366	AW Meteor NF13 (4X-FNA) (comp VZ462)	SWWAPS, Lasham	
WM367	AW Meteor NF13 <ff>	Jet Avn Preservation Grp, Long Marston	
WM571	DH112 Sea Venom FAW21 [VL]	Southampton Hall of Aviation	
WM729	DH113 Vampire NF10 <ff>	Mosquito Aircraft Museum, London Colney	
WM913	Hawker Sea Hawk FB5 (8162M) [456/J]	Newark Air Museum, Winthorpe	
WM961	Hawker Sea Hawk FB5 [J]	Caernarfon Air World	
WM969	Hawker Sea Hawk FB5 [10/Z]	Imperial War Museum, Duxford	
WN105	Hawker Sea Hawk FB3 (WF299/ 8164M)	Privately owned, Birlingham, Worcs	
WN108	Hawker Sea Hawk FB5 [033]	Ulster Aviation Society, Langford Lodge	
WN149	BP P108 Balliol T2	Boulton Paul Association, Wolverhampton	
WN411	Fairey Gannet AS1 (fuselage)	Privately owned, Southampton	
WN493	WS51 Dragonfly HR5	FAA Museum, RNAS Yeovilton	
WN499	WS51 Dragonfly HR5 [Y]	Caernarfon Air World	
WN516	BP P108 Balliol T2 <ff>	North-East Aircraft Museum, Usworth	
WN534	BP P108 Balliol T2 <ff>	Boulton Paul Association, Wolverhampton	
WN890	Hawker Hunter F2 <ff>	Aeroventure, Doncaster	
WN904	Hawker Hunter F2 (7544M) [3]	RE 39 Regt, Waterbeach, on display	
WN907	Hawker Hunter F2 (7416M) <ff>	Robertsbridge Aviation Society, Newhaven	
WN957	Hawker Hunter F5 <ff>	Privately owned, Llanbedr	
WP185	Hawker Hunter F5 (7583M)	Privately owned, Great Dunmow, Essex	
WP190	Hawker Hunter F5 (7582M/8473M/ WP180) [K]	Tangmere Military Aviation Museum	
WP250	DH113 Vampire NF10 <ff>	Privately owned,	
WP255	DH113 Vampire NF10 <ff>	Aeroventure, Doncaster	
WP270	EoN Eton TX1 (8598M)	Gr Manchester Mus of Science & Industry, stored	
WP271	EoN Eton TX1	Privately owned, stored Keevil	
WP308	Percival P57 Sea Prince T1 (G-GACA) [572/CU]	Gatwick Aviation Museum, Charlwood, Surrey	

WP313 – WR410

Notes	Serial	Type (other identity) [code]	Owner/operator, location or fate
	WP313	Percival P57 Sea Prince T1 [568/CU]	FAA Museum, stored RNAS Yeovilton
	WP314	Percival P57 Sea Prince T1 (8634M) [573/CU]	Privately owned, Carlisle Airport
	WP321	Percival P57 Sea Prince T1 (N7SY)	Bournemouth Aviation Museum
	WP515	EE Canberra B2 <ff>	Privately owned, Welshpool
	WP772	DHC1 Chipmunk T10 [Q] (wreck)	RAF Manston History Museum
	WP784	DHC1 Chipmunk T10 <ff>	Jet Avn Preservation Grp, Long Marston
	WP788	DHC1 Chipmunk T10 (G-BCHL)	Privately owned, Sleap
	WP790	DHC1 Chipmunk T10 (G-BBNC) [T]	Mosquito Aircraft Museum, London Colney
	WP795	DHC1 Chipmunk T10 (G-BVZZ) [901]	Privately owned, Lee-on-Solent
	WP800	DHC1 Chipmunk T10 (G-BCXN) [2]	Privately owned, Halton
	WP803	DHC1 Chipmunk T10 (G-HAPY) [G]	Privately owned, Booker
	WP805	DHC1 Chipmunk T10 (G-MAJR) [D]	Privately owned, Fareham
	WP808	DHC1 Chipmunk T10 (G-BDEU)	Privately owned, Binham
	WP809	DHC1 Chipmunk T10 (G-BVTX) [78]	Privately owned, Husbands Bosworth
	WP833	DHC1 Chipmunk T10 (G-BZDU) [H]	Privately owned, Blackpool
	WP835	DHC1 Chipmunk T10 (D-ERTY)	Privately owned, The Netherlands
	WP839	DHC1 Chipmunk T10 (G-BZXE) [A]	Privately owned, Perth
	WP840	DHC1 Chipmunk T10 (G-BXDM) [9]	Privately owned, Halton
	WP844	DHC1 Chipmunk T10 (G-BWOX) [85]	Privately owned, Shobdon
	WP856	DHC1 Chipmunk T10 (G-BVWP) [904]	Privately owned, Horsham
	WP857	DHC1 Chipmunk T10 (G-BDRJ) [24]	Privately owned, Elstree
	WP859	DHC1 Chipmunk T10 (G-BXCP) [E]	Privately owned, Spanhoe Lodge
	WP860	DHC1 Chipmunk T10 (G-BXDA) [6]	Privately owned, Perth
	WP863	DHC1 Chipmunk T10 (8360M/ G-ATJI) <ff>	No 1011 Sqn ATC, Boscombe Down
	WP871	DHC1 Chipmunk T10 [W]	AAC, Middle Wallop, for display
	WP896	DHC1 Chipmunk T10 (G-BWVY) [M]	Privately owned, White Waltham
	WP901	DHC1 Chipmunk T10 (G-BWNT) [B]	Privately owned, East Midlands Airport
	WP903	DHC1 Chipmunk T10 (G-BCGC)	Privately owned, Shoreham
	WP907	DHC1 Chipmunk T10 <ff> (7970M)	Currently not known
	WP912	DHC1 Chipmunk T10 (8467M)	RAF Museum, Cosford
	WP921	DHC1 Chipmunk T10 (G-ATJJ) <ff>	Privately owned, Brooklands
	WP925	DHC1 Chipmunk T10 (G-BXHA) [C]	Privately owned, Camberley
	WP927	DHC1 Chipmunk T10 (8216M/ G-ATJK) <ff>	No 1343 Sqn ATC, Odiham
	WP928	DHC1 Chipmunk T10 (G-BXGM) [D]	Privately owned, Shoreham
	WP929	DHC1 Chipmunk T10 (G-BXCV) [F]	Privately owned, Rush Green
	WP930	DHC1 Chipmunk T10 (G-BXHF) [J]	Privately owned, Redhill
	WP959	DHC1 Chipmunk T10 (G-BXCP) [E]	Privately owned, Spanhoe Lodge
	WP962	DHC1 Chipmunk T10 [C]	RAF Museum, Hendon
	WP964	DHC1 Chipmunk T10 [Y]	AAC Historic Aircraft Flight, Middle Wallop
	WP969	DHC1 Chipmunk T10 (comp WB685/G-ATHC) [C]	North-East Aircraft Museum, Usworth
	WP971	DHC1 Chipmunk T10 (G-ATHD)	Privately owned, Denham
	WP978	DHC1 Chipmunk T10 (7467M) <ff>	Currently not known
	WP983	DHC1 Chipmunk T10 (G-BXNN) [B]	Privately owned, Eggesford
	WP984	DHC1 Chipmunk T10 (G-BWTO) [H]	Privately owned, Little Gransden
	WR360	DH112 Venom FB50 (J-1626/ G-DHSS) [K]	Source Classic Jet Flight, Bournemouth
	WR410	DH112 Venom FB50 (J-1539/ G-DHUU/WE410)	Source Classic Jet Flight, Bournemouth

Serial	Type (other identity) [code]	Owner/operator, location or fate	Notes
WR410	DH112 Venom FB54 (J-1790/ G-BLKA) [N]	Privately owned, Martham, Norfolk	
WR421	DH112 Venom FB50 (J-1611/ G-DHTT)	Source Classic Jet Flight, Bournemouth	
WR539	DH112 Venom FB4 (8399M) <ff>	Mosquito Aircraft Museum, London Colney	
WR960	Avro 696 Shackleton AEW2 (8772M)	Gr Manchester Mus of Science & Industry	
WR963	Avro 696 Shackleton AEW2	Air Atlantique Historic Flight, Coventry	
WR971	Avro 696 Shackleton MR3 (8119M) [Q]	Fenland & W Norfolk Aviation Museum, Wisbech	
WR974	Avro 696 Shackleton MR3 (8117M) [K]	Gatwick Aviation Museum, Charlwood, Surrey	
WR977	Avro 696 Shackleton MR3 (8186M) [B]	Newark Air Museum, Winthorpe	
WR982	Avro 696 Shackleton MR3 (8106M) [J]	Gatwick Aviation Museum, Charlwood, Surrey	
WR985	Avro 696 Shackleton MR3 (8103M) [H]	Privately owned, Long Marston	
WS103	Gloster Meteor T7 [709/VL]	FAA Museum, stored RNAS Yeovilton	
WS692	Gloster Meteor NF12 (7605M) [C]	Newark Air Museum, Winthorpe	
WS726	Gloster Meteor NF14 (7960M) [G]	No 1855 Sqn ATC, Royton, Gr Manchester	
WS739	Gloster Meteor NF14 (7961M)	Newark Air Museum, Winthorpe	
WS760	Gloster Meteor NF14 (7964M)	Meteor Flight, stored Yatesbury	
WS774	Gloster Meteor NF14 (7959M)	Privately owned, Quedgeley, Glos	
WS776	Gloster Meteor NF14 (7716M) [K]	Privately owned, Sandtoft	
WS788	Gloster Meteor NF14 (7967M) [Z]	Yorkshire Air Museum, Elvington	
WS792	Gloster Meteor NF14 (7965M) [K]	Brighouse Bay Caravan Park, Borgue, D&G	
WS807	Gloster Meteor NF14 (7973M) [N]	Gloucestershire Avn Coll, stored Gloucester	
WS832	Gloster Meteor NF14 [W]	Solway Aviation Society, Carlisle	
WS838	Gloster Meteor NF14	Midland Air Museum, Coventry	
WS843	Gloster Meteor NF14 (7937M) [Y]	RAF Museum, stored Cosford	
WT121	Douglas Skyraider AEW1 [415/CU]	FAA Museum, stored RNAS Yeovilton	
WT205	EE Canberra B15	RAF Manston History Museum	
WT308	EE Canberra B(I)6	RN, Predannack Fire School	
WT309	EE Canberra B(I)6 <ff>	FAST, Farnborough	
WT319	EE Canberra B(I)6 <ff>	Privately owned, Lavendon, Bucks	
WT333	EE Canberra B6(mod) (G-BVXC)	Privately owned, Bruntingthorpe	
WT339	EE Canberra B(I)8 (8198M)	RAF Barkston Heath Fire Section	
WT480	EE Canberra T4 [AT]	RAF, stored Shawbury	
WT482	EE Canberra T4 <ff>	Privately owned	
WT483	EE Canberra T4 [83]	Privately owned, Long Marston	
WT486	EE Canberra T4 (8102M) <ff>	Flight Experience Workshop, Belfast	
WT507	EE Canberra PR7 (8131M/8548M) [44] <ff>	No 384 Sqn ATC, Mansfield	
WT509	EE Canberra PR7 [BR]	RAF Marham, BDRT	
WT510	EE Canberra T22 <ff>	Privately owned, Stock, Essex	
WT519	EE Canberra PR7 [CH]	RAF Wyton, Fire Section	
WT520	EE Canberra PR7 (8094M/8184M) <ff>	No 967 Sqn ATC, Warton	
WT525	EE Canberra T22 <ff>	Privately owned, South Woodham Ferrers	
WT532	EE Canberra PR7 (8728M/8890M) <ff>	Bournemouth Aviation Museum	
WT534	EE Canberra PR7 (8549M) [43] <ff>	Boscombe Down Museum	
WT536	EE Canberra PR7 (8063M) <ff>	Privately owned, Shirrell Heath, Hants	
WT537	EE Canberra PR7	BAE Systems Samlesbury, on display	
WT569	Hawker Hunter F1 (7491M)	No 2117 Sqn ATC, Kenfig Hill, Mid-Glamorgan	
WT612	Hawker Hunter F1 (7496M)	RAF Henlow on display	
WT619	Hawker Hunter F1 (7525M)	Gr Manchester Mus of Science & Industry	
WT648	Hawker Hunter F1 (7530M) <ff>	Boscombe Down Museum	
WT651	Hawker Hunter F1 (7532M) [C]	Newark Air Museum, Winthorpe	
WT660	Hawker Hunter F1 (7421M) [C]	Highland Aircraft Preservation Society, Inverness	
WT680	Hawker Hunter F1 (7533M) [J]	No 1429 Sqn ATC, at QinetiQ Aberporth	
WT684	Hawker Hunter F1 (7422M) <ff>	Privately owned, Lavendon, Bucks	
WT694	Hawker Hunter F1 (7510M)	Caernarfon Air World	
WT711	Hawker Hunter GA11 [833/DD]	Air Atlantique, Coventry	

Notes	Serial	Type (other identity) [code]	Owner/operator, location or fate
	WT720	Hawker Hunter F51 (RDAF E-408/ 8565M) [B]	RAF Sealand, on display
	WT722	Hawker Hunter T8C (G-BWGN) [878/VL]	Hunter Flying Club, Exeter
	WT723	Hawker Hunter PR11 (G-PRII) [866/VL,3]	Privately owned, Exeter
	WT744	Hawker Hunter GA11 [868/VL]	South West Aviation Heritage, Eaglescott
	WT746	Hawker Hunter F4 (7770M) [A]	Repainted as XF506
	WT799	Hawker Hunter T8C [879]	Hunter Flying Club, Exeter
	WT804	Hawker Hunter GA11 [831/DD]	FETC, Moreton-in-Marsh, Glos
	WT806	Hawker Hunter GA11	Northbrook College, Shoreham Airport
	WT859	Supermarine 544 <ff>	Privately owned, Booker
	WT867	Slingsby T31B Cadet TX3	Privately owned, Eaglescott
	WT877	Slingsby T31B Cadet TX3	Boulton Paul Association, Wolverhampton
	WT898	Slingsby T31B Cadet TX3 (BGA 3284/BGA 4412)	Privately owned, Rufforth
	WT899	Slingsby T31B Cadet TX3	Privately owned, stored Swindon
	WT901	Slingsby T31B Cadet TX3	Privately owned, stored Rothwell, Northants
	WT905	Slingsby T31B Cadet TX3	Privately owned, Keevil
	WT908	Slingsby T31B Cadet TX3 (BGA 3487)	Privately owned, Dunstable
	WT910	Slingsby T31B Cadet TX3 (BGA 3953)	Privately owned, Swansea
	WT933	Bristol 171 Sycamore 3 (G-ALSW/ 7709M)	Newark Air Museum, Winthorpe
	WV106	Douglas Skyraider AEW1 [427/C]	FAA Museum, stored Yeovilton
	WV198	Sikorsky S55 Whirlwind HAR21 (G-BJWY) [K]	Solway Aviation Society, Carlisle
	WV276	Hawker Hunter F4 (7847M) [D]	Privately owned, stored Scampton
	WV318	Hawker Hunter T7B (G-FFOX)	Delta Jets, Kemble
	WV322	Hawker Hunter T8C (G-BZSE/ 9096M) [Y]	Privately owned, Kemble
	WV332	Hawker Hunter F4 (7673M) <ff>	No 1254 Sqn ATC, Godalming
	WV372	Hawker Hunter T7 (G-BXFI) [R]	Privately owned, Kemble
	WV381	Hawker Hunter GA11 [732/VL] (fuselage)	UKAEA, Culham, Oxon
	WV382	Hawker Hunter GA11 [830/VL]	Jet Avn Preservation Grp, Long Marston
	WV383	Hawker Hunter T7	FAST, Farnborough
	WV396	Hawker Hunter T8C (9249M) [91]	RAF Valley, at main gate
	WV483	Percival P56 Provost T1 (7693M) [N-E]	Privately owned
	WV486	Percival P56 Provost T1 (7694M) [N-D]	Privately owned, Thatcham, Berks
	WV493	Percival P56 Provost T1 (G-BDYG/ 7696M) [29]	Royal Scottish Mus'm of Flight, stored E Fortune
	WV499	Percival P56 Provost T1 (G-BZRF/ 7698M) [P-G]	Privately owned, Sandtoft
	WV562	Percival P56 Provost T1 (7606M) [P-C]	RAF Museum, Cosford
	WV605	Percival P56 Provost T1 [T-B]	Norfolk & Suffolk Avn Museum, Flixton
	WV606	Percival P56 Provost T1 (7622M) [P-B]	Newark Air Museum, Winthorpe
	WV679	Percival P56 Provost T1 (7615M) [O-J]	Wellesbourne Wartime Museum
	WV703	Percival P66 Pembroke C1 (8108M/G-IIIM)	Privately owned, Tattershall Thorpe
	WV705	Percival P66 Pembroke C1 <ff>	Privately owned, Awbridge, Hants
	WV740	Percival P66 Pembroke C1 (G-BNPH)	Privately owned, Jersey
	WV746	Percival P66 Pembroke C1 (8938M)	RAF Museum, Cosford
	WV753	Percival P66 Pembroke C1 (8113M)	Cardiff International Airport Fire Section
	WV781	Bristol 171 Sycamore HR12 (G-ALTD/7839M)	Caernarfon Air World
	WV783	Bristol 171 Sycamore HR12 (G-ALSP/7841M)	RAF Museum Restoration Centre, Cosford
	WV787	EE Canberra B2/8 (8799M)	Newark Air Museum, Winthorpe
	WV795	Hawker Sea Hawk FGA6 (8151M)	Kennet Aviation, North Weald
	WV797	Hawker Sea Hawk FGA6 (8155M) [491/J]	Midland Air Museum, Coventry

Serial	Type (other identity) [code]	Owner/operator, location or fate	Notes
WV798	Hawker Sea Hawk FGA6 [026/CU]	SWWAPS, Lasham	
WV838	Hawker Sea Hawk FGA4 <ff>	Privately owned, Liverpool	
WV856	Hawker Sea Hawk FGA6 [163]	FAA Museum, RNAS Yeovilton	
WV903	Hawker Sea Hawk FGA4 (8153M) [128/C]	RNAS Yeovilton Fire Section	
WV908	Hawker Sea Hawk FGA6 (8154M) [188/A]	RN Historic Flight, Yeovilton	
WV910	Hawker Sea Hawk FGA6 <ff>	Boscombe Down Museum	
WV911	Hawker Sea Hawk FGA4 [115/C]	RN Historic Flight, Yeovilton	
WW138	DH112 Sea Venom FAW22 [227/Z]	FAA Museum, stored RNAS Yeovilton	
WW145	DH112 Sea Venom FAW22 [680/LM]	Royal Scottish Mus'm of Flight, E Fortune	
WW217	DH112 Sea Venom FAW22 [351]	Newark Air Museum, Winthorpe	
WW388	Percival P56 Provost T1 (7616M) [O-F]	Bomber County Aviation Museum, Hemswell	
WW421	Percival P56 Provost T1 (G-BZRE/ 7688M) [P-B]	Privately owned, Sandtoft	
WW442	Percival P56 Provost T1 (7618M) [N]	Gatwick Aviation Museum, Charlwood, Surrey	
WW444	Percival P56 Provost T1 [D]	Privately owned, Rugeley, Staffs	
WW447	Percival P56 Provost T1	Privately owned, Grazeley, Berks	
WW453	Percival P56 Provost T1 (G-TMKI) [W-S]	Privately owned, Clevedon	
WW654	Hawker Hunter GA11 [834/DD]	Privately owned, Ford, W Sussex	
WX788	DH112 Venom NF3	Aeroventure, Doncaster	
WX853	DH112 Venom NF3 (7443M)	Mosquito Aircraft Museum, London Colney	
WX905	DH112 Venom NF3 (7458M)	Newark Air Museum, Winthorpe	
WZ425	DH115 Vampire T11	Privately owned, Birlingham, Worcs	
WZ450	DH115 Vampire T11 <ff>	Lashenden Air Warfare Museum, Headcorn	
WZ464	DH115 Vampire T11 (N62430) [40]	Privately owned,	
WZ507	DH115 Vampire T11 (G-VTII) [74]	De Havilland Aviation, Bournemouth	
WZ515	DH115 Vampire T11 [60]	Solway Aviation Society, Carlisle	
WZ518	DH115 Vampire T11	North-East Aircraft Museum, Usworth	
WZ549	DH115 Vampire T11 (8118M) [F]	Ulster Aviation Society, Langford Lodge	
WZ553	DH115 Vampire T11 (G-DHYY) [40]	Source Classic Jet Flight, stored Bournemouth	
WZ557	DH115 Vampire T11	N Yorks Aircraft Recovery Centre, Chop Gate	
WZ572	DH115 Vampire T11 (8124M) [65] <ff>	Privately owned, Southampton	
WZ581	DH115 Vampire T11 <ff>	The Vampire Collection, Hemel Hempstead	
WZ584	DH115 Vampire T11 (G-BZRC) [K]	Privately owned, Sandtoft	
WZ589	DH115 Vampire T11 [19]	Lashenden Air Warfare Museum, Headcorn	
WZ589	DH115 Vampire T55 (U-1230/ G-DHZZ)	Source Classic Jet Flight, Bournemouth	
WZ590	DH115 Vampire T11 [19]	Imperial War Museum, Duxford	
WZ608	DH115 Vampire T11 [56] <ff>	Privately owned	
WZ620	DH115 Vampire T11 [68]	Privately owned	
WZ662	Auster AOP9 (G-BKVK)	Privately owned, Netheravon	
WZ706	Auster AOP9 (7851M/G-BURR)	Privately owned, Netheravon	
WZ711	Auster AOP9/Beagle E3 (G-AVHT)	Privately owned, Netheravon	
WZ721	Auster AOP9	Museum of Army Flying, Middle Wallop	
WZ724	Auster AOP9 (7432M)	AAC Middle Wallop, at main gate	
WZ729	Auster AOP9 (G-BXON)	Privately owned, Newark-on-Trent	
WZ736	Avro 707A (7868M)	Gr Manchester Mus of Science & Industry	
WZ744	Avro 707C (7932M)	RAF Museum, Cosford	
WZ753	Slingsby T38 Grasshopper TX1	Southampton Hall of Aviation	
WZ755	Slingsby T38 Grasshopper TX1 (BGA 3481)	Boulton Paul Association, Wolverhampton	
WZ767	Slingsby T38 Grasshopper TX1	North-East Aircraft Museum, stored Usworth	
WZ768	Slingsby T38 Grasshopper TX1 (comp XK820)	Privately owned, Kirton-in-Lindsey, Lincs	
WZ769	Slingsby T38 Grasshopper TX1	Privately owned,	
WZ772	Slingsby T38 Grasshopper TX1	Museum of Army Flying, Middle Wallop	
WZ779	Slingsby T38 Grasshopper TX1	Privately owned, Old Sarum	
WZ784	Slingsby T38 Grasshopper TX1	Solway Aviation Society, Carlisle	

Notes	Serial	Type (other identity) [code]	Owner/operator, location or fate
	WZ791	Slingsby T38 Grasshopper TX1 (8944M)	RAF Museum, Hendon
	WZ792	Slingsby T38 Grasshopper TX1	Privately owned, Sproughton
	WZ793	Slingsby T38 Grasshopper TX1	Whitgift School, Croydon
	WZ796	Slingsby T38 Grasshopper TX1	Privately owned, stored Nympsfield, Glos
	WZ798	Slingsby T38 Grasshopper TX1	Bournemouth Aviation Museum
	WZ816	Slingsby T38 Grasshopper TX1 (BGA 3979)	Privately owned, Redhill
	WZ819	Slingsby T38 Grasshopper TX1 (BGA 3498)	Privately owned, Halton
	WZ820	Slingsby T38 Grasshopper TX1	Sywell Aviation Museum
	WZ822	Slingsby T38 Grasshopper TX1	Aeroventure, stored Doncaster
	WZ824	Slingsby T38 Grasshopper TX1	Privately owned, stored Strathaven, Strathclyde
	WZ826	Vickers Valiant B(K)1 (XD826/ 7872M) <ff>	Privately owned, Foulness
	WZ827	Slingsby T38 Grasshopper TX1	RAFGSA, stored Bicester
	WZ828	Slingsby T38 Grasshopper TX1 (BGA 4421)	Privately owned, Bicester
	WZ831	Slingsby T38 Grasshopper TX1	Privately owned, stored Nympsfield, Glos
	WZ846	DHC1 Chipmunk T10 (G-BCSC/ 8439M)	No 1404 Sqn ATC, Chatham
	WZ847	DHC1 Chipmunk T10 (G-CPMK) [F]	Privately owned, Sleap
	WZ868	DHC1 Chipmunk T10 (G-BCIW) [H]	*Sold to Australia*
	WZ868	DHC1 Chipmunk T10 (WG322/ G-ARMF) [H]	*Currently not known*
	WZ869	DHC1 Chipmunk T10 (8019M) [R] <ff>	*Currently not known*
	WZ872	DHC1 Chipmunk T10 (G-BZGB) [E]	Privately owned, Newcastle
	WZ876	DHC1 Chipmunk T10 (G-BBWN) <ff>	Privately owned, Twyford
	WZ879	DHC1 Chipmunk T10 (G-BWUT) [73]	Privately owned, Earls Colne
	WZ882	DHC1 Chipmunk T10 (G-BXGP) [K]	Privately owned, Eaglescott
	XA109	DH115 Sea Vampire T22	Royal Scottish Mus'm of Flight, E Fortune
	XA127	DH115 Sea Vampire T22 <ff>	FAA Museum, stored RNAS Yeovilton
	XA129	DH115 Sea Vampire T22	FAA Museum, stored RNAS Yeovilton
	XA225	Slingsby T38 Grasshopper TX1	Privately owned, Upavon
	XA228	Slingsby T38 Grasshopper TX1	Royal Scottish Mus'm of Flight, E Fortune
	XA230	Slingsby T38 Grasshopper TX1 (BGA 4098)	Privately owned, Henlow
	XA231	Slingsby T38 Grasshopper TX1 (8888M)	RAF Manston History Museum
	XA240	Slingsby T38 Grasshopper TX1 (BGA 4556)	Privately owned, Keevil
	XA241	Slingsby T38 Grasshopper TX1	Shuttleworth Collection, Old Warden
	XA243	Slingsby T38 Grasshopper TX1 (8886M)	Privately owned, Gransden Lodge, Cambs
	XA244	Slingsby T38 Grasshopper TX1	Privately owned, Keevil
	XA282	Slingsby T31B Cadet TX3	Caernarfon Air World
	XA286	Slingsby T31B Cadet TX3	Privately owned, stored Rufforth
	XA289	Slingsby T31B Cadet TX3	Privately owned, Eaglescott
	XA290	Slingsby T31B Cadet TX3	Privately owned, stored Rufforth
	XA293	Slingsby T31B Cadet TX3	Privately owned, Breighton
	XA302	Slingsby T31B Cadet TX3 (BGA3786)	Privately owned, Syerston
	XA459	Fairey Gannet ECM6 [E]	Privately owned, Lambourn, Berks
	XA460	Fairey Gannet ECM6 [768/BY]	Deeside College, Connah's Quay, Clwyd
	XA466	Fairey Gannet COD4 [777/LM]	FAA Museum, stored Yeovilton
	XA508	Fairey Gannet T2 [627/GN]	FAA Museum, at Midland Air Museum, Coventry
	XA564	Gloster Javelin FAW1 (7464M)	RAF Museum, Cosford
	XA634	Gloster Javelin FAW4 (7641M)	RAF Leeming, on display
	XA699	Gloster Javelin FAW5 (7809M)	Midland Air Museum, Coventry
	XA847	EE P1B (8371M)	Privately owned, Stowmarket, Suffolk
	XA862	WS55 Whirlwind HAR1 (G-AMJT) [9]	The Helicopter Museum, Weston-super-Mare

Serial	Type (other identity) [code]	Owner/operator, location or fate	Notes
XA864	WS55 Whirlwind HAR1	FAA Museum, stored Yeovilton	
XA870	WS55 Whirlwind HAR1	Aeroventure, Doncaster	
XA880	DH104 Devon C2 (G-BVXR)	Privately owned, Kemble	
XA893	Avro 698 Vulcan B1 (8591M) <ff>	RAF Museum, Cosford	
XA903	Avro 698 Vulcan B1 <ff>	Privately owned, Wellesbourne Mountford	
XA917	HP80 Victor B1 (7827M) <ff>	Privately owned, Pitscottie, Fife	
XB259	Blackburn B101 Beverley C1 (G-AOAI)	Museum of Army Transport, Beverley	
XB261	Blackburn B101 Beverley C1 <ff>	Duxford Aviation Society, Duxford	
XB446	Grumman TBM-3 Avenger ECM6B	FAA Museum, Yeovilton	
XB480	Hiller HT1 [537]	FAA Museum, stored Yeovilton	
XB812	Canadair CL-13 Sabre F4 (9227M) [U]	RAF Museum, Hendon	
XD145	Saro SR53	RAF Museum, Cosford	
XD163	WS55 Whirlwind HAR10 (8645M) [X]	The Helicopter Museum, Weston-super-Mare	
XD165	WS55 Whirlwind HAR10 (8673M) [B]	Yorkshire Helicopter Preservation Group, Elvington	
XD215	VS Scimitar F1 <ff>	Privately owned, Cheltenham	
XD235	VS Scimitar F1 <ff>	Privately owned, Ingatestone, Essex	
XD317	VS Scimitar F1 [112/R]	FAA Museum, RNAS Yeovilton	
XD332	VS Scimitar F1 [194/C]	Southampton Hall of Aviation	
XD377	DH115 Vampire T11 (8203M) <ff>	Aeroventure, stored Doncaster	
XD382	DH115 Vampire T11 (8033M)	Anchor Surplus, Ripley, Derbys	
XD425	DH115 Vampire T11 <ff>	RAF Millom Museum, Haverigg	
XD434	DH115 Vampire T11 [25]	Fenland & W Norfolk Aviation Museum, Wisbech	
XD445	DH115 Vampire T11	Bomber County Aviation Museum, Hemswell	
XD447	DH115 Vampire T11 [50]	Jet Avn Preservation Grp, Long Marston	
XD452	DH115 Vampire T11 (7990M) [66] <ff>	Privately owned, Chester	
XD459	DH115 Vampire T11 [63] <ff>	East Midlands Airport Aeropark	
XD463	DH115 Vampire T11 (8023M)	Privately owned, Ripley, Derbyshire	
XD506	DH115 Vampire T11 (7983M)	Gloucestershire Avn Coll, stored Gloucester	
XD515	DH115 Vampire T11 (7998M/ XM515)	Privately owned, Rugeley, Staffs	
XD525	DH115 Vampire T11 (7882M) <ff>	Kinegar Camp, Hollywood, Northern Ireland	
XD528	DH115 Vampire T11 (8159M) <ff>	Gamston Aerodrome Fire Section	
XD534	DH115 Vampire T11 [41]	Military Aircraft Pres'n Grp, Barton	
XD536	DH115 Vampire T11 (7734M) [H]	Alleyn's School CCF, Northolt	
XD542	DH115 Vampire T11 (7604M) [N]	Montrose Air Station Museum	
XD547	DH115 Vampire T11 [Z] (composite)	Dumfries & Galloway Avn Mus, Dumfries	
XD593	DH115 Vampire T11 [50]	Newark Air Museum, Winthorpe	
XD595	DH115 Vampire T11 <ff>	Privately owned, Glentham, Lincs	
XD596	DH115 Vampire T11 (7939M)	Southampton Hall of Aviation	
XD599	DH115 Vampire T11 <ff>	Privately owned, Ingatestone, Essex	
XD602	DH115 Vampire T11 (7737M) (composite)	Privately owned, Wearside	
XD616	DH115 Vampire T11 [56]	Mosquito Aircraft Museum, stored Gloucester	
XD622	DH115 Vampire T11 (8160M)	No 2214 Sqn ATC, Usworth	
XD624	DH115 Vampire T11 [O]	Macclesfield Technical College	
XD626	DH115 Vampire T11 [Q]	Midland Air Museum, Coventry	
XD674	Hunting Jet Provost T1 (7570M) [T]	RAF Museum, stored Cosford	
XD693	Hunting Jet Provost T1 (XM129/ G-AOBU) [Z-Q]	Kennet Aviation, North Weald	
XD816	Vickers Valiant B(K)1 <ff>	Brooklands Museum, Weybridge	
XD818	Vickers Valiant B(K)1 (7894M)	RAF Museum, Hendon	
XD857	Vickers Valiant B(K)1 <ff>	RAF Manston History Museum	
XD875	Vickers Valiant B(K)1 <ff>	Newark Air Museum, Winthorpe	
XE317	Bristol 171 Sycamore HR14 (G-AMWO) [S-N]	Aeroventure, stored Doncaster	
XE327	Hawker Sea Hawk FGA6 [644/LH]	*Sold to Germany, October 2002*	
XE339	Hawker Sea Hawk FGA6 (8156M) [149/E]	RNAS Yeovilton Fire Section	

Notes	Serial	Type (other identity) [code]	Owner/operator, location or fate
	XE340	Hawker Sea Hawk FGA6 [131/Z]	FAA Museum, at Montrose Air Station Museum
	XE368	Hawker Sea Hawk FGA6 [200/J]	Privately owned, Bruntingthorpe
	XE489	Hawker Sea Hawk FGA6 (G-JETH)	Gatwick Aviation Museum, Charlwood, Surrey
	XE521	Fairey Rotodyne Y (parts)	The Helicopter Museum, Weston-super-Mare
	XE584	Hawker Hunter FGA9 <ff>	NW Aviation Heritage Group, Hooton Park
	XE597	Hawker Hunter FGA9 (8874M) <ff>	Privately owned, Bromsgrove
	XE601	Hawker Hunter FGA9	Boscombe Down Museum
	XE606	Hawker Hunter F6A (XJ673/8841M)	RAF Cottesmore, preserved
	XE624	Hawker Hunter FGA9 (8875M) [G]	Phoenix Aviation, Bruntingthorpe
	XE627	Hawker Hunter F6A [T]	Imperial War Museum, Duxford
	XE643	Hawker Hunter FGA9 (8586M) <ff>	RAF EPTT, Aldergrove
	XE664	Hawker Hunter F4 <ff>	Gloucestershire Avn Coll, stored Gloucester
	XE665	Hawker Hunter T8C (G-BWGM) [876/VL]	Hunter Flying Club, Exeter
	XE668	Hawker Hunter GA11 [832/DD]	RN, Predannack Fire School
	XE670	Hawker Hunter F4 (7762M/8585M) <ff>	RAF Museum, Cosford
	XE683	Hawker Hunter F51 (RDAF E-409) [G]	City of Norwich Aviation Museum
	XE685	Hawker Hunter GA11 (G-GAII) [861/VL]	Privately owned, Exeter
	XE689	Hawker Hunter GA11 (G-BWGK) [864/VL]	Hunter Flying Club, Exeter
	XE786	Slingsby T31B Cadet TX3	RAF, stored Arbroath
	XE793	Slingsby T31B Cadet TX3 (8666M)	Privately owned
	XE796	Slingsby T31B Cadet TX3	*Sold to the Netherlands*
	XE799	Slingsby T31B Cadet TX3 (8943M) [R]	RAFGSA, Syerston
	XE802	Slingsby T31B Cadet TX3	Privately owned,
	XE807	Slingsby T31B Cadet TX3 (BGA3545)	Privately owned, Halesland
	XE849	DH115 Vampire T11 (7928M) [V3]	Privately owned, Shobdon
	XE852	DH115 Vampire T11 [H]	No 2247 Sqn ATC, Hawarden
	XE855	DH115 Vampire T11	Midland Air Museum, Coventry
	XE856	DH115 Vampire T11 (G-DUSK)	Privately owned, Henlow
	XE864	DH115 Vampire T11(comp XD435) <ff>	Privately owned, Ingatstone, Essex
	XE872	DH115 Vampire T11 [62]	Midland Air Museum, Coventry
	XE874	DH115 Vampire T11 (8582M)	Montrose Air Station Museum
	XE897	DH115 Vampire T11 (XD403)	Privately owned, Errol, Tayside
	XE897	DH115 Vampire T55 (U-1214/ G-DHVV)	Source Classic Jet Flight, Bournemouth
	XE920	DH115 Vampire T11 (8196M/ G-VMPR) [A]	The Jet Fighter Experience, Swansea
	XE921	DH115 Vampire T11 [64] <ff>	Privately owned, Yarmouth, IOW
	XE935	DH115 Vampire T11	Aeroventure, Doncaster
	XE946	DH115 Vampire T11 (7473M) <ff>	RAF Cranwell Aviation Heritage Centre
	XE956	DH115 Vampire T11 (G-OBLN)	De Havilland Aviation, Bridgend
	XE979	DH115 Vampire T11 [54]	Privately owned, Birlingham, Worcs
	XE982	DH115 Vampire T11 (7564M) [01]	Privately owned, Dunkeswell
	XE985	DH115 Vampire T11 (*WZ476*)	De Havilland Aviation, Swansea
	XE993	DH115 Vampire T11 (8161M)	Privately owned, Cosford
	XE995	DH115 Vampire T11 [53]	Privately owned, High Halden, Kent
	XE998	DH115 Vampire T11 (*U-1215*)	Privately owned, Farnborough
	XF113	VS Swift F7 [19] <ff>	Boscombe Down Museum
	XF114	VS Swift F7 (G-SWIF)	Privately owned, Bicester
	XF303	Hawker Hunter F58A (J-4105/ G-BWOU) [105,A]	The Old Flying Machine Company, Scampton
	XF314	Hawker Hunter F51 (RDAF E-412) [N]	Privately owned, Booker
	XF321	Hawker Hunter T7	Hunter Flying Club, Exeter (spares use)
	XF324	Hawker Hunter F51 (RDAF E-427) [D]	British Aviation Heritage, Bruntingthorpe
	XF358	Hawker Hunter T8C [870/VL]	DPA/AFD/QinetiQ, stored Boscombe Down
	XF375	Hawker Hunter F6A (8736M/ G-BUEZ) [05]	Privately owned, Spanhoe
	XF382	Hawker Hunter F6A [15]	Midland Air Museum, Coventry

Serial	Type (other identity) [code]	Owner/operator, location or fate	Notes
XF383	Hawker Hunter F6 (8706M) <ff>	Privately owned, Kidlington	
XF418	Hawker Hunter F51 (RDAF E-430)	Gatwick Aviation Museum, Charlwood, Surrey	
XF506	Hawker Hunter F4 (WT746/7770M) [A]	Dumfries & Galloway Avn Mus, Dumfries	
XF509	Hawker Hunter F6 (8708M)	Humbrol Paints, Marfleet, E Yorkshire	
XF515	Hawker Hunter F6A (8830M/ G-KAXF) [R]	Kennet Aviation, North Weald	
XF516	Hawker Hunter F6A (8685M/ G-BVVC) [19]	Hunter Flying Club, Exeter	
XF519	Hawker Hunter FGA9 (8677M/) 8738M/9183M (comp XJ695) [J]	Scrapped at Manston, 2002	
XF522	Hawker Hunter F6 <ff>	No 1365 Sqn ATC, Aylesbury	
XF526	Hawker Hunter F6 (8679M) [78/E]	Privately owned, Birlingham, Worcs	
XF527	Hawker Hunter F6 (8680M)	RAF Halton, on display	
XF545	Percival P56 Provost T1 (7957M) [O-K]	Privately owned, Thatcham	
XF597	Percival P56 Provost T1 (G-BKFW) [AH]	Privately owned, Thatcham	
XF603	Percival P56 Provost T1 (G-KAPW)	Kennet Aviation, North Weald	
XF690	Percival P56 Provost T1 (8041M/ G-MOOS)	Kennet Aviation, North Weald	
XF708	Avro 716 Shackleton MR3 [203/C]	Imperial War Museum, Duxford	
XF785	Bristol 173 (7648M/G-ALBN)	Bristol Aero Collection, Kemble	
XF836	Percival P56 Provost T1 (8043M/ G-AWRY) [JG]	Privately owned, Thatcham	
XF844	Percival P56 Provost T1 [70]	British Aviation Heritage, Bruntingthorpe	
XF877	Percival P56 Provost T1 (G-AWVF) [JX]	Privately owned, Brimpton, Berks	
XF926	Bristol 188 (8368M)	RAF Museum, Cosford	
XF994	Hawker Hunter T8C [873/VL]	Boscombe Down Museum	
XF995	Hawker Hunter T8B (G-BZSF/ 9237M) [K]	Delta Jets, Kemble	
XG154	Hawker Hunter FGA9 (8863M) [54]	RAF Museum, Hendon	
XG160	Hawker Hunter F6A (8831M/ G-BWAF)	Bournemouth Aviation Museum	
XG164	Hawker Hunter F6 (8681M)	Privately owned, Wellington, Somerset	
XG172	Hawker Hunter F6A (8832M) [A]	City of Norwich Aviation Museum	
XG190	Hawker Hunter F51 (RDAF E-425) [C]	Midland Air Museum, Coventry	
XG193	Hawker Hunter FGA9 (XG297) (comp with WT741)	Bomber County Aviation Museum, Hemswell	
XG195	Hawker Hunter FGA9 <ff>	Shropshire Wartime Aircraft Recovery Grp Mus, Sleap	
XG196	Hawker Hunter F6A (8702M) [31]	Army, Mytchett, Surrey, on display	
XG209	Hawker Hunter F6 (8709M) <ff>	Privately owned, Chelmsford	
XG210	Hawker Hunter F6	Privately owned, Beck Row, Suffolk	
XG225	Hawker Hunter F6A (8713M) [S]	RAF Cosford on display	
XG226	Hawker Hunter F6A (8800M) [28] <ff>	No 1242 Sqn ATC, Faversham, Kent	
XG252	Hawker Hunter FGA9 (8840M) [U]	Privately owned, Bosbury, Hereford	
XG254	Hawker Hunter FGA9 (8881M)	Norfolk & Suffolk Avn Museum, Flixton	
XG274	Hawker Hunter F6 (8710M) [71]	Privately owned, Newmarket	
XG290	Hawker Hunter F6 (8711M) <ff>	Boscombe Down Museum	
XG297	Hawker Hunter FGA9 <ff>	Privately owned, Whitwell, Derbyshire	
XG325	EE Lightning F1 <ff>	No 1476 Sqn ATC, Southend	
XG329	EE Lightning F1 (8050M)	Privately owned, Flixton	
XG331	EE Lightning F1 <ff>	Gloucestershire Avn Coll, stored Gloucester	
XG337	EE Lightning F1 (8056M) [M]	RAF Museum, Cosford	
XG452	Bristol 192 Belvedere HC1 (7997M/G-BRMB)	The Helicopter Museum, Weston-super-Mare	
XG454	Bristol 192 Belvedere HC1 (8366M)	Gr Manchester Mus of Science & Industry	
XG462	Bristol 192 Belvedere HC1 <ff>	The Helicopter Museum, stored Weston-super-Mare	
XG474	Bristol 192 Belvedere HC1 (8367M) [O]	RAF Museum, Hendon	
XG502	Bristol 171 Sycamore HR14	Museum of Army Flying, Middle Wallop	
XG506	Bristol 171 Sycamore HR14 (7852M) <ff>	Privately owned, South Kirby	
XG518	Bristol 171 Sycamore HR14 (8009M) [S-E]	Norfolk & Suffolk Avn Museum, Flixton	

XG523 – XH837

Notes	Serial	Type (other identity) [code]	Owner/operator, location or fate
	XG523	Bristol 171 Sycamore HR14 <ff> [K]	Norfolk & Suffolk Avn Museum, Flixton
	XG544	Bristol 171 Sycamore HR14	Privately owned,
	XG547	Bristol 171 Sycamore HR14 (G-HAPR) [S-T]	The Helicopter Museum, Weston-super-Mare
	XG574	WS55 Whirlwind HAR3 [752/PO]	FAA Museum, stored RNAS Yeovilton
	XG577	WS55 Whirlwind HAR3 (9050M)	RAF Leconfield Crash Rescue Training
	XG588	WS55 Whirlwind HAR3 (G-BAMH/ VR-BEP)	East Midlands Airport Aeropark
	XG594	WS55 Whirlwind HAS7 [517/PO]	FAA Museum, at R. Scottish Mus'm of Flt, E Fortune
	XG596	WS55 Whirlwind HAS7 [66]	The Helicopter Museum, Weston-super-Mare
	XG613	DH112 Sea Venom FAW21	Imperial War Museum, Duxford
	XG629	DH112 Sea Venom FAW22	Privately owned, Stone, Staffs
	XG680	DH112 Sea Venom FAW22 [438]	North-East Aircraft Museum, Usworth
	XG691	DH112 Sea Venom FAW22 [93/J]	Gloucestershire Avn Coll, stored Gloucester
	XG692	DH112 Sea Venom FAW22 [668/LM]	Privately owned, Stockport
	XG730	DH112 Sea Venom FAW22 [499/A]	Mosquito Aircraft Museum, London Colney
	XG736	DH112 Sea Venom FAW22	Ulster Aviation Society, Newtownards
	XG737	DH112 Sea Venom FAW22 [220/Z]	Jet Avn Preservation Grp, stored Long Marston
	XG743	DH115 Sea Vampire T22 [597/LM]	Imperial War Museum, Duxford
	XG775	DH115 Vampire T55 (U-1219/ G-DHWW) [VL]	Source Classic Jet Flight, Bournemouth
	XG797	Fairey Gannet ECM6 [277]	Imperial War Museum, Duxford
	XG831	Fairey Gannet ECM6 [396]	Flambards Village Theme Park, Helston
	XG882	Fairey Gannet T5 (8754M) [771/LM]	Privately owned, Errol, Tayside
	XG883	Fairey Gannet T5 [773/BY]	FAA Museum, at Museum of Berkshire Aviation, Woodley
	XG900	Short SC1	Science Museum, South Kensington
	XG905	Short SC1	Ulster Folk & Transpt Mus, Holywood, Co Down
	XH131	EE Canberra PR9	RAF No 39(1 PRU) Sqn, Marham
	XH134	EE Canberra PR9	RAF No 39(1 PRU) Sqn, Marham
	XH135	EE Canberra PR9	RAF No 39(1 PRU) Sqn, Marham
	XH136	EE Canberra PR9 (8782M) [W] <ff>	Phoenix Aviation, Bruntingthorpe
	XH165	EE Canberra PR9 <ff>	Blyth Valley Aviation Collection, Walpole
	XH168	EE Canberra PR9	RAF No 39(1 PRU) Sqn, Marham
	XH169	EE Canberra PR9	RAF No 39(1 PRU) Sqn, Marham
	XH170	EE Canberra PR9 (8739M)	RAF Wyton, on display
	XH171	EE Canberra PR9 (8746M) [U]	RAF Museum, Cosford
	XH174	EE Canberra PR9 <ff>	RAF, stored Shawbury
	XH175	EE Canberra PR9 <ff>	Privately owned, Stock, Essex
	XH177	EE Canberra PR9 <ff>	Newark Air Museum, Winthorpe
	XH278	DH115 Vampire T11 (8595M/ 7866M) [42]	Yorkshire Air Museum, Elvington
	XH312	DH115 Vampire T11 [18]	Privately owned, Dodleston, Cheshire
	XH313	DH115 Vampire T11 (G-BZRD) [E]	Privately owned, Sandtoft
	XH318	DH115 Vampire T11 (7761M) [64]	Privately owned, Cadnam
	XH328	DH115 Vampire T11 <ff>	Privately owned, Duxford
	XH330	DH115 Vampire T11 [73]	Privately owned, Camberley, Surrey
	XH537	Avro 698 Vulcan B2MRR (8749M) <ff>	Bournemouth Aviation Museum
	XH558	Avro 698 Vulcan B2 (G-VLCN)	British Aviation Heritage, Bruntingthorpe
	XH560	Avro 698 Vulcan K2 <ff>	Privately owned, Foulness
	XH563	Avro 698 Vulcan B2MRR <ff>	Privately owned, Banchory, Fife
	XH568	EE Canberra B6(mod) (G-BVIC)	Classic Aviation Projects, Bruntingthorpe
	XH584	EE Canberra T4 (G-27-374) <ff>	Aeroventure, Doncaster
	XH592	HP80 Victor K1A (8429M) <ff>	Phoenix Aviation, Bruntingthorpe
	XH648	HP80 Victor K1A	Imperial War Museum, Duxford
	XH669	HP80 Victor K2 (9092M) <ff>	Privately owned, Foulness
	XH670	HP80 Victor SR2 <ff>	Privately owned, Foulness
	XH672	HP80 Victor K2	RAF Museum, Cosford
	XH673	HP80 Victor K2 (8911M)	RAF Marham, on display
	XH767	Gloster Javelin FAW9 (7955M) [A]	Yorkshire Air Museum, Elvington
	XH783	Gloster Javelin FAW7 (7798M) <ff>	Privately owned, Catford
	XH837	Gloster Javelin FAW7 (8032M) <ff>	Caernarfon Air World

Serial	Type (other identity) [code]	Owner/operator, location or fate	Notes
XH892	Gloster Javelin FAW9R (7982M) [J]	Norfolk & Suffolk Avn Museum, Flixton	
XH897	Gloster Javelin FAW9	Imperial War Museum, Duxford	
XH903	Gloster Javelin FAW9 (7938M) <ff>	Gloucestershire Avn Coll, stored Gloucester	
XH992	Gloster Javelin FAW8 (7829M) [P]	Newark Air Museum, Winthorpe	
XJ314	RR Thrust Measuring Rig	Science Museum, South Kensington	
XJ380	Bristol 171 Sycamore HR14 (8628M)	Montrose Air Station Museum	
XJ389	Fairey Jet Gyrodyne (XD759/ G-AJJP)	Museum of Berkshire Aviation, Woodley	
XJ409	WS55 Whirlwind HAR10 (XD779)	Maes Artro Craft Village, Llanbedr	
XJ435	WS55 Whirlwind HAR10 (XD804/ 8671M) [V]	RAF Manston History Museum, spares use	
XJ476	DH110 Sea Vixen FAW1 <ff>	No 424 Sqn ATC, Southampton Hall of Avn	
XJ481	DH110 Sea Vixen FAW1 [VL]	FAA Museum, stored RNAS Yeovilton	
XJ482	DH110 Sea Vixen FAW1 [713/VL]	Norfolk & Suffolk Avn Museum, Flixton	
XJ488	DH110 Sea Vixen FAW1 <ff>	Robertsbridge Aviation Society, Mayfield	
XJ494	DH110 Sea Vixen FAW2	Privately owned, Bruntingthorpe	
XJ560	DH110 Sea Vixen FAW2 (8142M) [242]	Newark Air Museum, Winthorpe	
XJ565	DH110 Sea Vixen FAW2 [127/E]	Mosquito Aircraft Museum, London Colney	
XJ571	DH110 Sea Vixen FAW2 (8140M) [242/R]	Privately owned, Brooklands Museum, Weybridge	
XJ575	DH110 Sea Vixen FAW2 <ff> [SAH-13]	Wellesbourne Wartime Museum	
XJ579	DH110 Sea Vixen FAW2 <ff>	Midland Air Museum, Coventry	
XJ580	DH110 Sea Vixen FAW2 [131/E]	Tangmere Military Aviation Museum	
XJ615	Hawker Hunter T8C(mod) (XF357/ G-BWGL)	Privately owned, Elvington	
XJ639	Hawker Hunter F6A (8687M) [H]	Hunter Flying Club, Exeter	
XJ714	Hawker Hunter FR10 (comp XG226)	Jet Avn Preservation Grp, Long Marston	
XJ723	WS55 Whirlwind HAR10	Montrose Air Station Museum	
XJ726	WS55 Whirlwind HAR10 [F]	Caernarfon Air World	
XJ727	WS55 Whirlwind HAR10 (8661M) [L]	RAF Manston History Museum	
XJ758	WS55 Whirlwind HAR10 <ff>	Privately owned, Welshpool	
XJ771	DH115 Vampire T55 (U-1215/ G-HELV)	Privately owned, Bournemouth	
XJ772	DH115 Vampire T11 [H]	Mosquito Aircraft Museum, London Colney	
XJ823	Avro 698 Vulcan B2A	Solway Aviation Society, Carlisle	
XJ824	Avro 698 Vulcan B2A	Imperial War Museum, Duxford	
XJ917	Bristol 171 Sycamore HR14 [H-S]	Bristol Sycamore Group, stored Kemble	
XJ918	Bristol 171 Sycamore HR14 (8190M)	RAF Museum, Cosford	
XK149	Hawker Hunter F6A (8714M) [L]	Privately owned, Bruntingthorpe	
XK416	Auster AOP9 (7855M/G-AYUA)	De Havilland Aviation, Swansea	
XK417	Auster AOP9 (G-AVXY)	Privately owned, Sutton in Ashfield	
XK418	Auster AOP9 (7976M)	SWWAPS, Lasham	
XK421	Auster AOP9 (8365M) (frame)	Aeroventure, stored Doncaster	
XK482	Saro Skeeter AOP12 (7840M/ G-BJWC) [C]	*Sold to Australia, 2002*	
XK488	Blackburn NA39 Buccaneer S2	FAA Museum, stored RNAS Yeovilton	
XK526	Blackburn NA39 Buccaneer S2 (8648M)	RAF Honington, at main gate	
XK527	Blackburn NA39 Buccaneer S2D (8818M) <ff>	Privately owned, North Wales	
XK532	Blackburn NA39 Buccaneer S1 (8867M) [632/LM]	The Fresson Trust, Inverness Airport	
XK533	Blackburn NA39 Buccaneer S1 <ff>	Royal Scottish Mus'm of Flight, E Fortune	
XK590	DH115 Vampire T11 [V]	Wellesbourne Wartime Museum	
XK623	DH115 Vampire T11 (*G-VAMP*) [56]	Caernarfon Air World	
XK624	DH115 Vampire T11 [32]	Norfolk & Suffolk Avn Museum, Flixton	
XK625	DH115 Vampire T11 [12]	Brenzett Aeronautical Museum	
XK627	DH115 Vampire T11	Privately owned, Barton	
XK632	DH115 Vampire T11 [67]	No 2370 Sqn ATC, Denham	
XK637	DH115 Vampire T11 [56]	RAF Millom Museum, Haverigg	

XK655 – XL609

Notes	Serial	Type (other identity) [code]	Owner/operator, location or fate
	XK655	DH106 Comet C2(RC) (G-AMXA) <ff>	Gatwick Airport, on display (BOAC colours)
	XK695	DH106 Comet C2(RC) (G-AMXH/ 9164M) <ff>	Mosquito Aircraft Museum, London Colney
	XK699	DH106 Comet C2 (7971M)	RAF Lyneham on display
	XK724	Folland Gnat F1 (7715M)	RAF Museum, Cosford
	XK740	Folland Gnat F1 (8396M)	Southampton Hall of Aviation
	XK741	Folland Gnat F1 (fuselage)	Midland Air Museum, Coventry
	XK776	ML Utility 1	Museum of Army Flying, Middle Wallop
	XK788	Slingsby T38 Grasshopper TX1	Privately owned, Sproughton
	XK789	Slingsby T38 Grasshopper TX1	Midland Air Museum, stored Coventry
	XK790	Slingsby T38 Grasshopper TX1	Privately owned, stored Husbands Bosworth
	XK819	Slingsby T38 Grasshopper TX1	Privately owned, Selby
	XK822	Slingsby T38 Grasshopper TX1	Privately owned, Kenley
	XK895	DH104 Sea Devon C20 (G-SDEV) [19/CU]	Privately owned, Shoreham
	XK896	DH104 Sea Devon C20 (G-RNAS) (fuselage)	Privately owned, Filton (spares use)
	XK907	WS55 Whirlwind HAS7 [U]	Midland Air Museum, Coventry
	XK911	WS55 Whirlwind HAS7 [519/PO]	Privately owned, Adlington, Lancs
	XK936	WS55 Whirlwind HAS7 [62]	Imperial War Museum, Duxford
	XK940	WS55 Whirlwind HAS7 (G-AYXT) [911]	The Helicopter Museum, Weston-super-Mare
	XK944	WS55 Whirlwind HAS7	No 617 Sqn ATC, Malpas, Cheshire
	XK970	WS55 Whirlwind HAR10 (8789M)	Privately owned, Dunkeswell
	XL149	Blackburn B101 Beverley C1 (7988M) <ff>	Newark Air Museum, Winthorpe
	XL160	HP80 Victor K2 (8910M) <ff>	HP Victor Association, Walpole
	XL164	HP80 Victor K2 (9215M) <ff>	Gatwick Aviation Museum, Charlwood, Surrey
	XL188	HP80 Victor K2 (9100M) (fuselage)	RAF Kinloss Fire Section
	XL190	HP80 Victor K2 (9216M) <ff>	RAF Manston History Museum
	XL231	HP80 Victor K2	Yorkshire Air Museum, Elvington
	XL318	Avro 698 Vulcan B2 (8733M)	RAF Museum, Hendon
	XL319	Avro 698 Vulcan B2	North-East Aircraft Museum, Usworth
	XL360	Avro 698 Vulcan B2A	Midland Air Museum, Coventry
	XL388	Avro 698 Vulcan B2 <ff>	Blyth Valley Aviation Collection, Walpole
	XL391	Avro 698 Vulcan B2	Privately owned, Blackpool
	XL426	Avro 698 Vulcan B2 (G-VJET)	Vulcan Restoration Trust, Southend
	XL445	Avro 698 Vulcan K2 (8811M) <ff>	Blyth Valley Aviation Collection, Walpole
	XL449	Fairey Gannet AEW3 <ff>	Privately owned, Camberley, Surrey
	XL472	Fairey Gannet AEW3 [044/R]	Gatwick Aviation Museum, Charlwood, Surrey
	XL497	Fairey Gannet AEW3 [041/R]	RN, Prestwick
	XL500	Fairey Gannet AEW3 [CU]	World Naval Base, Chatham
	XL502	Fairey Gannet AEW3 (8610M/ G-BMYP)	Privately owned, Sandtoft
	XL503	Fairey Gannet AEW3 [070/E]	FAA Museum, RNAS Yeovilton
	XL563	Hawker Hunter T7 (9218M)	Privately owned, Bosbury, Hereford
	XL564	Hawker Hunter T7 (fuselage)	Boscombe Down Museum
	XL565	Hawker Hunter T7 (parts of WT745)	Privately owned, Bruntingthorpe
	XL567	Hawker Hunter T7 (8723M) [84]	Scrapped
	XL568	Hawker Hunter T7A (9224M) [C]	RAF Museum, Cosford
	XL569	Hawker Hunter T7 (8833M) [SC]	East Midlands Airport Aeropark
	XL571	Hawker Hunter T7 (XL572/8834M/ G-HNTR) [V]	Yorkshire Air Museum, Elvington
	XL573	Hawker Hunter T7 (G-BVGH)	Privately owned, Exeter
	XL577	Hawker Hunter T7 (G-BXKF/ 8676M)	Delta Jets, Kemble
	XL578	Hawker Hunter T7 (fuselage) [77]	Privately owned, Kemble
	XL580	Hawker Hunter T8M [723]	FAA Museum, RNAS Yeovilton
	XL586	Hawker Hunter T7 <rf>	Delta Jets, Kemble
	XL587	Hawker Hunter T7 (8807M/ G-HPUX) [Z]	The Old Flying Machine Company, stored Scampton
	XL591	Hawker Hunter T7	Gatwick Aviation Museum, Charlwood, Surrey
	XL592	Hawker Hunter T7 (8836M) [Y]	Hunter Flying Club, Exeter
	XL601	Hawker Hunter T7 (G-BZSR) [874/VL]	Classic Fighters, Brustem, Belgium
	XL602	Hawker Hunter T8M (G-BWFT)	Hunter Flying Club, Exeter
	XL609	Hawker Hunter T7 <ff>	Boscombe Down Museum

Serial	Type (other identity) [code]	Owner/operator, location or fate	Notes
XL612	Hawker Hunter T7 [2]	DPA/AFD/QinetiQ Boscombe Down, wfu	
XL618	Hawker Hunter T7 (8892M) [05]	Caernarfon Air World	
XL621	Hawker Hunter T7 (G-BNCX)	Privately owned, Brooklands Museum	
XL623	Hawker Hunter T7 (8770M)	The Planets Leisure Centre, Woking	
XL629	EE Lightning T4	DPA/QinetiQ Boscombe Down, at main gate	
XL703	SAL Pioneer CC1 (8034M)	RAF Museum, Cosford	
XL714	DH82A Tiger Moth II (T6099/ G-AOGR)	Privately owned, Swanton Morley	
XL716	DH82A Tiger Moth II (T7363/ G-AOIL)	Privately owned, Chandlers Ford	
XL735	Saro Skeeter AOP12	Privately owned, Tattershall Thorpe	
XL738	Saro Skeeter AOP12 (7860M)	Privately owned, Ivybridge, Devon	
XL739	Saro Skeeter AOP12	AAC Wattisham, on display	
XL762	Saro Skeeter AOP12 (8017M)	Royal Scottish Mus'm of Flight, E Fortune	
XL763	Saro Skeeter AOP12	Privately owned, Ivybridge, Devon	
XL764	Saro Skeeter AOP12 (7940M) [J]	Newark Air Museum, Winthorpe	
XL765	Saro Skeeter AOP12	Privately owned, Melksham, Wilts	
XL770	Saro Skeeter AOP12 (8046M)	Southampton Hall of Aviation	
XL809	Saro Skeeter AOP12 (G-BLIX)	Privately owned, Wilden, Beds	
XL811	Saro Skeeter AOP	The Helicopter Museum, Weston-super-Mare	
XL812	Saro Skeeter AOP12 (G-SARO)	Privately owned, Old Buckenham	
XL813	Saro Skeeter AOP12	Museum of Army Flying, Middle Wallop	
XL814	Saro Skeeter AOP12	AAC Historic Aircraft Flight, Middle Wallop	
XL824	Bristol 171 Sycamore HR14 (8021M)	Gr Manchester Mus of Science & Industry	
XL829	Bristol 171 Sycamore HR14	Bristol Industrial Museum	
XL840	WS55 Whirlwind HAS7	Privately owned, Bawtry	
XL847	WS55 Whirlwind HAS7 [83]	AAC Middle Wallop Fire Section	
XL853	WS55 Whirlwind HAS7 [PO]	FAA Museum, stored RNAS Yeovilton	
XL875	WS55 Whirlwind HAR9	Perth Technical College	
XL929	Percival P66 Pembroke C1 (G-BNPU)	D-Day Museum, Shoreham Airport	
XL954	Percival P66 Pembroke C1 (9042M/N4234C/G-BXES)	Air Atlantique Historic Flight, Coventry	
XL993	SAL Twin Pioneer CC1 (8388M)	RAF Museum, Cosford	
XM135	BAC Lightning F1 [B]	Imperial War Museum, Duxford	
XM144	BAC Lightning F1 (8417M) <ff>	Privately owned, Booker	
XM169	BAC Lightning F1A (8422M) <ff>	N Yorks Aircraft Recovery Centre, Chop Gate	
XM172	BAC Lightning F1A (8427M)	Privately owned, Booker	
XM173	BAC Lightning F1A (8414M) [A]	RAF Bentley Priory, at main gate	
XM191	BAC Lightning F1A (7854M/ 8590M) <ff>	RAF EPTT, Bottesford	
XM192	BAC Lightning F1A (8413M) [K]	Bomber County Aviation Museum, Hemswell	
XM223	DH104 Devon C2 (G-BWWC) [J]	Air Atlantique, Coventry	
XM279	EE Canberra B(I)8 <ff>	Privately owned, Flixton	
XM300	WS58 Wessex HAS1	Welsh Industrial & Maritime Mus'm, stored Cardiff	
XM328	WS58 Wessex HAS3 [653/PO]	SFDO, RNAS Culdrose	
XM330	WS58 Wessex HAS1	The Helicopter Museum, Weston-super-Mare	
XM349	Hunting Jet Provost T3A (9046M) [T]	Global Aviation, Binbrook	
XM350	Hunting Jet Provost T3A (9036M) [89]	Aeroventure, Doncaster	
XM351	Hunting Jet Provost T3 (8078M) [Y]	RAF Museum, Cosford	
XM355	Hunting Jet Provost T3 (8229M) [D]	Privately owned, Shobdon	
XM358	Hunting Jet Provost T3A (8987M) [53]	Privately owned, Llanwrtyd Wells, Powys	
XM362	Hunting Jet Provost T3 (8230M)	RAF No 1 SoTT, Cosford	
XM363	Hunting Jet Provost T3 <ff>	*Currently not known*	
XM365	Hunting Jet Provost T3A (G-BXBH) [37]	Privately owned, Norwich	
XM369	Hunting Jet Provost T3 (8084M) [C]	Privately owned, Portsmouth	
XM370	Hunting Jet Provost T3A (G-BVSP) [10]	Privately owned, Long Marston	
XM372	Hunting Jet Provost T3A (8917M) [55]	RAF Linton-on-Ouse Fire Section	
XM375	Hunting Jet Provost T3 (8231M) [B]	RAF Cottesmore Fire Section	

Notes	Serial	Type (other identity) [code]	Owner/operator, location or fate
	XM383	Hunting Jet Provost T3A [90]	Newark Air Museum, Winthorpe
	XM402	Hunting Jet Provost T3 (8055AM) [J]	Fenland & W Norfolk Aviation Museum, Wisbech
	XM404	Hunting Jet Provost T3 (8055BM)	FETC, Moreton-in-Marsh, Glos
	XM409	Hunting Jet Provost T3 (8082M) <rf>	Air Scouts, Guernsey Airport
	XM410	Hunting Jet Provost T3 (8054AM) [B]	DEODS, Chattenden, Kent
	XM411	Hunting Jet Provost T3 (8434M) <ff>	Aeroventure, Doncaster
	XM412	Hunting Jet Provost T3A (9011M) [41]	Privately owned, Kinross, Scotland
	XM414	Hunting Jet Provost T3A (8996M)	Flight Experience Workshop, Belfast
	XM417	Hunting Jet Provost T3 (8054BM) [D] <ff>	Privately owned, Hednesford, Staffs
	XM419	Hunting Jet Provost T3A (8990M) [102]	DARA Training School, RAF St Athan
	XM424	Hunting Jet Provost T3A (G-BWDS)	Privately owned, North Weald
	XM425	Hunting Jet Provost T3A (8995M) [88]	Privately owned, Longton, Staffs
	XM463	Hunting Jet Provost T3A [38] (fuselage)	RAF Museum, Hendon
	XM468	Hunting Jet Provost T3 (8081M)	Privately owned, Terrington St Clement
	XM470	Hunting Jet Provost T3A (G-BWZZ) [12]	Privately owned, Hawarden
	XM473	Hunting Jet Provost T3A (8974M/ G-TINY)	Bedford College, instructional use
	XM474	Hunting Jet Provost T3 (8121M) <ff>	No 1940 Sqn ATC, Levenshulme
	XM478	Hunting Jet Provost T3A (8983M/ G-BXDL)	Privately owned, Swansea
	XM479	Hunting Jet Provost T3A (G-BVEZ) [54]	Privately owned, Newcastle
	XM480	Hunting Jet Provost T3 (8080M)	4x4 Car Centre, Chesterfield
	XM496	Bristol 253 Britannia C1 (EL-WXA)	Britannia Preservation Society, Kemble
	XM529	Saro Skeeter AOP12 (7979M/ G-BDNS)	Privately owned, Handforth
	XM553	Saro Skeeter AOP12 (G-AWSV)	Privately owned, Middle Wallop
	XM555	Saro Skeeter AOP12 (8027M)	RAF Museum, Cosford
	XM561	Saro Skeeter AOP12 (7980M)	Aeroventure, Doncaster
	XM564	Saro Skeeter AOP12	National Tank Museum, Bovington
	XM569	Avro 698 Vulcan B2 <ff>	Gloucestershire Avn Coll, stored Gloucester
	XM575	Avro 698 Vulcan B2A (G-BLMC)	East Midlands Airport Aeropark
	XM594	Avro 698 Vulcan B2	Newark Air Museum, Winthorpe
	XM597	Avro 698 Vulcan B2	Royal Scottish Mus'm of Flight, E Fortune
	XM598	Avro 698 Vulcan B2 (8778M)	RAF Museum, Cosford
	XM602	Avro 698 Vulcan B2 (8771M) <ff>	Avro Aircraft Heritage Society, Woodford
	XM603	Avro 698 Vulcan B2	Avro Aircraft Heritage Society, Woodford
	XM607	Avro 698 Vulcan B2 (8779M)	RAF Waddington, on display
	XM612	Avro 698 Vulcan B2	City of Norwich Aviation Museum
	XM652	Avro 698 Vulcan B2 <ff>	Privately owned, Welshpool
	XM655	Avro 698 Vulcan B2 (G-VULC)	Privately owned, Wellesbourne Mountford
	XM660	WS55 Whirlwind HAS7 [78]	RAF Millom Museum, Haverigg
	XM685	WS55 Whirlwind HAS7 (G-AYZJ) [513/PO]	Newark Air Museum, Winthorpe
	XM692	HS Gnat T1 <ff>	Thameside Aviation Museum, East Tilbury
	XM693	HS Gnat T1 (7891M)	BAE Systems Hamble, on display
	XM693	HS Gnat T1 (8618M/XP504/ G-TIMM) [04]	Kennet Aviation, North Weald
	XM697	HS Gnat T1 (G-NAAT)	Privately owned, Exeter
	XM708	HS Gnat T1 (8573M)	Privately owned, Lytham St Annes
	XM715	HP80 Victor K2	British Aviation Heritage, Bruntingthorpe
	XM717	HP80 Victor K2 <ff>	RAF Museum, Hendon
	XM819	Lancashire EP9 Prospector (G-APXW)	Museum of Army Flying, Middle Wallop
	XM833	WS58 Wessex HAS3	SWWAPS, Lasham
	XM868	WS58 Wessex HAS1 [517]	*Scrapped at Predannack by April 2002*
	XM870	WS58 Wessex HAS3 [PO]	RN, Predannack Fire School
	XM874	WS58 Wessex HAS1 [521/CU]	*Scrapped at Predannack by April 2002*
	XM927	WS58 Wessex HAS3 (8814M) [660/PO]	RAF Shawbury Fire Section

Serial	Type (other identity) [code]	Owner/operator, location or fate	Notes
XN126	WS55 Whirlwind HAR10 (8655M) [S]	Pinewood Studios, Elstree	
XN157	Slingsby T21B Sedbergh TX1 (BGA 3255)	Privately owned, stored Long Mynd	
XN185	Slingsby T21B Sedbergh TX1 (8942M/BGA 4077)	RAFGSA, Syerston	
XN187	Slingsby T21B Sedbergh TX1 (BGA 3903)	Privately owned, Seighford	
XN198	Slingsby T31B Cadet TX3	Privately owned, Challock Lees	
XN238	Slingsby T31B Cadet TX3 <ff>	Aeroventure, stored Doncaster	
XN239	Slingsby T31B Cadet TX3 (8889M) [G]	Welsh National Museum, Cardiff	
XN243	Slingsby T31B Cadet TX3 (BGA 3145)	Privately owned, Bicester	
XN246	Slingsby T31B Cadet TX3	Southampton Hall of Aviation	
XN258	WS55 Whirlwind HAR9 [589/CU]	North-East Aircraft Museum, Usworth	
XN263	WS55 Whirlwind HAS7	Privately owned, Bosham, W Sussex	
XN297	WS55 Whirlwind HAR9 (XN311) [12]	Privately owned, Hull	
XN298	WS55 Whirlwind HAR9 [810/LS]	International Fire Training Centre, Chorley	
XN299	WS55 Whirlwind HAS7 [758]	Tangmere Military Aviation Museum	
XN304	WS55 Whirlwind HAS7 [64]	Norfolk & Suffolk Avn Museum, Flixton	
XN332	Saro P531 (G-APNV) [759]	FAA Museum, stored RNAS Yeovilton	
XN334	Saro P531	FAA Museum, stored RNAS Yeovilton	
XN341	Saro Skeeter AOP12 (8022M)	Stondon Transport Mus & Garden Centre, Beds	
XN344	Saro Skeeter AOP12 (8018M)	Science Museum, South Kensington	
XN351	Saro Skeeter AOP12 (G-BKSC)	Privately owned, Ipswich	
XN380	WS55 Whirlwind HAS7	RAF Manston History Museum	
XN385	WS55 Whirlwind HAS7	Botany Bay Villages, Chorley, Lancs	
XN386	WS55 Whirlwind HAR9 [435/ED]	Aeroventure, Doncaster	
XN412	Auster AOP9	Auster 9 Group, Melton Mowbray	
XN435	Auster AOP9 (G-BGBU)	Privately owned, Egham	
XN437	Auster AOP9 (G-AXWA)	Privately owned, North Weald	
XN441	Auster AOP9 (G-BGKT)	Privately owned, Wickenby	
XN459	Hunting Jet Provost T3A (G-BWOT)	Transair(UK) Ltd, North Weald	
XN462	Hunting Jet Provost T3A [17]	FAA Museum, stored RNAS Yeovilton	
XN466	Hunting Jet Provost T3A [29] <ff>	No 1005 Sqn ATC, Radcliffe, Gtr Manchester	
XN492	Hunting Jet Provost T3 (8079M) <ff>	Privately owned, Haydock	
XN493	Hunting Jet Provost T3 (XN137) <ff>	Privately owned, Camberley	
XN494	Hunting Jet Provost T3A (9012M) [43]	Crawley Technical College	
XN497	Hunting Jet Provost T3A [52]	Privately owned, Newby Wiske	
XN500	Hunting Jet Provost T3A [48]	Oxford Avn Services Ltd, Oxford, ground instruction	
XN501	Hunting Jet Provost T3A (8958M) [G]	Privately owned, Billockby, Norfolk	
XN503	Hunting Jet Provost T3 <ff>	No 1284 Sqn ATC, Milford Haven	
XN508	Hunting Jet Provost T3A <ff>	RAF/DARA, St Athan	
XN510	Hunting Jet Provost T3A (G-BXBI) [40]	Privately owned, Sproughton	
XN511	Hunting Jet Provost T3 [64] <ff>	Aeroventure, Doncaster	
XN549	Hunting Jet Provost T3 (8235M) [32,P]	RAF Shawbury Fire Section	
XN550	Hunting Jet Provost T3 <ff>	Privately owned, Stone, Staffs	
XN551	Hunting Jet Provost T3A (8984M)	DARA Training School, RAF St Athan	
XN554	Hunting Jet Provost T3 (8436M) [K]	RAF North Luffenham Training Area	
XN573	Hunting Jet Provost T3 [E] <ff>	Newark Air Museum, Winthorpe	
XN577	Hunting Jet Provost T3A (8956M) [89,F]	Privately owned, Billockby, Norfolk	
XN579	Hunting Jet Provost T3A (9137M) [14]	RAF North Luffenham Training Area	
XN582	Hunting Jet Provost T3A (8957M) [95,H]	Arbury College, Cambridge	
XN584	Hunting Jet Provost T3A (9014M) [E]	Phoenix Aviation, Bruntingthorpe	
XN586	Hunting Jet Provost T3A (9039M) [91,S]	Brooklands Technical College	
XN589	Hunting Jet Provost T3A (9143M) [46]	RAF Linton-on-Ouse, on display	

Notes	Serial	Type (other identity) [code]	Owner/operator, location or fate
	XN592	Hunting Jet Provost T3 <ff>	No 1105 Sqn ATC, Winchester
	XN593	Hunting Jet Provost T3A (8988M) [97,Q]	Privately owned, Billockby, Norfolk
	XN594	Hunting Jet Provost T3 (8234M/ XN458)	Privately owned, Ashington, W Sussex
	XN597	Hunting Jet Provost T3 (7984M) <ff>	RAF Millom Museum, Haverigg
	XN607	Hunting Jet Provost T3 <ff>	N Yorks Aircraft Recovery Centre, Chop Gate
	XN629	Hunting Jet Provost T3A (G-BVEG/ G-KNOT) [49]	Privately owned, Norwich
	XN632	Hunting Jet Provost T3 (8352M)	Privately owned, Birlingham, Worcs
	XN634	Hunting Jet Provost T3A <ff>	Privately owned, Sproughton
	XN634	Hunting Jet Provost T3A [53] <rf>	BAE Systems Warton Fire Section
	XN636	Hunting Jet Provost T3A (9045M) [15]	Privately owned
	XN637	Hunting Jet Provost T3 (G-BKOU) [03]	Privately owned, Cranfield
	XN647	DH110 Sea Vixen FAW2 <ff>	Privately owned, stored Bruntingthorpe
	XN650	DH110 Sea Vixen FAW2 <ff>	Privately owned, Welshpool
	XN651	DH110 Sea Vixen FAW2 <ff>	Privately owned, stored Lavendon, Bucks
	XN657	DH110 Sea Vixen D3 [TR-1]	Privately owned, Yateley, Hants
	XN685	DH110 Sea Vixen FAW2 (8173M) [03/VL]	Midland Air Museum, Coventry
	XN696	DH110 Sea Vixen FAW2 <ff>	Blyth Valley Aviation Collection, stored Walpole
	XN714	Hunting H126	RAF Museum, Cosford
	XN726	EE Lightning F2A (8545M) <ff>	Boscombe Down Museum
	XN728	EE Lightning F2A (8546M) [V]	Privately owned, Balderton, Notts
	XN734	EE Lightning F3A (8346M/ G-BNCA) <ff>	Privately owned, Cranfield
	XN774	EE Lightning F2A (8551M) <ff>	Privately owned, Boston
	XN776	EE Lightning F2A (8535M) [C]	Royal Scottish Mus'm of Flight, E Fortune
	XN795	EE Lightning F2A <ff>	Privately owned, Foulness
	XN817	AW660 Argosy C1	QinetiQ West Freugh Fire Section
	XN819	AW660 Argosy C1 (8205M) <ff>	Newark Air Museum, Winthorpe
	XN923	HS Buccaneer S1 [13]	Gatwick Aviation Museum, Charlwood, Surrey
	XN928	HS Buccaneer S1 (8179M) <ff>	Privately owned, Kent
	XN957	HS Buccaneer S1	FAA Museum, RNAS Yeovilton
	XN964	HS Buccaneer S1 [613/LM]	Newark Air Museum, Winthorpe
	XN967	HS Buccaneer S1 <ff>	Muckleburgh Collection, Weybourne, Norfolk
	XN972	HS Buccaneer S1 (8183M/XN962) <ff>	RAF Museum, Hendon
	XN974	HS Buccaneer S2A	Yorkshire Air Museum, Elvington
	XN981	HS Buccaneer S2B	Privately owned, Errol, Scotland
	XN983	HS Buccaneer S2B <ff>	Fenland & W Norfolk Aviation Museum, Wisbech
	XP110	WS58 Wessex HAS3 [55/FL]	RN AESS, HMS Sultan, Gosport, BDRT
	XP137	WS58 Wessex HAS3 [711/DD]	SFDO, RNAS Culdrose
	XP142	WS58 Wessex HAS3	FAA Museum, Yeovilton
	XP150	WS58 Wessex HAS3 [LS]	FETC, Moreton-in-Marsh, Glos
	XP160	WS58 Wessex HAS1	RN, Predannack Fire School
	XP165	WS Scout AH1	The Helicopter Museum, Weston-super-Mare
	XP166	WS Scout AH1 (G-APVL)	Privately owned, East Dereham, Norfolk
	XP190	WS Scout AH1	Aeroventure, Doncaster
	XP191	WS Scout AH1	Privately owned, Dunkeswell
	XP226	Fairey Gannet AEW3 [073/E]	Newark Air Museum, Winthorpe
	XP241	Auster AOP9	Privately owned, Eggesford
	XP242	Auster AOP9 (G-BUCI)	AAC Historic Aircraft Flight, Middle Wallop
	XP244	Auster AOP9 (7864M/M7922)	Privately owned, Stretton on Dunsmore
	XP248	Auster AOP9 (7863M/WZ679)	Privately owned, Sandy, Beds
	XP254	Auster AOP11 (G-ASCC)	Privately owned, Tollerton
	XP279	Auster AOP9 (G-BWKK)	Privately owned, Popham
	XP280	Auster AOP9	Snibston Discovery Park, Coalville
	XP281	Auster AOP9	Imperial War Museum, Duxford
	XP283	Auster AOP9 (7859M) (frame)	Privately owned
	XP286	Auster AOP9	Privately owned, Eggesford
	XP299	WS55 Whirlwind HAR10 (8726M)	RAF Museum, Cosford
	XP330	WS55 Whirlwind HAR10	CAA Fire School, Tees-side Airport

Serial	Type (other identity) [code]	Owner/operator, location or fate	Notes
XP344	WS55 Whirlwind HAR10 (8764M) [H723]	RAF North Luffenham Training Area	
XP345	WS55 Whirlwind HAR10 (8792M) [UN]	Yorkshire Helicopter Preservation Group, Doncaster	
XP346	WS55 Whirlwind HAR10 (8793M)	Privately owned, Long Marston	
XP350	WS55 Whirlwind HAR10	Privately owned	
XP351	WS55 Whirlwind HAR10 (8672M) [Z]	RAF Shawbury, on display	
XP355	WS55 Whirlwind HAR10 (8463M/ G-BEBC)	City of Norwich Aviation Museum	
XP359	WS55 Whirlwind HAR10 (8447M)	*Scrapped*	
XP360	WS55 Whirlwind HAR10 [V]	Privately owned, Upper Hill, nr Leominster	
XP398	WS55 Whirlwind HAR10 (8794M)	Gatwick Aviation Museum, Charlwood, Surrey	
XP399	WS55 Whirlwind HAR10	Privately owned, Rettendon, Essex	
XP404	WS55 Whirlwind HAR10 (8682M)	The Helicopter Museum, Weston-super-Mare	
XP411	AW660 Argosy C1 (8442M) [C]	RAF Museum, Cosford	
XP454	Slingsby T38 Grasshopper TX1	Wellingborough School, Wellingborough	
XP463	Slingsby T38 Grasshopper TX1	Privately owned, Rufforth	
XP488	Slingsby T38 Grasshopper TX1	Fenland & W Norfolk Aviation Museum, stored Wisbech	
XP492	Slingsby T38 Grasshopper TX1 (BGA 3480)	Privately owned, Gallows Hill, Dorset	
XP493	Slingsby T38 Grasshopper TX1	Privately owned, stored Aston Down	
XP494	Slingsby T38 Grasshopper TX1	Privately owned, Rattlesden, Suffolk	
XP502	HS Gnat T1 (8576M)	Privately owned, Kemble	
XP505	HS Gnat T1	Science Museum, Wroughton	
XP516	HS Gnat T1 (8580M) [16]	QinetiQ Structures Dept, Farnborough	
XP540	HS Gnat T1 (8608M) [62]	Arbury College, Cambridge	
XP542	HS Gnat T1 (8575M) [42]	R. Military College of Science, Shrivenham	
XP556	Hunting Jet Provost T4 (9027M) [B]	RAF Cranwell Aviation Heritage Centre	
XP557	Hunting Jet Provost T4 (8494M) [72]	Bomber County Aviation Museum, Hemswell	
XP558	Hunting Jet Provost T4 (8627M) [20]	Privately owned, Sproughton	
XP563	Hunting Jet Provost T4 (9028M) [C]	Privately owned, Sproughton	
XP568	Hunting Jet Provost T4	Jet Avn Preservation Grp, Long Marston	
XP573	Hunting Jet Provost T4 (8236M) [19]	Jersey Airport Fire Section	
XP585	Hunting Jet Provost T4 (8407M) [24]	NE Wales Institute, Wrexham	
XP627	Hunting Jet Provost T4	North-East Aircraft Museum, Usworth	
XP629	Hunting Jet Provost T4 (9026M) [P]	RAF North Luffenham Training Area	
XP638	Hunting Jet Provost T4 (9034M) [A]	Privately owned, Ystrad Mynach, Mid Glamorgan	
XP640	Hunting Jet Provost T4 (8501M) [27]	Yorkshire Air Museum, Elvington	
XP642	Hunting Jet Provost T4 <ff>	Privately owned, Lavendon, Bucks	
XP672	Hunting Jet Provost T4 (8458M/ G-RAFI) [03]	Privately owned, North Weald	
XP677	Hunting Jet Provost T4 (8587M) <ff>	*Scrapped at East Grinstead, November 2001*	
XP680	Hunting Jet Provost T4 (8460M)	FETC, Moreton-in-Marsh, Glos	
XP686	Hunting Jet Provost T4 (8401M/ 8502M) [G]	RAF North Luffenham Training Area	
XP688	Hunting Jet Provost T4 (9031M)	Botany Bay Villages, Chorley, Lancs	
XP701	BAC Lightning F3 (8924M) <ff>	Robertsbridge Aviation Society, Mayfield	
XP703	BAC Lightning F3 <ff>	The Cockpit Collection, RAF Coltishall	
XP706	BAC Lightning F3 (8925M)	Aeroventure, Doncaster	
XP743	BAC Lightning F3 <ff>	No 351 Sqn ATC, Burton-upon-Trent	
XP745	BAC Lightning F3 (8453M) <ff>	Greenford Haulage, West London	
XP772	DHC2 Beaver AL1 (G-BUCJ)	AAC Historic Aircraft Flight, stored Duxford	
XP775	DHC2 Beaver AL1	Privately owned	
XP820	DHC2 Beaver AL1	AAC Historic Aircraft Flight, Middle Wallop	
XP821	DHC2 Beaver AL1 [MCO]	Museum of Army Flying, Middle Wallop	
XP822	DHC2 Beaver AL1	Museum of Army Flying, Middle Wallop	
XP831	Hawker P.1127 (8406M)	Science Museum, South Kensington	
XP841	Handley-Page HP115	FAA Museum, RNAS Yeovilton	
XP846	WS Scout AH1 [B,H] (fuselage)	RE 39 Regt, Waterbeach, instructional use	
XP847	WS Scout AH1	Museum of Army Flying, Middle Wallop	
XP848	WS Scout AH1	AAC Arborfield, on display	

Notes	Serial	Type (other identity) [code]	Owner/operator, location or fate
	XP849	WS Scout AH1 (G-CBUH)	Privately owned, East Dereham, Norfolk
	XP853	WS Scout AH1	Privately owned, Dunkeswell
	XP854	WS Scout AH1 (7898M/TAD043)	Bedford College, instructional use
	XP855	WS Scout AH1	Army SEAE, Arborfield
	XP856	WS Scout AH1	Privately owned, Dunkeswell
	XP883	WS Scout AH1	Privately owned, Oaksey Park, Wilts
	XP884	WS Scout AH1	AAC Middle Wallop, instructional use
	XP885	WS Scout AH1	AAC Wattisham, instructional use
	XP886	WS Scout AH1	Yeovil College
	XP888	WS Scout AH1	Privately owned, Sproughton
	XP890	WS Scout AH1 [G] (fuselage)	Privately owned, Ipswich
	XP893	WS Scout AH1	AAC Middle Wallop, BDRT
	XP899	WS Scout AH1 [D]	Army SEAE, Arborfield
	XP900	WS Scout AH1	AAC Wattisham, instructional use
	XP902	WS Scout AH1 <ff>	Aeroventure, stored Doncaster
	XP905	WS Scout AH1	Privately owned, Sproughton
	XP907	WS Scout AH1 (G-SROE)	Privately owned, Wattisham
	XP910	WS Scout AH1	Museum of Army Flying, Middle Wallop
	XP919	DH110 Sea Vixen FAW2 (8163M) [706/VL]	Blyth Valley Aviation Collection, Walpole
	XP924	DH110 Sea Vixen D3 (G-CVIX)	De Havilland Aviation, Bournemouth
	XP925	DH110 Sea Vixen FAW2 [752] <ff>	No 1268 Sqn ATC, Haslemere, Surrey
	XP956	DH110 Sea Vixen FAW2	*Scrapped*
	XP980	Hawker P.1127	FAA Museum, RNAS Yeovilton
	XP984	Hawker P.1127	Brooklands Museum, Weybridge
	XR220	BAC TSR2 (7933M)	RAF Museum, Cosford
	XR222	BAC TSR2	Imperial War Museum, Duxford
	XR232	Sud Alouette AH2 (F-WEIP)	Museum of Army Flying, Middle Wallop
	XR239	Auster AOP9	Privately owned, Stretton on Dunsmore
	XR240	Auster AOP9 (G-BDFH)	Privately owned, Widmerpool
	XR241	Auster AOP9 (G-AXRR)	The Aircraft Restoration Co, Duxford
	XR244	Auster AOP9	AAC Historic Aircraft Flight, Middle Wallop
	XR246	Auster AOP9 (7862M/G-AZBU)	Privately owned, North Coates
	XR267	Auster AOP9 (G-BJXR)	Privately owned, Widmerpool
	XR271	Auster AOP9	Royal Artillery Experience, Woolwich
	XR371	SC5 Belfast C1	RAF Museum, Cosford
	XR379	Sud Alouette AH2	AAC Historic Aircraft Flight, Middle Wallop
	XR453	WS55 Whirlwind HAR10 (8873M) [A]	RAF Odiham, on gate
	XR458	WS55 Whirlwind HAR10 (8662M) [H]	Museum of Army Flying, Middle Wallop
	XR485	WS55 Whirlwind HAR10 [Q]	Norfolk & Suffolk Avn Museum, Flixton
	XR486	WS55 Whirlwind HCC12 (8727M/ G-RWWW)	The Helicopter Museum, Weston-super-Mare
	XR497	WS58 Wessex HC2 [F]	*To Uruguayan Navy, June 2002*
	XR498	WS58 Wessex HC2 [X]	RAF, stored Shawbury
	XR499	WS58 Wessex HC2 [W]	RN AESS, *HMS Sultan*, Gosport
	XR501	WS58 Wessex HC2	Army, Keogh Barracks, Aldershot, instructional use
	XR502	WS58 Wessex HC2 [Z]	Privately owned, Colsterworth
	XR503	WS58 Wessex HC2	MoD FSCTE, Manston
	XR506	WS58 Wessex HC2 [V]	RAF, stored Shawbury
	XR507	WS58 Wessex HC2	Privately owned, Hixon, Staffs
	XR508	WS58 Wessex HC2 [B]	RN AESS, *HMS Sultan*, Gosport
	XR511	WS58 Wessex HC2 [L]	RAF, stored Shawbury
	XR516	WS58 Wessex HC2 [WB]	RAF Shawbury, instructional use
	XR517	WS58 Wessex HC2 [N]	Shoreham Airport, on display
	XR518	WS58 Wessex HC2 [J]	RN AESS, *HMS Sultan*, Gosport
	XR520	WS58 Wessex HC2	RN AESS, *HMS Sultan*, Gosport
	XR523	WS58 Wessex HC2 [M]	RN *HMS Raleigh*, Torpoint, instructional use
	XR525	WS58 Wessex HC2 [G]	RAF, stored Shawbury
	XR526	WS58 Wessex HC2 (8147M)	The Helicopter Museum, Weston-super-Mare
	XR528	WS58 Wessex HC2	SFDO, RNAS Culdrose
	XR529	WS58 Wessex HC2 [E]	RAF Aldergrove, for display
	XR534	HS Gnat T1 (8578M) [65]	Newark Air Museum, Winthorpe
	XR537	HS Gnat T1 (8642M/G-NATY) [T]	Bournemouth Aviation Museum
	XR538	HS Gnat T1 (8621M/G-RORI) [01]	Privately owned, Kemble
	XR571	HS Gnat T1 (8493M)	RAF *Red Arrows*, Scampton, on display
	XR574	HS Gnat T1 (8631M) [72]	RAF No 1 SoTT, Cosford
	XR588	WS58 Wessex HC2 [*Hearts*]	RAF Akrotiri (for disposal)

Serial	Type (other identity) [code]	Owner/operator, location or fate	Notes
XR595	WS Scout AH1 (G-BWHU) [M]	Privately owned, Staddon Heights, Devon	
XR597	WS Scout AH1 (fuselage)	Privately owned, Sproughton	
XR601	WS Scout AH1	Army SEAE, Arborfield	
XR627	WS Scout AH1 [X]	Privately owned, Sproughton	
XR628	WS Scout AH1	Privately owned, Ipswich	
XR629	WS Scout AH1 (fuselage)	Privately owned, Ipswich	
XR635	WS Scout AH1	Privately owned, Sproughton	
XR650	Hunting Jet Provost T4 (8459M) [28]	Boscombe Down Museum	
XR654	Hunting Jet Provost T4 <ff>	Privately owned, Chester	
XR658	Hunting Jet Provost T4 (8192M)	Deeside College, Connah's Quay, Clwyd	
XR662	Hunting Jet Provost T4 (8410M) [25]	Boulton Paul Association, Wolverhampton	
XR672	Hunting Jet Provost T4 (8495M) [50]	RAF Halton, Fire Section	
XR673	Hunting Jet Provost T4 (G-BXLO/ 9032M) [L]	Privately owned, North Weald	
XR681	Hunting Jet Provost T4 (8588M) <ff>	Robertsbridge Aviation Society, Mayfield	
XR700	Hunting Jet Provost T4 (8589M) <ff>	RAF EPTT, Aldergrove	
XR713	BAC Lightning F3 (8935M) [C]	RAF Leuchars, on display	
XR718	BAC Lightning F6 (8932M) [DA]	Blyth Valley Aviation Collection, Walpole	
XR724	BAC Lightning F6 (G-BTSY)	The Lightning Association, Binbrook	
XR725	BAC Lightning F6	Privately owned, Binbrook	
XR726	BAC Lightning F6 <ff>	Privately owned, Harrogate	
XR728	BAC Lightning F6 [JS]	Lightning Preservation Grp, Bruntingthorpe	
XR747	BAC Lightning F6 <ff>	Privately owned, Cubert, Cornwall	
XR749	BAC Lightning F3 (8934M) [DA]	Tees-side Airport, on display	
XR751	BAC Lightning F3	Privately owned, Tremar, Cornwall	
XR753	BAC Lightning F6 (8969M) [BP]	RAF Leeming on display	
XR753	BAC Lightning F53 (really ZF578)	Tangmere Military Aviation Museum	
XR754	BAC Lightning F6 (8972M) <ff>	Aeroventure, Doncaster	
XR755	BAC Lightning F6	Privately owned, Callington, Cornwall	
XR757	BAC Lightning F6 <ff>	Privately owned, Grainthorpe, Lincs	
XR759	BAC Lightning F6 <ff>	Privately owned, Haxey, Lincs	
XR770	BAC Lightning F6 [AA]	Privately owned, Grainthorpe, Lincs	
XR771	BAC Lightning F6 [BM]	Midland Air Museum, Coventry	
XR806	BAC VC10 C1K <ff>	RAF Brize Norton, BDRT	
XR807	BAC VC10 C1K	RAF/DARA, stored St Athan	
XR808	BAC VC10 C1K	RAF No 10 Sqn, Brize Norton	
XR810	BAC VC10 C1K	RAF No 10 Sqn, Brize Norton	
XR944	Wallis WA116 (G-ATTB)	RAF Museum, Hendon	
XR954	HS Gnat T1 (8570M) [30]	Source Classic Jet Flight, stored Bournemouth	
XR955	HS Gnat T1 [SAH-2]	Privately owned, Leavesden	
XR977	HS Gnat T1 (8640M) [3]	RAF Museum, Cosford	
XR991	HS Gnat T1 (8624M/XS102/ G-MOUR)	Privately owned, Kemble	
XR993	HS Gnat T1 (8620M/XP534/ G-BVPP)	Kennet Aviation, North Weald	
XS100	HS Gnat T1 (8561M) <ff>	Privately owned, Ongar	
XS101	HS Gnat T1 (8638M) (G-GNAT)	Privately owned, Cranfield	
XS122	WS58 Wessex HAS3 [655/PO]	RN AESS, HMS Sultan, Gosport	
XS149	WS58 Wessex HAS3 [661/GL]	The Helicopter Museum, Weston-super-Mare	
XS165	Hiller UH12E (G-ASAZ) [37]	Privately owned, Sherburn-in-Elmet	
XS176	Hunting Jet Provost T4 (8514M) <ff>	Privately owned, Stamford	
XS177	Hunting Jet Provost T4 (9044M) [N]	RAF Cosford	
XS179	Hunting Jet Provost T4 (8237M) [20]	University of Salford, Manchester	
XS180	Hunting Jet Provost T4 (8238M) [21]	RAF St Athan, Fire Section	
XS181	Hunting Jet Provost T4 (9033M) <ff>	Privately owned, Bruntingthorpe	
XS183	Hunting Jet Provost T4 <ff>	Privately owned, Plymouth	
XS186	Hunting Jet Provost T4 (8408M) [M]	RAF North Luffenham Training Area	
XS209	Hunting Jet Provost T4 (8409M)	Privately owned, Bruntingthorpe	

XS215 – XS713

Notes	Serial	Type (other identity) [code]	Owner/operator, location or fate
	XS215	Hunting Jet Provost T4 (8507M) [17]	RAF Halton
	XS216	Hunting Jet Provost T4 <ff>	No 2357 Sqn ATC, Goole
	XS217	Hunting Jet Provost T4 (9029M)	Privately owned, Bruntingthorpe
	XS218	Hunting Jet Provost T4 (8508M) <ff>	No 447 Sqn ATC, Henley-on-Thames, Berks
	XS231	BAC Jet Provost T5 (G-ATAJ)	Privately owned, Barnstaple
	XS235	DH106 Comet 4C (G-CPDA)	British Aviation Heritage, Bruntingthorpe
	XS416	BAC Lightning T5	Privately owned, Grainthorpe, Lincs
	XS417	BAC Lightning T5 [DZ]	Newark Air Museum, Winthorpe
	XS420	BAC Lightning T5	Privately owned, Walpole St Andrew, Norfolk
	XS421	BAC Lightning T5 <ff>	Privately owned, Foulness
	XS456	BAC Lightning T5 [DX]	Privately owned, Wainfleet
	XS457	BAC Lightning T5 <ff>	Privately owned, Grainthorpe, Lincs
	XS458	BAC Lightning T5 [T]	T5 Projects, Cranfield
	XS459	BAC Lightning T5 [AW]	Fenland & W Norfolk Aviation Museum, Wisbech
	XS463	WS Wasp HAS1 (comp XT431)	Privately owned, Sproughton
	XS481	WS58 Wessex HU5	Aeroventure, Doncaster
	XS482	WS58 Wessex HU5 [A/D]	RAF Manston History Museum
	XS485	WS58 Wessex HC5C (comp XR503) [Hearts]	Scrapped at Gosport by October 2002
	XS486	WS58 Wessex HU5 (9272M) [524/CU,F]	No 93 Sqn ATC, Bath
	XS488	WS58 Wessex HU5 (9056M) [XK]	RN AESS, HMS Sultan, Gosport
	XS489	WS58 Wessex HU5 [R]	RN AESS, HMS Sultan, Gosport
	XS492	WS58 Wessex HU5 [623]	RN/DARA, stored Fleetlands
	XS493	WS58 Wessex HU5	RN/DARA, stored Fleetlands
	XS496	WS58 Wessex HU5 [625/PO]	RN AESS, HMS Sultan, Gosport
	XS498	WS58 Wessex HC5C (comp XS677) [WK]	Privately owned, Hixon, Staffs
	XS507	WS58 Wessex HU5	RN AESS, HMS Sultan, Gosport
	XS508	WS58 Wessex HU5	FAA Museum, stored RNAS Yeovilton
	XS510	WS58 Wessex HU5 [626/PO]	RN AESS, HMS Sultan, Gosport
	XS511	WS58 Wessex HU5 [M]	RN AESS, HMS Sultan, Gosport
	XS513	WS58 Wessex HU5 [419/CU]	RN AESS, HMS Sultan, Gosport
	XS514	WS58 Wessex HU5 [L]	RN AESS, HMS Sultan, Gosport
	XS515	WS58 Wessex HU5 [N]	Army, Keogh Barracks, Aldershot, instructional use
	XS516	WS58 Wessex HU5 [Q]	RN, Predannack Fire School
	XS517	WS58 Wessex HC5C [Diamonds] (comp XS679)	Scrapped at Gosport by October 2002
	XS520	WS58 Wessex HU5 [F]	RN AESS, HMS Sultan, Gosport
	XS522	WS58 Wessex HU5 [ZL]	RN, Predannack Fire School
	XS527	WS Wasp HAS1	FAA Museum, stored RNAS Yeovilton
	XS529	WS Wasp HAS1	RN, Predannack Fire School
	XS539	WS Wasp HAS1 [435]	DARA Fleetlands Apprentice School
	XS567	WS Wasp HAS1 [434/E]	Imperial War Museum, Duxford
	XS568	WS Wasp HAS1 [441]	RN AESS, HMS Sultan, Gosport
	XS569	WS Wasp HAS1	DARA Fleetlands Apprentice School
	XS570	WS Wasp HAS1 [445/P]	Warship Preservation Trust, Birkenhead
	XS576	DH110 Sea Vixen FAW2 [125/E]	Imperial War Museum, Duxford
	XS587	DH110 Sea Vixen FAW(TT)2 (8828M/G-VIXN)	Gatwick Aviation Museum, Charlwood, Surrey
	XS590	DH110 Sea Vixen FAW2 [131/E]	FAA Museum, RNAS Yeovilton
	XS596	HS Andover C1(PR)	DPA/AFD/Open Skies, Boscombe Down
	XS598	HS Andover C1 (fuselage)	FETC, Moreton-in-Marsh, Glos
	XS606	HS Andover C1	DPA/ETPS, Boscombe Down
	XS639	HS Andover E3A	RAF Museum, Cosford
	XS641	HS Andover C1(PR) (9198M) [Z]	RAF No 1 SoTT, Cosford
	XS643	HS Andover E3A (9278M)	Scrapped at Manston, 2001
	XS646	HS Andover C1(mod)	DPA/AFD/QinetiQ, Boscombe Down
	XS652	Slingsby T45 Swallow TX1 (BGA 1107)	Privately owned, Rufforth
	XS674	WS58 Wessex HC2 [R]	Privately owned, Sproughton
	XS675	WS58 Wessex HC2 [Spades]	RAF Akrotiri (for disposal)
	XS695	HS Kestrel FGA1	RAF Museum Restoration Centre, Cosford
	XS709	HS125 Dominie T1 [M]	RAF No 3 FTS/55(R) Sqn, Cranwell
	XS710	HS125 Dominie T1 (9259M) [O]	RAF No 1 SoTT, Cosford
	XS711	HS125 Dominie T1 [L]	RAF No 3 FTS/55(R) Sqn, Cranwell
	XS712	HS125 Dominie T1 [A]	RAF No 3 FTS/55(R) Sqn, Cranwell
	XS713	HS125 Dominie T1 [C]	RAF No 3 FTS/55(R) Sqn, Cranwell

Serial	Type (other identity) [code]	Owner/operator, location or fate	Notes
XS714	HS125 Dominie T1 (9246M) [P]	MoD FSCTE, Manston	
XS726	HS125 Dominie T1 (9273M) [T]	RAF No 1 SoTT, Cosford	
XS727	HS125 Dominie T1 [D]	RAF No 3 FTS/55(R) Sqn, Cranwell	
XS728	HS125 Dominie T1 [E]	RAF No 3 FTS/55(R) Sqn, Cranwell	
XS729	HS125 Dominie T1 (9275M) [G]	RAF No 1 SoTT, Cosford	
XS730	HS125 Dominie T1 [H]	RAF No 3 FTS/55(R) Sqn, Cranwell	
XS731	HS125 Dominie T1 [J]	RAF No 3 FTS/55(R) Sqn, Cranwell	
XS733	HS125 Dominie T1 (9276M) [Q]	RAF No 1 SoTT, Cosford	
XS734	HS125 Dominie T1 (9260M) [N]	RAF No 1 SoTT, Cosford	
XS735	HS125 Dominie T1 [R]	DARA Training School, RAF St Athan	
XS736	HS125 Dominie T1 [S]	RAF No 3 FTS/55(R) Sqn, Cranwell	
XS737	HS125 Dominie T1 [K]	RAF No 3 FTS/55(R) Sqn, Cranwell	
XS738	HS125 Dominie T1 (9274M) [U]	RAF No 1 SoTT, Cosford	
XS739	HS125 Dominie T1 [F]	RAF No 3 FTS/55(R) Sqn, Cranwell	
XS743	Beagle B206Z Basset CC1	DPA/ETPS, Boscombe Down	
XS765	Beagle B206Z Basset CC1 (G-BSET)	Privately owned, Cranfield	
XS770	Beagle B206Z Basset CC1 (G-HRHI)	Privately owned, Cranfield	
XS790	HS748 Andover CC2 <ff>	Boscombe Down Museum	
XS791	HS748 Andover CC2 (fuselage)	Privately owned, Ely	
XS862	WS58 Wessex HAS3	Privately owned, Hixon, Staffs	
XS863	WS58 Wessex HAS1	Imperial War Museum, Duxford	
XS866	WS58 Wessex HAS1 [520/CU]	Sea Scouts, South Littleton, Worcs	
XS868	WS58 Wessex HAS1	RN, Predannack Fire School	
XS870	WS58 Wessex HAS1 [PO]		
XS871	WS58 Wessex HAS1 (8457M) [265]	Privately owned, Chippenham, Wilts	
XS876	WS58 Wessex HAS1 [523/PO]	SFDO, RNAS Culdrose	
XS881	WS58 Wessex HAS1	RN, Predannack Fire School	
XS885	WS58 Wessex HAS1 [512/DD]	SFDO, RNAS Culdrose	
XS886	WS58 Wessex HAS1 [527/CU]	Sea Scouts, Evesham, Worcs	
XS887	WS58 Wessex HAS1 [403/FI]	Flambards Village Theme Park, Helston	
XS888	WS58 Wessex HAS1 [521]	Guernsey Airport Fire Section	
XS897	BAC Lightning F6	Aeroventure, Doncaster	
XS898	BAC Lightning F6 <ff>	Privately owned, Lavendon, Bucks	
XS899	BAC Lightning F6 <ff>	The Cockpit Collection, RAF Coltishall	
XS903	BAC Lightning F6 [BA]	Yorkshire Air Museum, Elvington	
XS904	BAC Lightning F6 [BQ]	Lightning Preservation Grp, Bruntingthorpe	
XS919	BAC Lightning F6	Wonderland Pleasure Park, Farnsfield, Notts	
XS922	BAC Lightning F6 (8973M) <ff>	The Air Defence Collection, Salisbury	
XS923	BAC Lightning F6 <ff>	Privately owned, Welshpool	
XS925	BAC Lightning F6 (8961M) [BA]	RAF Museum, Hendon	
XS928	BAC Lightning F6 [D]	BAE Systems Warton, on display	
XS932	BAC Lightning F6 <ff>	FAST, Farnborough	
XS933	BAC Lightning F6 <ff>	Privately owned, Farnham	
XS936	BAC Lightning F6	Castle Motors, Liskeard, Cornwall	
XT108	Agusta-Bell 47G-3 Sioux AH1 [U]	Museum of Army Flying, Middle Wallop	
XT123	WS Sioux AH1 (XT827) [D]	AAC Middle Wallop, at main gate	
XT131	Agusta-Bell 47G-3 Sioux AH1 [B]	AAC Historic Aircraft Flight, Middle Wallop	
XT133	Agusta-Bell 47G-3 Sioux AH1 (7923M)	Royal Engineers' Museum, stored Chattenden	
XT140	Agusta-Bell 47G-3 Sioux AH1	Perth Technical College	
XT141	Agusta-Bell 47G-3 Sioux AH1	Privately owned, Dunkeswell	
XT148	Agusta-Bell 47G-3 Sioux AH1	The Helicopter Museum, stored Weston-super-Mare	
XT150	Agusta-Bell 47G-3 Sioux AH1 (7883M) [R]	AAC Netheravon, at main gate	
XT151	WS Sioux AH1 [W]	Museum of Army Flying, stored Middle Wallop	
XT175	WS Sioux AH1 (TAD175)	Privately owned, Cambs	
XT176	WS Sioux AH1 [U]	FAA Museum, stored Yeovilton	
XT190	WS Sioux AH1	The Helicopter Museum, Weston-super-Mare	
XT200	WS Sioux AH1 [F]	Newark Air Museum, Winthorpe	
XT223	WS Sioux AH1 (G-BGZK/G-XTUN)	Privately owned, Sherburn-in-Elmet	
XT236	WS Sioux AH1 (frame only)	North-East Aircraft Museum, stored Usworth	
XT242	WS Sioux AH1 (composite) [12]	Aeroventure, Doncaster	
XT257	WS58 Wessex HAS3 (8719M)	Privately owned, East Grinstead	
XT277	HS Buccaneer S2A (8853M) <ff>	Privately owned, Welshpool	

Notes	Serial	Type (other identity) [code]	Owner/operator, location or fate
	XT280	HS Buccaneer S2A <ff>	Privately owned, Strathclyde
	XT284	HS Buccaneer S2A (8855M) <ff>	Privately owned, Felixstowe
	XT288	HS Buccaneer S2B (9134M)	Royal Scottish Museum of Flight, stored E Fortune
	XT420	WS Wasp HAS1 (G-CBUI) [606]	Privately owned, Thruxton
	XT422	WS Wasp HAS1 [324]	Privately owned, Burgess Hill
	XT427	WS Wasp HAS1 [606]	FAA Museum, stored RNAS Yeovilton
	XT434	WS Wasp HAS1 [455]	DARA Fleetlands Apprentice School
	XT435	WS Wasp HAS1 (NZ3907/G-RIMM) [430]	Privately owned, Cranfield
	XT437	WS Wasp HAS1 [423]	Boscombe Down Museum
	XT439	WS Wasp HAS1 [605]	Privately owned, Hemel Hempstead
	XT443	WS Wasp HAS1 [422/AU]	The Helicopter Museum, Weston-super-Mare
	XT453	WS58 Wessex HU5 [A/B]	RN AESS, HMS Sultan, Gosport
	XT455	WS58 Wessex HU5 [U]	RN AESS, HMS Sultan, Gosport
	XT456	WS58 Wessex HU5 (8941M) [XZ]	RAF Aldergrove, BDRT
	XT458	WS58 Wessex HU5 [622]	RN AESS, HMS Sultan, Gosport
	XT460	WS58 Wessex HU5	RN AESS, HMS Sultan, Gosport, BDRT
	XT463	WS58 Wessex HC5C (comp XR508) [Clubs]	Privately owned, Hixon, Staffs
	XT466	WS58 Wessex HU5 (8921M) [XV]	RN AESS, HMS Sultan, Gosport
	XT467	WS58 Wessex HU5 (8922M) [BF]	Privately owned, Dunkeswell
	XT468	WS58 Wessex HU5 (comp XT460) [628]	RN, Predannack Fire School
	XT469	WS58 Wessex HU5 (8920M)	RAF No 16 MU, Stafford, ground instruction
	XT472	WS58 Wessex HU5 [XC]	The Helicopter Museum, Weston-super-Mare
	XT474	WS58 Wessex HU5 [820]	RN AESS, HMS Sultan, Gosport
	XT480	WS58 Wessex HU5 [468/RG]	RN/DARA, Fleetlands
	XT482	WS58 Wessex HU5 [ZM/VL]	FAA Museum, RNAS Yeovilton
	XT484	WS58 Wessex HU5 [H]	RN AESS, HMS Sultan, Gosport
	XT485	WS58 Wessex HU5	RN AESS, HMS Sultan, Gosport
	XT575	Vickers Viscount 837 <ff>	Brooklands Museum, Weybridge
	XT595	McD F-4K Phantom FG1 (8851M) <ff>	Currently not known
	XT596	McD F-4K Phantom FG1	FAA Museum, RNAS Yeovilton
	XT597	McD F-4K Phantom FG1	Boscombe Down Museum
	XT601	WS58 Wessex HC2 (9277M) (composite)	RAF Odiham, BDRT
	XT602	WS58 Wessex HC2	Scrapped at Gosport by October 2002
	XT604	WS58 Wessex HC2	East Midlands Airport Aeropark
	XT607	WS58 Wessex HC2 [P]	RN AESS, HMS Sultan, Gosport
	XT617	WS Scout AH1	AAC Wattisham, on display
	XT621	WS Scout AH1	R. Military College of Science, Shrivenham
	XT623	WS Scout AH1	Army SEAE, Arborfield
	XT626	WS Scout AH1 [Q]	AAC Historic Aircraft Flt, Middle Wallop
	XT630	WS Scout AH1 (G-BXRL) [X]	Privately owned, Bruntingthorpe
	XT631	WS Scout AH1 [D]	Privately owned, Ipswich
	XT632	WS Scout AH1 (G-BZBD)	Privately owned, Oaksey Park, Wilts (spares use)
	XT633	WS Scout AH1	Army SEAE, Arborfield
	XT634	WS Scout AH1 (G-BYRX) [T]	Privately owned, Humberside
	XT638	WS Scout AH1 [N]	AAC Middle Wallop, at gate
	XT640	WS Scout AH1	Privately owned, Sproughton
	XT643	WS Scout AH1 [Z]	Army, Thorpe Camp, East Wretham
	XT645	WS Scout AH1 (fuselage)	Privately owned, Ipswich
	XT668	WS58 Wessex HC2 [S]	RAF, stored Shawbury
	XT670	WS58 Wessex HC2	RN AESS, HMS Sultan, Gosport, BDRT
	XT671	WS58 Wessex HC2 (G-BYRC) [D]	Privately owned, Redhill
	XT672	WS58 Wessex HC2 [WE]	Privately owned, Hixon, Staffs
	XT676	WS58 Wessex HC2 [I]	RAF, stored Shawbury
	XT680	WS58 Wessex HC2 [Diamonds]	RAF Akrotiri (for disposal)
	XT681	WS58 Wessex HC2 (9279M) [U]	RAF Benson, BDRT
	XT761	WS58 Wessex HU5	RN AESS, HMS Sultan, Gosport
	XT762	WS58 Wessex HU5	RN, Predannack Fire School
	XT764	WS58 Wessex HU5 [G]	Scrapped at Gosport by October 2002
	XT765	WS58 Wessex HU5 [J]	RN AESS, HMS Sultan, Gosport
	XT769	WS58 Wessex HU5 [823]	FAA Museum, RNAS Yeovilton
	XT770	WS58 Wessex HU5 (9055M) [P]	Privately owned, Shawell, Leics
	XT771	WS58 Wessex HU5 [620/PO]	RN AESS, HMS Sultan, Gosport
	XT772	WS58 Wessex HU5 (8805M)	SARTU RAF Valley, ground instruction

Serial	Type (other identity) [code]	Owner/operator, location or fate	Notes
XT773	WS58 Wessex HU5 (9123M) [822/CU]	RAF/DARA, St Athan, BDRT	
XT778	WS Wasp HAS1 [430]	FAA Museum, stored Yeovilton	
XT780	WS Wasp HAS1 [636]	DARA Fleetlands Apprentice School	
XT781	WS Wasp HAS1 (NZ3908/G-KAWW) [426]	Privately owned, Swansea	
XT787	WS Wasp HAS1 (NZ3905/G-KAXT)	Kennet Aviation, North Weald	
XT788	WS Wasp HAS1 (G-BMIR) [316] (painted as XT78?)	Privately owned, Dunkeswell	
XT793	WS Wasp HAS1 (G-BZPP) [456]	Privately owned, Otley	
XT803	WS Sioux AH1 [Y]	Privately owned, Panshanger	
XT852	McD YF-4M Phantom FGR2	QinetiQ West Freugh Fire Section	
XT863	McD F-4K Phantom FG1 <ff>	Privately owned, Cowes, IOW	
XT864	McD F-4K Phantom FG1 (8998M/XT684) [BJ]	RAF Leuchars on display	
XT891	McD F-4M Phantom FGR2 (9136M) [Z]	RAF Coningsby, at main gate	
XT903	McD F-4M Phantom FGR2 <ff>	RAF Museum Restoration Centre, Cosford	
XT905	McD F-4M Phantom FGR2 [P]	RAF North Luffenham Training Area	
XT907	McD F-4M Phantom FGR2 (9151M) [W]	DEODS, Chattenden, Kent	
XT914	McD F-4M Phantom FGR2 [Z]	RAF Brampton, Cambs, on display	
XV101	BAC VC10 C1K	RAF No 10 Sqn, Brize Norton	
XV102	BAC VC10 C1K	RAF No 10 Sqn, Brize Norton	
XV103	BAC VC10 C1K	*Scrapped at RAF St Athan Nov 2002*	
XV104	BAC VC10 C1K	RAF No 10 Sqn, Brize Norton	
XV105	BAC VC10 C1K	RAF No 10 Sqn, Brize Norton	
XV106	BAC VC10 C1K	RAF/DARA, St Athan	
XV107	BAC VC10 C1K	RAF No 10 Sqn, Brize Norton	
XV108	BAC VC10 C1K	RAF No 10 Sqn, Brize Norton	
XV109	BAC VC10 C1K	RAF No 10 Sqn, Brize Norton	
XV118	WS Scout AH1 (9141M)	RAF Air Movements School, Brize Norton	
XV121	WS Scout AH1 (G-BYKJ)	Privately owned, Oaksey Park, Wilts	
XV122	WS Scout AH1 [D]	R. Military College of Science, Shrivenham	
XV123	WS Scout AH1	Privately owned, Ipswich	
XV124	WS Scout AH1 [W]	Army SEAE, Arborfield	
XV126	WS Scout AH1 (G-SCTA) [X]	Privately owned, Thruxton	
XV127	WS Scout AH1	Museum of Army Flying, Middle Wallop	
XV130	WS Scout AH1 (G-BWJW) [R]	Privately owned, Redhill	
XV131	WS Scout AH1 [Y]	AAC 70 Aircraft Workshops, Middle Wallop, BDRT	
XV134	WS Scout AH1 (G-BWLX) [P]	*Repainted as G-BWLX*	
XV136	WS Scout AH1 [X]	AAC Netheravon, on display	
XV137	WS Scout AH1 (G-CRUM)	Privately owned, Glenrothes	
XV137	WS Scout AH1 (XV139)	Yeovil College	
XV138	WS Scout AH1	Privately owned, East Dereham, Norfolk	
XV140	WS Scout AH1 (G-KAXL) [K]	Kennet Aviation, North Weald	
XV141	WS Scout AH1	REME Museum, Arborfield	
XV147	HS Nimrod MR1(mod) (fuselage)	BAE Systems, Warton	
XV148	HS Nimrod MR1(mod) <ff>	Privately owned, Guildford	
XV161	HS Buccaneer S2B (9117M) <ff>	Privately owned, Strathclyde	
XV165	HS Buccaneer S2B <ff>	FAST, Farnborough	
XV168	HS Buccaneer S2B	BAE Systems Brough, on display	
XV177	Lockheed C-130K Hercules C3	RAF Lyneham Transport Wing	
XV179	Lockheed C-130K Hercules C1	RAF Lyneham Transport Wing	
XV181	Lockheed C-130K Hercules C3	Marshalls, Cambridge (for Austria)	
XV183	Lockheed C-130K Hercules C3	*Returned to LMAC, 25 June 2002*	
XV184	Lockheed C-130K Hercules C3	RAF Lyneham Transport Wing	
XV188	Lockheed C-130K Hercules C3	RAF Lyneham Transport Wing	
XV190	Lockheed C-130K Hercules C3	*Returned to LMAC, 25 June 2002*	
XV196	Lockheed C-130K Hercules C1	RAF Lyneham Transport Wing	
XV197	Lockheed C-130K Hercules C3	RAF Lyneham Transport Wing	
XV199	Lockheed C-130K Hercules C3	RAF Lyneham Transport Wing	
XV200	Lockheed C-130K Hercules C1	RAF Lyneham Transport Wing	
XV201	Lockheed C-130K Hercules C1K (fuselage)	Marshalls, Cambridge	
XV202	Lockheed C-130K Hercules C3	RAF Lyneham Transport Wing	
XV205	Lockheed C-130K Hercules C1	RAF Lyneham Transport Wing	
XV206	Lockheed C-130K Hercules C1	RAF Lyneham Transport Wing	
XV208	Lockheed C-130K Hercules W2	DPA/AFD/QinetiQ, Boscombe Down	
XV209	Lockheed C-130K Hercules C3	RAF Lyneham Transport Wing	

Notes	Serial	Type (other identity) [code]	Owner/operator, location or fate
	XV212	Lockheed C-130K Hercules C3	RAF Lyneham Transport Wing
	XV214	Lockheed C-130K Hercules C3	RAF Lyneham Transport Wing
	XV217	Lockheed C-130K Hercules C3	RAF Lyneham Transport Wing
	XV220	Lockheed C-130K Hercules C3	RAF Lyneham Transport Wing
	XV221	Lockheed C-130K Hercules C3	RAF Lyneham Transport Wing
	XV222	Lockheed C-130K Hercules C3	*Returned to LMAC, 4 November 2001*
	XV226	HS Nimrod MR2	RAF Kinloss MR Wing
	XV227	HS Nimrod MR2	RAF Kinloss MR Wing
	XV228	HS Nimrod MR2	RAF Kinloss MR Wing
	XV229	HS Nimrod MR2	RAF Kinloss MR Wing
	XV230	HS Nimrod MR2	RAF Kinloss MR Wing
	XV231	HS Nimrod MR2	RAF Kinloss MR Wing
	XV232	HS Nimrod MR2	RAF Kinloss MR Wing
	XV235	HS Nimrod MR2	RAF Kinloss MR Wing
	XV236	HS Nimrod MR2	RAF Kinloss MR Wing
	XV237	HS Nimrod MR2 <ff>	Privately owned, St Austell
	XV238	HS Nimrod <R> (parts of G-ALYW)	RAF EPTT, Bottesford
	XV240	HS Nimrod MR2	RAF Kinloss MR Wing
	XV241	HS Nimrod MR2	RAF Kinloss MR Wing
	XV243	HS Nimrod MR2	RAF Kinloss MR Wing
	XV244	HS Nimrod MR2	RAF Kinloss MR Wing
	XV245	HS Nimrod MR2	RAF Kinloss MR Wing
	XV246	HS Nimrod MR2	RAF Kinloss MR Wing
	XV248	HS Nimrod MR2	RAF Kinloss MR Wing
	XV249	HS Nimrod R1	RAF No 51 Sqn, Waddington
	XV250	HS Nimrod MR2	RAF Kinloss MR Wing
	XV252	HS Nimrod MR2	RAF Kinloss MR Wing
	XV253	HS Nimrod MR2 (9118M)	DPA/BAE Systems, Woodford
	XV254	HS Nimrod MR2	RAF Kinloss MR Wing
	XV255	HS Nimrod MR2	RAF Kinloss MR Wing
	XV259	BAe Nimrod AEW3 <ff>	Privately owned, Carlisle
	XV260	HS Nimrod MR2	RAF Kinloss MR Wing
	XV263	BAe Nimrod AEW3P (8967M) <ff>	BAE Systems, Warton, instructional use
	XV263	BAe Nimrod AEW3P (8967M) <rf>	DPA/BAE Systems, Woodford
	XV268	DHC2 Beaver AL1 (G-BVER)	Privately owned, Cumbernauld
	XV277	HS P.1127(RAF)	Royal Scottish Mus'm of Flight, E Fortune
	XV279	HS P.1127(RAF) (8566M)	RAF Harrier Maintenance School, Wittering
	XV280	HS P.1127(RAF) <ff>	RNAS Yeovilton Fire Section
	XV290	Lockheed C-130K Hercules C3	RAF Lyneham Transport Wing
	XV291	Lockheed C-130K Hercules C1	Marshalls, Cambridge (for Austria)
	XV292	Lockheed C-130K Hercules C1	Marshalls, Cambridge (for Austria)
	XV294	Lockheed C-130K Hercules C3	RAF Lyneham Transport Wing
	XV295	Lockheed C-130K Hercules C1	RAF Lyneham Transport Wing
	XV296	Lockheed C-130K Hercules C1K (fuselage)	Marshalls, Cambridge
	XV299	Lockheed C-130K Hercules C3	RAF Lyneham Transport Wing
	XV301	Lockheed C-130K Hercules C3	RAF Lyneham Transport Wing
	XV302	Lockheed C-130K Hercules C3	Marshalls, Cambridge, fatigue test airframe
	XV303	Lockheed C-130K Hercules C3	RAF Lyneham Transport Wing
	XV304	Lockheed C-130K Hercules C3	RAF Lyneham Transport Wing
	XV305	Lockheed C-130K Hercules C3	RAF Lyneham Transport Wing
	XV307	Lockheed C-130K Hercules C3	RAF Lyneham Transport Wing
	XV328	BAC Lightning T5 <ff>	Phoenix Aviation, Bruntingthorpe
	XV333	HS Buccaneer S2B [234/H]	FAA Museum, RNAS Yeovilton
	XV337	HS Buccaneer S2C (8852M) <ff>	Privately owned, Diseworth, Leics
	XV344	HS Buccaneer S2C	QinetiQ Farnborough, on display
	XV350	HS Buccaneer S2B	East Midlands Airport Aeropark
	XV352	HS Buccaneer S2B <ff>	RAF Manston History Museum
	XV353	HS Buccaneer S2B (9144M) <ff>	Privately owned, Dalkeith
	XV359	HS Buccaneer S2B [035/R]	RNAS Culdrose, on display
	XV361	HS Buccaneer S2B	Ulster Aviation Society, Langford Lodge
	XV370	Sikorsky SH-3D [260]	RN AESS, *HMS Sultan*, Gosport
	XV371	WS61 Sea King HAS1(DB) [261]	RN AESS, *HMS Sultan*, Gosport
	XV372	WS61 Sea King HAS1	SFDO, RNAS Culdrose
	XV399	McD F-4M Phantom FGR2 <ff>	Privately owned,
	XV401	McD F-4M Phantom FGR2	Boscombe Down Museum
	XV402	McD F-4M Phantom FGR2 <ff>	Robertsbridge Aviation Society, Mayfield
	XV406	McD F-4M Phantom FGR2 (9098M) [CK]	Solway Aviation Society, Carlisle
	XV408	McD F-4M Phantom FGR2 (9165M) [Z]	RAF Halton

Serial	Type (other identity) [code]	Owner/operator, location or fate	Notes
XV411	McD F-4M Phantom FGR2 (9103M) [L]	MoD FSCTE, Manston	
XV415	McD F-4M Phantom FGR2 (9163M) [E]	RAF Boulmer, on display	
XV420	McD F-4M Phantom FGR2 (9247M) [BT]	RAF Neatishead, at main gate	
XV424	McD F-4M Phantom FGR2 (9152M) [I]	RAF Museum, Hendon	
XV426	McD F-4M Phantom FGR2 <ff>	The Cockpit Collection, RAF Coltishall	
XV426	McD F-4M Phantom FGR2 [P] <rf>	RAF Coningsby, BDRT	
XV435	McD F-4M Phantom FGR2 [R]	QinetiQ Llanbedr Fire Section	
XV460	McD F-4M Phantom FGR2 <ff>	No 2214 Sqn ATC, Usworth	
XV474	McD F-4M Phantom FGR2 [T]	The Old Flying Machine Company, Duxford	
XV490	McD F-4M Phantom FGR2 <ff>	Privately owned, Nantwich	
XV497	McD F-4M Phantom FGR2 [D]	RAF No 23 Sqn Waddington, (preserved)	
XV498	McD F-4M Phantom FGR2 (XV500/9113M) [U]	RAF St Athan, on display	
XV499	McD F-4M Phantom FGR2 <ff>	RAF Leeming, WLT	
XV581	McD F-4K Phantom FG1 (9070M) <ff>	No 2481 Sqn ATC, Bridge of Don	
XV582	McD F-4K Phantom FG1 (9066M) [M]	RAF Leuchars, on display	
XV586	McD F-4K Phantom FG1 (9067M) [AJ]	RAF Leuchars, on display	
XV591	McD F-4K Phantom FG1 <ff>	RAF Museum, Cosford	
XV625	WS Wasp HAS1 [471]	RN, stored *HMS Sultan*, Gosport	
XV629	WS Wasp HAS1	AAC Middle Wallop, BDRT	
XV631	WS Wasp HAS1 (fuselage)	QinetiQ Acoustics Dept, Farnborough	
XV642	WS61 Sea King HAS2A [259]	RN AESS, *HMS Sultan*, Gosport	
XV643	WS61 Sea King HAS6 [262]	RAF St Athan, BDRT	
XV647	WS61 Sea King HU5 [707]	RN No 771 Sqn, Prestwick	
XV648	WS61 Sea King HU5SAR [708/PW]	RN No 771 Sqn, Prestwick	
XV649	WS61 Sea King ASaC7 [180/CU]	RN No 849 Sqn, HQ Flt, Culdrose	
XV650	WS61 Sea King AEW2 [181/CU]	RN AMG, Culdrose	
XV651	WS61 Sea King HU5 [599/CU]	RN/DARA, Fleetlands	
XV653	WS61 Sea King HAS6 [513/CU]	RAF No 1 SoTT, Cosford	
XV654	WS61 Sea King HAS6 [705] (wreck)	RN AESS, *HMS Sultan*, Gosport	
XV655	WS61 Sea King HAS6 [270/N]	RN, stored *HMS Sultan*, Gosport	
XV656	WS61 Sea King AEW2 [180]	RN No 849 Sqn, HQ Flt, Culdrose	
XV657	WS61 Sea King HAS5 (*ZA135*) [32/DD]	SFDO, RNAS Culdrose	
XV659	WS61 Sea King HAS6 (93..M) [510/CU]	RAF No 1 SoTT, Cosford	
XV660	WS61 Sea King HAS6 [69]	RN, stored *HMS Sultan*, Gosport	
XV661	WS61 Sea King HU5SAR [821]	RN No 771 Sqn, Culdrose	
XV663	WS61 Sea King HAS6	RN, stored *HMS Sultan*, Gosport	
XV664	WS61 Sea King ASaC7 [187/R]	RN No 849 Sqn, A Flt, Culdrose	
XV665	WS61 Sea King HAS6 [507/CU]	RN, stored *HMS Sultan*, Gosport	
XV666	WS61 Sea King HU5SAR [823]	RN No 771 Sqn, Culdrose	
XV669	WS61 Sea King HAS1 [10]	RN/DARA, Fleetlands	
XV670	WS61 Sea King HU5 [588]	RN/Westland Helicopters, Weston-super-Mare	
XV671	WS61 Sea King ASaC7 [181/CU]	RN No 849 Sqn, HQ Flt, Culdrose	
XV672	WS61 Sea King ASaC7	RN No 849 Sqn, HQ Flt, Culdrose	
XV673	WS61 Sea King HU5 SAR [827]	RN/DARA, Fleetlands	
XV674	WS61 Sea King HAS6 [015/L]	RN No 820 Sqn, Culdrose	
XV675	WS61 Sea King HAS6 [701/PW]	RN, stored *HMS Sultan*, Gosport	
XV676	WS61 Sea King HAS6 [506]	RN/DARA, stored Fleetlands	
XV677	WS61 Sea King HAS6 [269]	RN, stored *HMS Sultan*, Gosport	
XV696	WS61 Sea King HAS6 [267/N]	RN, stored *HMS Sultan*, Gosport	
XV697	WS61 Sea King ASaC7 [185]	RN AMG, Culdrose (conversion)	
XV699	WS61 Sea King HU5SAR [708]	RN/DARA, stored Fleetlands	
XV700	WS61 Sea King HAS6C [005/CU]	RN AMG, Yeovilton (conversion)	
XV701	WS61 Sea King HAS6 [268/N]	RN, stored *HMS Sultan*, Gosport	
XV703	WS61 Sea King HAS6C [828]	RN AMG, Yeovilton (conversion)	
XV704	WS61 Sea King ASaC7 [186]	RN No 849 Sqn, HQ Flt, Culdrose	
XV705	WS61 Sea King HU5 [821/CU]	RN, stored *HMS Sultan*, Gosport	
XV706	WS61 Sea King HAS6 [017/L]	RN ETS, Culdrose	
XV707	WS61 Sea King ASaC7	RN AMG, Culdrose	
XV708	WS61 Sea King HAS6 [501/CU]	RN, stored *HMS Sultan*, Gosport	
XV709	WS61 Sea King HAS6 [263]	RAF St Mawgan, instructional use	

Notes	Serial	Type (other identity) [code]	Owner/operator, location or fate
	XV710	WS61 Sea King HAS6 (93..M) [264]	RAF No 1 SoTT, Cosford
	XV711	WS61 Sea King HAS6 [515/CT]	RN, stored *HMS Sultan*, Gosport
	XV712	WS61 Sea King HAS6 [269]	RN AESS, *HMS Sultan*, Gosport
	XV713	WS61 Sea King HAS6 [018]	RN, stored *HMS Sultan*, Gosport
	XV714	WS61 Sea King ASaC7 [188]	RN No 849 Sqn, A Flt, Culdrose
	XV720	WS58 Wessex HC2	RAF Benson, instructional use
	XV721	WS58 Wessex HC2 [H]	RAF, stored Shawbury
	XV722	WS58 Wessex HC2 [WH]	Privately owned, Hixon, Staffs
	XV723	WS58 Wessex HC2 [Q]	*To Uruguayan Navy, June 2002*
	XV724	WS58 Wessex HC2	RN AESS, *HMS Sultan*, Gosport
	XV725	WS58 Wessex HC2 [C]	RN AESS, *HMS Sultan*, Gosport
	XV726	WS58 Wessex HC2 [J]	RAF, stored Shawbury
	XV728	WS58 Wessex HC2 [A]	Newark Air Museum, Winthorpe
	XV729	WS58 Wessex HC2 (G-HANA)	Privately owned, Redhill
	XV730	WS58 Wessex HC2 [*Clubs*]	RAF Akrotiri (for disposal)
	XV731	WS58 Wessex HC2 [Y]	Privately owned,
	XV732	WS58 Wessex HCC4	RAF Museum, Hendon
	XV733	WS58 Wessex HCC4	The Helicopter Museum, Weston-super-Mare
	XV741	HS Harrier GR3 [41]	SFDO, RNAS Culdrose
	XV744	HS Harrier GR3 (9167M) [3K]	R. Military College of Science, Shrivenham
	XV748	HS Harrier GR3 [3D]	Yorkshire Air Museum, Elvington
	XV751	HS Harrier GR3	Privately owned, Bruntingthorpe
	XV752	HS Harrier GR3 (9078M) [B,HF]	RAF No 1 SoTT, Cosford
	XV753	HS Harrier GR3 (9075M) [53]	SFDO, RNAS Culdrose
	XV755	HS Harrier GR3 [M]	RNAS Yeovilton Fire Section
	XV759	HS Harrier GR3 [O] <ff>	Privately owned, Luton, Beds
	XV779	HS Harrier GR3 (8931M)	RAF Wittering on display
	XV783	HS Harrier GR3 [83]	SFDO, RNAS Culdrose
	XV784	HS Harrier GR3 (8909M) <ff>	Boscombe Down Museum
	XV786	HS Harrier GR3 <ff>	RNAS Culdrose
	XV786	HS Harrier GR3 [S] <rf>	RN, Predannack Fire School
	XV798	HS Harrier GR1(mod)	Bristol Aero Collection, stored Kemble
	XV804	HS Harrier GR3 (9280M) [O]	RAF North Luffenham Training Area
	XV808	HS Harrier GR3 (9076M) [08]	SFDO, RNAS Culdrose
	XV810	HS Harrier GR3 (9038M) [K]	Privately owned, Bruntingthorpe
	XV814	DH106 Comet 4 (G-APDF) <ff>	Privately owned, Chipping Campden
	XV863	HS Buccaneer S2B (9115M/ 9139M/9145M) [S]	RAF Lossiemouth
	XV864	HS Buccaneer S2B (9234M)	MoD FSCTE, Manston
	XV865	HS Buccaneer S2B (9226M)	Privately owned, Duxford
	XV867	HS Buccaneer S2B <ff>	N Yorks Aircraft Recovery Centre, Chop Gate
	XW175	HS Harrier T4(VAAC)	DPA/AFD/QinetiQ, Boscombe Down
	XW198	WS Puma HC1	RAF No 230 Sqn, Aldergrove
	XW199	WS Puma HC1	RAF No 33 Sqn, Benson
	XW200	WS Puma HC1 (wreck)	RAF, stored Shawbury
	XW201	WS Puma HC1	RAF No 230 Sqn, Aldergrove
	XW202	WS Puma HC1	RAF No 230 Sqn, Aldergrove
	XW204	WS Puma HC1	RAF No 230 Sqn, Aldergrove
	XW206	WS Puma HC1	RAF No 230 Sqn, Aldergrove
	XW207	WS Puma HC1	DPA/Eurocopter, Marignane, France (on repair)
	XW208	WS Puma HC1	DPA/Westland Helicopters, Weston-super-Mare
	XW209	WS Puma HC1	RAF No 33 Sqn, Benson
	XW210	WS Puma HC1 (comp XW215)	RAF No 230 Sqn, Aldergrove
	XW211	WS Puma HC1	RAF No 33 Sqn, Benson
	XW212	WS Puma HC1	RAF No 33 Sqn, Benson
	XW213	WS Puma HC1	RAF No 230 Sqn, Aldergrove
	XW214	WS Puma HC1	RAF No 230 Sqn, Aldergrove
	XW216	WS Puma HC1	RAF/DARA, stored Fleetlands
	XW217	WS Puma HC1	RAF No 33 Sqn, Benson
	XW218	WS Puma HC1	RAF No 33 Sqn, Benson
	XW219	WS Puma HC1	RAF No 230 Sqn, Aldergrove
	XW220	WS Puma HC1	RAF No 230 Sqn, Aldergrove
	XW221	WS Puma HC1	RAF No 230 Sqn, Aldergrove
	XW222	WS Puma HC1	RAF No 33 Sqn, Benson
	XW223	WS Puma HC1	RAF No 33 Sqn, Benson
	XW224	WS Puma HC1	RAF No 230 Sqn, Aldergrove
	XW225	WS Puma HC1	RAF Benson, spares use
	XW226	WS Puma HC1	RAF No 33 Sqn, Benson

Serial	Type (other identity) [code]	Owner/operator, location or fate	Notes
XW227	WS Puma HC1	RAF PASF, Benson (wreck)	
XW229	WS Puma HC1	RAF No 33 Sqn, Benson	
XW231	WS Puma HC1	RAF No 230 Sqn, Aldergrove	
XW232	WS Puma HC1	RAF No 33 Sqn, Benson	
XW234	WS Puma HC1	RAF PASF, Benson (wreck)	
XW235	WS Puma HC1	RAF No 33 Sqn, Benson	
XW236	WS Puma HC1	RAF No 33 Sqn, Benson	
XW237	WS Puma HC1	RAF No 230 Sqn, Aldergrove	
XW241	Sud SA330E Puma	QinetiQ Avionics & Sensors Dept, Farnborough	
XW249	Cushioncraft CC7	Privately owned, Bruntingthorpe	
XW264	HS Harrier T2 <ff>	Gloucestershire Avn Coll, stored	
XW265	HS Harrier T4A [W]	RAF No 1 SoTT, Cosford	
XW267	HS Harrier T4 [SA]	Territorial Army, Toton, Notts	
XW269	HS Harrier T4	DPA/QinetiQ, Boscombe Down, BDRT	
XW270	HS Harrier T4 (fuselage)	Phoenix Aviation, Bruntingthorpe	
XW271	HS Harrier T4 [71]	SFDO, RNAS Culdrose	
XW272	HS Harrier T4 (8783M) (fuselage) (comp XV281)	Marsh Lane Technical School, Preston	
XW276	Aérospatiale SA341 Gazelle (F-ZWRI)	Newark Air Museum, Winthorpe	
XW281	WS Scout AH1 (G-BYNZ) [T]	Privately owned, Wembury, Devon	
XW283	WS Scout AH1 [U]	RM, stored Yeovilton	
XW284	WS Scout AH1 [A] (fuselage)	Privately owned, Ipswich	
XW289	BAC Jet Provost T5A (G-BVXT/ G-JPVA) [73]	Kennet Aviation, North Weald	
XW290	BAC Jet Provost T5A (9199M) [41,MA]	RAF No 1 SoTT, Cosford	
XW292	BAC Jet Provost T5A (9128M) [32]	RAF No 1 SoTT, Cosford	
XW293	BAC Jet Provost T5 (G-BWCS) [Z]	Privately owned, Sandtoft	
XW294	BAC Jet Provost T5A (9129M) [45]	RAF No 1 SoTT, Cosford	
XW299	BAC Jet Provost T5A (9146M) [60,MB]	RAF No 1 SoTT, Cosford	
XW301	BAC Jet Provost T5A (9147M) [63,MC]	RAF No 1 SoTT, Cosford	
XW303	BAC Jet Provost T5A (9119M) [127]	RAF No 1 SoTT, Cosford	
XW304	BAC Jet Provost T5 (9172M) [MD]	RAF No 1 SoTT, Cosford	
XW309	BAC Jet Provost T5 (9179M) [V,ME]	RAF No 1 SoTT, Cosford	
XW311	BAC Jet Provost T5 (9180M) [W,MF]	RAF No 1 SoTT, Cosford	
XW312	BAC Jet Provost T5A (9109M) [64]	RAF No 1 SoTT, Cosford	
XW315	BAC Jet Provost T5A <ff>	Privately owned, Wolverhampton	
XW318	BAC Jet Provost T5A (9190M) [78,MG]	RAF No 1 SoTT, Cosford	
XW320	BAC Jet Provost T5A (9015M) [71]	RAF No 1 SoTT, Cosford	
XW321	BAC Jet Provost T5A (9154M) [62,MH]	RAF No 1 SoTT, Cosford	
XW323	BAC Jet Provost T5A (9166M) [86]	RAF Museum, Hendon	
XW324	BAC Jet Provost T5 (G-BWSG)	Privately owned, North Weald	
XW325	BAC Jet Provost T5B (G-BWGF) [E]	Privately owned, Blackpool	
XW327	BAC Jet Provost T5A (9130M) [62]	RAF No 1 SoTT, Cosford	
XW328	BAC Jet Provost T5A (9177M) [75,MI]	RAF No 1 SoTT, Cosford	
XW330	BAC Jet Provost T5A (9195M) [82,MJ]	RAF No 1 SoTT, Cosford	
XW333	BAC Jet Provost T5A (G-BVTC)	Global Aviation, Humberside	
XW335	BAC Jet Provost T5A (9061M) [74]	RAF No 1 SoTT, Cosford	
XW351	BAC Jet Provost T5A (9062M) [31]	RAF No 1 SoTT, Cosford	
XW353	BAC Jet Provost T5A (9090M) [3]	RAF Cranwell, on display	
XW358	BAC Jet Provost T5A (9181M) [59,MK]	RAF No 1 SoTT, Cosford	
XW360	BAC Jet Provost T5A (9153M) [61,ML]	RAF No 1 SoTT, Cosford	
XW361	BAC Jet Provost T5A (9192M) [81,MM]	RAF No 1 SoTT, Cosford	
XW363	BAC Jet Provost T5A [36]	BAE Systems North West Heritage Group, Warton	
XW364	BAC Jet Provost T5A (9188M) [35,MN]	RAF No 1 SoTT, Cosford	
XW365	BAC Jet Provost T5A (9018M) [73]	RAF No 1 SoTT, Cosford	

Notes	Serial	Type (other identity) [code]	Owner/operator, location or fate
	XW366	BAC Jet Provost T5A (9097M) [75]	RAF No 1 SoTT, Cosford
	XW367	BAC Jet Provost T5A (9193M) [64,MO]	RAF No 1 SoTT, Cosford
	XW370	BAC Jet Provost T5A (9196M) [72,MP]	RAF No 1 SoTT, Cosford
	XW375	BAC Jet Provost T5A (9149M) [52]	RAF No 1 SoTT, Cosford
	XW404	BAC Jet Provost T5A (9049M)	DARA Training School, RAF St Athan
	XW405	BAC Jet Provost T5A (9187M) [J,MQ]	RAF No 1 SoTT, Cosford
	XW409	BAC Jet Provost T5A (9047M)	DARA Training School, RAF St Athan
	XW410	BAC Jet Provost T5A (9125M) [80,MR]	RAF No 1 SoTT, Cosford
	XW413	BAC Jet Provost T5A (9126M) [69]	RAF No 1 SoTT, Cosford
	XW416	BAC Jet Provost T5A (9191M) [84,MS]	RAF No 1 SoTT, Cosford
	XW418	BAC Jet Provost T5A (9173M) [MT]	RAF No 1 SoTT, Cosford
	XW419	BAC Jet Provost T5A (9120M) [125]	RAF No 1 SoTT, Cosford
	XW420	BAC Jet Provost T5A (9194M) [83,MU]	RAF No 1 SoTT, Cosford
	XW421	BAC Jet Provost T5A (9111M) [60]	RAF No 1 SoTT, Cosford
	XW423	BAC Jet Provost T5A (G-BWUW) [14]	Privately owned, Little Snoring
	XW425	BAC Jet Provost T5A (9200M) [H,MV]	RAF No 1 SoTT, Cosford
	XW427	BAC Jet Provost T5A (9124M) [67]	RAF No 1 SoTT, Cosford
	XW430	BAC Jet Provost T5A (9176M) [77,MW]	RAF No 1 SoTT, Cosford
	XW432	BAC Jet Provost T5A (9127M) [76,MX]	RAF No 1 SoTT, Cosford
	XW433	BAC Jet Provost T5A (G-JPRO)	Global Aviation, Humberside
	XW434	BAC Jet Provost T5A (9091M) [78,MY]	RAF No 1 SoTT, Cosford
	XW436	BAC Jet Provost T5A (9148M) [68]	RAF No 1 SoTT, Cosford
	XW527	HS Buccaneer S2B <ff>	Privately owned, Wittering
	XW528	HS Buccaneer S2B (8861M) [C]	Burnt at Coningsby, 2002
	XW530	HS Buccaneer S2B	Buccaneer Service Station, Elgin
	XW541	HS Buccaneer S2B (8858M) <ff>	Privately owned, Welshpool
	XW544	HS Buccaneer S2B (8857M) [Y]	Privately owned, Kemble
	XW547	HS Buccaneer S2B (9095M/ 9169M) [R]	RAF Museum, Cosford
	XW550	HS Buccaneer S2B <ff>	Privately owned, West Horndon, Essex
	XW563	SEPECAT Jaguar S (XX822/ 8563M)	RAF Coltishall, on display
	XW566	SEPECAT Jaguar B	QinetiQ Avionics & Sensors Dept, Farnborough
	XW613	WS Scout AH1 (G-BXRS) [W]	Privately owned, Bembridge
	XW616	WS Scout AH1	AAC Dishforth, instructional use
	XW630	HS Harrier GR3	RNAS Yeovilton, Fire Section
	XW635	Beagle D5/180 (G-AWSW)	Privately owned, Spanhoe Lodge
	XW664	HS Nimrod R1	RAF No 51 Sqn, Waddington
	XW665	HS Nimrod R1	RAF No 51 Sqn, Waddington
	XW666	HS Nimrod R1 <ff>	Aeroventure, Doncaster
	XW750	HS748 Series 107	DPA/AFD/QinetiQ, Boscombe Down
	XW763	HS Harrier GR3 (9002M/9041M) <ff>	Privately owned, Bruntingthorpe
	XW768	HS Harrier GR3 (9072M) [N]	RAF No 1 SoTT, Cosford
	XW784	Mitchell-Procter Kittiwake I (G-BBRN) [VL]	Privately owned, Henstridge
	XW795	WS Scout AH1	Blessingbourne Museum, Fivemiletown, Co Tyrone, NI
	XW796	WS Scout AH1	Privately owned, Sproughton
	XW835	WS Lynx	AAC Wattisham, Fire Section
	XW838	WS Lynx (TAD 009)	Army SEAE, Arborfield
	XW839	WS Lynx	The Helicopter Museum, Weston-super-Mare
	XW844	WS Gazelle AH1	DARA Fleetlands Apprentice School
	XW845	WS Gazelle HT2 (G-CBSA) [47/CU]	Privately owned, Redhill
	XW846	WS Gazelle AH1	AAC No 665 Sqn/5 Regt, Aldergrove
	XW847	WS Gazelle AH1 [H]	RM No 847 Sqn, Yeovilton
	XW848	WS Gazelle AH1 [D]	AAC No 671 Sqn/2 Regt, Middle Wallop
	XW849	WS Gazelle AH1 [G]	RM No 847 Sqn, Yeovilton

Serial	Type (other identity) [code]	Owner/operator, location or fate	Notes
XW851	WS Gazelle AH1	RM No 847 Sqn, Yeovilton	
XW852	WS Gazelle HCC4	RAF No 1 SoTT, Cosford	
XW853	WS Gazelle HT2 [53/CU]	Privately owned, Somerset	
XW854	WS Gazelle HT2 (G-CBSD) [46/CU]	Privately owned, Redhill	
XW855	WS Gazelle HCC4	RAF, stored Shawbury	
XW856	WS Gazelle HT2 (G-GAZL) [49/CU]	Privately owned, Kirknewton	
XW857	WS Gazelle HT2 (G-CBSB) [55/CU]	Privately owned, Redhill	
XW858	WS Gazelle HT3 (G-DMSS) [C]	Privately owned, Kirkham, Lincs	
XW860	WS Gazelle HT2 (TAD021)	Army SEAE, Arborfield	
XW861	WS Gazelle HT2 (G-BZFJ) [52/CU]	Privately owned, Ford, W Sussex	
XW862	WS Gazelle HT3 (G-CBKC) [D]	Privately owned, Stapleford Tawney	
XW863	WS Gazelle HT2 (TAD022) [42/CU]	Army SEAE, Arborfield	
XW864	WS Gazelle HT2 [54/CU]	FAA Museum, stored RNAS Yeovilton	
XW865	WS Gazelle AH1 [5C]	AAC No 29 Flt, BATUS, Suffield, Canada	
XW866	WS Gazelle HT3 (G-BXTH) [E]	Flightline Ltd, Southend	
XW868	WS Gazelle HT2 (G-CBKD) [50/CU]	Privately owned, Stapleford Tawney	
XW870	WS Gazelle HT3 [F]	MoD FSCTE, Manston	
XW871	WS Gazelle HT2 (G-CBSC) [44/CU]	Privately owned, Redhill	
XW885	WS Gazelle AH1 (G-ZZEL)	Privately owned, Thruxton	
XW887	WS Gazelle HT2 (G-CBFD) [FL]	Privately owned, Hungerford	
XW888	WS Gazelle AH1 (TAD017)	Army SEAE, Arborfield	
XW889	WS Gazelle AH1 (TAD018)	Army SEAE, Arborfield	
XW890	WS Gazelle HT2	RNAS Yeovilton, on display	
XW892	WS Gazelle AH1 [C]	AAC, stored Shawbury	
XW893	WS Gazelle AH1 <ff>	Privately owned, East Garston, Bucks	
XW895	WS Gazelle HT2 (G-BXZD) [51/CU]	Privately owned, Barnard Castle	
XW897	WS Gazelle AH1 [Y]	AAC No 658 Sqn/7 Regt, Netheravon	
XW898	WS Gazelle HT3 (G-CBXT) [G]	Privately owned, East Garston, Bucks	
XW899	WS Gazelle AH1 [Z]	AAC No 658 Sqn/7 Regt, Netheravon	
XW900	WS Gazelle AH1 (TAD900)	Army SEAE, Arborfield	
XW902	WS Gazelle HT3 [H]	DPA/QinetiQ, Boscombe Down, spares use	
XW903	WS Gazelle AH1 (G-BZYC)	Privately owned, East Garston, Bucks	
XW904	WS Gazelle AH1 [H]	AAC No 666(V) Sqn/7 Regt, Netheravon	
XW906	WS Gazelle HT3 [J]	QinetiQ Boscombe Down, Apprentice School	
XW907	WS Gazelle HT2 (G-DFKI) [48/CU]	Repainted as G-DFKI by July 2002	
XW908	WS Gazelle AH1 [A]	AAC No 666(V) Sqn/7 Regt, Netheravon	
XW909	WS Gazelle AH1	AAC No 656 Sqn/9 Regt, Dishforth	
XW910	WS Gazelle HT3 (G-BXZE) [K]	Crashed 3 September 2001, Hickstead	
XW912	WS Gazelle AH1 (TAD019)	Army SEAE, Arborfield	
XW913	WS Gazelle AH1	AAC No 662 Sqn/3 Regt, Wattisham	
XW917	HS Harrier GR3 (8975M)	RAF Cottesmore, at main gate	
XW919	HS Harrier GR3 [W]	R. Military College of Science, Shrivenham	
XW922	HS Harrier GR3 (8885M)	MoD FSCTE, Manston	
XW923	HS Harrier GR3 (8724M) <ff>	RAF Wittering, Fire Section	
XW924	HS Harrier GR3 (9073M) [G]	RAF Cottesmore, preserved	
XW934	HS Harrier T4 [Y]	DPA, QinetiQ Farnborough (wfu)	
XW986	HS Buccaneer S2B	To South Africa as ZU-NIP, August 2002	
XX105	BAC 1-11/201AC (G-ASJD)	DPA/AFD/QinetiQ, Boscombe Down	
XX108	SEPECAT Jaguar GR3	DPA/DARA, St Athan	
XX109	SEPECAT Jaguar GR1 (8918M) [US]	RAF Coltishall, ground instruction	
XX110	SEPECAT Jaguar GR1 (8955M) [EP]	RAF No 1 SoTT, Cosford	
XX110	SEPECAT Jaguar GR1 <R> (BAPC 169)	RAF No 1 SoTT, Cosford	
XX112	SEPECAT Jaguar GR3A [EA]	RAF No 6 Sqn, Coltishall	
XX115	SEPECAT Jaguar GR1 (8821M) (fuselage)	RAF No 1 SoTT, Cosford	
XX116	SEPECAT Jaguar GR3A [EO]	RAF No 6 Sqn, Coltishall	
XX117	SEPECAT Jaguar GR3 [PA]	RAF No 16(R) Sqn, Coltishall	
XX119	SEPECAT Jaguar GR3A (8898M) [GD]	RAF No 54 Sqn, Coltishall	
XX121	SEPECAT Jaguar GR1 [EQ]	Privately owned, Charlwood, Surrey	
XX139	SEPECAT Jaguar T4 [PT]	RAF No 16(R) Sqn, Coltishall	

XX140 – XX237

Notes	Serial	Type (other identity) [code]	Owner/operator, location or fate
	XX140	SEPECAT Jaguar T2 (9008M) [D,JJ]	Privately owned, Charlwood, Surrey
	XX141	SEPECAT Jaguar T2A [T]	AMIF, RAFC Cranwell
	XX144	SEPECAT Jaguar T2A [U]	RAF, stored Shawbury
	XX145	SEPECAT Jaguar T2A	DPA/ETPS, Boscombe Down
	XX146	SEPECAT Jaguar T4 [GT]	RAF No 54 Sqn, Coltishall
	XX150	SEPECAT Jaguar T4 [PW]	RAF No 16(R) Sqn, Coltishall
	XX153	WS Lynx AH1	Westland Helicopters, Yeovil
	XX154	HS Hawk T1	DPA/ETPS, Boscombe Down
	XX156	HS Hawk T1	RAF No 4 FTS/*208(R) Sqn*, Valley
	XX157	HS Hawk T1A	RAF/DARA, St Athan
	XX158	HS Hawk T1A	RAF No 4 FTS/*19(R) Sqn*, Valley
	XX159	HS Hawk T1A	RAF No 4 FTS/*208(R) Sqn*, Valley
	XX160	HS Hawk T1 [CP]	RAF No 100 Sqn, Leeming
	XX161	HS Hawk T1W	RAF No 4 FTS/*208(R) Sqn*, Valley
	XX162	HS Hawk T1	RAF Aviation Medicine Flt, Boscombe Down
	XX165	HS Hawk T1	RN FRADU, Culdrose
	XX167	HS Hawk T1W	RN FRADU, Culdrose
	XX168	HS Hawk T1 [CH]	RAF No 100 Sqn, Leeming
	XX169	HS Hawk T1	RAF No 4 FTS/*208(R) Sqn*, Valley
	XX170	HS Hawk T1	RAF/DARA, St Athan
	XX171	HS Hawk T1	RN FRADU, Culdrose
	XX172	HS Hawk T1	RAF/DARA, St Athan
	XX173	HS Hawk T1	RN FRADU, Culdrose
	XX174	HS Hawk T1	RAF No 4 FTS/*208(R) Sqn*, Valley
	XX175	HS Hawk T1	RAF No 4 FTS/*208(R) Sqn*, Valley
	XX176	HS Hawk T1W	RAF No 4 FTS/*19(R) Sqn*, Valley
	XX177	HS Hawk T1	RAF No 4 FTS/*208(R) Sqn*, Valley
	XX178	HS Hawk T1W	RN FRADU, Culdrose
	XX179	HS Hawk T1W	RAF *Red Arrows*, Scampton
	XX181	HS Hawk T1W	RAF No 4 FTS/*208(R) Sqn*, Valley
	XX183	HS Hawk T1	RAF/DARA, St Athan
	XX184	HS Hawk T1	RN FRADU, Culdrose
	XX185	HS Hawk T1	RAF No 4 FTS/*208(R) Sqn*, Valley
	XX187	HS Hawk T1A	RAF/DARA, St Athan
	XX188	HS Hawk T1A	RAF No 100 Sqn, Leeming
	XX189	HS Hawk T1A	RAF No 4 FTS/*19(R) Sqn*, Valley
	XX190	HS Hawk T1A	RAF No 4 FTS/*208(R) Sqn*, Valley
	XX191	HS Hawk T1A [CC]	RAF No 100 Sqn, Leeming
	XX194	HS Hawk T1A [CO]	RAF No 100 Sqn/JFACSTU, Leeming
	XX195	HS Hawk T1W	RAF No 4 FTS/*208(R) Sqn*, Valley
	XX196	HS Hawk T1A	RAF No 4 FTS/*208(R) Sqn*, Valley
	XX198	HS Hawk T1A	RAF/DARA, St Athan
	XX199	HS Hawk T1A	RAF/DARA, St Athan
	XX200	HS Hawk T1A	RAF No 4 FTS, Valley
	XX201	HS Hawk T1A	RAF No 4 FTS/*19(R) Sqn*, Valley
	XX202	HS Hawk T1A	RAF No 4 FTS/*19(R) Sqn*, Valley
	XX203	HS Hawk T1A	RAF No 4 FTS, Valley
	XX204	HS Hawk T1A	RAF No 4 FTS/*208(R) Sqn*, Valley
	XX205	HS Hawk T1A	RAF No 4 FTS/*208(R) Sqn*, Valley
	XX217	HS Hawk T1A [CC]	RAF/DARA, St Athan
	XX218	HS Hawk T1A	RAF No 4 FTS, Valley
	XX219	HS Hawk T1A	RAF No 4 FTS/*208(R) Sqn*, Valley
	XX220	HS Hawk T1A	RAF No 4 FTS/*208(R) Sqn*, Valley
	XX221	HS Hawk T1A	RAF No 4 FTS/*19(R) Sqn*, Valley
	XX222	HS Hawk T1A	RAF No 4 FTS, Valley
	XX223	HS Hawk T1 <ff>	Privately owned, Charlwood, Surrey
	XX224	HS Hawk T1W	RN FRADU, Culdrose
	XX225	HS Hawk T1	RAF No 4 FTS/*208(R) Sqn*, Valley
	XX226	HS Hawk T1	RN FRADU, Culdrose
	XX226	HS Hawk T1 <R> (*XX263/* BAPC 152)	RAF EPTT, Bottesford
	XX227	HS Hawk T1A	RAF *Red Arrows*, Scampton
	XX228	HS Hawk T1A [CG]	RAF No 100 Sqn, Leeming
	XX230	HS Hawk T1A	RAF No 4 FTS/*208(R) Sqn*, Valley
	XX231	HS Hawk T1W	RN FRADU, Culdrose
	XX232	HS Hawk T1	RAF No 4 FTS/*208(R) Sqn*, Valley
	XX233	HS Hawk T1	RAF *Red Arrows*, Scampton
	XX234	HS Hawk T1	RN FRADU, Culdrose
	XX235	HS Hawk T1W	RAF No 4 FTS/*208(R) Sqn*, Valley
	XX236	HS Hawk T1W	RAF/DARA, St Athan
	XX237	HS Hawk T1	RAF *Red Arrows*, Scampton

Serial	Type (other identity) [code]	Owner/operator, location or fate	Notes
XX238	HS Hawk T1	RN FRADU, Culdrose	
XX239	HS Hawk T1W	RAF No 4 FTS/*208(R) Sqn*, Valley	
XX240	HS Hawk T1	RN FRADU, Culdrose	
XX242	HS Hawk T1	RAF/DARA, St Athan	
XX244	HS Hawk T1	RAF No 4 FTS, Valley	
XX245	HS Hawk T1	RAF No 4 FTS/*208(R) Sqn*, Valley	
XX246	HS Hawk T1A	RAF No 4 FTS/*19(R) Sqn*, Valley	
XX246	HS Hawk T1A <rf>	RAF CTTS, St Athan	
XX247	HS Hawk T1A [CM]	RAF No 100 Sqn, Leeming	
XX248	HS Hawk T1A [CJ]	RAF No 100 Sqn, Leeming	
XX250	HS Hawk T1	RAF/DARA, St Athan	
XX252	HS Hawk T1A (fuselage)	Privately owned, Charlwood, Surrey	
XX253	HS Hawk T1A	RAF *Red Arrows*, Scampton	
XX253	HS Hawk T1 <R> (*XX297/*BAPC 171)	RAF EPTT, Bottesford	
XX254	HS Hawk T1A <ff>	RAF/DARA, St Athan	
XX254	HS Hawk T1A	DPA/BAE Systems, stored Scampton	
XX254	HS Hawk T1A <R>	Privately owned, Marlow, Bucks	
XX255	HS Hawk T1A	RAF No 4 FTS, Valley	
XX256	HS Hawk T1A	RAF No 4 FTS/*19(R) Sqn*, Valley	
XX258	HS Hawk T1A	RAF/DARA, St Athan	
XX260	HS Hawk T1A	RAF *Red Arrows*, Scampton	
XX261	HS Hawk T1A	RAF No 4 FTS/*208(R) Sqn*, Valley	
XX263	HS Hawk T1A	RAF/DARA, St Athan	
XX264	HS Hawk T1A	RAF *Red Arrows*, Scampton	
XX265	HS Hawk T1A	RN FRADU, Culdrose	
XX266	HS Hawk T1A	RAF *Red Arrows*, Scampton	
XX278	HS Hawk T1A [CD]	RAF No 100 Sqn, Leeming	
XX280	HS Hawk T1A	RAF No 4 FTS/*19(R) Sqn*, Valley	
XX281	HS Hawk T1A	RAF No 4 FTS/*208(R) Sqn*, Valley	
XX283	HS Hawk T1W	RAF No 4 FTS/*19(R) Sqn*, Valley	
XX284	HS Hawk T1A [CA]	RAF No 100 Sqn, Leeming	
XX285	HS Hawk T1A [CB]	RAF No 100 Sqn, Leeming	
XX286	HS Hawk T1A	RAF No 4 FTS/*208(R) Sqn*, Valley	
XX287	HS Hawk T1A	RAF No 4 FTS/*19(R) Sqn*, Valley	
XX289	HS Hawk T1A [CI]	RAF/DARA, St Athan	
XX290	HS Hawk T1W	RAF No 4 FTS/*208(R) Sqn*, Valley	
XX292	HS Hawk T1W	RAF *Red Arrows*, Scampton	
XX294	HS Hawk T1	RAF *Red Arrows*, Scampton	
XX295	HS Hawk T1W	RAF No 4 FTS/*19(R) Sqn*, Valley	
XX296	HS Hawk T1	RAF No 4 FTS/*19(R) Sqn*, Valley	
XX299	HS Hawk T1W [CS]	RAF No 100 Sqn, Leeming	
XX301	HS Hawk T1A	RAF No 4 FTS/*208(R) Sqn*, Valley	
XX303	HS Hawk T1A	RAF No 4 FTS/*208(R) Sqn*, Valley	
XX304	HS Hawk T1A <ff>	RAF, stored Shawbury	
XX304	HS Hawk T1A <rf>	Cardiff International Airport Fire Section	
XX306	HS Hawk T1A	RAF *Red Arrows*, Scampton	
XX307	HS Hawk T1	RAF No 4 FTS, Valley	
XX308	HS Hawk T1	RAF *Red Arrows*, Scampton	
XX309	HS Hawk T1	RAF No 4 FTS, Valley	
XX310	HS Hawk T1W	RAF No 4 FTS/*208(R) Sqn*, Valley	
XX311	HS Hawk T1	RAF No 4 FTS/*19(R) Sqn*, Valley	
XX312	HS Hawk T1W [CK]	RAF No 100 Sqn, Leeming	
XX313	HS Hawk T1W	RAF/DARA, St Athan	
XX314	HS Hawk T1W [CN]	RAF No 100 Sqn, Leeming	
XX315	HS Hawk T1A	RAF No 4 FTS/*19(R) Sqn*, Valley	
XX316	HS Hawk T1A	RAF No 4 FTS/*19(R) Sqn*, Valley	
XX317	HS Hawk T1A	RAF No 4 FTS/*19(R) Sqn*, Valley	
XX318	HS Hawk T1A	RAF No 4 FTS/*19(R) Sqn*, Valley	
XX319	HS Hawk T1A	RAF No 4 FTS/*208(R) Sqn*, Valley	
XX320	HS Hawk T1A	RAF No 4 FTS, Valley	
XX321	HS Hawk T1A	RAF No 4 FTS/*208(R) Sqn*, Valley	
XX322	HS Hawk T1A	RAF/DARA, St Athan	
XX323	HS Hawk T1A	RAF No 4 FTS/*19(R) Sqn*, Valley	
XX324	HS Hawk T1A	RAF No 4 FTS/*19(R) Sqn*, Valley	
XX325	HS Hawk T1A [CT]	RAF No 100 Sqn, Leeming	
XX326	HS Hawk T1A <ff>	RAF/DARA, St Athan	
XX326	HS Hawk T1A	DPA/BAE Systems, Brough (on rebuild)	
XX327	HS Hawk T1	RAF Aviation Medicine Flt, Boscombe Down	
XX329	HS Hawk T1A	RAF No 4 FTS/*19(R) Sqn*, Valley	
XX330	HS Hawk T1A [CL]	RAF/DARA, St Athan	
XX331	HS Hawk T1A	RAF No 4 FTS/*19(R) Sqn*, Valley	

Notes	Serial	Type (other identity) [code]	Owner/operator, location or fate
	XX332	HS Hawk T1A	RAF/DARA, St Athan
	XX335	HS Hawk T1A [CR]	RAF No 100 Sqn, Leeming
	XX337	HS Hawk T1A	RAF No 4 FTS/*208(R) Sqn*, Valley
	XX338	HS Hawk T1W	RAF No 4 FTS/*19(R) Sqn*, Valley
	XX339	HS Hawk T1A	RAF No 4 FTS/*208(R) Sqn*, Valley
	XX341	HS Hawk T1 ASTRA [1]	DPA/ETPS, Boscombe Down
	XX342	HS Hawk T1 [2]	DPA/ETPS, Boscombe Down
	XX343	HS Hawk T1 [3] (wreck)	Boscombe Down Museum
	XX344	HS Hawk T1 (8847M) (fuselage)	QinetiQ Farnborough Fire Section
	XX345	HS Hawk T1A	RAF No 4 FTS/*208(R) Sqn*, Valley
	XX346	HS Hawk T1A	RAF No 4 FTS, Valley
	XX348	HS Hawk T1A	RAF No 4 FTS/*19(R) Sqn*, Valley
	XX349	HS Hawk T1W [CE]	RAF No 100 Sqn/JFACSTU, Leeming
	XX350	HS Hawk T1A	RAF No 4 FTS, Valley
	XX351	HS Hawk T1A [CQ]	RAF No 100 Sqn, Leeming
	XX352	HS Hawk T1A	*Crashed 15 February 2002, Valley*
	XX370	WS Gazelle AH1	AAC No 665 Sqn/5 Regt, Aldergrove
	XX371	WS Gazelle AH1	AAC No 12 Flt, Brüggen
	XX372	WS Gazelle AH1	AAC 3 Regt, Wattisham
	XX375	WS Gazelle AH1	AAC No 8 Flt, Middle Wallop
	XX378	WS Gazelle AH1 [Q]	AAC No 671 Sqn/2 Regt, Middle Wallop
	XX379	WS Gazelle AH1	AAC No 669 Sqn/4 Regt, Wattisham
	XX380	WS Gazelle AH1 [A]	RM No 847 Sqn, Yeovilton
	XX381	WS Gazelle AH1	AAC No 662 Sqn/3 Regt, Wattisham
	XX382	WS Gazelle HT3 (G-BZYB) [M]	Privately owned, East Garston, Bucks
	XX383	WS Gazelle AH1 [D]	AAC No 666(V) Sqn/7 Regt, Netheravon
	XX384	WS Gazelle AH1	AAC/DARA, stored Fleetlands
	XX385	WS Gazelle AH1	RAF No 7 Sqn, Odiham
	XX386	WS Gazelle AH1	AAC No 12 Flt, Brüggen
	XX387	WS Gazelle AH1 (TAD 014)	Army SEAE, Arborfield
	XX388	WS Gazelle AH1	Privately owned, East Garston, Bucks
	XX389	WS Gazelle AH1	AAC No 656 Sqn/9 Regt, Dishforth
	XX391	WS Gazelle HT2 [56/CU]	*Sold as ZK-HTB, July 2001*
	XX392	WS Gazelle AH1	AAC No 3(V) Flt/7 Regt, Leuchars
	XX393	WS Gazelle AH1 (fuselage)	Privately owned, Wellington, Somerset
	XX394	WS Gazelle AH1 [X]	AAC No 654 Sqn/4 Regt, Wattisham
	XX396	WS Gazelle HT3 (8718M) [N]	ATF, RAFC Cranwell
	XX398	WS Gazelle AH1	Privately owned, East Garston, Bucks
	XX399	WS Gazelle AH1 [D]	RM No 847 Sqn, Yeovilton
	XX403	WS Gazelle AH1	AAC No 671 Sqn/2 Regt, Middle Wallop
	XX405	WS Gazelle AH1	AAC No 665 Sqn/5 Regt, Aldergrove
	XX406	WS Gazelle HT3 (G-CBSH) [P]	Privately owned, Redhill
	XX409	WS Gazelle AH1	AAC 4 Regt, Wattisham
	XX411	WS Gazelle AH1	Aeroventure, Doncaster
	XX411	WS Gazelle AH1 <rf>	FAA Museum, RNAS Yeovilton
	XX412	WS Gazelle AH1 [B]	RM No 847 Sqn, Yeovilton
	XX413	WS Gazelle AH1 [C]	Privately owned, East Garston, Bucks
	XX414	WS Gazelle AH1	AAC/DARA, stored Fleetlands
	XX416	WS Gazelle AH1	AAC No 9 Regt, Dishforth
	XX417	WS Gazelle AH1	AAC No 667 Sqn, Middle Wallop
	XX418	WS Gazelle AH1	Privately owned, East Garston, Bucks
	XX419	WS Gazelle AH1	AAC No 656 Sqn/9 Regt, Dishforth
	XX431	WS Gazelle HT2 (9300M) [43/CU]	RAF Shawbury, for display
	XX432	WS Gazelle AH1	AAC No 665 Sqn/5 Regt, Aldergrove
	XX433	WS Gazelle AH1 [F]	Privately owned, Hungerford
	XX435	WS Gazelle AH1 [V]	AAC No 658 Sqn/7 Regt, Netheravon
	XX436	WS Gazelle HT2 (G-CBSE) [39/CU]	Privately owned, Redhill
	XX437	WS Gazelle AH1	AAC No 669 Sqn/4 Regt, Wattisham
	XX438	WS Gazelle AH1	AAC No 9 Regt, Dishforth
	XX439	WS Gazelle AH1	AAC No 9 Regt, Dishforth
	XX440	WS Gazelle AH1 (G-BCHN)	DARA Fleetlands Apprentice School
	XX442	WS Gazelle AH1 [E]	AAC No 666(V) Sqn/7 Regt, Netheravon
	XX443	WS Gazelle AH1 [Y]	AAC Stockwell Hall, Middle Wallop, instructional use
	XX444	WS Gazelle AH1	AAC No 25 Flt, Belize
	XX445	WS Gazelle AH1 [T]	AAC/DARA, stored Fleetlands
	XX447	WS Gazelle AH1 [D1]	AAC No 671 Sqn/2 Regt, Middle Wallop
	XX448	WS Gazelle AH1	AAC No 664 Sqn/9 Regt, Dishforth
	XX449	WS Gazelle AH1	AAC No 664 Sqn/9 Regt, Dishforth
	XX450	WS Gazelle AH1 [D]	Privately owned, East Garston, Bucks
	XX453	WS Gazelle AH1	AAC 3 Regt, Wattisham
	XX454	WS Gazelle AH1 (TAD 023) (fuselage)	Army SEAE, Arborfield

Serial	Type (other identity) [code]	Owner/operator, location or fate	Notes
XX455	WS Gazelle AH1	AAC/DARA, Fleetlands	
XX456	WS Gazelle AH1	AAC No 3(V) Flt/7 Regt, Leuchars	
XX457	WS Gazelle AH1 <ff>	Jet Avn Preservation Grp, Long Marston	
XX460	WS Gazelle AH1	AAC No 662 Sqn/3 Regt, Wattisham	
XX462	WS Gazelle AH1 [W]	AAC No 658 Sqn/7 Regt, Netheravon	
XX467	HS Hunter T66B/T7 (XL605/ G-TVII) [86]	Privately owned, Kemble	
XX475	HP137 Jetstream T2 (N1036S)	DPA/QinetiQ, West Freugh	
XX476	HP137 Jetstream T2 (N1037S) [561/CU]	RN No 750 Sqn, Culdrose	
XX477	HP137 Jetstream T1 (G-AXXS/ 8462M) <ff>	Privately owned, Askern, Doncaster	
XX478	HP137 Jetstream T2 (G-AXXT) [564/CU]	RN No 750 Sqn, Culdrose	
XX479	HP137 Jetstream T2 (G-AXUR)	RN, Predannack Fire School	
XX481	HP137 Jetstream T2 (G-AXUP) [560/CU]	RN No 750 Sqn, Culdrose	
XX482	SA Jetstream T1 [J]	RAF No 3 FTS/45(R) Sqn, Cranwell	
XX483	SA Jetstream T2 <ff>	Dumfries & Galloway Avn Mus, Dumfries	
XX484	SA Jetstream T2 [566/CU]	RN No 750 Sqn, Culdrose	
XX486	SA Jetstream T2 [569/CU]	RN No 750 Sqn, Culdrose	
XX487	SA Jetstream T2 [568/CU]	RN No 750 Sqn, Culdrose	
XX488	SA Jetstream T2 [562/CU]	RN No 750 Sqn, Culdrose	
XX491	SA Jetstream T1 [K]	RAF No 3 FTS/45(R) Sqn, Cranwell	
XX492	SA Jetstream T1 [A]	RAF No 3 FTS/45(R) Sqn, Cranwell	
XX493	SA Jetstream T1 [L]	RAF No 3 FTS/45(R) Sqn, Cranwell	
XX494	SA Jetstream T1 [B]	RAF No 3 FTS/45(R) Sqn, Cranwell	
XX495	SA Jetstream T1 [C]	RAF No 3 FTS/45(R) Sqn, Cranwell	
XX496	SA Jetstream T1 [D]	RAF No 3 FTS/45(R) Sqn, Cranwell	
XX497	SA Jetstream T1 [E]	RAF No 3 FTS/45(R) Sqn, Cranwell	
XX498	SA Jetstream T1 [F]	RAF No 3 FTS/45(R) Sqn, Cranwell	
XX499	SA Jetstream T1 [G]	RAF No 3 FTS/45(R) Sqn, Cranwell	
XX500	SA Jetstream T1 [H]	RAF No 3 FTS/45(R) Sqn, Cranwell	
XX510	WS Lynx HAS2 [69/DD]	SFDO, RNAS Culdrose	
XX513	SA Bulldog T1 (G-KKKK) [10]	Privately owned, Meppershall	
XX514	SA122 Bulldog (G-BWIB)	Sold to the US, 2002	
XX515	SA Bulldog T1 (G-CBBC) [4]	Privately owned, Blackbushe	
XX518	SA Bulldog T1 (G-UDOG) [S]	Privately owned, Sleap	
XX520	SA Bulldog T1 (9288M) [A]	No 172 Sqn ATC, Haywards Heath	
XX521	SA Bulldog T1 (G-CBEH) [H]	Privately owned, East Dereham, Norfolk	
XX522	SA Bulldog T1 (G-DAWG) [06]	Privately owned, Sleap	
XX524	SA Bulldog T1 (G-DDOG) [04]	Privately owned, North Weald	
XX525	SA Bulldog T1 (G-CBJJ) [8]	Privately owned, Norwich	
XX526	SA Bulldog T1 [C]	Sold as N3014T, January 2002	
XX528	SA Bulldog T1 (G-BZON) [D]	Privately owned, Carlisle	
XX530	SA Bulldog T1 (XX637/9197M) [F]	Rolls-Royce, Renfrew	
XX534	SA Bulldog T1 (G-EDAV) [B]	Privately owned,	
XX537	SA Bulldog T1 (G-CBCB) [C]	Privately owned, Elstree	
XX538	SA Bulldog T1 (G-TDOG) [O]	Privately owned, Bewdley, Worcs	
XX539	SA Bulldog T1 [L]	Privately owned, Wellesbourne Mountford	
XX543	SA Bulldog T1 (G-CBAB) [F]	Privately owned, Duxford	
XX546	SA Bulldog T1 (G-CBCO) [03]	Privately owned, Great Oakley	
XX548	SA Bulldog T1 [06]	Sold as C-FLBD, January 2002	
XX549	SA Bulldog T1 (G-CBID) [6]	Privately owned,	
XX550	SA Bulldog T1 (G-CBBL) [Z]	Privately owned, Fenland	
XX551	SA Bulldog T1 (G-BZDP) [E]	Privately owned, Wellesbourne Mountford	
XX553	SA Bulldog T1 [07]	Sold as N415BD, 2001	
XX554	SA Bulldog T1 (G-BZMD) [09]	Privately owned, Wellesbourne Mountford	
XX557	SA Bulldog T1	Privately owned, Paull, Yorks	
XX561	SA Bulldog T1 (G-BZEP) [7]	Privately owned, Biggin Hill	
XX562	SA Bulldog T1 [18]	Sold as N427VC, December 2001	
XX611	SA Bulldog T1 (G-CBDK) [7]	Privately owned, Coventry	
XX612	SA Bulldog T1 (G-BZXC) [A,03]	Privately owned, Sleap	
XX614	SA Bulldog T1 (G-GGRR) [V]	Privately owned, White Waltham	
XX619	SA Bulldog T1 (G-CBBW) [T]	Privately owned, Coventry	
XX621	SA Bulldog T1 (G-CBEF) [H]	Privately owned, Spanhoe Lodge	
XX623	SA Bulldog T1 [M]	Privately owned, Hurstbourne Tarrant	
XX624	SA Bulldog T1 (G-KDOG) [E]	Privately owned, North Weald	
XX625	SA Bulldog T1 (G-CBBR) [01,N]	Privately owned, Lincs	
XX626	SA Bulldog T1 (9290M) [W,02]	DARA Training School, RAF St Athan	
XX628	SA Bulldog T1 (G-CBFU) [9]	Privately owned, Faversham	
XX629	SA Bulldog T1 (G-BZXZ) [V]	Privately owned, Sleap	
XX630	SA Bulldog T1 (G-SIJW) [5]	Privately owned, Sleap	

Notes	Serial	Type (other identity) [code]	Owner/operator, location or fate
	XX631	SA Bulldog T1 (G-BZXS) [W]	Privately owned, Newport, Ireland
	XX633	SA Bulldog T1 [X]	Privately owned, Mansfield
	XX634	SA Bulldog T1 [T]	Privately owned, Wellesbourne Mountford
	XX635	SA Bulldog T1 (8767M)	DARA Training School, RAF St Athan
	XX636	SA Bulldog T1 (G-CBFP) [Y]	Privately owned, Biggin Hill
	XX638	SA Bulldog T1 (G-DOGG)	Privately owned, Bourne Park, Hants
	XX639	SA Bulldog T1 [D]	*Sold as F-AZTF, 2002*
	XX653	SA Bulldog T1 [E]	DPA/QinetiQ, stored Boscombe Down
	XX654	SA Bulldog T1 [3]	RAF, stored Shawbury
	XX655	SA Bulldog T1 [V]	*Scrapped at Manston, August 2001*
	XX656	SA Bulldog T1 [C]	Privately owned, Wellesbourne Mountford
	XX657	SA Bulldog T1 [U]	*Sold to New Zealand, May 2002*
	XX658	SA Bulldog T1 (G-BZPS) [07]	Privately owned, Wellesbourne Mountford
	XX659	SA Bulldog T1 [E]	Privately owned, Hixon, Staffs
	XX664	SA Bulldog T1 (G-CBCT) [04]	Privately owned, Sleap
	XX665	SA Bulldog T1	No 2409 Sqn ATC, Halton
	XX667	SA Bulldog T1 (G-BZFN) [16]	Privately owned, Staverton
	XX668	SA Bulldog T1 (G-CBAN) [1]	Privately owned, Colerne
	XX669	SA Bulldog T1 (8997M) [B]	Privately owned, Hurstbourne Tarrant, Hants
	XX670	SA Bulldog T1 [C]	*Sold as N50UP, December 2001*
	XX671	SA Bulldog T1 [D]	Privately owned, Wellesbourne Mountford
	XX672	SA Bulldog T1 [E]	Barry Technical College, Cardiff Airport
	XX685	SA Bulldog T1 (G-BZLB) [11]	*Sold as N709AB, November 2002*
	XX686	SA Bulldog T1 (9291M) [5]	DARA Training School, RAF St Athan
	XX687	SA Bulldog T1 [F]	Barry Technical College, Cardiff Airport
	XX689	SA Bulldog T1 [D]	*Sold as N689BD, 2001*
	XX690	SA Bulldog T1 [A]	James Watt College, Greenock
	XX692	SA Bulldog T1 (G-BZMH) [A]	Privately owned, Wellesbourne Mountford
	XX693	SA Bulldog T1 (G-BZML) [07]	Privately owned, Elmsett
	XX694	SA Bulldog T1 (G-CBBS) [E]	Privately owned, Egginton
	XX695	SA Bulldog T1 (G-CBBT) [3]	Privately owned, Egginton
	XX698	SA Bulldog T1 (G-BZME) [9]	Privately owned, Breighton
	XX699	SA Bulldog T1 (G-CBCV) [F]	Privately owned, Egginton
	XX700	SA Bulldog T1 (G-CBEK) [17]	Privately owned, Blackbushe
	XX702	SA Bulldog T1 (G-CBCR) [ ]	Privately owned, Egginton
	XX705	SA Bulldog T1 [5]	QinetiQ Boscombe Down, Apprentice School
	XX706	SA Bulldog T1 [1]	*Sold as N3043A, April 2002*
	XX707	SA Bulldog T1 (G-CBDS) [4]	Privately owned, Sleap
	XX708	SA Bulldog T1 [3]	*Sold as N708BD, April 2002*
	XX711	SA Bulldog T1 (G-CBBU) [X]	Privately owned, Egginton
	XX713	SA Bulldog T1 (G-CBJK) [2]	Privately owned, Norwich
	XX720	SEPECAT Jaguar GR3A [GB]	RAF No 54 Sqn, Coltishall
	XX722	SEPECAT Jaguar GR1 (fuselage)	RAF St Mawgan, BDRT
	XX723	SEPECAT Jaguar GR3A [GQ]	RAF No 54 Sqn, Coltishall
	XX724	SEPECAT Jaguar GR3A [GC]	RAF No 54 Sqn, Coltishall
	XX725	SEPECAT Jaguar GR3A	RAF AWC/SAOEU, Boscombe Down
	XX725	SEPECAT Jaguar GR1 <R> (BAPC 150/*XX718*) [GU]	RAF EPTT, Bottesford
	XX726	SEPECAT Jaguar GR1 (8947M) [EB]	RAF No 1 SoTT, Cosford
	XX727	SEPECAT Jaguar GR1 (8951M) [ER]	RAF No 1 SoTT, Cosford
	XX729	SEPECAT Jaguar GR3A [EL]	RAF No 6 Sqn, Coltishall
	XX730	SEPECAT Jaguar GR1 (8952M) [EC]	RAF No 1 SoTT, Cosford
	XX734	SEPECAT Jaguar GR1 (8816M) (fuselage)	Gatwick Aviation Museum, Charlwood
	XX736	SEPECAT Jaguar GR1 (9110M) <ff>	BAE Systems Brough
	XX737	SEPECAT Jaguar GR3A [EE]	RAF No 6 Sqn, Coltishall
	XX738	SEPECAT Jaguar GR3A [GG]	RAF No 54 Sqn, Coltishall
	XX739	SEPECAT Jaguar GR1 (8902M) [I]	RAF No 1 SoTT, Cosford
	XX741	SEPECAT Jaguar GR1A [04]	RAF, stored Shawbury
	XX743	SEPECAT Jaguar GR1 (8949M) [EG]	RAF No 1 SoTT, Cosford
	XX744	SEPECAT Jaguar GR1	Privately owned, Sproughton
	XX745	SEPECAT Jaguar GR1A [GV]	RAF, stored Shawbury
	XX746	SEPECAT Jaguar GR1 (8895M) [09]	RAF No 1 SoTT, Cosford
	XX747	SEPECAT Jaguar GR1 (8903M)	ATF, RAFC Cranwell
	XX748	SEPECAT Jaguar GR3A [GQ]	RAF No 54 Sqn, Coltishall

Serial	Type (other identity) [code]	Owner/operator, location or fate	Notes
XX751	SEPECAT Jaguar GR1 (8937M) [10]	RAF No 1 SoTT, Cosford	
XX752	SEPECAT Jaguar GR3A [FC]	RAF No 41 Sqn, Coltishall	
XX753	SEPECAT Jaguar GR1 (9087M) <ff>	RAF EPTT, Bottesford	
XX756	SEPECAT Jaguar GR1 (8899M) [AM]	RAF No 1 SoTT, Cosford	
XX757	SEPECAT Jaguar GR1 (8948M) [CU]	RAF No 1 SoTT, Cosford	
XX761	SEPECAT Jaguar GR1 (8600M) <ff>	Boscombe Down Museum	
XX763	SEPECAT Jaguar GR1 (9009M)	DARA Training School, RAF St Athan	
XX764	SEPECAT Jaguar GR1 (9010M)	DARA Training School, RAF St Athan	
XX765	SEPECAT Jaguar ACT	RAF Museum, Cosford	
XX766	SEPECAT Jaguar GR3A [PE]	RAF No 16(R) Sqn, Coltishall	
XX767	SEPECAT Jaguar GR3A [GE]	RAF No 54 Sqn, Coltishall	
XX818	SEPECAT Jaguar GR1 (8945M) [DE]	RAF No 1 SoTT, Cosford	
XX819	SEPECAT Jaguar GR1 (8923M) [CE]	RAF No 1 SoTT, Cosford	
XX821	SEPECAT Jaguar GR1 (8896M) [P]	AMIF, RAFC Cranwell	
XX824	SEPECAT Jaguar GR1 (9019M) [AD]	RAF No 1 SoTT, Cosford	
XX825	SEPECAT Jaguar GR1 (9020M) [BN]	RAF No 1 SoTT, Cosford	
XX826	SEPECAT Jaguar GR1 (9021M) [34,JH]	RAF No 1 SoTT, Cosford	
XX829	SEPECAT Jaguar T2A [GZ]	RAF, stored Shawbury	
XX830	SEPECAT Jaguar T2 <ff>	The Cockpit Collection, RAF Coltishall	
XX832	SEPECAT Jaguar T2A [EZ]	RAF, stored Shawbury	
XX833	SEPECAT Jaguar T2B	RAF AWC/SAOEU, Boscombe Down	
XX835	SEPECAT Jaguar T4 [FY]	RAF No 41 Sqn, Coltishall	
XX836	SEPECAT Jaguar T2A [X]	RAF, stored Shawbury	
XX837	SEPECAT Jaguar T2 (8978M) [Z]	RAF No 1 SoTT, Cosford	
XX838	SEPECAT Jaguar T4 [PR]	RAF No 16(R) Sqn, Coltishall	
XX839	SEPECAT Jaguar T2B (9256M)	*Scrapped at St Athan, May 2002*	
XX840	SEPECAT Jaguar T4 [PS]	RAF No 16(R) Sqn, Coltishall	
XX841	SEPECAT Jaguar T4 [PQ]	RAF No 16(R) Sqn, Coltishall	
XX842	SEPECAT Jaguar T2A [PX]	RAF No 16(R) Sqn, Coltishall	
XX845	SEPECAT Jaguar T4 [ET]	RAF No 6 Sqn, Coltishall	
XX846	SEPECAT Jaguar T4 [PV]	RAF No 16(R) Sqn, Coltishall	
XX847	SEPECAT Jaguar T4 [PY]	RAF No 16(R) Sqn, Coltishall	
XX885	HS Buccaneer S2B (9225M/G-HHAA)	The Old Flying Machine Company, Scampton	
XX888	HS Buccaneer S2B <ff>	Privately owned, Barnstaple	
XX889	HS Buccaneer S2B	Gloucestershire Avn Coll, stored Gloucester	
XX892	HS Buccaneer S2B <ff>	Privately owned, Perthshire	
XX893	HS Buccaneer S2B <ff>	Privately owned,	
XX894	HS Buccaneer S2B [020/R]	Buccaneer Supporters Club, Farnborough	
XX895	HS Buccaneer S2B <ff>	Privately owned, Oxford	
XX897	HS Buccaneer S2B(mod)	Bournemouth Aviation Museum	
XX899	HS Buccaneer S2B <ff>	Midland Air Museum, Coventry	
XX900	HS Buccaneer S2B	British Aviation Heritage, Bruntingthorpe	
XX901	HS Buccaneer S2B	Yorkshire Air Museum, Elvington	
XX907	WS Lynx AH1	QinetiQ Structures Dept, Farnborough	
XX910	WS Lynx HAS2	The Helicopter Museum, Weston-super-Mare	
XX914	BAC VC10/1103 (8777M) <rf>	RAF Air Movements School, Brize Norton	
XX919	BAC 1-11/402AP (PI-C1121) <ff>	Boscombe Down Museum	
XX946	Panavia Tornado (P02) (8883M)	RAF Museum, Hendon	
XX947	Panavia Tornado (P03) (8797M)	RAF Museum, Cosford	
XX948	Panavia Tornado (P06) (8879M) [P]	RAF No 1 SoTT, Cosford	
XX955	SEPECAT Jaguar GR1A [GK]	RAF, stored Shawbury	
XX956	SEPECAT Jaguar GR1 (8950M) [BE]	RAF No 1 SoTT, Cosford	
XX958	SEPECAT Jaguar GR1 (9022M) [BK,JG]	RAF No 1 SoTT, Cosford	
XX959	SEPECAT Jaguar GR1 (8953M) [CJ]	RAF No 1 SoTT, Cosford	

Notes	Serial	Type (other identity) [code]	Owner/operator, location or fate
	XX962	SEPECAT Jaguar GR1B (9257M) [E]	RAF No 1 SoTT, Cosford
	XX965	SEPECAT Jaguar GR1A [C]	AMIF, RAFC Cranwell
	XX966	SEPECAT Jaguar GR1 (8904M) [EL]	RAF No 1 SoTT, Cosford
	XX967	SEPECAT Jaguar GR1 (9006M) [AC,JD]	RAF No 1 SoTT, Cosford
	XX968	SEPECAT Jaguar GR1 (9007M) [AJ,JE]	RAF No 1 SoTT, Cosford
	XX969	SEPECAT Jaguar GR1 (8897M) [01]	RAF No 1 SoTT, Cosford
	XX970	SEPECAT Jaguar GR3A [EH]	RAF No 6 Sqn, Coltishall
	XX974	SEPECAT Jaguar GR3 [PB]	RAF No 16(R) Sqn, Coltishall
	XX975	SEPECAT Jaguar GR1 (8905M) [07]	RAF No 1 SoTT, Cosford
	XX976	SEPECAT Jaguar GR1 (8906M) [BD]	RAF No 1 SoTT, Cosford
	XX977	SEPECAT Jaguar GR1 (9132M) [DL,05]	DARA, RAF St Athan, BDRT
	XX979	SEPECAT Jaguar GR1A (9306M) (fuselage)	RAF Coltishall, instructional use
	XZ101	SEPECAT Jaguar GR1A (9282M) [D]	DPA/QinetiQ Boscombe Down, GI use
	XZ103	SEPECAT Jaguar GR3A [FP]	RAF No 41 Sqn, Coltishall
	XZ104	SEPECAT Jaguar GR3A [FM]	RAF No 41 Sqn, Coltishall
	XZ106	SEPECAT Jaguar GR3A [FR]	RAF No 41 Sqn, Coltishall
	XZ107	SEPECAT Jaguar GR3 [FH]	RAF No 41 Sqn, Coltishall
	XZ109	SEPECAT Jaguar GR3A	RAF/DARA, St Athan (conversion)
	XZ112	SEPECAT Jaguar GR3A [GA]	RAF No 54 Sqn, Coltishall
	XZ113	SEPECAT Jaguar GR3 [FD]	RAF/DARA, St Athan
	XZ114	SEPECAT Jaguar GR1A [FB]	RAF, stored Shawbury
	XZ115	SEPECAT Jaguar GR3 [PD]	RAF No 16(R) Sqn, Coltishall
	XZ117	SEPECAT Jaguar GR3 [EP]	RAF No 6 Sqn, Coltishall
	XZ118	SEPECAT Jaguar GR3 [FF]	RAF No 41 Sqn, Coltishall
	XZ119	SEPECAT Jaguar GR1A [F]	AMIF, RAFC Cranwell
	XZ129	HS Harrier GR3 [ETS]	RN ETS, Yeovilton
	XZ130	HS Harrier GR3 (9079M) [A,HE]	RAF No 1 SoTT, Cosford
	XZ131	HS Harrier GR3 (9174M) <ff>	No 2156 Sqn ATC, Brierley Hill, W Midlands
	XZ132	HS Harrier GR3 (9168M) [C]	ATF, RAFC Cranwell
	XZ133	HS Harrier GR3 [10]	Imperial War Museum, Duxford
	XZ135	HS Harrier GR3 (8848M) <ff>	RAF EPTT, Bottesford
	XZ138	HS Harrier GR3 (9040M) <ff>	RAFC Cranwell, Trenchard Hall
	XZ145	HS Harrier T4 [45]	SFDO, RNAS Culdrose
	XZ146	HS Harrier T4 (9281M) [S]	RAF Wittering, for display
	XZ170	WS Lynx AH9	DPA/Westland Helicopters, Yeovil
	XZ171	WS Lynx AH7	AAC No 656 Sqn/9 Regt, Dishforth
	XZ172	WS Lynx AH7	AAC No 655 Sqn/5 Regt, Aldergrove
	XZ173	WS Lynx AH7	AAC No 661 Sqn/1 Regt, Brüggen
	XZ174	WS Lynx AH7	AAC No 662 Sqn/3 Regt, Wattisham
	XZ175	WS Lynx AH7	AAC No 25 Flt, Belize
	XZ176	WS Lynx AH7	AAC/DARA stored, Fleetlands
	XZ177	WS Lynx AH7	AAC/DARA, Fleetlands
	XZ178	WS Lynx AH7	AAC No 661 Sqn/1 Regt, Brüggen
	XZ179	WS Lynx AH7	AAC/DARA, Fleetlands
	XZ180	WS Lynx AH7 [R]	RM No 847 Sqn, Yeovilton
	XZ181	WS Lynx AH1	Westland Helicopters, Yeovil, wfu
	XZ182	WS Lynx AH7 [M]	RM/DARA, Fleetlands
	XZ183	WS Lynx AH7	AAC/DARA, stored Fleetlands
	XZ184	WS Lynx AH7 [Z]	AAC/DARA, Fleetlands
	XZ185	WS Lynx AH7	AAC/DARA, stored Fleetlands
	XZ187	WS Lynx AH7	AAC/DARA, stored Fleetlands
	XZ188	WS Lynx AH7	Army SEAE, Arborfield
	XZ190	WS Lynx AH7	AAC No 9 Regt, Dishforth
	XZ191	WS Lynx AH7 [A]	AAC No 671 Sqn/2 Regt, Middle Wallop
	XZ192	WS Lynx AH7	DPA/Westland Helicopters, Weston-super-Mare (on rebuild)
	XZ193	WS Lynx AH7 [I]	AAC No 671 Sqn/2 Regt, Middle Wallop
	XZ194	WS Lynx AH7	AAC No 3 Regt, Wattisham
	XZ195	WS Lynx AH7	AAC/DARA, stored Fleetlands
	XZ196	WS Lynx AH7	AAC No 4 Regt, Wattisham
	XZ197	WS Lynx AH7	AAC

Serial	Type (other identity) [code]	Owner/operator, location or fate	Notes
XZ198	WS Lynx AH7	AAC/DARA, Fleetlands	
XZ203	WS Lynx AH7 [L]	AAC No 671 Sqn/2 Regt, Middle Wallop	
XZ205	WS Lynx AH7	AAC No 655 Sqn/5 Regt, Aldergrove	
XZ206	WS Lynx AH7	AAC No 25 Flt, Belize	
XZ207	WS Lynx AH7	AAC/DARA, Fleetlands (damaged)	
XZ208	WS Lynx AH7	AAC No 669 Sqn/4 Regt, Wattisham	
XZ209	WS Lynx AH7	AAC No 655 Sqn/5 Regt, Aldergrove	
XZ210	WS Lynx AH7	AAC No 656 Sqn/9 Regt, Dishforth	
XZ211	WS Lynx AH7	AAC No 655 Sqn/5 Regt, Aldergrove	
XZ212	WS Lynx AH7	AAC No 1 Regt, Brüggen	
XZ213	WS Lynx AH1 (TAD 213)	DARA Fleetlands Apprentice School	
XZ214	WS Lynx AH7	AAC No 657 Sqn, Odiham	
XZ215	WS Lynx AH7 [4]	AAC No 655 Sqn/5 Regt, Aldergrove	
XZ216	WS Lynx AH7	AAC No 661 Sqn/1 Regt, Brüggen	
XZ217	WS Lynx AH7	AAC No 664 Sqn/9 Regt, Dishforth	
XZ218	WS Lynx AH7	AAC/DARA, Fleetlands	
XZ219	WS Lynx AH7	AAC No 3 Regt, Wattisham	
XZ220	WS Lynx AH7	AAC No 661 Sqn/1 Regt, Brüggen	
XZ221	WS Lynx AH7	AAC No 654 Sqn/4 Regt, Wattisham	
XZ222	WS Lynx AH7	AAC No 657 Sqn, Odiham	
XZ228	WS Lynx HAS3S [425/KT]	RN No 815 Sqn, *Kent* Flt, Yeovilton	
XZ229	WS Lynx HAS3S [422/SU]	RN No 815 Sqn, *Sutherland* Flt, Yeovilton	
XZ230	WS Lynx HAS3S [302]	RN/DARA, stored Fleetlands	
XZ232	WS Lynx HAS3S [350/CL]	RN No 815 Sqn, *Cumberland* Flt, Yeovilton	
XZ233	WS Lynx HAS3(ICE)	RN AMG, Yeovilton	
XZ234	WS Lynx HAS3S [633]	RN No 702 Sqn, Yeovilton	
XZ235	WS Lynx HAS3S [304]	RN No 815 Sqn, Yeovilton	
XZ236	WS Lynx HMA8	DPA/DARA, stored Fleetlands	
XZ237	WS Lynx HAS3S [301]	RN No 815 Sqn, HQ Flt, Yeovilton	
XZ238	WS Lynx HAS3S(ICE) [435/EE]	RN/DARA, Fleetlands	
XZ239	WS Lynx HAS3S [344/GW]	RN No 815 Sqn, *Glasgow* Flt, Yeovilton	
XZ241	WS Lynx HAS3S(ICE) [435/EE]	RN No 815 Sqn, *Endurance* Flt, Yeovilton	
XZ243	WS Lynx HAS3 <ff>	RNAS Culdrose, Fire Section	
XZ245	WS Lynx HAS3S [348/CM]	RN AMG, Yeovilton	
XZ246	WS Lynx HAS3S(ICE) [434/EE]	RN No 815 Sqn, *Endurance* Flt, Yeovilton	
XZ248	WS Lynx HAS3S [638]	RN No 702 Sqn, Yeovilton	
XZ250	WS Lynx HAS3S [631]	RN No 702 Sqn, Yeovilton	
XZ252	WS Lynx HAS3S	RN MASU, Fleetlands	
XZ254	WS Lynx HAS3S [634]	RN No 702 Sqn, Yeovilton	
XZ255	WS Lynx HMA8 [462/WM]	RN/DARA, stored Fleetlands	
XZ256	WS Lynx HMA8 [474/RM]	*Crashed 12 June 2002, Atlantic Ocean*	
XZ257	WS Lynx HMA8 [640]	RN No 702 Sqn, Yeovilton	
XZ286	BAe Nimrod AEW3 <rf>	RAF Kinloss Fire Section	
XZ287	BAe Nimrod AEW3 (9140M) (fuselage)	RAF TSW, Stafford	
XZ290	WS Gazelle AH1	AAC No 665 Sqn/5 Regt, Aldergrove	
XZ291	WS Gazelle AH1	AAC No 12 Flt, Brüggen	
XZ292	WS Gazelle AH1	AAC No 9 Regt, Dishforth	
XZ294	WS Gazelle AH1 [X]	AAC No 658 Sqn/7 Regt, Netheravon	
XZ295	WS Gazelle AH1	AAC No 12 Flt, Brüggen	
XZ296	WS Gazelle AH1	RAF No 7 Sqn, Odiham	
XZ298	WS Gazelle AH1	AAC No 656 Sqn/9 Regt, Dishforth	
XZ299	WS Gazelle AH1	AAC/DARA, Fleetlands	
XZ300	WS Gazelle AH1 [L] (wreck)	Army, Bramley, Hants	
XZ301	WS Gazelle AH1 [U]	AAC No 664 Sqn/9 Regt, Dishforth	
XZ303	WS Gazelle AH1	AAC No 663 Sqn/3 Regt, Wattisham	
XZ304	WS Gazelle AH1	AAC No 6(V) Flt/7 Regt, Shawbury	
XZ305	WS Gazelle AH1 (TAD020)	Army SEAE, Arborfield	
XZ307	WS Gazelle AH1	DARA Fleetlands Apprentice School	
XZ308	WS Gazelle AH1	AAC No 4 Regt, Wattisham	
XZ309	WS Gazelle AH1	AAC No 6(V) Flt/7 Regt, Shawbury	
XZ311	WS Gazelle AH1	AAC No 6(V) Flt/7 Regt, Shawbury	
XZ312	WS Gazelle AH1	AAC No 9 Regt, Dishforth	
XZ313	WS Gazelle AH1	AAC No 667 Sqn, Middle Wallop	
XZ314	WS Gazelle AH1	AAC No 8 Flt, Middle Wallop	
XZ315	WS Gazelle AH1	Privately owned, Sproughton	
XZ316	WS Gazelle AH1 [B]	AAC No 666(V) Sqn/7 Regt, Netheravon	
XZ318	WS Gazelle AH1 (fuselage)	AAC/DARA, stored Fleetlands	
XZ320	WS Gazelle AH1	AAC/DARA, Fleetlands	
XZ321	WS Gazelle AH1	AAC No 665 Sqn/5 Regt, Aldergrove	
XZ322	WS Gazelle AH1 (9283M) [N]	DARA, RAF St Athan, BDRT	
XZ323	WS Gazelle AH1	AAC No 16 Flt, Dhekelia, Cyprus	

Notes	Serial	Type (other identity) [code]	Owner/operator, location or fate
	XZ324	WS Gazelle AH1	AAC No 3(V) Flt/7 Regt, Leuchars
	XZ325	WS Gazelle AH1 [T]	Army SEAE, Arborfield
	XZ326	WS Gazelle AH1	AAC No 665 Sqn/5 Regt, Aldergrove
	XZ327	WS Gazelle AH1	AAC No 3(V) Flt/7 Regt, Leuchars
	XZ328	WS Gazelle AH1	AAC No 662 Sqn/3 Regt, Wattisham
	XZ329	WS Gazelle AH1 (G-BZYD) [J]	Privately owned, East Garston, Bucks
	XZ330	WS Gazelle AH1 [Y]	AAC, Middle Wallop (damaged)
	XZ331	WS Gazelle AH1	AAC No 654 Sqn/4 Regt, Wattisham
	XZ332	WS Gazelle AH1 [O]	Army SEAE, Arborfield
	XZ333	WS Gazelle AH1 [A]	Army SEAE, Arborfield
	XZ334	WS Gazelle AH1	AAC No 665 Sqn/5 Regt, Aldergrove
	XZ335	WS Gazelle AH1	AAC No 6(V) Flt/7 Regt, Shawbury
	XZ337	WS Gazelle AH1	AAC No 664 Sqn/9 Regt, Dishforth
	XZ338	WS Gazelle AH1	AAC/DARA, stored Fleetlands
	XZ339	WS Gazelle AH1	*Crashed 19 July 2002, in Irish Sea off Ballykelly*
	XZ340	WS Gazelle AH1 [5B]	AAC No 29 Flt, BATUS, Suffield, Canada
	XZ341	WS Gazelle AH1	AAC No 665 Sqn/5 Regt, Aldergrove
	XZ342	WS Gazelle AH1	AAC No 8 Flt, Credenhill
	XZ343	WS Gazelle AH1	DARA, Fleetlands, hack
	XZ344	WS Gazelle AH1	AAC No 9 Regt, Dishforth
	XZ345	WS Gazelle AH1 [M]	AAC No 671 Sqn/2 Regt, Middle Wallop
	XZ346	WS Gazelle AH1	AAC No 665 Sqn/5 Regt, Aldergrove
	XZ347	WS Gazelle AH1	AAC No 3 Regt, Wattisham
	XZ348	WS Gazelle AH1 (wreck)	AAC/DARA, stored Fleetlands
	XZ349	WS Gazelle AH1 [G1]	AAC No 671 Sqn/2 Regt, Middle Wallop
	XZ355	SEPECAT Jaguar GR3A [FJ]	RAF No 41 Sqn, Coltishall
	XZ356	SEPECAT Jaguar GR3A [GF]	RAF No 54 Sqn, Coltishall
	XZ357	SEPECAT Jaguar GR3A [FK]	RAF No 41 Sqn, Coltishall
	XZ358	SEPECAT Jaguar GR1A [L]	AMIF, RAFC Cranwell
	XZ360	SEPECAT Jaguar GR3 [FN]	RAF No 41 Sqn, Coltishall
	XZ361	SEPECAT Jaguar GR3 [FT]	RAF, stored Shawbury
	XZ363	SEPECAT Jaguar GR1A <R> (*XX824*/BAPC 151) [A]	RAF EPTT, Bottesford
	XZ364	SEPECAT Jaguar GR3A [GJ]	RAF No 54 Sqn, Coltishall
	XZ366	SEPECAT Jaguar GR3A [FS]	RAF No 41 Sqn, Coltishall
	XZ367	SEPECAT Jaguar GR3 [GP]	RAF Coltishall, GI use
	XZ368	SEPECAT Jaguar GR1 [8900M] [AG]	RAF No 1 SoTT, Cosford
	XZ369	SEPECAT Jaguar GR3A [EF]	RAF No 6 Sqn, Coltishall
	XZ370	SEPECAT Jaguar GR1 (9004M) [JB]	RAF No 1 SoTT, Cosford
	XZ371	SEPECAT Jaguar GR1 (8907M) [AP]	RAF No 1 SoTT, Cosford
	XZ372	SEPECAT Jaguar GR3 [ED]	RAF No 41 Sqn, Coltishall
	XZ374	SEPECAT Jaguar GR1 (9005M) [JC]	RAF No 1 SoTT, Cosford
	XZ375	SEPECAT Jaguar GR1A (9255M) (fuselage)	RAF Coltishall, instructional use
	XZ377	SEPECAT Jaguar GR3A [EG]	RAF No 6 Sqn, Coltishall
	XZ378	SEPECAT Jaguar GR1A [EP]	RAF, stored Shawbury
	XZ382	SEPECAT Jaguar GR1 (8908M)	Privately owned, Bruntingthorpe
	XZ383	SEPECAT Jaguar GR1 (8901M) [AF]	RAF No 1 SoTT, Cosford
	XZ384	SEPECAT Jaguar GR1 (8954M) [BC]	RAF No 1 SoTT, Cosford
	XZ385	SEPECAT Jaguar GR3 [PC]	RAF No 16(R) Sqn, Coltishall
	XZ389	SEPECAT Jaguar GR1 (8946M) [BL]	RAF No 1 SoTT, Cosford
	XZ390	SEPECAT Jaguar GR1 (9003M) [35,JA]	RAF No 1 SoTT, Cosford
	XZ391	SEPECAT Jaguar GR3A [EB]	RAF No 6 Sqn, Coltishall
	XZ392	SEPECAT Jaguar GR3A [PF]	RAF No 16(R) Sqn, Coltishall
	XZ394	SEPECAT Jaguar GR3 [GN]	RAF No 54 Sqn, Coltishall
	XZ396	SEPECAT Jaguar GR1A [EM]	RAF/DARA, St Athan
	XZ398	SEPECAT Jaguar GR3 [FA]	RAF No 41 Sqn, Coltishall
	XZ399	SEPECAT Jaguar GR3A [EJ]	RAF No 6 Sqn, Coltishall
	XZ400	SEPECAT Jaguar GR3A [GR]	RAF No 54 Sqn, Coltishall
	XZ431	HS Buccaneer S2B (9233M) <ff>	Phoenix Aviation, Bruntingthorpe
	XZ439	BAe Sea Harrier FA2	RN/DARA, stored St Athan
	XZ440	BAe Sea Harrier FA2 [127/R]	RN No 800 Sqn, Yeovilton
	XZ455	BAe Sea Harrier FA2 [001] (wreck)	*Scrapped at Yeovilton*
	XZ459	BAe Sea Harrier FA2	RN/DARA, stored St Athan

Serial	Type (other identity) [code]	Owner/operator, location or fate	Notes
XZ493	BAe Sea Harrier FRS1 (comp XV760) [001/N]	FAA Museum, RNAS Yeovilton	
XZ493	BAe Sea Harrier FRS1 <ff>	RN Yeovilton, Fire Section	
XZ494	BAe Sea Harrier FA2	RN/DARA, stored St Athan	
XZ497	BAe Sea Harrier FA2 [001/L]	RN No 801 Sqn, Yeovilton	
XZ499	BAe Sea Harrier FA2 [003]	FAA Museum, stored Yeovilton	
XZ559	Slingsby T61F Venture T2 (G-BUEK)	Privately owned, Tibenham	
XZ570	WS61 Sea King HAS5(mod)	RN, stored *HMS Sultan*, Gosport	
XZ571	WS61 Sea King HAS6 [016/L]	RN No 820 Sqn, Culdrose	
XZ574	WS61 Sea King HAS6 [829/CU]	RN No 771 Sqn, Culdrose	
XZ575	WS61 Sea King HU5	DPA/AFD/QinetiQ, Boscombe Down	
XZ576	WS61 Sea King HAS6	DPA/AFD/QinetiQ, Boscombe Down	
XZ578	WS61 Sea King HU5 [709/PW]	RN No 771 Sqn, Prestwick	
XZ579	WS61 Sea King HAS6 [707/PW]	RN, stored *HMS Sultan*, Gosport	
XZ580	WS61 Sea King HAS6 [704/PW]	RN/DARA, Fleetlands	
XZ581	WS61 Sea King HAS6 [69/CU]	RN, stored *HMS Sultan*, Gosport	
XZ585	WS61 Sea King HAR3	RAF No 203 (R) Sqn, Akrotiri	
XZ586	WS61 Sea King HAR3	RAF HMF, St Mawgan	
XZ587	WS61 Sea King HAR3	RAF No 202 Sqn, D Flt, Lossiemouth	
XZ588	WS61 Sea King HAR3	RAF HMF, St Mawgan	
XZ589	WS61 Sea King HAR3	RAF No 22 Sqn, C Flt, Valley	
XZ590	WS61 Sea King HAR3	RAF No 202 Sqn, A Flt, Boulmer	
XZ591	WS61 Sea King HAR3	RAF No 203 (R) Sqn, Akrotiri	
XZ592	WS61 Sea King HAR3	RAF/DARA, Fleetlands	
XZ593	WS61 Sea King HAR3	RAF No 202 Sqn, E Flt, Leconfield	
XZ594	WS61 Sea King HAR3	RAF No 202 Sqn, E Flt, Leconfield	
XZ595	WS61 Sea King HAR3	RAF No 203 (R) Sqn, Akrotiri	
XZ596	WS61 Sea King HAR3	RAF HMF, St Mawgan	
XZ597	WS61 Sea King HAR3	RAF HMF, St Mawgan	
XZ598	WS61 Sea King HAR3	RAF No 22 Sqn, C Flt, Valley	
XZ599	WS61 Sea King HAR3	RAF/DARA, Fleetlands (damaged)	
XZ605	WS Lynx AH7 [Y]	RM No 847 Sqn, Yeovilton	
XZ606	WS Lynx AH7	AAC No 667 Sqn, Middle Wallop	
XZ607	WS Lynx AH7	AAC No 656 Sqn/9 Regt, Dishforth	
XZ608	WS Lynx AH7	AAC No 657 Sqn, Odiham	
XZ609	WS Lynx AH7	AAC No 657 Sqn, Odiham	
XZ611	WS Lynx AH7	AAC No 9 Regt, Dishforth	
XZ612	WS Lynx AH7 [N]	RM No 847 Sqn, Yeovilton	
XZ613	WS Lynx AH7 [F]	AAC/DARA, Fleetlands	
XZ614	WS Lynx AH7 [X]	RM No 847 Sqn, Yeovilton	
XZ615	WS Lynx AH7	AAC No 655 Sqn/5 Regt, Aldergrove	
XZ616	WS Lynx AH7	AAC No 657 Sqn, Odiham	
XZ617	WS Lynx AH7	AAC No 656 Sqn/9 Regt, Dishforth	
XZ630	Panavia Tornado GR1 (8976M)	DARA, RAF St Athan, BDRT	
XZ631	Panavia Tornado GR1	DPA/BAE Systems, Warton	
XZ641	WS Lynx AH7	AAC No 7 Air Assault Battalion, Wattisham	
XZ642	WS Lynx AH7	AAC No 663 Sqn/3 Regt, Wattisham	
XZ643	WS Lynx AH7	AAC No 654 Sqn/4 Regt, Wattisham	
XZ645	WS Lynx AH7	AAC No 4 Regt, Wattisham	
XZ646	WS Lynx AH7	AAC No 657 Sqn, Odiham	
XZ646	WS Lynx AH7 (really XZ649)	QinetiQ Structures Dept, Farnborough	
XZ647	WS Lynx AH7	AAC No 667 Sqn, Middle Wallop	
XZ648	WS Lynx AH7	AAC No 4 Regt, Wattisham	
XZ651	WS Lynx AH7	AAC No 657 Sqn, Odiham	
XZ652	WS Lynx AH7 [T]	AAC No 671 Sqn/2 Regt, Middle Wallop	
XZ653	WS Lynx AH7	AAC No 657 Sqn, Odiham	
XZ654	WS Lynx AH7	AAC No 655 Sqn/5 Regt, Aldergrove	
XZ655	WS Lynx AH7	AAC/DARA, stored Fleetlands	
XZ661	WS Lynx AH1	AAC No 655 Sqn/5 Regt, Aldergrove	
XZ663	WS Lynx AH7	AAC/DARA, stored Fleetlands	
XZ665	WS Lynx AH7	Privately owned, Staverton	
XZ666	WS Lynx AH7	Army SEAE, Arborfield	
XZ668	WS Lynx AH7 [UN] (wreckage)	AAC Middle Wallop	
XZ669	WS Lynx AH7	AAC No 662 Sqn/3 Regt, Wattisham	
XZ670	WS Lynx AH7	AAC No 656 Sqn/9 Regt, Dishforth	
XZ671	WS Lynx AH7 <ff>	Westland Helicopters, Yeovil, instructional use	
XZ672	WS Lynx AH7	AAC No 655 Sqn/5 Regt, Aldergrove	
XZ673	WS Lynx AH7	AAC/DARA, Fleetlands	
XZ674	WS Lynx AH7	AAC/DARA, stored Fleetlands	
XZ675	WS Lynx AH7 [E]	AAC No 671 Sqn/2 Regt, Middle Wallop	
XZ676	WS Lynx AH7	AAC No 655 Sqn/5 Regt, Aldergrove	

XZ677 – ZA111

Notes	Serial	Type (other identity) [code]	Owner/operator, location or fate
	XZ677	WS Lynx AH7	AAC No 655 Sqn/5 Regt, Aldergrove
	XZ678	WS Lynx AH7	AAC No 662 Sqn/3 Regt, Wattisham
	XZ679	WS Lynx AH7	AAC No 664 Sqn/9 Regt, Dishforth
	XZ680	WS Lynx AH7	AAC No 1 Regt, Brüggen
	XZ689	WS Lynx HMA8 [363/MA]	RN No 815 Sqn, *Marlborough* Flt, Yeovilton
	XZ690	WS Lynx HMA8 [375/SM]	RN No 815 Sqn, *Somerset* Flt, Yeovilton
	XZ691	WS Lynx HMA8 [670]	RN/DARA, stored Fleetlands
	XZ692	WS Lynx HMA8 [306]	RN No 815 Sqn, HQ Flt, Yeovilton
	XZ693	WS Lynx HAS3S [639]	RN No 702 Sqn, Yeovilton
	XZ694	WS Lynx HAS3S [411/EB]	RN No 815 Sqn, *Edinburgh* Flt, Yeovilton
	XZ695	WS Lynx HMA8 [308]	RN No 815 Sqn, Yeovilton
	XZ696	WS Lynx HAS3S [336/CF]	RN No 815 Sqn, *Cardiff* Flt, Yeovilton
	XZ697	WS Lynx HMA8 [437/GT]	RN No 815 Sqn, *Grafton* Flt, Yeovilton
	XZ698	WS Lynx HMA8 [427/SB]	RN No 815 Sqn, *St Albans* Flt, Yeovilton
	XZ699	WS Lynx HAS3S [303]	RN/DARA, Fleetlands
	XZ719	WS Lynx HMA8 [317]	RN No 815 Sqn OEU, Yeovilton
	XZ720	WS Lynx HAS3S [302]	RN/DARA, Fleetlands
	XZ721	WS Lynx HMA8 [332/LP]	RN No 815 Sqn, *Liverpool* Flt, Yeovilton
	XZ722	WS Lynx HMA8 [365/AY]	RN No 815 Sqn, *Argyll* Flt, Yeovilton
	XZ723	WS Lynx HMA8	RN/DARA, Fleetlands
	XZ724	WS Lynx HAS3S [426/PD]	RN No 815 Sqn, *Portland* Flt, Yeovilton
	XZ725	WS Lynx HMA8 [474/RM]	RN No 815 Sqn, *Richmond* Flt, Yeovilton
	XZ726	WS Lynx HMA8 [365]	RN AMG, Yeovilton
	XZ727	WS Lynx HAS3S [303]	RN No 815 Sqn, HQ Flt, Yeovilton
	XZ728	WS Lynx HMA8 [415/MM]	RN/DARA, stored Fleetlands
	XZ729	WS Lynx HMA8 [318]	RN No 815 Sqn OEU, Yeovilton
	XZ730	WS Lynx HAS3CTS [632]	RN No 702 Sqn, Yeovilton
	XZ731	WS Lynx HMA8 [307]	RN/DARA, stored Fleetlands
	XZ732	WS Lynx HMA8 [420/EX]	RN No 815 Sqn, *Exeter* Flt, Yeovilton
	XZ733	WS Lynx HAS3S [462/WM]	RN No 815 Sqn, *Westminster* Flt, Yeovilton
	XZ735	WS Lynx HAS3S [348/CM]	RN AMG, Yeovilton
	XZ736	WS Lynx HMA8 [388/CT]	RN No 815 Sqn, *Campbeltown* Flt, Yeovilton
	XZ920	WS61 Sea King HU5SAR [822/CU]	RN No 771 Sqn, Culdrose
	XZ921	WS61 Sea King HAS6 [269/N]	RN AMG, Culdrose
	XZ922	WS61 Sea King HAS6C [WA]	RN/DARA, Fleetlands
	XZ930	WS Gazelle HT3 [Q]	RN AESS, *HMS Sultan*, Gosport
	XZ932	WS Gazelle HT3 [S]	*Sold as 3D-HGW, 2001*
	XZ933	WS Gazelle HT3 [T]	DPA/QinetiQ, Boscombe Down, spares use
	XZ934	WS Gazelle HT3 (G-CBSI) [U]	Privately owned, Redhill
	XZ935	WS Gazelle HCC4	RAF No 1 SoTT, Cosford
	XZ936	WS Gazelle HT2 [6]	DPA/ETPS, Boscombe Down
	XZ937	WS Gazelle HT2 (G-CBKA) [Y]	Privately owned, Stapleford Tawney
	XZ938	WS Gazelle HT2 [45/CU]	RAF No 1 SoTT, Cosford
	XZ939	WS Gazelle HT2 [9]	DPA/ETPS, Boscombe Down
	XZ940	WS Gazelle HT2 (G-CBBV) [O]	Privately owned, Redhill
	XZ941	WS Gazelle HT2 [B]	DARA Training School, RAF St Athan, BDRT
	XZ942	WS Gazelle HT2 [42/CU]	AAC, Middle Wallop, instructional use
	XZ964	BAe Harrier GR3 [D]	Royal Engineers Museum, Chatham
	XZ966	BAe Harrier GR3 (9221M) [G]	MoD FSCTE, Manston
	XZ968	BAe Harrier GR3 (9222M) [3G]	Muckleborough Collection, Weybourne
	XZ969	BAe Harrier GR3 [69]	SFDO, RNAS Culdrose
	XZ971	BAe Harrier GR3 (9219M) [G]	RAF, stored Shawbury
	XZ987	BAe Harrier GR3 (9185M) [C]	RAF Stafford, at main gate
	XZ990	BAe Harrier GR3 <ff>	No 1220 Sqn ATC, March, Cambs
	XZ990	BAe Harrier GR3 <rf>	RAF Wittering, derelict
	XZ991	BAe Harrier GR3 (9162M) [3A]	DARA, RAF St Athan, BDRT
	XZ993	BAe Harrier GR3 (9240M) (fuselage)	DARA, RAF St Athan, fire training
	XZ994	BAe Harrier GR3 (9170M) [U]	RAF Air Movements School, Brize Norton
	XZ995	BAe Harrier GR3 (G-CBGK/ 9220M) [3G]	Privately owned, Lowestoft
	XZ996	BAe Harrier GR3 [96]	SFDO, RNAS Culdrose
	XZ997	BAe Harrier GR3 (9122M) [V]	RAF Museum, Hendon
	ZA101	BAe Hawk 100 (G-HAWK)	DPA/BAE Systems, Warton
	ZA105	WS61 Sea King HAR3	RAF No 78 Sqn, Mount Pleasant, FI
	ZA110	BAe Jetstream T2 (F-BTMI) [563/CU]	RN No 750 Sqn, Culdrose
	ZA111	BAe Jetstream T2 (9Q-CTC) [565/CU]	RN No 750 Sqn, Culdrose

Serial	Type (other identity) [code]	Owner/operator, location or fate	Notes
ZA126	WS61 Sea King HAS6 [504/CU]	RN, stored *HMS Sultan*, Gosport	
ZA127	WS61 Sea King HAS6 [509/CU]	RN, stored *HMS Sultan*, Gosport	
ZA128	WS61 Sea King HAS6 [010]	RN, stored *HMS Sultan*, Gosport	
ZA129	WS61 Sea King HAS6 [502/CU]	Westland Helicopters, Yeovil	
ZA130	WS61 Sea King HU5SAR [824]	RN No 771 Sqn, Culdrose	
ZA131	WS61 Sea King HAS6 [271/N]	RN, stored *HMS Sultan*, Gosport	
ZA133	WS61 Sea King HAS6 [013]	RN No 820 Sqn, Culdrose	
ZA134	WS61 Sea King HU5SAR [825/CU]	RN AMG, Culdrose	
ZA135	WS61 Sea King HAS6 [705/PW]	RN No 820 Sqn, Culdrose	
ZA136	WS61 Sea King HAS6 [018/L]	RN, AESS, *HMS Sultan*, Gosport (wreck)	
ZA137	WS61 Sea King HU5SAR [820/CU]	RN AMG, Culdrose	
ZA142	BAe VC10 K2 (G-ARVI) [C]	RAF/DARA, St Athan, wfu	
ZA147	BAe VC10 K3 (5H-MMT) [F]	RAF No 101 Sqn, Brize Norton	
ZA148	BAe VC10 K3 (5Y-ADA) [G]	RAF No 101 Sqn, Brize Norton	
ZA149	BAe VC10 K3 (5X-UVJ) [H]	RAF No 101 Sqn, Brize Norton	
ZA150	BAe VC10 K3 (5H-MOG)	RAF No 101 Sqn, Brize Norton	
ZA166	WS61 Sea King HU5 [189/CU]	RN/DARA, stored Fleetlands	
ZA167	WS61 Sea King HU5SAR [821/CU]	RN No 771 Sqn, Culdrose	
ZA168	WS61 Sea King HAS6 [011/L]	RN No 820 Sqn, Culdrose	
ZA169	WS61 Sea King HAS6 [515/CW]	RN No 771 Sqn, Culdrose	
ZA170	WS61 Sea King HU5	RN MASU, Fleetlands	
ZA175	BAe Sea Harrier FA2 [717]	FAA Museum, stored Yeovilton	
ZA176	BAe Sea Harrier FA2 [126/R]	RN No 800 Sqn, Yeovilton	
ZA195	BAe Sea Harrier FA2	RN, Yeovilton, instructional use	
ZA250	BAe Harrier T52 (G-VTOL)	Brooklands Museum, Weybridge	
ZA254	Panavia Tornado F2 (9253M) (fuselage)	RAF Coningsby, instructional use	
ZA267	Panavia Tornado F2 (9284M)	RAF Marham, instructional use	
ZA291	WS61 Sea King HC4 [WX]	RN No 848 Sqn, Yeovilton	
ZA292	WS61 Sea King HC4 [ZR]	DPA/Westland Helicopters, Weston-super-Mare	
ZA293	WS61 Sea King HC4 [WO]	RN No 848 Sqn, Yeovilton	
ZA295	WS61 Sea King HC4 [ZR]	RN AMG, Yeovilton	
ZA296	WS61 Sea King HC4 [VO]	RN No 846 Sqn, Yeovilton	
ZA297	WS61 Sea King HC4 [C]	RN No 845 Sqn, Yeovilton	
ZA298	WS61 Sea King HC4 [G]	RN No 845 Sqn, Yeovilton	
ZA299	WS61 Sea King HC4 [VV]	RN No 846 Sqn, Yeovilton	
ZA310	WS61 Sea King HC4 [WY]	RN No 848 Sqn, Yeovilton	
ZA312	WS61 Sea King HC4 [ZS]	RN/DARA, Fleetlands	
ZA313	WS61 Sea King HC4 [M]	RN No 845 Sqn, Yeovilton	
ZA314	WS61 Sea King HC4 [F]	RN No 845 Sqn, Yeovilton	
ZA319	Panavia Tornado GR1	Army, Bicester, on display	
ZA320	Panavia Tornado GR1 (fuselage)	RAF No 1 SoTT, Cosford	
ZA321	Panavia Tornado GR1 [TAB]	*To the USA, July 2002*	
ZA322	Panavia Tornado GR1 (9334M) [TAC]	RAF Marham, WLT	
ZA323	Panavia Tornado GR1 [TAZ]	RAF/DARA, stored St Athan	
ZA324	Panavia Tornado GR1 [TAY]	RAF Lossiemouth, BDRT	
ZA325	Panavia Tornado GR1 [TAX]	RAF/DARA, stored St Athan	
ZA326	Panavia Tornado GR1P	DPA/AFD/QinetiQ, Boscombe Down	
ZA327	Panavia Tornado GR1	DPA/BAE Systems, Warton	
ZA328	Panavia Tornado GR1	DPA/BAE Systems, Warton	
ZA352	Panavia Tornado GR1 (fuselage)	Privately owned, Chesterfield (for scrapping)	
ZA353	Panavia Tornado GR1 [B-53]	DPA/AFD/QinetiQ, Boscombe Down	
ZA354	Panavia Tornado GR1	DPA/BAE Systems, Warton	
ZA355	Panavia Tornado GR1 [TAA]	RAF Lossiemouth, WLT	
ZA356	Panavia Tornado GR1 [P]	Privately owned, Chesterfield (for scrapping)	
ZA357	Panavia Tornado GR1 [TTV]	RAF/DARA, stored St Athan	
ZA358	Panavia Tornado GR1	RAF St Athan Fire Section	
ZA359	Panavia Tornado GR1	BAE Systems Warton, Overseas Customer Training Centre	
ZA360	Panavia Tornado GR1 <ff>	RAF Marham, instructional use	
ZA361	Panavia Tornado GR1 [TD]	RAF ASF, Marham	
ZA362	Panavia Tornado GR1	RAF, Lossiemouth, wfu	
ZA365	Panavia Tornado GR4 [AJ-Y]	RAF No 617 Sqn, Lossiemouth	
ZA367	Panavia Tornado GR4 [FW]	RAF No 12 Sqn, Lossiemouth	
ZA369	Panavia Tornado GR4A [U]	RAF No 2 Sqn, Marham	
ZA370	Panavia Tornado GR4A [DB]	RAF No 31 Sqn, Marham	
ZA371	Panavia Tornado GR4A [C]	RAF No 2 Sqn, Marham	
ZA372	Panavia Tornado GR4A [E]	RAF No 2 Sqn, Marham	
ZA373	Panavia Tornado GR4A [H]	RAF No 2 Sqn, Marham	

Notes	Serial	Type (other identity) [code]	Owner/operator, location or fate
	ZA374	Panavia Tornado GR1 [TTA]	*To the USAF Museum, October 2002*
	ZA375	Panavia Tornado GR1 (9335M) [AJ-W]	RAF Marham, BDRT
	ZA393	Panavia Tornado GR4 [FE]	RAF No 12 Sqn, Lossiemouth
	ZA395	Panavia Tornado GR4A [N]	RAF No 2 Sqn, Marham
	ZA398	Panavia Tornado GR4A [S]	RAF No 2 Sqn, Marham
	ZA399	Panavia Tornado GR1 [AJ-C]	RAF/DARA, stored St Athan
	ZA400	Panavia Tornado GR4A [T]	RAF No 2 Sqn, Marham
	ZA401	Panavia Tornado GR4A [P]	RAF No 13 Sqn, Marham
	ZA402	Panavia Tornado GR4A	DPA/BAE Systems, Warton (conversion)
	ZA404	Panavia Tornado GR4A [W]	RAF No 2 Sqn, Marham
	ZA405	Panavia Tornado GR4A [Y]	RAF No 2 Sqn, Marham
	ZA406	Panavia Tornado GR4 [FU]	RAF No 12 Sqn, Lossiemouth
	ZA407	Panavia Tornado GR1 (9336M) [AJ-N]	RAF Marham, for display
	ZA409	Panavia Tornado GR1 [VII]	RAF Lossiemouth, wfu
	ZA410	Panavia Tornado GR4 [DX]	RAF No 31 Sqn, Marham
	ZA411	Panavia Tornado GR1 [TT]	RAF/DARA, stored St Athan
	ZA412	Panavia Tornado GR4 [TT]	RAF No 15(R) Sqn, Lossiemouth
	ZA446	Panavia Tornado GR4 [E]	DPA/BAE Systems, Warton (conversion)
	ZA447	Panavia Tornado GR4	DPA/BAE Systems, Warton
	ZA449	Panavia Tornado GR4 [AJ-N]	RAF No 617 Sqn, Lossiemouth
	ZA450	Panavia Tornado GR1	RAF No 1 SoTT, Cosford
	ZA452	Panavia Tornado GR4 [TJ]	DPA/BAE Systems, Warton (conversion)
	ZA453	Panavia Tornado GR4 [TB]	DPA/BAE Systems, Warton (conversion)
	ZA455	Panavia Tornado GR1 [F]	Privately owned, Chesterfield (for scrapping)
	ZA456	Panavia Tornado GR4 [AJ-Q]	DPA/BAE Systems, Warton (conversion)
	ZA457	Panavia Tornado GR1 [AJ-J]	RAF/DARA, stored St Athan
	ZA458	Panavia Tornado GR4 [DG]	RAF No 31 Sqn, Marham
	ZA459	Panavia Tornado GR1 [TQ]	RAF, St Athan
	ZA460	Panavia Tornado GR1 [AJ-A]	*Scrapped at St Athan, February 2002*
	ZA461	Panavia Tornado GR4 [FD]	RAF, St Athan
	ZA462	Panavia Tornado GR4 [AJ-P]	RAF No 617 Sqn, Lossiemouth
	ZA463	Panavia Tornado GR4 [TL]	RAF No 15(R) Sqn, Lossiemouth
	ZA465	Panavia Tornado GR1 [FF]	Imperial War Museum, Duxford
	ZA466	Panavia Tornado GR1 <ff>	RAF St Athan Fire Section
	ZA469	Panavia Tornado GR4 [TM]	DPA/BAE Systems, Warton (conversion)
	ZA470	Panavia Tornado GR4	RAF, Lossiemouth
	ZA471	Panavia Tornado GR1 (fuselage)	*Scrapped at St Athan, March 2002*
	ZA472	Panavia Tornado GR4 [AE]	RAF No 9 Sqn, Marham
	ZA473	Panavia Tornado GR4	DPA/BAE Systems, Warton (conversion)
	ZA474	Panavia Tornado GR1	RAF Lossiemouth, wfu
	ZA475	Panavia Tornado GR1	RAF Lossiemouth, on display
	ZA490	Panavia Tornado GR1 (fuselage)	Privately owned, Chesterfield (for scrapping)
	ZA491	Panavia Tornado GR4 [TI]	DPA/BAE Systems, Warton (conversion)
	ZA492	Panavia Tornado GR4 [TE]	DPA/BAE Systems, Warton (conversion)
	ZA541	Panavia Tornado GR4 [DZ]	RAF No 31 Sqn, Marham
	ZA542	Panavia Tornado GR4 [DM]	RAF No 31 Sqn, Marham
	ZA543	Panavia Tornado GR4 [FO]	RAF No 15(R) Sqn, Lossiemouth
	ZA544	Panavia Tornado GR4 [FZ]	RAF No 617 Sqn, Lossiemouth
	ZA546	Panavia Tornado GR4 [FF]	RAF No 12 Sqn, Lossiemouth
	ZA547	Panavia Tornado GR4 [DC]	RAF No 31 Sqn, Marham
	ZA548	Panavia Tornado GR4 [III]	RAF No 2 Sqn, Marham
	ZA549	Panavia Tornado GR4 [AJ-Z]	RAF No 617 Sqn, Lossiemouth
	ZA550	Panavia Tornado GR4 [DD]	RAF No 31 Sqn, Marham
	ZA551	Panavia Tornado GR4 [AX]	RAF No 9 Sqn, Marham
	ZA552	Panavia Tornado GR4 [TX]	RAF No 15(R) Sqn, Lossiemouth
	ZA553	Panavia Tornado GR4 [DI]	RAF No 31 Sqn, Marham
	ZA554	Panavia Tornado GR4 [BF]	RAF No 14 Sqn, Lossiemouth
	ZA556	Panavia Tornado GR4 [AK]	RAF No 9 Sqn, Marham
	ZA556	Panavia Tornado GR1 <R> (ZA368/BAPC 155) [Z]	RAF EPTT, Bottesford
	ZA557	Panavia Tornado GR4 [TJ]	RAF No 15(R) Sqn, Lossiemouth
	ZA559	Panavia Tornado GR4 [AD]	RAF No 9 Sqn, Marham
	ZA560	Panavia Tornado GR4 [BC]	RAF No 14 Sqn, Lossiemouth
	ZA562	Panavia Tornado GR4 [TO]	RAF No 15(R) Sqn, Lossiemouth
	ZA563	Panavia Tornado GR4 [AG]	RAF No 9 Sqn, Marham
	ZA564	Panavia Tornado GR4 [DK]	RAF No 31 Sqn, Marham
	ZA585	Panavia Tornado GR4 [AH]	RAF No 9 Sqn, Marham
	ZA587	Panavia Tornado GR4 [AJ-M]	RAF No 617 Sqn, Lossiemouth
	ZA588	Panavia Tornado GR4 [BB]	RAF No 14 Sqn, Lossiemouth

Serial	Type (other identity) [code]	Owner/operator, location or fate	Notes
ZA589	Panavia Tornado GR4 [DN]	RAF No 31 Sqn, Marham	
ZA590	Panavia Tornado GR1	*Scrapped at St Athan, February 2002*	
ZA591	Panavia Tornado GR4 [DJ]	RAF No 31 Sqn, Marham	
ZA592	Panavia Tornado GR4 [BJ]	RAF No 14 Sqn, Lossiemouth	
ZA594	Panavia Tornado GR4 [TS]	RAF No 15(R) Sqn, Lossiemouth	
ZA595	Panavia Tornado GR4 [VIII]	RAF No 13 Sqn, Marham	
ZA596	Panavia Tornado GR4 [BL]	RAF No 14 Sqn, Lossiemouth	
ZA597	Panavia Tornado GR4 [AJ-O]	RAF No 617 Sqn, Lossiemouth	
ZA598	Panavia Tornado GR4 [TW]	RAF No 15(R) Sqn, Lossiemouth	
ZA599	Panavia Tornado GR4 [VI]	*Crashed 17 May 2002, into River Humber near Brough*	
ZA600	Panavia Tornado GR4 [AJ-L]	RAF No 617 Sqn, Lossiemouth	
ZA601	Panavia Tornado GR4 [TE]	RAF No 15(R) Sqn, Lossiemouth	
ZA602	Panavia Tornado GR4 [BY]	RAF No 14 Sqn, Lossiemouth	
ZA604	Panavia Tornado GR4 [TY]	RAF No 15(R) Sqn, Lossiemouth	
ZA606	Panavia Tornado GR4 [BD]	RAF No 14 Sqn, Lossiemouth	
ZA607	Panavia Tornado GR4 [AB]	RAF No 9 Sqn, Marham	
ZA608	Panavia Tornado GR4 [TN]	RAF No 15(R) Sqn, Lossiemouth	
ZA609	Panavia Tornado GR4	RAF AWC/SAOEU, Boscombe Down	
ZA611	Panavia Tornado GR4 [TK]	RAF No 15(R) Sqn, Lossiemouth	
ZA612	Panavia Tornado GR4 [TZ]	RAF No 15(R) Sqn, Lossiemouth	
ZA613	Panavia Tornado GR4	DPA/BAE Systems, Warton (conversion)	
ZA614	Panavia Tornado GR4 [AJ-J]	RAF No 617 Sqn, Lossiemouth	
ZA634	Slingsby T61F Venture T2 (G-BUHA) [C]	Privately owned, Rufforth	
ZA670	B-V Chinook HC2 (N37010)	RAF/DARA, Fleetlands	
ZA671	B-V Chinook HC2 (N37011)	RAF No 18 Sqn, Odiham	
ZA673	B-V Chinook HC2 (N37016)	RAF No 18 Sqn, Odiham	
ZA674	B-V Chinook HC2 (N37019)	RAF No 27 Sqn, Odiham	
ZA675	B-V Chinook HC2 (N37020)	RAF No 7 Sqn, Odiham	
ZA676	B-V Chinook HC1 (N37021/9230M) [FG] (wreck)	AAC, Wattisham	
ZA677	B-V Chinook HC2 (N37022) [EG]	RAF No 7 Sqn, Odiham	
ZA678	B-V Chinook HC1 (N37023/9229M) [EZ] (wreck)	RAF Odiham, BDRT	
ZA679	B-V Chinook HC2 (N37025)	RAF No 18 Sqn, Odiham	
ZA680	B-V Chinook HC2 (N37026)	RAF No 27 Sqn, Odiham	
ZA681	B-V Chinook HC2 (N37027)	RAF No 27 Sqn, Odiham	
ZA682	B-V Chinook HC2 (N37029) [BT]	RAF No 18 Sqn, Odiham	
ZA683	B-V Chinook HC2 (N37030) [BD]	RAF No 18 Sqn, Odiham	
ZA684	B-V Chinook HC2 (N37031) [EL]	RAF No 7 Sqn, Odiham	
ZA704	B-V Chinook HC2 (N37033) [EJ]	RAF/DARA, Fleetlands (wreck)	
ZA705	B-V Chinook HC2 (N37035) [BE]	RAF No 27 Sqn, Odiham	
ZA707	B-V Chinook HC2 (N37040)	RAF No 7 Sqn, Odiham	
ZA708	B-V Chinook HC2 (N37042) [EC]	RAF No 18 Sqn, Odiham	
ZA709	B-V Chinook HC2 (N37043) [EQ]	RAF No 27 Sqn, Odiham	
ZA710	B-V Chinook HC2 (N37044) [NC]	RAF No 27 Sqn, Odiham	
ZA711	B-V Chinook HC2 (N37046) [BA]	RAF No 18 Sqn, Odiham	
ZA712	B-V Chinook HC2 (N37047)	RAF No 27 Sqn, Odiham	
ZA713	B-V Chinook HC2 (N37048)	RAF No 27 Sqn, Odiham	
ZA714	B-V Chinook HC2 (N37051) [NT]	RAF No 27 Sqn, Odiham	
ZA717	B-V Chinook HC1 (N37056/9238M) (wreck)	Trenchard Hall, RAF Cranwell, instructional use	
ZA718	B-V Chinook HC2 (N37058) [BN]	RAF No 18 Sqn, Odiham	
ZA720	B-V Chinook HC2 (N37060) [BR]	RAF No 18 Sqn, Odiham	
ZA726	WS Gazelle AH1 [F1]	AAC No 671 Sqn/2 Regt, Middle Wallop	
ZA728	WS Gazelle AH1 [E]	RM No 847 Sqn, Yeovilton	
ZA729	WS Gazelle AH1	AAC, Wattisham, BDRT	
ZA730	WS Gazelle AH1	Privately owned, Somerset	
ZA731	WS Gazelle AH1	AAC No 29 Flt, BATUS, Suffield, Canada	
ZA733	WS Gazelle AH1	DARA Fleetlands Apprentice School	
ZA734	WS Gazelle AH1	AAC No 25 Flt, Belize	
ZA735	WS Gazelle AH1	AAC No 25 Flt, Belize	
ZA736	WS Gazelle AH1	AAC No 29 Flt, BATUS, Suffield, Canada	
ZA737	WS Gazelle AH1	Museum of Army Flying, Middle Wallop	
ZA766	WS Gazelle AH1	AAC/DARA, stored Fleetlands	
ZA768	WS Gazelle AH1 [F] (wreck)	AAC/DARA, stored Fleetlands	
ZA769	WS Gazelle AH1 [K]	Army SEAE, Arborfield	
ZA771	WS Gazelle AH1	AAC No 664 Sqn/9 Regt, Dishforth	
ZA772	WS Gazelle AH1	AAC No 665 Sqn/5 Regt, Aldergrove	
ZA773	WS Gazelle AH1 [F]	AAC No 666(V) Sqn/7 Regt, Netheravon	
ZA774	WS Gazelle AH1	AAC/DARA, stored Fleetlands	
ZA775	WS Gazelle AH1	AAC No 665 Sqn/5 Regt, Aldergrove	

Notes	Serial	Type (other identity) [code]	Owner/operator, location or fate
	ZA776	WS Gazelle AH1 [F]	RM No 847 Sqn, Yeovilton
	ZA802	WS Gazelle HT3 (G-CBSJ) [W]	Privately owned, Redhill
	ZA803	WS Gazelle HT3 [X]	Privately owned, Angmering, W Sussex
	ZA804	WS Gazelle HT3 [I]	DPA/QinetiQ Boscombe Down, spares use
	ZA934	WS Puma HC1 [BZ]	RAF No 230 Sqn, Aldergrove
	ZA935	WS Puma HC1	RAF No 33 Sqn, Benson
	ZA936	WS Puma HC1	RAF No 33 Sqn, Benson
	ZA937	WS Puma HC1	RAF No 33 Sqn, Benson
	ZA938	WS Puma HC1	RAF No 33 Sqn, Benson
	ZA939	WS Puma HC1	RAF No 230 Sqn, Aldergrove
	ZA940	WS Puma HC1	RAF No 230 Sqn, Algergrove
	ZA947	Douglas Dakota C3 [YS-H]	RAF BBMF, Coningsby
	ZB500	WS Lynx 800 (G-LYNX/ZA500)	The Helicopter Museum, Weston-super-Mare
	ZB506	WS61 Sea King Mk 4X	DPA/AFD/QinetiQ, Boscombe Down
	ZB507	WS61 Sea King HC4 [ZN]	RN No 848 Sqn, Yeovilton
	ZB600	BAe Harrier T8I	*To Indian Navy as IN656, 15 September 2002*
	ZB601	BAe Harrier T4 (fuselage)	RNAS Yeovilton, Fire Section
	ZB602	BAe Harrier T8I	*To Indian Navy as IN655, 15 September 2002*
	ZB603	BAe Harrier T8 [724]	RN/DARA, St Athan
	ZB604	BAe Harrier T8 [722]	RN No 899 Sqn, Yeovilton
	ZB605	BAe Harrier T8 [720]	*Crashed 5 December 2002, Wittering*
	ZB615	SEPECAT Jaguar T2A	DPA/AFD/QinetiQ, Boscombe Down
	ZB625	WS Gazelle HT3 [N]	DPA/AFD/QinetiQ, Boscombe Down
	ZB627	WS Gazelle HT3 (G-CBSK) [A]	Privately owned, Redhill
	ZB629	WS Gazelle HCC4	*Sold as G-CBSK, October 2002*
	ZB646	WS Gazelle HT2 (G-CBGZ) [59/CU]	Privately owned, Knebworth
	ZB647	WS Gazelle HT2 (G-CBSF) [40/CU]	Privately owned, Redhill
	ZB649	WS Gazelle HT2 (G-SIVJ) [VL]	Privately owned, Redhill
	ZB665	WS Gazelle AH1	AAC No 665 Sqn/5 Regt, Aldergrove
	ZB667	WS Gazelle AH1	AAC No 16 Flt, Dhekelia, Cyprus
	ZB668	WS Gazelle AH1 (TAD 015)	Army SEAE, Arborfield
	ZB669	WS Gazelle AH1	AAC/DARA, Fleetlands
	ZB670	WS Gazelle AH1	AAC No 665 Sqn/5 Regt, Aldergrove
	ZB671	WS Gazelle AH1 [2]	AAC No 29 Flt, BATUS, Suffield, Canada
	ZB672	WS Gazelle AH1	Army Training Regiment, Winchester
	ZB673	WS Gazelle AH1	AAC No 671 Sqn/2 Regt, Middle Wallop
	ZB674	WS Gazelle AH1	AAC No 665 Sqn/5 Regt, Aldergrove
	ZB676	WS Gazelle AH1	RM No 847 Sqn, Yeovilton
	ZB677	WS Gazelle AH1	AAC No 29 Flt, BATUS, Suffield, Canada
	ZB678	WS Gazelle AH1	Army SEAE, Arborfield
	ZB679	WS Gazelle AH1	AAC No 16 Flt, Dhekelia, Cyprus
	ZB682	WS Gazelle AH1	AAC/DARA, Fleetlands
	ZB683	WS Gazelle AH1	AAC No 665 Sqn/5 Regt, Aldergrove
	ZB684	WS Gazelle AH1	RAF Air Movements School, Brize Norton
	ZB685	WS Gazelle AH1	Privately owned, Sproughton
	ZB686	WS Gazelle AH1 <ff>	AAC Middle Wallop, instructional use
	ZB688	WS Gazelle AH1	AAC No 671 Sqn/2 Regt, Middle Wallop
	ZB689	WS Gazelle AH1	AAC No 665 Sqn/5 Regt, Aldergrove
	ZB690	WS Gazelle AH1	AAC No 16 Flt, Dhekelia, Cyprus
	ZB691	WS Gazelle AH1	AAC No 4 Regt, Wattisham
	ZB692	WS Gazelle AH1	AAC No 4 Regt, Wattisham
	ZB693	WS Gazelle AH1	AAC No 665 Sqn/5 Regt, Aldergrove
	ZD230	BAC Super VC10 K4 (G-ASGA) [K]	RAF No 101 Sqn, Brize Norton
	ZD234	BAC Super VC10 (G-ASGF/8700M)	RAF Brize Norton, tanker simulator
	ZD235	BAC Super VC10 K4 (G-ASGG) [L]	RAF/DARA, stored St Athan
	ZD240	BAC Super VC10 K4 (G-ASGL) [M]	RAF No 101 Sqn, Brize Norton
	ZD241	BAC Super VC10 K4 (G-ASGM) [N]	RAF No 101 Sqn, Brize Norton
	ZD242	BAC Super VC10 K4 (G-ASGP)	RAF No 101 Sqn, Brize Norton
	ZD249	WS Lynx HAS3S [637]	RN No 702 Sqn, Yeovilton
	ZD250	WS Lynx HAS3S	RN/DARA, Fleetlands
	ZD251	WS Lynx HAS3S [636]	RN No 702 Sqn, Yeovilton
	ZD252	WS Lynx HMA8 [671]	RN/DARA, Fleetlands
	ZD254	WS Lynx HAS3S [635]	RN No 702 Sqn, Yeovilton

Serial	Type (other identity) [code]	Owner/operator, location or fate	Notes
ZD255	WS Lynx HAS3S [372/NL]	RN No 815 Sqn, *Northumberland* Flt, Yeovilton	
ZD257	WS Lynx HMA8 [474]	RN/DARA, Fleetlands	
ZD258	WS Lynx HMA8 (*XZ258*) [319]	RN No 815 Sqn OEU, Yeovilton	
ZD259	WS Lynx HMA8 [407/YK]	RN No 815 Sqn, *York* Flt, Yeovilton	
ZD260	WS Lynx HMA8 [360/MC]	RN No 815 Sqn, *Manchester* Flt, Yeovilton	
ZD261	WS Lynx HMA8 [309]	RN No 815 Sqn, HQ Flt, Yeovilton	
ZD262	WS Lynx HMA8	RN AMG, Yeovilton	
ZD263	WS Lynx HAS3S [305]	RN No 815 Sqn, HQ Flt, Yeovilton	
ZD264	WS Lynx HAS3S [334/SN]	RN No 815 Sqn, *Southampton* Flt, Yeovilton	
ZD265	WS Lynx HMA8 [404/IR]	RN No 815 Sqn, *Iron Duke* Flt, Yeovilton	
ZD266	WS Lynx HMA8	DPA/AFD/QinetiQ, Boscombe Down	
ZD267	WS Lynx HMA8	DPA/Westland Helicopters, Yeovil	
ZD268	WS Lynx HMA8	RN/DARA, Fleetlands	
ZD272	WS Lynx AH7 [H]	AAC No 671 Sqn/2 Regt, Middle Wallop	
ZD273	WS Lynx AH7	AAC No 655 Sqn/5 Regt, Aldergrove	
ZD274	WS Lynx AH7	AAC No 3 Regt, Wattisham	
ZD276	WS Lynx AH7 [X]	AAC No 671 Sqn/2 Regt, Middle Wallop	
ZD277	WS Lynx AH7	AAC No 1 Regt, Brüggen	
ZD278	WS Lynx AH7 [A]	AAC No 655 Sqn/5 Regt, Aldergrove	
ZD279	WS Lynx AH7	AAC/DARA, Fleetlands	
ZD280	WS Lynx AH7	AAC No 661 Sqn/1 Regt, Brüggen	
ZD281	WS Lynx AH7 [K]	AAC No 671 Sqn/2 Regt, Middle Wallop	
ZD282	WS Lynx AH7 [L]	RM No 847 Sqn, Yeovilton	
ZD283	WS Lynx AH7	AAC No 655 Sqn/5 Regt, Aldergrove	
ZD284	WS Lynx AH7 [H]	AAC No 1 Regt, Brüggen	
ZD285	WS Lynx AH7	DPA/AFD/QinetiQ, Boscombe Down	
ZD318	BAe Harrier GR7A	DPA/BAE Systems, Warton	
ZD319	BAe Harrier GR7	DPA/BAE Systems, Warton	
ZD320	BAe Harrier GR7	DPA/BAE Systems, Warton	
ZD321	BAe Harrier GR7 [02]	RAF No 1 Sqn, Cottesmore	
ZD322	BAe Harrier GR7 [03]	RAF No 4 Sqn, Cottesmore	
ZD323	BAe Harrier GR7 [04]	RAF No 4 Sqn, Cottesmore	
ZD327	BAe Harrier GR7 [08]	RAF HOCU/No 20(R) Sqn, Wittering	
ZD328	BAe Harrier GR7 [09]	RAF No 4 Sqn, Cottesmore	
ZD329	BAe Harrier GR7 [10]	RAF No 4 Sqn, Cottesmore	
ZD330	BAe Harrier GR7 [11]	RAF No 4 Sqn, Cottesmore	
ZD346	BAe Harrier GR7 [13]	RAF No 3 Sqn, Cottesmore	
ZD347	BAe Harrier GR7 [14]	RAF/DARA, St Athan	
ZD348	BAe Harrier GR7	RAF/DARA, stored St Athan	
ZD350	BAe Harrier GR5 (9189M) <ff>	DARA, RAF St Athan, BDRT	
ZD351	BAe Harrier GR7 (fuselage)	RAF/DARA, stored St Athan	
ZD352	BAe Harrier GR7 [19]	RAF No 4 Sqn, Cottesmore	
ZD353	BAe Harrier GR5 (fuselage)	BAE Systems, Warton	
ZD354	BAe Harrier GR7 [21]	RAF No 3 Sqn, Cottesmore	
ZD375	BAe Harrier GR7 [23]	RAF No 1 Sqn, Cottesmore	
ZD376	BAe Harrier GR7 [24]	RAF No 1 Sqn, Cottesmore	
ZD378	BAe Harrier GR7 [26]	RAF HOCU/No 20(R) Sqn, Wittering	
ZD379	BAe Harrier GR7 [27]	RAF No 3 Sqn, Cottesmore	
ZD380	BAe Harrier GR7 [28]	RAF HOCU/No 20(R) Sqn, Wittering	
ZD401	BAe Harrier GR7 [30]	RAF No 3 Sqn, Cottesmore	
ZD402	BAe Harrier GR7 [31]	RAF HOCU/No 20(R) Sqn, Wittering	
ZD403	BAe Harrier GR7 [32]	RAF/DARA, stored St Athan	
ZD404	BAe Harrier GR7 [33]	RAF HOCU/No 20(R) Sqn, Wittering	
ZD405	BAe Harrier GR7 [34]	RAF No 4 Sqn, Cottesmore	
ZD406	BAe Harrier GR7 [35]	RAF No 4 Sqn, Cottesmore	
ZD407	BAe Harrier GR7 [36]	RAF HOCU/No 20(R) Sqn, Wittering	
ZD408	BAe Harrier GR7 [37]	RAF HOCU/No 20(R) Sqn, Wittering	
ZD409	BAe Harrier GR7 [38]	RAF No 4 Sqn, Cottesmore	
ZD410	BAe Harrier GR7 [39]	RAF No 3 Sqn, Cottesmore	
ZD411	BAe Harrier GR7	RAF AWC/SAOEU, Boscombe Down	
ZD412	BAe Harrier GR5 (fuselage)	RAF/DARA, St Athan, instructional use	
ZD431	BAe Harrier GR7 [43]	RAF HOCU/No 20(R) Sqn, Wittering	
ZD433	BAe Harrier GR7 [45]	RAF HOCU/No 20(R) Sqn, Wittering	
ZD435	BAe Harrier GR7 [47]	RAF No 4 Sqn, Cottesmore	
ZD436	BAe Harrier GR7 [48]	RAF/DARA, St Athan	
ZD437	BAe Harrier GR7 [49]	RAF HOCU/No 20(R) Sqn, Wittering	
ZD438	BAe Harrier GR7 [50]	RAF No 1 Sqn, Cottesmore	
ZD461	BAe Harrier GR7 [51]	RAF No 1 Sqn, Cottesmore	
ZD462	BAe Harrier GR7 (9302M) [52]	RAF No 1 SoTT, Cosford	
ZD463	BAe Harrier GR7 [53]	RAF No 3 Sqn, Cottesmore	

Notes	Serial	Type (other identity) [code]	Owner/operator, location or fate
	ZD464	BAe Harrier GR7 [54]	Crashed 2 August 2002, into North Sea off Lowestoft
	ZD465	BAe Harrier GR7 [55]	RAF/DARA, stored St Athan
	ZD466	BAe Harrier GR7 [56]	RAF HOCU/No 20(R) Sqn, Wittering
	ZD467	BAe Harrier GR7 [57]	RAF No 1 Sqn, Cottesmore
	ZD468	BAe Harrier GR7 [58]	RAF No 1 Sqn, Cottesmore
	ZD469	BAe Harrier GR7 [59]	RAF No 4 Sqn, Cottesmore
	ZD470	BAe Harrier GR7 [60]	RAF No 4 Sqn, Cottesmore
	ZD476	WS61 Sea King HC4 [WU]	RN No 848 Sqn, Yeovilton
	ZD477	WS61 Sea King HC4 [H]	RN No 845 Sqn, Yeovilton
	ZD478	WS61 Sea King HC4 [VX]	RN/DARA, Fleetlands
	ZD479	WS61 Sea King HC4 [ZV]	RN No 848 Sqn, Yeovilton
	ZD480	WS61 Sea King HC4 [E]	RN No 845 Sqn, Yeovilton
	ZD559	WS Lynx AH5X	DPA/AFD/QinetiQ, Boscombe Down
	ZD560	WS Lynx AH7	DPA/ETPS, Boscombe Down
	ZD565	WS Lynx HMA8 [361/NF]	RN AMG, Yeovilton
	ZD566	WS Lynx HMA8 [670]	RN No 702 Sqn, Yeovilton
	ZD574	B-V Chinook HC2 (N37077)	RAF No 27 Sqn, Odiham
	ZD575	B-V Chinook HC2 (N37078)	RAF No 18 Sqn, Odiham
	ZD578	BAe Sea Harrier FA2 [000, 122]	RN AMG, Yeovilton, on display
	ZD579	BAe Sea Harrier FA2 [128/R]	RN No 800 Sqn, Yeovilton
	ZD580	BAe Sea Harrier FA2	Privately owned, Sproughton
	ZD581	BAe Sea Harrier FA2	RN/DARA, stored St Athan
	ZD582	BAe Sea Harrier FA2 [124/R]	RN No 800 Sqn, Yeovilton
	ZD607	BAe Sea Harrier FA2	RAF St Athan, BDRT
	ZD608	BAe Sea Harrier FA2 [731]	RN, St Athan, spares recovery
	ZD610	BAe Sea Harrier FA2 [126/R]	RN No 800 Sqn, Yeovilton
	ZD611	BAe Sea Harrier FA2	RN AMG, Yeovilton, wfu
	ZD612	BAe Sea Harrier FA2 [129]	RN No 800 Sqn, Yeovilton
	ZD613	BAe Sea Harrier FA2 [711]	RN/DARA, stored St Athan
	ZD614	BAe Sea Harrier FA2 [122/R]	Privately owned, Sproughton
	ZD615	BAe Sea Harrier FA2	RN/DARA, stored St Athan
	ZD620	BAe 125 CC3	RAF No 32(The Royal) Sqn, Northolt
	ZD621	BAe 125 CC3	RAF No 32(The Royal) Sqn, Northolt
	ZD625	WS61 Sea King HC4 [VZ]	RN No 846 Sqn, Yeovilton
	ZD626	WS61 Sea King HC4 [ZZ]	RN No 848 Sqn, Yeovilton
	ZD627	WS61 Sea King HC4 [VR]	RN No 846 Sqn, Yeovilton
	ZD630	WS61 Sea King HAS6 [012/L]	RN No 820 Sqn, Culdrose
	ZD631	WS61 Sea King HAS6 [66] (fuselage)	RN, Predannack Fire School
	ZD633	WS61 Sea King HAS6 [014/L]	RN, stored HMS Sultan, Gosport
	ZD634	WS61 Sea King HAS6 [503]	RN No 771 Sqn, Culdrose
	ZD636	WS61 Sea King AEW2 [183/L]	RN No 849 Sqn, B Flt, Culdrose
	ZD637	WS61 Sea King HAS6 [700/PW]	RN, stored HMS Sultan, Gosport
	ZD658	Schleicher ASW-19B Valiant TX1 [YX]	Sold as BGA 2894
	ZD667	BAe Harrier GR3 (9201M) [67]	SFDO, RNAS Culdrose
	ZD668	BAe Harrier GR3 (G-CBCU) [3E]	Privately owned, Lowestoft
	ZD670	BAe Harrier GR3 [3A]	The Trocadero, Leicester Square, London
	ZD703	BAe 125 CC3	RAF No 32(The Royal) Sqn, Northolt
	ZD704	BAe 125 CC3	RAF No 32(The Royal) Sqn, Northolt
	ZD707	Panavia Tornado GR4 [BU]	RAF, St Athan
	ZD708	Panavia Tornado GR4	DPA/BAE Systems, Warton
	ZD709	Panavia Tornado GR4 [DH]	RAF No 31 Sqn, Marham
	ZD710	Panavia Tornado GR1 <ff>	Privately owned, Barnstaple
	ZD711	Panavia Tornado GR4 [II]	RAF No 2 Sqn, Marham
	ZD712	Panavia Tornado GR4 [TR]	RAF No 15(R) Sqn, Lossiemouth
	ZD713	Panavia Tornado GR4 [AJ-F]	RAF No 617 Sqn, Lossiemouth
	ZD714	Panavia Tornado GR4 [AJ-W]	RAF No 617 Sqn, Lossiemouth
	ZD715	Panavia Tornado GR4 [AM]	RAF No 9 Sqn, Marham
	ZD716	Panavia Tornado GR4 [AJ]	RAF No 9 Sqn, Marham
	ZD719	Panavia Tornado GR4 [BS]	RAF No 14 Sqn, Lossiemouth
	ZD720	Panavia Tornado GR4 [TA]	RAF No 15(R) Sqn, Lossiemouth
	ZD739	Panavia Tornado GR4	RAF AWC/SAOEU, Boscombe Down
	ZD740	Panavia Tornado GR4 [DR]	RAF No 31 Sqn, Marham
	ZD741	Panavia Tornado GR4 [BZ]	RAF No 14 Sqn, Lossiemouth
	ZD742	Panavia Tornado GR4 [FY]	RAF No 12 Sqn, Lossiemouth
	ZD743	Panavia Tornado GR4 [TQ]	RAF No 2 Sqn, Marham
	ZD744	Panavia Tornado GR4 [FD]	RAF No 12 Sqn, Lossiemouth
	ZD745	Panavia Tornado GR4 [DA]	RAF No 31 Sqn, Marham
	ZD746	Panavia Tornado GR4 [TH]	RAF No 15(R) Sqn, Lossiemouth
	ZD747	Panavia Tornado GR4 [AL]	RAF No 9 Sqn, Marham
	ZD748	Panavia Tornado GR4 [FC]	RAF No 12 Sqn, Lossiemouth

Serial	Type (other identity) [code]	Owner/operator, location or fate	Notes
ZD749	Panavia Tornado GR4 [AP]	RAF No 9 Sqn, Marham	
ZD788	Panavia Tornado GR4 [BT]	RAF, St Athan	
ZD789	Panavia Tornado GR1 <ff>	RAF, stored Shawbury	
ZD790	Panavia Tornado GR4 [FM]	RAF No 12 Sqn, Lossiemouth	
ZD792	Panavia Tornado GR4	RAF AWC/SAOEU, Boscombe Down	
ZD793	Panavia Tornado GR4 [TB]	RAF No 15(R) Sqn, Lossiemouth	
ZD810	Panavia Tornado GR4 [TD]	RAF No 15(R) Sqn, Lossiemouth	
ZD811	Panavia Tornado GR4 [BK]	RAF No 14 Sqn, Lossiemouth	
ZD812	Panavia Tornado GR4 [TU]	RAF No 15(R) Sqn, Lossiemouth	
ZD842	Panavia Tornado GR4 [TV]	RAF No 15(R) Sqn, Lossiemouth	
ZD843	Panavia Tornado GR4	RAF, Marham	
ZD844	Panavia Tornado GR4 [AJ-A]	RAF No 617 Sqn, Lossiemouth	
ZD847	Panavia Tornado GR4 [AA]	RAF No 9 Sqn, Marham	
ZD848	Panavia Tornado GR4 [AE]	RAF, Lossiemouth, WLT	
ZD849	Panavia Tornado GR4 [FG]	RAF No 12 Sqn, Lossiemouth	
ZD850	Panavia Tornado GR4 [AJ-T]	RAF No 617 Sqn, Lossiemouth	
ZD851	Panavia Tornado GR4 [FP]	RAF No 12 Sqn, Lossiemouth	
ZD890	Panavia Tornado GR4 [FR]	RAF No 12 Sqn, Lossiemouth	
ZD892	Panavia Tornado GR4 [TG]	RAF No 15(R) Sqn, Lossiemouth	
ZD895	Panavia Tornado GR4 [TI]	RAF No 15(R) Sqn, Lossiemouth	
ZD899	Panavia Tornado F2	DPA/BAE Systems, Warton	
ZD900	Panavia Tornado F2 (comp ZE343) (fuselage)	Privately owned, Chesterfield for scrapping	
ZD901	Panavia Tornado F2 (comp ZE154) (fuselage)	Scrapped, August 2002	
ZD902	Panavia Tornado F2A(TIARA)	DPA/AFD/QinetiQ, Boscombe Down	
ZD903	Panavia Tornado F2 (comp ZE728) (fuselage)	RAF St Athan Fire Section	
ZD905	Panavia Tornado F2 (comp ZE258) (fuselage)	Privately owned, Chesterfield for scrapping	
ZD906	Panavia Tornado F2 (comp ZE294) <ff>	RAF Leuchars, BDRT	
ZD932	Panavia Tornado F2 (comp ZE255) (fuselage)	RAF St Athan, BDRT	
ZD933	Panavia Tornado F2 (comp ZE729) (fuselage)	DARA, St Athan, instructional use	
ZD934	Panavia Tornado F2 (comp ZE786) <ff>	RAF Leeming, GI use	
ZD935	Panavia Tornado F2 (comp ZE793) <ff>	RAF, stored Shawbury	
ZD936	Panavia Tornado F2 (comp ZE251) <ff>	DS&TL, Bedford	
ZD938	Panavia Tornado F2 (comp ZE295) <ff>	RAF, stored Shawbury	
ZD939	Panavia Tornado F2 (comp ZE292) <ff>	RAF Cosford, instructional use	
ZD940	Panavia Tornado F2 (comp ZE288) (fuselage)	RAF St Athan Fire Section	
ZD948	Lockheed TriStar KC1 (G-BFCA)	RAF No 216 Sqn, Brize Norton	
ZD949	Lockheed TriStar K1 (G-BFCB)	RAF No 216 Sqn, Brize Norton	
ZD950	Lockheed TriStar KC1 (G-BFCC)	RAF No 216 Sqn, Brize Norton	
ZD951	Lockheed TriStar K1 (G-BFCD)	RAF No 216 Sqn, Brize Norton	
ZD952	Lockheed TriStar KC1 (G-BFCE)	RAF No 216 Sqn, Brize Norton	
ZD953	Lockheed TriStar KC1 (G-BFCF)	RAF No 216 Sqn, Brize Norton	
ZD974	Schempp-Hirth Kestrel TX1 [SY]	Sold as BGA 2875	
ZD975	Schempp-Hirth Kestrel TX1 [SZ]	Sold as BGA 2876	
ZD980	B-V Chinook HC2 (N37082)	RAF No 18 Sqn, Odiham	
ZD981	B-V Chinook HC2 (N37083) [BH]	RAF No 18 Sqn, Odiham	
ZD982	B-V Chinook HC2 (N37085) [BI]	RAF No 18 Sqn, Odiham	
ZD983	B-V Chinook HC2 (N37086)	RAF No 7 Sqn, Odiham	
ZD984	B-V Chinook HC2 (N37088) [BJ]	RAF No 18 Sqn, Odiham	
ZD990	BAe Harrier T8 [721]	RN/DARA, St Athan	
ZD991	BAe Harrier T8 (9228M) [722/VL]	Privately owned, Sproughton	
ZD992	BAe Harrier T8 [724/VL]	Scrapped at Yeovilton	
ZD993	BAe Harrier T8 [723/VL]	RN No 899 Sqn, Yeovilton	
ZD996	Panavia Tornado GR4A [I]	RAF No 13 Sqn, Marham	
ZE116	Panavia Tornado GR4A [X]	RAF No 13 Sqn, Marham	
ZE154	Panavia Tornado F3 (comp ZD901) [LT]	RAF No 11 Sqn, Leeming	
ZE155	Panavia Tornado F3	DPA/BAE Systems, Warton	
ZE156	Panavia Tornado F3 [UX]	RAF F3 OCU/No 56(R) Sqn, Coningsby	
ZE157	Panavia Tornado F3 [GK]	RAF No 25 Sqn, Leeming	

Notes	Serial	Type (other identity) [code]	Owner/operator, location or fate
	ZE158	Panavia Tornado F3 [UW]	RAF No 25 Sqn, Leeming
	ZE159	Panavia Tornado F3 [UV]	RAF No 111 Sqn, Leuchars
	ZE160	Panavia Tornado F3 [TX]	RAF F3 OCU/No 56(R) Sqn, Coningsby
	ZE161	Panavia Tornado F3 [UU]	RAF No 43 Sqn, Leuchars
	ZE162	Panavia Tornado F3 [UR]	RAF, Leuchars
	ZE163	Panavia Tornado F3 (comp ZG753) [TW]	RAF No 43 Sqn, Leuchars
	ZE164	Panavia Tornado F3 [UQ]	RAF, stored Coningsby
	ZE165	Panavia Tornado F3 [UP]	RAF No 5 Sqn, Coningsby
	ZE168	Panavia Tornado F3 [UN]	RAF AWC/F3 OEU, Coningsby
	ZE199	Panavia Tornado F3 [TV]	RAF F3 OCU/No 56(R) Sqn, Coningsby
	ZE200	Panavia Tornado F3 [UM]	RAF No 11 Sqn, Leeming
	ZE201	Panavia Tornado F3 [UL]	RAF AWC/F3 OEU, Coningsby
	ZE203	Panavia Tornado F3 [UK]	RAF No 11 Sqn, Leeming
	ZE204	Panavia Tornado F3 [UJ]	RAF No 25 Sqn, Leeming
	ZE206	Panavia Tornado F3 [UI]	RAF No 43 Sqn, Leuchars
	ZE207	Panavia Tornado F3 [GC]	RAF No 111 Sqn, Leuchars
	ZE209	Panavia Tornado F3 [AX]	EADS, Munich
	ZE250	Panavia Tornado F3 [TR]	RAF F3 OCU/No 56(R) Sqn, Coningsby
	ZE251	Panavia Tornado F3 (comp ZD936) [UF]	RAF No 11 Sqn, Leeming
	ZE253	Panavia Tornado F3 [AC]	RAF/DARA, stored St Athan
	ZE254	Panavia Tornado F3 (comp ZD941) [UD]	RAF No 25 Sqn, Leeming
	ZE255	Panavia Tornado F3 (comp ZD932) [UC]	RAF No 25 Sqn, Leeming
	ZE256	Panavia Tornado F3 [TP]	RAF F3 OCU/No 56(R) Sqn, Coningsby
	ZE257	Panavia Tornado F3 [UB]	RAF No 43 Sqn, Leuchars
	ZE258	Panavia Tornado F3 (comp ZD905) [UA]	RAF F3 OCU/No 56(R) Sqn, Coningsby
	ZE287	Panavia Tornado F3 [TO]	RAF No 11 Sqn, Leeming
	ZE288	Panavia Tornado F3 (comp ZD940) [AT]	RAF No 43 Sqn, Leuchars
	ZE289	Panavia Tornado F3 [VX]	RAF No 111 Sqn, Leuchars
	ZE290	Panavia Tornado F3	RAF/DARA, stored St Athan
	ZE291	Panavia Tornado F3 [VW]	RAF No 43 Sqn, Leuchars
	ZE292	Panavia Tornado F3 (comp ZD939) [YY]	RAF No 25 Sqn, Leeming
	ZE293	Panavia Tornado F3 [HT]	RAF/DARA, stored St Athan
	ZE294	Panavia Tornado F3 (comp ZD906) [YX]	RAF No 25 Sqn, Leeming
	ZE295	Panavia Tornado F3 (comp ZD938) [AY]	RAF No 11 Sqn, Leeming
	ZE296	Panavia Tornado F3 [AD]	RAF/DARA, stored St Athan
	ZE338	Panavia Tornado F3 [YV]	RAF No 43 Sqn, Leuchars
	ZE339	Panavia Tornado F3	RAF/DARA, stored St Athan
	ZE340	Panavia Tornado F3 (ZE758/ 9298M) [GO]	RAF No 1 SoTT, Cosford
	ZE341	Panavia Tornado F3 [YU]	RAF No 25 Sqn, Leeming
	ZE342	Panavia Tornado F3 [YS]	RAF No 111 Sqn, Leuchars
	ZE343	Panavia Tornado F3 (comp ZD900) [TI]	RAF F3 OCU/No 56(R) Sqn, Coningsby
	ZE350	McD F-4J(UK) Phantom (9080M) <ff>	Privately owned, Ingatestone, Essex
	ZE352	McD F-4J(UK) Phantom (9086M) <ff>	Privately owned, Hooton Park, Cheshire
	ZE356	McD F-4J(UK) Phantom (9060M) [Q]	RAF Waddington, BDRT
	ZE360	McD F-4J(UK) Phantom (9059M) [O]	MoD FSCTE, Manston
	ZE368	WS61 Sea King HAR3	RAF No 202 Sqn, A Flt, Boulmer
	ZE369	WS61 Sea King HAR3	RAF No 78 Sqn, Mount Pleasant, FI
	ZE370	WS61 Sea King HAR3	RAF No 202 Sqn, D Flt, Lossiemouth
	ZE375	WS Lynx AH9 [2,9]	AAC No 653 Sqn/3 Regt, Wattisham
	ZE376	WS Lynx AH9	AAC No 659 Sqn/4 Regt, Wattisham
	ZE378	WS Lynx AH7	AAC/DARA, Fleetlands
	ZE379	WS Lynx AH7	AAC/DARA, stored Fleetlands
	ZE380	WS Lynx AH9	AAC No 659 Sqn/4 Regt, Wattisham
	ZE381	WS Lynx AH7	AAC No 657 Sqn, Odiham
	ZE382	WS Lynx AH9	AAC No 659 Sqn/4 Regt, Wattisham
	ZE395	BAe 125 CC3	RAF No 32 (The Royal) Sqn, Northolt
	ZE396	BAe 125 CC3	RAF No 32 (The Royal) Sqn, Northolt
	ZE410	Agusta A109A (AE-334)	AAC No 8 Flt, Credenhill

Serial	Type (other identity) [code]	Owner/operator, location or fate	Notes
ZE411	Agusta A109A (AE-331)	AAC No 8 Flt, Credenhill	
ZE412	Agusta A109A	AAC No 8 Flt, Credenhill	
ZE413	Agusta A109A	AAC No 8 Flt, Credenhill	
ZE418	WS61 Sea King AEW2 [185]	RN No 849 Sqn, B Flt, Culdrose	
ZE420	WS61 Sea King AEW2 [184/L]	RN No 849 Sqn, B Flt, Culdrose	
ZE422	WS61 Sea King HAS6 [508/CT]	RN No 771 Sqn, Culdrose	
ZE425	WS61 Sea King HC4 [J]	RN No 845 Sqn, Yeovilton	
ZE426	WS61 Sea King HC4 [ZW]	RN No 848 Sqn, Yeovilton	
ZE427	WS61 Sea King HC4 [B]	RN No 845 Sqn, Yeovilton	
ZE428	WS61 Sea King HC4 [VS]	RN No 846 Sqn, Yeovilton	
ZE432	BAC 1-11/479FU (DQ-FBV)	DPA/ETPS, Boscombe Down	
ZE433	BAC 1-11/479FU (DQ-FBQ)	DPA/GEC-Ferranti, Edinburgh	
ZE438	BAe Jetstream T3 [76]	RN FOMA/Heron Flight, Yeovilton	
ZE439	BAe Jetstream T3 [77]	RN, stored Shawbury	
ZE440	BAe Jetstream T3 [78]	RN FOMA/Heron Flight, Yeovilton	
ZE441	BAe Jetstream T3 [79]	RN FOMA/Heron Flight, Yeovilton	
ZE449	SA330L Puma HC1 (9017M/ PA-12)	RAF No 33 Sqn, Benson	
ZE477	WS Lynx 3	The Helicopter Museum, Weston-super-Mare	
ZE495	Grob G103 Viking T1 (BGA3000) [VA]	RAF No 622 VGS, Upavon	
ZE496	Grob G103 Viking T1 (BGA3001) [VB]	RAF No 634 VGS, St Athan	
ZE498	Grob G103 Viking T1 (BGA3003) [VC]	RAF No 614 VGS, Wethersfield	
ZE499	Grob G103 Viking T1 (BGA3004) [VD]	RAF No 615 VGS, Kenley	
ZE501	Grob G103 Viking T1 (BGA3006) [VE]	RAF No 636 VGS, Swansea	
ZE502	Grob G103 Viking T1 (BGA3007) [VF]	RAF No 614 VGS, Wethersfield	
ZE503	Grob G103 Viking T1 (BGA3008) [VG]	RAF No 645 VGS, Catterick	
ZE504	Grob G103 Viking T1 (BGA3009) [VH]	RAF No 634 VGS, St Athan	
ZE520	Grob G103 Viking T1 (BGA3010) [VJ]	RAF No 636 VGS, Swansea	
ZE521	Grob G103 Viking T1 (BGA3011) [VK]	RAF No 626 VGS, Predannack	
ZE522	Grob G103 Viking T1 (BGA3012) [VL]	RAF No 634 VGS, St Athan	
ZE524	Grob G103 Viking T1 (BGA3014) [VM]	RAF No 645 VGS, Catterick	
ZE526	Grob G103 Viking T1 (BGA3016) [VN]	RAF ACCGS, Syerston	
ZE527	Grob G103 Viking T1 (BGA3017) [VP]	RAF ACCGS, Syerston	
ZE528	Grob G103 Viking T1 (BGA3018) [VQ]	RAF No 614 VGS, Wethersfield	
ZE529	Grob G103 Viking T1 (BGA3019) (comp ZE655) [VR]	RAF No 614 VGS, Wethersfield	
ZE530	Grob G103 Viking T1 (BGA3020) [VS]	RAF No 611 VGS, Watton	
ZE531	Grob G103 Viking T1 (BGA3021) [VT]	RAF No 615 VGS, Kenley	
ZE532	Grob G103 Viking T1 (BGA3022) [VU]	RAF CGMF, Syerston	
ZE533	Grob G103 Viking T1 (BGA3023) [VV]	RAF No 622 VGS, Upavon	
ZE534	Grob G103 Viking T1 (BGA3024) [VW]	RAF No 645 VGS, Catterick	
ZE550	Grob G103 Viking T1 (BGA3025) [VX]	RAF No 614 VGS, Wethersfield	
ZE551	Grob G103 Viking T1 (BGA3026) [VY]	RAF No 614 VGS, Wethersfield	
ZE552	Grob G103 Viking T1 (BGA3027) [VZ]	RAF No 661 VGS, Kirknewton	
ZE553	Grob G103 Viking T1 (BGA3028) [WA]	RAF No 611 VGS, Watton	
ZE554	Grob G103 Viking T1 (BGA3029) [WB]	RAF No 611 VGS, Watton	

Notes	Serial	Type (other identity) [code]	Owner/operator, location or fate
	ZE555	Grob G103 Viking T1 (BGA3030) [WC]	RAF No 645 VGS, Catterick
	ZE556	Grob G103 Viking T1 (BGA3031) [WD]	RAF CGMF, Syerston (damaged)
	ZE557	Grob G103 Viking T1 (BGA3032) [WE]	RAF No 622 VGS, Upavon
	ZE558	Grob G103 Viking T1 (BGA3033) [WF]	RAF No 615 VGS, Kenley
	ZE559	Grob G103 Viking T1 (BGA3034) [WG]	RAF No 631 VGS, Sealand
	ZE560	Grob G103 Viking T1 (BGA3035) [WH]	RAF No 661 VGS, Kirknewton
	ZE561	Grob G103 Viking T1 (BGA3036) [WJ]	RAF No 625 VGS, Hullavington
	ZE562	Grob G103 Viking T1 (BGA3037) [WK]	RAF No 626 VGS, Predannack
	ZE563	Grob G103 Viking T1 (BGA3038) [WL]	RAF No 631 VGS, Sealand
	ZE564	Grob G103 Viking T1 (BGA3039) [WN]	RAF No 621 VGS, Hullavington
	ZE584	Grob G103 Viking T1 (BGA3040) [WP]	RAF CGMF, Syerston
	ZE585	Grob G103 Viking T1 (BGA3041) [WQ]	RAF No 626 VGS, Predannack
	ZE586	Grob G103 Viking T1 (BGA3042) [WR]	RAF No 631 VGS, Sealand
	ZE587	Grob G103 Viking T1 (BGA3043) [WS]	RAF No 611 VGS, Watton
	ZE589	Grob G103 Viking T1 (BGA3045)	Rebuilt as BGA 3045, 2002
	ZE590	Grob G103 Viking T1 (BGA3046) [WT]	RAF No 661 VGS, Kirknewton
	ZE591	Grob G103 Viking T1 (BGA3047) [WU]	RAF No 631 VGS, Sealand
	ZE592	Grob G103 Viking T1 (BGA3048) [WV]	RAF No 615 VGS, Kenley
	ZE593	Grob G103 Viking T1 (BGA3049) [WW]	RAF No 621 VGS, Hullavington
	ZE594	Grob G103 Viking T1 (BGA3050) [WX]	RAF CGMF, Syerston
	ZE595	Grob G103 Viking T1 (BGA3051) [WY]	RAF No 622 VGS, Upavon
	ZE600	Grob G103 Viking T1 (BGA3052) [WZ]	RAF No 622 VGS, Upavon
	ZE601	Grob G103 Viking T1 (BGA3053) [XA]	RAF No 611 VGS, Watton
	ZE602	Grob G103 Viking T1 (BGA3054) [XB]	RAF CGMF, Syerston
	ZE603	Grob G103 Viking T1 (BGA3055) [XC]	RAF No 636 VGS, Swansea
	ZE604	Grob G103 Viking T1 (BGA3056) [XD]	RAF CGMF, Syerston
	ZE605	Grob G103 Viking T1 (BGA3057) [XE]	RAF CGMF, Syerston
	ZE606	Grob G103 Viking T1 (BGA3058) [XF]	RAF No 621 VGS, Hullavington
	ZE607	Grob G103 Viking T1 (BGA3059) [XG]	RAF No 625 VGS, Hullavington
	ZE608	Grob G103 Viking T1 (BGA3060) [XH]	RAF No 625 VGS, Hullavington
	ZE609	Grob G103 Viking T1 (BGA3061) [XJ]	RAF No 661 VGS, Kirknewton
	ZE610	Grob G103 Viking T1 (BGA3062) [XK]	RAF No 611 VGS, Watton
	ZE611	Grob G103 Viking T1 (BGA3063) [XL]	RAF No 611 VGS, Watton
	ZE613	Grob G103 Viking T1 (BGA3065) [XM]	RAF No 625 VGS, Hullavington
	ZE614	Grob G103 Viking T1 (BGA3066) [XN]	RAF No 631 VGS, Sealand
	ZE625	Grob G103 Viking T1 (BGA3067) [XP]	RAF No 625 VGS, Hullavington
	ZE626	Grob G103 Viking T1 (BGA3068) [XQ]	RAF No 626 VGS, Predannack

Serial	Type (other identity) [code]	Owner/operator, location or fate	Notes
ZE627	Grob G103 Viking T1 (BGA3069) [XR]	RAF No 634 VGS, St Athan	
ZE628	Grob G103 Viking T1 (BGA3070) [XS]	RAF No 662 VGS, Arbroath	
ZE629	Grob G103 Viking T1 (BGA3071) [XT]	RAF No 662 VGS, Arbroath	
ZE630	Grob G103 Viking T1 (BGA3072) [XU]	RAF No 662 VGS, Arbroath	
ZE631	Grob G103 Viking T1 (BGA3073) [XV]	RAF No 662 VGS, Arbroath	
ZE632	Grob G103 Viking T1 (BGA3074) [XW]	RAF No 645 VGS, Catterick	
ZE633	Grob G103 Viking T1 (BGA3075) [XX]	RAF No 614 VGS, Wethersfield	
ZE635	Grob G103 Viking T1 (BGA3077) [XY]	RAF No 625 VGS, Hullavington	
ZE636	Grob G103 Viking T1 (BGA3078) [XZ]	RAF No 636 VGS, Swansea	
ZE637	Grob G103 Viking T1 (BGA3079) [YA]	RAF No 622 VGS, Upavon	
ZE650	Grob G103 Viking T1 (BGA3080) [YB]	RAF No 661 VGS, Kirknewton	
ZE651	Grob G103 Viking T1 (BGA3081) [YC]	RAF No 661 VGS, Kirknewton	
ZE652	Grob G103 Viking T1 (BGA3082) [YD]	RAF ACCGS, Syerston	
ZE653	Grob G103 Viking T1 (BGA3083) [YE]	RAF No 661 VGS, Kirknewton	
ZE656	Grob G103 Viking T1 (BGA3086) [YH]	RAF No 622 VGS, Upavon	
ZE657	Grob G103 Viking T1 (BGA3087) [YJ]	RAF No 615 VGS, Kenley	
ZE658	Grob G103 Viking T1 (BGA3088) [YK]	RAF No 621 VGS, Hullavington	
ZE659	Grob G103 Viking T1 (BGA3089) [YL]	Privately owned, Warminster	
ZE677	Grob G103 Viking T1 (BGA3090) [YM]	RAF No 645 VGS, Catterick	
ZE678	Grob G103 Viking T1 (BGA3091) [YN]	RAF No 621 VGS, Hullavington	
ZE679	Grob G103 Viking T1 (BGA3092) [YP]	RAF No 622 VGS, Upavon	
ZE680	Grob G103 Viking T1 (BGA3093) [YQ]	RAF No 662 VGS, Arbroath	
ZE681	Grob G103 Viking T1 (BGA3094) [YR]	RAF No 615 VGS, Kenley	
ZE682	Grob G103 Viking T1 (BGA3095) [YS]	RAF No 662 VGS, Arbroath	
ZE683	Grob G103 Viking T1 (BGA3096) [YT]	RAF No 661 VGS, Kirknewton	
ZE684	Grob G103 Viking T1 (BGA3097) [YU]	RAF No 621 VGS, Hullavington	
ZE685	Grob G103 Viking T1 (BGA3098) [YV]	RAF No 631 VGS, Sealand	
ZE686	Grob G103 Viking T1 (BGA3099)	DPA/Slingsby Kirkbymoorside	
ZE690	BAe Sea Harrier FA2 [005]	RN No 801 Sqn, Yeovilton	
ZE691	BAe Sea Harrier FA2	Privately owned, Sproughton	
ZE692	BAe Sea Harrier FA2 [718]	RN No 899 Sqn, Yeovilton	
ZE693	BAe Sea Harrier FA2 [714]	RN No 899 Sqn, Yeovilton	
ZE694	BAe Sea Harrier FA2 [004]	RN No 801 Sqn, Yeovilton	
ZE695	BAe Sea Harrier FA2 [718]	Privately owned, Sproughton	
ZE696	BAe Sea Harrier FA2 [715]	RN No 899 Sqn, Yeovilton	
ZE697	BAe Sea Harrier FA2 [006]	RN No 801 Sqn, Yeovilton	
ZE698	BAe Sea Harrier FA2 [123/R]	RN No 800 Sqn, Yeovilton	
ZE700	BAe 146 CC2 (G-6-021)	RAF No 32(The Royal) Sqn, Northolt	
ZE701	BAe 146 CC2 (G-6-029)	RAF No 32(The Royal) Sqn, Northolt	
ZE702	BAe 146 CC2 (G-6-124)	Repainted as G-CBXY, Nov 2002	
ZE704	Lockheed TriStar C2 (N508PA)	RAF No 216 Sqn, Brize Norton	
ZE705	Lockheed TriStar C2 (N509PA)	RAF No 216 Sqn, Brize Norton	
ZE706	Lockheed TriStar C2A (N503PA)	RAF No 216 Sqn, Brize Norton	
ZE728	Panavia Tornado F3 (comp ZD903) [TH]	RAF No 25 Sqn, Leeming	

Notes	Serial	Type (other identity) [code]	Owner/operator, location or fate
	ZE729	Panavia Tornado F3 (comp ZD933) [YR]	RAF No 11 Sqn, Leeming
	ZE731	Panavia Tornado F3 [YP]	RAF No 11 Sqn, Leeming
	ZE734	Panavia Tornado F3 [GB]	RAF No 111 Sqn, Leuchars
	ZE735	Panavia Tornado F3 [AL]	RAF F3 OCU/No 56(R) Sqn, Coningsby
	ZE736	Panavia Tornado F3 (comp ZD937) [YN]	RAF/DARA, St Athan
	ZE737	Panavia Tornado F3 [FF]	RAF No 43 Sqn, Leuchars
	ZE755	Panavia Tornado F3 [YL]	RAF No 25 Sqn, Leeming
	ZE756	Panavia Tornado F3	RAF/DARA, stored St Athan
	ZE757	Panavia Tornado F3 [YJ]	RAF No 25 Sqn, Leeming
	ZE758	Panavia Tornado F3 [YI]	RAF/DARA, St Athan
	ZE758	Panavia Tornado F3 (ZE340/ 9298M) [GO]	Repainted as ZE340
	ZE763	Panavia Tornado F3 [YE]	RAF No 11 Sqn, Leeming
	ZE764	Panavia Tornado F3 [YD]	RAF No 111 Sqn, Leuchars
	ZE785	Panavia Tornado F3 [YC]	RAF AWC/F3 OEU, Coningsby
	ZE786	Panavia Tornado F3 (comp ZD934) [AN]	RAF F3 OCU/No 56(R) Sqn, Coningsby
	ZE788	Panavia Tornado F3 [YA]	RAF No 111 Sqn, Leuchars
	ZE790	Panavia Tornado F3 [VU]	RAF No 25 Sqn, Leeming
	ZE791	Panavia Tornado F3 [XY]	RAF No 111 Sqn, Leuchars
	ZE793	Panavia Tornado F3 (comp ZD935) [TE]	RAF No 111 Sqn, Leuchars
	ZE794	Panavia Tornado F3	RAF No 25 Sqn, Leeming
	ZE808	Panavia Tornado F3 [XV]	RAF No 25 Sqn, Leeming
	ZE810	Panavia Tornado F3 [XU]	RAF No 43 Sqn, Leuchars
	ZE812	Panavia Tornado F3 [XR]	RAF F3 OCU/No 56(R) Sqn, Coningsby
	ZE831	Panavia Tornado F3 [XQ]	RAF No 25 Sqn, Leeming
	ZE834	Panavia Tornado F3 [XO]	RAF No 111 Sqn, Leuchars
	ZE838	Panavia Tornado F3 [XL]	RAF No 43 Sqn, Leuchars
	ZE839	Panavia Tornado F3 [XK]	RAF No 11 Sqn, Leeming
	ZE887	Panavia Tornado F3 [DJ]	RAF No 11 Sqn, Leeming
	ZE888	Panavia Tornado F3 [TC]	RAF F3 OCU/No 56(R) Sqn, Coningsby
	ZE889	Panavia Tornado F3 [XI]	RAF F3 OCU/No 56(R) Sqn, Coningsby
	ZE907	Panavia Tornado F3 [FM]	RAF No 11 Sqn, Leeming
	ZE908	Panavia Tornado F3 [TB]	RAF F3 OCU/No 56(R) Sqn, Coningsby
	ZE934	Panavia Tornado F3 [TA]	RAF F3 OCU/No 56(R) Sqn, Coningsby
	ZE936	Panavia Tornado F3 [XF]	RAF No 25 Sqn, Leeming
	ZE941	Panavia Tornado F3 [KT]	RAF F3 OCU/No 56(R) Sqn, Coningsby
	ZE942	Panavia Tornado F3 [XE]	RAF No 5 Sqn, Coningsby
	ZE961	Panavia Tornado F3 [XD]	RAF F3 OCU/No 56(R) Sqn, Coningsby
	ZE962	Panavia Tornado F3 [XC]	RAF No 25 Sqn, Leeming
	ZE963	Panavia Tornado F3 [YT]	RAF No 111 Sqn, Leuchars
	ZE964	Panavia Tornado F3 [GN]	RAF/DARA, St Athan
	ZE965	Panavia Tornado F3 [WT]	RAF F3 OCU/No 56(R) Sqn, Coningsby
	ZE966	Panavia Tornado F3 [VT]	RAF F3 OCU/No 56(R) Sqn, Coningsby
	ZE967	Panavia Tornado F3 [UT]	RAF No 111 Sqn, Leuchars
	ZE968	Panavia Tornado F3 [XB]	RAF No 111 Sqn, Leuchars
	ZE969	Panavia Tornado F3 [XA]	RAF No 25 Sqn, Leeming
	ZE982	Panavia Tornado F3 [VV]	RAF No 25 Sqn, Leeming
	ZE983	Panavia Tornado F3 [WY]	RAF No 111 Sqn, Leuchars
	ZF116	WS61 Sea King HC4 [ZP]	RN No 848 Sqn, Yeovilton
	ZF117	WS61 Sea King HC4 [VQ]	RN No 846 Sqn, Yeovilton
	ZF118	WS61 Sea King HC4 [VP]	RN No 846 Sqn, Yeovilton
	ZF119	WS61 Sea King HC4 [VW]	RN No 846 Sqn, Yeovilton
	ZF120	WS61 Sea King HC4 [K]	RN No 845 Sqn, Yeovilton
	ZF121	WS61 Sea King HC4 [VT]	RN No 846 Sqn, Yeovilton
	ZF122	WS61 Sea King HC4 [VU]	RN No 846 Sqn, Yeovilton
	ZF123	WS61 Sea King HC4 [ZQ]	RN FSAIU, Yeovilton
	ZF124	WS61 Sea King HC4 [L]	RN No 845 Sqn, Yeovilton
	ZF130	BAe 125-600B (G-BLUW) (fuselage)	Scrapped Farnborough January 03
	ZF135	Shorts Tucano T1	RAF No 1 FTS, Linton-on-Ouse
	ZF136	Shorts Tucano T1	RAF No 1 FTS, Linton-on-Ouse
	ZF137	Shorts Tucano T1	RAF No 1 FTS, Linton-on-Ouse
	ZF138	Shorts Tucano T1	RAF No 1 FTS, Linton-on-Ouse
	ZF139	Shorts Tucano T1	RAF No 1 FTS, Linton-on-Ouse
	ZF140	Shorts Tucano T1	RAF No 1 FTS, Linton-on-Ouse
	ZF141	Shorts Tucano T1	RAF, stored Shawbury
	ZF142	Shorts Tucano T1	RAF No 1 FTS, Linton-on-Ouse
	ZF143	Shorts Tucano T1	RAF No 1 FTS, Linton-on-Ouse

Serial	Type (other identity) [code]	Owner/operator, location or fate	Notes
ZF144	Shorts Tucano T1	RAF No 1 FTS, Linton-on-Ouse	
ZF145	Shorts Tucano T1	RAF No 1 FTS, Linton-on-Ouse	
ZF160	Shorts Tucano T1	RAF, stored Shawbury	
ZF161	Shorts Tucano T1	RAF No 1 FTS, Linton-on-Ouse	
ZF162	Shorts Tucano T1	RAF No 1 FTS, Linton-on-Ouse	
ZF163	Shorts Tucano T1	RAF, stored Shawbury	
ZF164	Shorts Tucano T1	RAF, stored Shawbury	
ZF165	Shorts Tucano T1	RAF, stored Shawbury	
ZF166	Shorts Tucano T1	RAF, stored Shawbury	
ZF167	Shorts Tucano T1	RAF, stored Shawbury	
ZF168	Shorts Tucano T1	RAF No 1 FTS, Linton-on-Ouse	
ZF169	Shorts Tucano T1	RAF, stored Shawbury	
ZF170	Shorts Tucano T1	RAF No 1 FTS, Linton-on-Ouse	
ZF171	Shorts Tucano T1	RAF, stored Shawbury	
ZF172	Shorts Tucano T1	RAF, stored Shawbury	
ZF200	Shorts Tucano T1	RAF, stored Shawbury	
ZF201	Shorts Tucano T1	RAF, stored Shawbury	
ZF202	Shorts Tucano T1	RAF No 1 FTS, Linton-on-Ouse	
ZF203	Shorts Tucano T1	RAF No 1 FTS, Linton-on-Ouse	
ZF204	Shorts Tucano T1	RAF, stored Shawbury	
ZF205	Shorts Tucano T1	RAF, stored Shawbury	
ZF206	Shorts Tucano T1	RAF No 1 FTS, Linton-on-Ouse	
ZF207	Shorts Tucano T1	RAF No 1 FTS, Linton-on-Ouse	
ZF208	Shorts Tucano T1	RAF No 1 FTS, Linton-on-Ouse	
ZF209	Shorts Tucano T1	RAF No 1 FTS, Linton-on-Ouse	
ZF210	Shorts Tucano T1	RAF No 1 FTS, Linton-on-Ouse	
ZF211	Shorts Tucano T1	RAF, stored Shawbury	
ZF212	Shorts Tucano T1	RAF No 1 FTS, Linton-on-Ouse	
ZF238	Shorts Tucano T1	RAF No 1 FTS, Linton-on-Ouse	
ZF239	Shorts Tucano T1	RAF, stored Shawbury	
ZF240	Shorts Tucano T1	RAF No 1 FTS, Linton-on-Ouse	
ZF241	Shorts Tucano T1	RAF No 1 FTS, Linton-on-Ouse	
ZF242	Shorts Tucano T1	RAF No 1 FTS, Linton-on-Ouse	
ZF243	Shorts Tucano T1	RAF No 1 FTS, Linton-on-Ouse	
ZF244	Shorts Tucano T1	RAF No 1 FTS, Linton-on-Ouse	
ZF245	Shorts Tucano T1	RAF, stored Shawbury	
ZF263	Shorts Tucano T1	RAF, stored Shawbury	
ZF264	Shorts Tucano T1	RAF, stored Shawbury	
ZF265	Shorts Tucano T1	RAF, stored Shawbury	
ZF266	Shorts Tucano T1	RAF No 1 FTS, Linton-on-Ouse	
ZF267	Shorts Tucano T1	RAF, stored Shawbury	
ZF268	Shorts Tucano T1	RAF No 1 FTS, Linton-on-Ouse	
ZF269	Shorts Tucano T1	RAF No 1 FTS, Linton-on-Ouse	
ZF284	Shorts Tucano T1	RAF, stored Shawbury	
ZF285	Shorts Tucano T1	RAF, stored Shawbury	
ZF286	Shorts Tucano T1	RAF No 1 FTS, Linton-on-Ouse	
ZF287	Shorts Tucano T1	RAF, stored Shawbury	
ZF288	Shorts Tucano T1	RAF, stored Shawbury	
ZF289	Shorts Tucano T1	RAF No 1 FTS, Linton-on-Ouse	
ZF290	Shorts Tucano T1	RAF No 1 FTS, Linton-on-Ouse	
ZF291	Shorts Tucano T1	RAF No 1 FTS, Linton-on-Ouse	
ZF292	Shorts Tucano T1	RAF No 1 FTS, Linton-on-Ouse	
ZF293	Shorts Tucano T1	RAF No 1 FTS, Linton-on-Ouse	
ZF294	Shorts Tucano T1	RAF No 1 FTS, Linton-on-Ouse	
ZF295	Shorts Tucano T1	RAF No 1 FTS, Linton-on-Ouse	
ZF315	Shorts Tucano T1	RAF No 1 FTS, Linton-on-Ouse	
ZF317	Shorts Tucano T1	RAF No 1 FTS, Linton-on-Ouse	
ZF318	Shorts Tucano T1	RAF, stored Shawbury	
ZF319	Shorts Tucano T1	RAF No 1 FTS, Linton-on-Ouse	
ZF320	Shorts Tucano T1	RAF No 1 FTS, Linton-on-Ouse	
ZF338	Shorts Tucano T1	RAF No 1 FTS, Linton-on-Ouse	
ZF339	Shorts Tucano T1	RAF No 1 FTS, Linton-on-Ouse	
ZF340	Shorts Tucano T1	RAF, stored Shawbury	
ZF341	Shorts Tucano T1	RAF No 1 FTS, Linton-on-Ouse	
ZF342	Shorts Tucano T1	RAF No 1 FTS, Linton-on-Ouse	
ZF343	Shorts Tucano T1	RAF No 1 FTS, Linton-on-Ouse	
ZF344	Shorts Tucano T1	RAF, stored Shawbury	
ZF345	Shorts Tucano T1	RAF No 1 FTS, Linton-on-Ouse	
ZF346	Shorts Tucano T1	RAF No 1 FTS, Linton-on-Ouse	
ZF347	Shorts Tucano T1	RAF No 1 FTS, Linton-on-Ouse	
ZF348	Shorts Tucano T1	RAF No 1 FTS, Linton-on-Ouse	
ZF349	Shorts Tucano T1	RAF No 1 FTS, Linton-on-Ouse	
ZF350	Shorts Tucano T1	RAF, stored Shawbury	

Notes	Serial	Type (other identity) [code]	Owner/operator, location or fate
	ZF372	Shorts Tucano T1	RAF, stored Shawbury
	ZF373	Shorts Tucano T1	RAF, stored Shawbury
	ZF374	Shorts Tucano T1	RAF, stored Shawbury
	ZF375	Shorts Tucano T1	RAF No 1 FTS, Linton-on-Ouse
	ZF376	Shorts Tucano T1	RAF, stored Shawbury
	ZF377	Shorts Tucano T1	RAF No 1 FTS, Linton-on-Ouse
	ZF378	Shorts Tucano T1	RAF No 1 FTS, Linton-on-Ouse
	ZF379	Shorts Tucano T1	RAF No 1 FTS, Linton-on-Ouse
	ZF380	Shorts Tucano T1	RAF, stored Shawbury
	ZF405	Shorts Tucano T1	RAF No 1 FTS, Linton-on-Ouse
	ZF406	Shorts Tucano T1	RAF No 1 FTS, Linton-on-Ouse
	ZF407	Shorts Tucano T1	RAF No 1 FTS, Linton-on-Ouse
	ZF408	Shorts Tucano T1	RAF, stored Shawbury
	ZF409	Shorts Tucano T1	RAF No 1 FTS, Linton-on-Ouse
	ZF410	Shorts Tucano T1	RAF No 1 FTS, Linton-on-Ouse
	ZF411	Shorts Tucano T1	RAF, stored Shawbury
	ZF412	Shorts Tucano T1	RAF, stored Shawbury
	ZF413	Shorts Tucano T1	RAF No 1 FTS, Linton-on-Ouse
	ZF414	Shorts Tucano T1	RAF, stored Shawbury
	ZF415	Shorts Tucano T1	RAF, stored Shawbury
	ZF416	Shorts Tucano T1	RAF No 1 FTS, Linton-on-Ouse
	ZF417	Shorts Tucano T1	RAF No 1 FTS, Linton-on-Ouse
	ZF418	Shorts Tucano T1	RAF No 1 FTS, Linton-on-Ouse
	ZF445	Shorts Tucano T1	RAF No 1 FTS, Linton-on-Ouse
	ZF446	Shorts Tucano T1	RAF No 1 FTS, Linton-on-Ouse
	ZF447	Shorts Tucano T1	RAF No 1 FTS, Linton-on-Ouse
	ZF448	Shorts Tucano T1	RAF No 1 FTS, Linton-on-Ouse
	ZF449	Shorts Tucano T1	RAF, stored Shawbury
	ZF450	Shorts Tucano T1	RAF, stored Shawbury
	ZF483	Shorts Tucano T1	RAF No 1 FTS, Linton-on-Ouse
	ZF484	Shorts Tucano T1	RAF No 1 FTS, Linton-on-Ouse
	ZF485	Shorts Tucano T1 (G-BULU)	RAF No 1 FTS, Linton-on-Ouse
	ZF486	Shorts Tucano T1	RAF No 1 FTS, Linton-on-Ouse
	ZF487	Shorts Tucano T1	RAF No 1 FTS, Linton-on-Ouse
	ZF488	Shorts Tucano T1	RAF, stored Shawbury
	ZF489	Shorts Tucano T1	RAF No 1 FTS, Linton-on-Ouse
	ZF490	Shorts Tucano T1	RAF No 1 FTS, Linton-on-Ouse
	ZF491	Shorts Tucano T1	RAF No 1 FTS, Linton-on-Ouse
	ZF492	Shorts Tucano T1	RAF No 1 FTS, Linton-on-Ouse
	ZF510	Shorts Tucano T1	DPA/AFD/QinetiQ, Boscombe Down
	ZF511	Shorts Tucano T1	DPA/AFD/QinetiQ, Boscombe Down
	ZF512	Shorts Tucano T1	RAF No 1 FTS, Linton-on-Ouse
	ZF513	Shorts Tucano T1	RAF No 1 FTS, Linton-on-Ouse
	ZF514	Shorts Tucano T1	RAF No 1 FTS, Linton-on-Ouse
	ZF515	Shorts Tucano T1	RAF No 1 FTS, Linton-on-Ouse
	ZF516	Shorts Tucano T1	RAF, stored Shawbury
	ZF534	BAe EAP	Loughborough University
	ZF537	WS Lynx AH9	AAC No 653 Sqn/3 Regt, Wattisham
	ZF538	WS Lynx AH9	AAC No 659 Sqn/4 Regt, Wattisham
	ZF539	WS Lynx AH9	AAC No 7 Air Assault Battalion, Wattisham
	ZF540	WS Lynx AH9	AAC/DARA, stored Fleetlands
	ZF557	WS Lynx HMA8	RN AMG, Yeovilton
	ZF558	WS Lynx HMA8 [307]	RN No 815 Sqn, HQ Flt, Yeovilton
	ZF560	WS Lynx HMA8 [345/NC]	RN No 815 Sqn, *Newcastle* Flt, Yeovilton
	ZF562	WS Lynx HMA8 [361/NF]	RN AMG, Yeovilton
	ZF563	WS Lynx HMA8 [306]	RN No 815 Sqn, HQ Flt, Yeovilton
	ZF573	PBN 2T Islander CC2A (G-SRAY)	RAF Northolt Station Flight
	ZF579	BAC Lightning F53	Gatwick Aviation Museum, Charlwood
	ZF580	BAC Lightning F53	BAE Systems Samlesbury, at main gate
	ZF581	BAC Lightning F53	Privately owned, Rochester
	ZF582	BAC Lightning F53 <ff>	Privately owned, Reading
	ZF583	BAC Lightning F53	Solway Aviation Society, Carlisle
	ZF584	BAC Lightning F53	Ferranti Ltd, South Gyle, Edinburgh
	ZF587	BAC Lightning F53 <ff>	Lashenden Air Warfare Museum, Headcorn
	ZF588	BAC Lightning F53 [L]	East Midlands Airport Aeropark
	ZF590	BAC Lightning F53 <rf>	Privately owned, Grainthorpe, Lincs
	ZF592	BAC Lightning F53	City of Norwich Aviation Museum
	ZF593	BAC Lightning F53 (fuselage)	Pontypridd Technical College
	ZF594	BAC Lightning F53	North-East Aircraft Museum, Usworth
	ZF595	BAC Lightning F55 (fuselage)	Privately owned, Grainthorpe, Lincs
	ZF596	BAC Lightning T55 <ff>	BAe North-West Heritage Group Warton

Serial	Type (other identity) [code]	Owner/operator, location or fate	Notes
ZF622	Piper PA-31 Navajo Chieftain 350 (N3548Y)	DPA/AFD/QinetiQ, Boscombe Down	
ZF641	EHI-101 [PP1]	SFDO, RNAS Culdrose	
ZF649	EHI-101 Merlin [PP5]	RN AESS, *HMS Sultan*, Gosport	
ZG101	EHI-101 (mock-up) [GB]	Westland Helicopters/Agusta, Yeovil	
ZG471	BAe Harrier GR7 [61]	RAF No 4 Sqn, Cottesmore	
ZG472	BAe Harrier GR7 [62]	RAF No 4 Sqn, Cottesmore	
ZG474	BAe Harrier GR7 [64]	RAF No 3 Sqn, Cottesmore	
ZG477	BAe Harrier GR7 [67]	RAF No 3 Sqn, Cottesmore	
ZG478	BAe Harrier GR7 [68]	RAF No 1 Sqn, Cottesmore	
ZG479	BAe Harrier GR7 [69]	RAF AWC/SAOEU, Boscombe Down	
ZG480	BAe Harrier GR7 [70]	RAF No 3 Sqn, Cottesmore	
ZG500	BAe Harrier GR7 [71]	RAF No 1 Sqn, Cottesmore	
ZG501	BAe Harrier GR7 [72]	RAF No 4 Sqn, Cottesmore	
ZG502	BAe Harrier GR7 [73]	RAF No 3 Sqn, Cottesmore	
ZG503	BAe Harrier GR7 [74]	RAF No 4 Sqn, Cottesmore	
ZG504	BAe Harrier GR7 [75]	RAF No 1 Sqn, Cottesmore	
ZG505	BAe Harrier GR7 [76]	RAF No 4 Sqn, Cottesmore	
ZG506	BAe Harrier GR7 [77]	RAF No 3 Sqn, Cottesmore	
ZG507	BAe Harrier GR7 [78]	RAF No 1 Sqn, Cottesmore	
ZG508	BAe Harrier GR7 [79]	RAF No 3 Sqn, Cottesmore	
ZG509	BAe Harrier GR7 [80]	RAF/DARA, St Athan	
ZG510	BAe Harrier GR7 [81]	RAF No 4 Sqn, Cottesmore	
ZG511	BAe Harrier GR7 [82]	RAF No 3 Sqn, Cottesmore	
ZG512	BAe Harrier GR7 [83]	DPA/BAE Systems, Warton	
ZG530	BAe Harrier GR7 [84]	RAF No 3 Sqn, Cottesmore	
ZG531	BAe Harrier GR7 [85]	RAF No 4 Sqn, Cottesmore	
ZG705	Panavia Tornado GR4A [J]	RAF No 13 Sqn, Marham	
ZG706	Panavia Tornado GR1A [E]	RAF/DARA, stored St Athan	
ZG707	Panavia Tornado GR4A [B]	RAF No 13 Sqn, Marham	
ZG709	Panavia Tornado GR4A [V]	RAF No 13 Sqn, Marham	
ZG710	Panavia Tornado GR4A [D]	RAF No 13 Sqn, Marham	
ZG711	Panavia Tornado GR4A [O]	RAF No 2 Sqn, Marham	
ZG712	Panavia Tornado GR4A [F]	RAF No 13 Sqn, Marham	
ZG713	Panavia Tornado GR4A [G]	RAF No 13 Sqn, Marham	
ZG714	Panavia Tornado GR4A [Q]	RAF No 2 Sqn, Marham	
ZG726	Panavia Tornado GR4A [K]	RAF No 13 Sqn, Marham	
ZG727	Panavia Tornado GR4A [L]	RAF No 13 Sqn, Marham	
ZG729	Panavia Tornado GR4A [M]	RAF No 13 Sqn, Marham	
ZG731	Panavia Tornado F3 [WV]	RAF AWC/F3 OEU, Coningsby	
ZG750	Panavia Tornado GR4 [DY]	RAF No 31 Sqn, Marham	
ZG751	Panavia Tornado F3 [WP]	RAF No 25 Sqn, Leeming	
ZG752	Panavia Tornado GR4 [TM]	RAF No 15(R) Sqn, Lossiemouth	
ZG753	Panavia Tornado F3 [WO]	RAF No 1435 Flt, Mount Pleasant, FI	
ZG754	Panavia Tornado GR4 [TP]	RAF No 15(R) Sqn, Lossiemouth	
ZG755	Panavia Tornado F3 [WN]	RAF No 11 Sqn, Leeming	
ZG756	Panavia Tornado GR4 [BX]	RAF No 14 Sqn, Lossiemouth	
ZG757	Panavia Tornado F3 [WM]	RAF No 43 Sqn, Leuchars	
ZG769	Panavia Tornado GR4	RAF/DARA, St Athan (damaged)	
ZG770	Panavia Tornado F3 [WK]	RAF F3 OCU/No 56(R) Sqn, Coningsby	
ZG771	Panavia Tornado GR4 [AZ]	RAF No 9 Sqn, Marham	
ZG772	Panavia Tornado F3 [WJ]	RAF No 1435 Flt, Mount Pleasant, FI	
ZG773	Panavia Tornado GR4	DPA/BAE Systems, Warton	
ZG774	Panavia Tornado F3 [WI]	RAF No 11 Sqn, Leeming	
ZG775	Panavia Tornado GR4 [FB]	RAF No 12 Sqn, Lossiemouth	
ZG776	Panavia Tornado F3	RAF No 1435 Flt, Mount Pleasant, FI	
ZG777	Panavia Tornado GR4 [TC]	RAF No 15(R) Sqn, Lossiemouth	
ZG778	Panavia Tornado F3 [WG]	RAF No 43 Sqn, Leuchars	
ZG779	Panavia Tornado GR4 [FA]	RAF No 12 Sqn, Lossiemouth	
ZG780	Panavia Tornado F3 [WF]	RAF No 11 Sqn, Leeming	
ZG791	Panavia Tornado GR4 [BI]	RAF/DARA, St Athan	
ZG792	Panavia Tornado GR4 [AJ-G]	RAF No 617 Sqn, Lossiemouth	
ZG793	Panavia Tornado F3 [WE]	RAF No 11 Sqn, Leeming	
ZG794	Panavia Tornado GR4 [F]	RAF No 15(R) Sqn, Lossiemouth	
ZG795	Panavia Tornado F3 [WD]	RAF No 1435 Flt, Mount Pleasant, FI	
ZG796	Panavia Tornado F3 [WC]	RAF F3 OCU/No 56(R) Sqn, Coningsby	
ZG797	Panavia Tornado F3 [WB]	RAF No 43 Sqn, Leuchars	
ZG798	Panavia Tornado F3 [WA]	RAF No 43 Sqn, Leuchars	
ZG799	Panavia Tornado F3 [VS]	RAF No 43 Sqn, Leuchars	
ZG816	WS61 Sea King HAS6 [014/L]	RN No 820 Sqn, Culdrose	
ZG817	WS61 Sea King HAS6 [702/PW]	RN, *HMS Sultan*, Gosport	
ZG818	WS61 Sea King HAS6 [707/PW]	RN, stored *HMS Sultan*, Gosport	

ZG819 – ZH184

Notes	Serial	Type (other identity) [code]	Owner/operator, location or fate
	ZG819	WS61 Sea King HAS6 [265/N]	RN, *HMS Sultan*, Gosport
	ZG820	WS61 Sea King HC4 [A]	RN No 845 Sqn, Yeovilton
	ZG821	WS61 Sea King HC4 [D]	RN No 845 Sqn, Yeovilton
	ZG822	WS61 Sea King HC4 [VN]	RN No 846 Sqn, Yeovilton
	ZG844	PBN 2T Islander AL1 (G-BLNE)	AAC AFWF, Middle Wallop
	ZG845	PBN 2T Islander AL1 (G-BLNT)	AAC AFWF, Middle Wallop
	ZG846	PBN 2T Islander AL1 (G-BLNU)	AAC No 1 Flt, Aldergrove
	ZG847	PBN 2T Islander AL1 (G-BLNV)	AAC No 1 Flt, Aldergrove
	ZG848	PBN 2T Islander AL1 (G-BLNY)	AAC No 1 Flt, Aldergrove
	ZG857	BAe Harrier GR7 [89]	RAF No 1 Sqn, Cottesmore
	ZG858	BAe Harrier GR7	RAF AWC/SAOEU, Boscombe Down
	ZG859	BAe Harrier GR7 [91]	RAF No 4 Sqn, Cottesmore
	ZG860	BAe Harrier GR9	DPA/BAE Systems, Warton (conversion)
	ZG862	BAe Harrier GR7 [94]	RAF AWC/SAOEU, Boscombe Down
	ZG875	WS61 Sea King HAS6 [013/L]	RN, stored *HMS Sultan*, Gosport (damaged)
	ZG879	Powerchute Raider Mk 1	DPA/Powerchute, Hereford
	ZG884	WS Lynx AH9	DPA/Westland Helicopters, Yeovil
	ZG885	WS Lynx AH9 [7]	AAC No 653 Sqn/3 Regt, Wattisham
	ZG886	WS Lynx AH9	AAC No 659 Sqn/4 Regt, Wattisham
	ZG887	WS Lynx AH9	AAC No 653 Sqn/3 Regt, Wattisham
	ZG888	WS Lynx AH9	AAC/DARA, Fleetlands
	ZG889	WS Lynx AH9	AAC/DARA, stored Fleetlands
	ZG914	WS Lynx AH9	AAC/DARA, Fleetlands
	ZG915	WS Lynx AH9 [7]	AAC/DARA, Fleetlands
	ZG916	WS Lynx AH9 [8]	AAC No 653 Sqn/3 Regt, Wattisham
	ZG917	WS Lynx AH9	AAC No 659 Sqn/4 Regt, Wattisham
	ZG918	WS Lynx AH9	AAC No 659 Sqn/4 Regt, Wattisham
	ZG919	WS Lynx AH9	AAC No 653 Sqn/3 Regt, Wattisham
	ZG920	WS Lynx AH9	AAC No 659 Sqn/4 Regt, Wattisham
	ZG921	WS Lynx AH9	AAC No 653 Sqn/3 Regt, Wattisham
	ZG922	WS Lynx AH9	AAC/DARA, Fleetlands
	ZG923	WS Lynx AH9	AAC No 653 Sqn/3 Regt, Wattisham
	ZG969	Pilatus PC-9 (HB-HQE)	BAE Systems Warton
	ZG989	PBN 2T Islander ASTOR (G-DLRA)	DPA/Britten-Norman, Bembridge
	ZG993	PBN 2T Islander AL1 (G-BOMD)	AAC No 1 Flight, Aldergrove
	ZG994	PBN 2T Islander AL1 (G-BPLN) (fuselage)	AAC/DARA, stored St Athan
	ZH101	Boeing E-3D Sentry AEW1	RAF No 8 Sqn/No 23 Sqn, Waddington
	ZH102	Boeing E-3D Sentry AEW1	RAF No 8 Sqn/No 23 Sqn, Waddington
	ZH103	Boeing E-3D Sentry AEW1	RAF No 8 Sqn/No 23 Sqn, Waddington
	ZH104	Boeing E-3D Sentry AEW1	RAF No 8 Sqn/No 23 Sqn, Waddington
	ZH105	Boeing E-3D Sentry AEW1	RAF No 8 Sqn/No 23 Sqn, Waddington
	ZH106	Boeing E-3D Sentry AEW1	RAF No 8 Sqn/No 23 Sqn, Waddington
	ZH107	Boeing E-3D Sentry AEW1	RAF/Marshalls, Cambridge
	ZH115	Grob G109B Vigilant T1 [TA]	RAF No 616 VGS, Henlow
	ZH116	Grob G109B Vigilant T1 [TB]	RAF ACCGS/No 644 VGS, Syerston
	ZH117	Grob G109B Vigilant T1 [TC]	RAF No 642 VGS, Linton-on-Ouse
	ZH118	Grob G109B Vigilant T1 [TD]	RAF No 612 VGS, Abingdon
	ZH119	Grob G109B Vigilant T1 [TE]	RAF No 632 VGS, Ternhill
	ZH120	Grob G109B Vigilant T1 [TF]	RAF No 613 VGS, Halton
	ZH121	Grob G109B Vigilant T1 [TG]	RAF No 633 VGS, Cosford
	ZH122	Grob G109B Vigilant T1 [TH]	RAF No 664 VGS, Newtownards
	ZH123	Grob G109B Vigilant T1 [TJ]	RAF No 637 VGS, Little Rissington
	ZH124	Grob G109B Vigilant T1 [TK]	RAF No 642 VGS, Linton-on-Ouse
	ZH125	Grob G109B Vigilant T1 [TL]	RAF No 633 VGS, Cosford
	ZH126	Grob G109B Vigilant T1 (D-KGRA) [TM]	RAF No 637 VGS, Little Rissington
	ZH127	Grob G109B Vigilant T1 (D-KEEC) [TN]	RAF No 642 VGS, Linton-on-Ouse
	ZH128	Grob G109B Vigilant T1 [TP]	RAF No 624 VGS, Chivenor RMB
	ZH129	Grob G109B Vigilant T1 [TQ]	RAF No 635 VGS, Samlesbury
	ZH139	BAe Harrier GR7 <R> (BAPC 191/ *ZD472*)	RAF EPTT, Bottesford
	ZH141	AS355F-1 Twin Squirrel HCC1 (G-OILX)	RAF No 32(The Royal) Sqn, Northolt
	ZH144	Grob G109B Vigilant T1 [TR]	RAF No 616 VGS, Henlow
	ZH145	Grob G109B Vigilant T1 [TS]	RAF No 618 VGS, Odiham
	ZH146	Grob G109B Vigilant T1 [TT]	RAF No 624 VGS, Chivenor RMB
	ZH147	Grob G109B Vigilant T1 [TU]	RAF No 632 VGS, Ternhill
	ZH148	Grob G109B Vigilant T1 [TV]	RAF No 613 VGS, Halton
	ZH184	Grob G109B Vigilant T1 [TW]	RAF CGMF, Syerston

Serial	Type (other identity) [code]	Owner/operator, location or fate	Notes
ZH185	Grob G109B Vigilant T1 [TX]	RAF No 663 VGS, Kinloss	
ZH186	Grob G109B Vigilant T1 [TY]	RAF No 613 VGS, Halton	
ZH187	Grob G109B Vigilant T1 [TZ]	RAF No 633 VGS, Cosford	
ZH188	Grob G109B Vigilant T1 [UA]	RAF No 612 VGS, Abingdon	
ZH189	Grob G109B Vigilant T1 [UB]	RAF ACCGS/No 644 VGS, Syerston	
ZH190	Grob G109B Vigilant T1 [UC]	RAF No 663 VGS, Kinloss	
ZH191	Grob G109B Vigilant T1 [UD]	RAF No 616 VGS, Henlow	
ZH192	Grob G109B Vigilant T1 [UE]	RAF No 635 VGS, Samlesbury	
ZH193	Grob G109B Vigilant T1 [UF]	RAF No 612 VGS, Abingdon	
ZH194	Grob G109B Vigilant T1 [UG]	RAF No 624 VGS, Chivenor RMB	
ZH195	Grob G109B Vigilant T1 [UH]	RAF No 642 VGS, Linton-on-Ouse	
ZH196	Grob G109B Vigilant T1 [UJ]	RAF No 612 VGS, Abingdon	
ZH197	Grob G109B Vigilant T1 [UK]	RAF CGMF, Syerston	
ZH200	BAe Hawk 200	BAE Systems Warton, Overseas Customer Training Centre	
ZH205	Grob G109B Vigilant T1 [UL]	RAF No 613 VGS, Halton	
ZH206	Grob G109B Vigilant T1 [UM]	RAF CGMF, Syerston	
ZH207	Grob G109B Vigilant T1 [UN]	RAF No 632 VGS, Ternhill	
ZH208	Grob G109B Vigilant T1 [UP]	RAF ACCGS/No 644 VGS, Syerston	
ZH209	Grob G109B Vigilant T1 [UQ]	RAF No 664 VGS, Newtownards	
ZH211	Grob G109B Vigilant T1 [UR]	RAF No 618 VGS, Odiham	
ZH247	Grob G109B Vigilant T1 [US]	RAF No 618 VGS, Odiham	
ZH248	Grob G109B Vigilant T1 [UT]	RAF CGMF, Syerston	
ZH249	Grob G109B Vigilant T1 [UU]	RAF No 633 VGS, Cosford	
ZH257	B-V CH-47C Chinook (AE-520/9217M)	RAF/DARA, Fleetlands	
ZH263	Grob G109B Vigilant T1 [UV]	RAF No 632 VGS, Ternhill	
ZH264	Grob G109B Vigilant T1 [UW]	RAF No 616 VGS, Henlow	
ZH265	Grob G109B Vigilant T1 [UX]	RAF No 663 VGS, Kinloss	
ZH266	Grob G109B Vigilant T1 [UY]	RAF No 635 VGS, Samlesbury	
ZH267	Grob G109B Vigilant T1 [UZ]	RAF ACCGS/No 644 VGS, Syerston	
ZH268	Grob G109B Vigilant T1 [SA]	RAF No 613 VGS, Halton	
ZH269	Grob G109B Vigilant T1 [SB]	RAF No 642 VGS, Linton-on-Ouse	
ZH270	Grob G109B Vigilant T1 [SC]	RAF No 616 VGS, Henlow	
ZH271	Grob G109B Vigilant T1 [SD]	RAF ACCGS/No 644 VGS, Syerston	
ZH278	Grob G109B Vigilant T1 (D-KAIS) [SF]	RAF No 633 VGS, Cosford	
ZH279	Grob G109B Vigilant T1 (D-KNPS) [SG]	RAF No 635 VGS, Samlesbury	
ZH536	PBN 2T Islander CC2 (G-BSAH)	RAF Northolt Station Flight	
ZH540	WS61 Sea King HAR3A	RAF No 22 Sqn, A Flt, Chivenor RMB	
ZH541	WS61 Sea King HAR3A	RAF No 22 Sqn, B Flt, Wattisham	
ZH542	WS61 Sea King HAR3A	RAF No 22 Sqn, B Flt, Wattisham	
ZH543	WS61 Sea King HAR3A	RAF No 22 Sqn, A Flt, Chivenor RMB	
ZH544	WS61 Sea King HAR3A	RAF HMF, St Mawgan	
ZH545	WS61 Sea King HAR3A	RAF No 22 Sqn, A Flt, Chivenor RMB	
ZH552	Panavia Tornado F3 [AB]	RAF/DARA, St Athan	
ZH553	Panavia Tornado F3 [AB]	RAF F3 OCU/No 56(R) Sqn, Coningsby	
ZH554	Panavia Tornado F3	RAF AWC/F3 OEU, Coningsby	
ZH555	Panavia Tornado F3 [CV]	RAF F3 OCU/No 56(R) Sqn, Coningsby	
ZH556	Panavia Tornado F3 [OT]	RAF No 111 Sqn, Leuchars	
ZH557	Panavia Tornado F3 [NT]	RAF No 25 Sqn, Leeming	
ZH559	Panavia Tornado F3 [MT]	RAF F3 OCU/No 56(R) Sqn, Coningsby	
ZH588	Eurofighter Typhoon (DA2)	DPA/BAE Systems, Warton	
ZH590	Eurofighter Typhoon (DA4)	DPA/BAE Systems, Warton	
ZH653	BAe Harrier T10	DPA/BAE Systems, Warton	
ZH654	BAe Harrier T10	DPA/QinetiQ, stored Boscombe Down (wreck)	
ZH655	BAe Harrier T10 [Q]	RAF/DARA, stored St Athan (damaged)	
ZH656	BAe Harrier T10 [104]	RAF No 1 Sqn, Cottesmore	
ZH657	BAe Harrier T10 [105]	RAF HOCU/No 20(R) Sqn, Wittering	
ZH658	BAe Harrier T10 [106]	RAF HOCU/No 20(R) Sqn, Wittering	
ZH659	BAe Harrier T10 [107]	RAF HOCU/No 20(R) Sqn, Wittering	
ZH660	BAe Harrier T10 [108]	RAF HOCU/No 20(R) Sqn, Wittering	
ZH661	BAe Harrier T10 [109]	RAF HOCU/No 20(R) Sqn, Wittering	
ZH662	BAe Harrier T10 [110]	RAF HOCU/No 20(R) Sqn, Wittering	
ZH663	BAe Harrier T10 [111]	RAF HOCU/No 20(R) Sqn, Wittering	
ZH664	BAe Harrier T10 [112]	RAF HOCU/No 20(R) Sqn, Wittering	
ZH665	BAe Harrier T10 [113]	RAF HOCU/No 20(R) Sqn, Wittering	
ZH762	Westinghouse Skyship 500 (G-SKSC)	Exported to the US	
ZH763	BAC 1-11/539GL (G-BGKE)	DPA/AFD/QinetiQ, Boscombe Down	
ZH775	B-V Chinook HC2 (N7424J) [NS]	RAF No 27 Sqn, Odiham	

Notes	Serial	Type (other identity) [code]	Owner/operator, location or fate
	ZH776	B-V Chinook HC2 (N7424L) [ES]	RAF No 7 Sqn, Odiham
	ZH777	B-V Chinook HC2 (N7424M) [BS]	RAF/DARA, Fleetlands
	ZH796	BAe Sea Harrier FA2 [716/VL]	RN/DARA, stored St Athan
	ZH797	BAe Sea Harrier FA2 [002]	RN No 801 Sqn, Yeovilton
	ZH798	BAe Sea Harrier FA2 [123]	RN No 800 Sqn, Yeovilton
	ZH799	BAe Sea Harrier FA2 [730]	RN/DARA, stored St Athan
	ZH800	BAe Sea Harrier FA2 [719]	RN No 899 Sqn, Yeovilton
	ZH801	BAe Sea Harrier FA2 [712]	RN No 899 Sqn, Yeovilton
	ZH802	BAe Sea Harrier FA2 [711]	RN No 899 Sqn, Yeovilton
	ZH803	BAe Sea Harrier FA2 [003/R]	RN No 801 Sqn, Yeovilton
	ZH804	BAe Sea Harrier FA2 [125/R]	RN No 800 Sqn, Yeovilton
	ZH805	BAe Sea Harrier FA2 [730]	RN/DARA, St Athan
	ZH806	BAe Sea Harrier FA2 [122/R]	RN No 800 Sqn, Yeovilton
	ZH807	BAe Sea Harrier FA2 [711]	RN FSAIU, Yeovilton (damaged)
	ZH808	BAe Sea Harrier FA2 [712]	RN AMG, Yeovilton
	ZH809	BAe Sea Harrier FA2 [710]	RN No 899 Sqn, Yeovilton
	ZH810	BAe Sea Harrier FA2 [716]	RN No 899 Sqn, Yeovilton
	ZH811	BAe Sea Harrier FA2 [731]	RN No 899 Sqn, Yeovilton
	ZH812	BAe Sea Harrier FA2	RN/DARA, stored St Athan
	ZH813	BAe Sea Harrier FA2 [000]	RN No 801 Sqn, Yeovilton
	ZH814	Bell 212 (G-BGMH)	AAC No 7 Flt, Brunei
	ZH815	Bell 212 (G-BGCZ)	AAC No 7 Flt, Brunei
	ZH816	Bell 212 (G-BGMG)	AAC No 7 Flt, Brunei
	ZH821	EHI-101 Merlin HM1	DPA/Westland Helicopters, Yeovil
	ZH822	EHI-101 Merlin HM1	DPA/Westland Helicopters, Yeovil
	ZH823	EHI-101 Merlin HM1	DPA/Westland Helicopters, Yeovil
	ZH824	EHI-101 Merlin HM1	DPA/AFD/QinetiQ, Boscombe Down
	ZH825	EHI-101 Merlin HM1 [583/CU]	RN AMG, Culdrose
	ZH826	EHI-101 Merlin HM1	RN/DARA, stored Fleetlands
	ZH827	EHI-101 Merlin HM1	RN/DARA, stored Fleetlands
	ZH828	EHI-101 Merlin HM1 [583/CU]	DPA/Westland Helicopters, Yeovil
	ZH829	EHI-101 Merlin HM1	DPA/Westland Helicopters, Yeovil
	ZH830	EHI-101 Merlin HM1	DPA/AFD/QinetiQ, Boscombe Down
	ZH831	EHI-101 Merlin HM1	RN AMG, Culdrose
	ZH832	EHI-101 Merlin HM1	DPA/AFD/QinetiQ, Boscombe Down
	ZH833	EHI-101 Merlin HM1 [587]	RN AMG, Culdrose
	ZH834	EHI-101 Merlin HM1	RN No 700M OEU, Culdrose
	ZH835	EHI-101 Merlin HM1	RN AMG, Culdrose
	ZH836	EHI-101 Merlin HM1 [582/CU]	RN AMG, Culdrose
	ZH837	EHI-101 Merlin HM1	DPA/Westland Helicopters, Yeovil
	ZH838	EHI-101 Merlin HM1	RN AMG, Culdrose
	ZH839	EHI-101 Merlin HM1 [539/CU]	RN No 700M OEU, Culdrose
	ZH840	EHI-101 Merlin HM1	RN AMG, Culdrose
	ZH841	EHI-101 Merlin HM1	RN AMG, Culdrose
	ZH842	EHI-101 Merlin HM1	RN AMG, Culdrose
	ZH843	EHI-101 Merlin HM1 [533/CU]	RN No 700M OEU, Culdrose
	ZH844	EHI-101 Merlin HM1	RN FSAIU, Yeovilton (damaged)
	ZH845	EHI-101 Merlin HM1 [535]	RN No 700M OEU, Culdrose
	ZH846	EHI-101 Merlin HM1 [535]	RN AMG, Culdrose
	ZH847	EHI-101 Merlin HM1	DPA/Westland Helicopters, Yeovil
	ZH848	EHI-101 Merlin HM1 [388/LA]	RN No 824 Sqn, *Lancaster* Flt, Culdrose
	ZH849	EHI-101 Merlin HM1	RN No 824 Sqn, Culdrose
	ZH850	EHI-101 Merlin HM1	RN No 824 Sqn, Culdrose
	ZH851	EHI-101 Merlin HM1 [267]	RN No 824 Sqn, Culdrose
	ZH852	EHI-101 Merlin HM1 [583/CU]	RN No 824 Sqn, Culdrose
	ZH853	EHI-101 Merlin HM1	RN No 824 Sqn, Culdrose
	ZH854	EHI-101 Merlin HM1 [580/CU]	RN AMG, Culdrose
	ZH855	EHI-101 Merlin HM1	RN No 824 Sqn, Culdrose
	ZH856	EHI-101 Merlin HM1 [267/R]	RN No 814 Sqn, Culdrose
	ZH857	EHI-101 Merlin HM1 [268/R]	RN No 814 Sqn, Culdrose
	ZH858	EHI-101 Merlin HM1 [415/MM]	RN No 824 Sqn, Culdrose
	ZH859	EHI-101 Merlin HM1 [584]	RN No 824 Sqn, Culdrose
	ZH860	EHI-101 Merlin HM1 [269/R]	RN No 814 Sqn, Culdrose
	ZH861	EHI-101 Merlin HM1	RN No 824 Sqn, Culdrose
	ZH862	EHI-101 Merlin HM1	RN No 824 Sqn, Culdrose
	ZH863	EHI-101 Merlin HM1 [537/CU]	RN No 700M OEU, Culdrose
	ZH864	EHI-101 Merlin HM1	RN AMG, Culdrose
	ZH865	Lockheed C-130J-30 Hercules C4 (N130JA)	DPA/AFD/QinetiQ, Boscombe Down
	ZH866	Lockheed C-130J-30 Hercules C4 (N130JE)	RAF Lyneham Transport Wing
	ZH867	Lockheed C-130J-30 Hercules C4 (N130JJ)	RAF Lyneham Transport Wing

Serial	Type (other identity) [code]	Owner/operator, location or fate	Notes
ZH868	Lockheed C-130J-30 Hercules C4 (N130JN)	RAF Lyneham Transport Wing	
ZH869	Lockheed C-130J-30 Hercules C4 (N130JV)	RAF Lyneham Transport Wing	
ZH870	Lockheed C-130J-30 Hercules C4 (N73235/N78235)	RAF Lyneham Transport Wing	
ZH871	Lockheed C-130J-30 Hercules C4 (N73238)	DPA/AFD/QinetiQ, Boscombe Down	
ZH872	Lockheed C-130J-30 Hercules C4 (N4249Y)	RAF Lyneham Transport Wing	
ZH873	Lockheed C-130J-30 Hercules C4 (N4242N)	RAF Lyneham Transport Wing	
ZH874	Lockheed C-130J-30 Hercules C4 (N41030)	RAF Lyneham Transport Wing	
ZH875	Lockheed C-130J-30 Hercules C4 (N4099R)	RAF Lyneham Transport Wing	
ZH876	Lockheed C-130J-30 Hercules C4 (N4080M)	RAF Lyneham Transport Wing	
ZH877	Lockheed C-130J-30 Hercules C4 (N4081M)	RAF Lyneham Transport Wing	
ZH878	Lockheed C-130J-30 Hercules C4 (N73232)	RAF Lyneham Transport Wing	
ZH879	Lockheed C-130J-30 Hercules C4 (N4080M)	RAF Lyneham Transport Wing	
ZH880	Lockheed C-130J Hercules C5 (N73238)	DPA/AFD/QinetiQ, Boscombe Down	
ZH881	Lockheed C-130J Hercules C5 (N4081M)	RAF Lyneham Transport Wing	
ZH882	Lockheed C-130J Hercules C5 (N4099R)	RAF Lyneham Transport Wing	
ZH883	Lockheed C-130J Hercules C5 (N4242N)	RAF Lyneham Transport Wing	
ZH884	Lockheed C-130J Hercules C5 (N4249Y)	RAF Lyneham Transport Wing	
ZH885	Lockheed C-130J Hercules C5 (N41030)	RAF Lyneham Transport Wing	
ZH886	Lockheed C-130J Hercules C5 (N73235)	RAF Lyneham Transport Wing	
ZH887	Lockheed C-130J Hercules C5 (N4187W)	RAF Lyneham Transport Wing	
ZH888	Lockheed C-130J Hercules C5 (N4187)	RAF Lyneham Transport Wing	
ZH889	Lockheed C-130J Hercules C5 (N4099R)	RAF Lyneham Transport Wing	
ZH890	Grob G109B Vigilant T1 [SE]	RAF ACCGS/No 644 VGS, Syerston	
ZH891	B-V Chinook HC2A (N20075)	RAF No 18 Sqn, Odiham	
ZH892	B-V Chinook HC2A (N2019V) [BL]	RAF No 18 Sqn, Odiham	
ZH893	B-V Chinook HC2A (N2025L) [BM]	RAF No 18 Sqn, Odiham	
ZH894	B-V Chinook HC2A (N2026E) [BO]	RAF No 18 Sqn, Odiham	
ZH895	B-V Chinook HC2A (N2034K) [BP]	RAF No 18 Sqn, Odiham	
ZH896	B-V Chinook HC2A (N2038G)	RAF ASF, Odiham	
ZH897	B-V Chinook HC3 (N2045G)	DPA/AFD/QinetiQ, Boscombe Down	
ZH898	B-V Chinook HC3 (N2057Q)	DPA/AFD/QinetiQ, Boscombe Down	
ZH899	B-V Chinook HC3 (N2057R)	DPA/AFD/QinetiQ, Boscombe Down	
ZH900	B-V Chinook HC3 (N2060H)	DPA/AFD/QinetiQ, Boscombe Down	
ZH901	B-V Chinook HC3 (N2060M)	DPA/AFD/QinetiQ, Boscombe Down	
ZH902	B-V Chinook HC3 (N2064W)	DPA/AFD/QinetiQ, Boscombe Down	
ZH903	B-V Chinook HC3 (N20671)	RAF No 7 Sqn, Odiham	
ZH904	B-V Chinook HC3 (N2083K)	Boeing, Philadelphia, for RAF	
ZJ100	BAe Hawk 102D	BAE Systems Warton	
ZJ117	EHI-101 Merlin HC3	DPA/AFD/QinetiQ, Boscombe Down	
ZJ118	EHI-101 Merlin HC3 [B]	DPA/AFD/QinetiQ, Boscombe Down	
ZJ119	EHI-101 Merlin HC3 [C]	DPA/AFD/QinetiQ, Boscombe Down	
ZJ120	EHI-101 Merlin HC3	DPA/Westland Helicopters, Yeovil	
ZJ121	EHI-101 Merlin HC3 [E]	RAF No 28 Sqn, Benson	
ZJ122	EHI-101 Merlin HC3 [F]	RAF No 28 Sqn, Benson	
ZJ123	EHI-101 Merlin HC3 [G]	RAF No 28 Sqn, Benson	
ZJ124	EHI-101 Merlin HC3 [H]	RAF No 28 Sqn, Benson	
ZJ125	EHI-101 Merlin HC3 [J]	RAF No 28 Sqn, Benson	
ZJ126	EHI-101 Merlin HC3 [K]	RAF No 28 Sqn, Benson	
ZJ127	EHI-101 Merlin HC3 [L]	RAF No 28 Sqn, Benson	
ZJ128	EHI-101 Merlin HC3 [M]	RAF No 28 Sqn, Benson	

Notes	Serial	Type (other identity) [code]	Owner/operator, location or fate
	ZJ129	EHI-101 Merlin HC3 [N]	RAF No 28 Sqn, Benson
	ZJ130	EHI-101 Merlin HC3	DPA/AFD/QinetiQ, Boscombe Down
	ZJ131	EHI-101 Merlin HC3 [P]	RAF No 28 Sqn, Benson
	ZJ132	EHI-101 Merlin HC3 [Q]	RAF No 28 Sqn, Benson
	ZJ133	EHI-101 Merlin HC3 [R]	RAF No 28 Sqn, Benson
	ZJ134	EHI-101 Merlin HC3 [S]	RAF No 28 Sqn, Benson
	ZJ135	EHI-101 Merlin HC3 [T]	RAF No 28 Sqn, Benson
	ZJ136	EHI-101 Merlin HC3 [U]	RAF No 28 Sqn, Benson
	ZJ137	EHI-101 Merlin HC3 [W]	RAF No 28 Sqn, Benson
	ZJ138	EHI-101 Merlin HC3 [X]	RAF No 28 Sqn, Benson
	ZJ139	AS355F-1 Twin Squirrel HCC1 (G-NUTZ)	RAF No 32 (The Royal) Sqn, Northolt
	ZJ140	AS355F-1 Twin Squirrel HCC1 (G-FFHI)	RAF No 32 (The Royal) Sqn, Northolt
	ZJ164	AS365N-2 Dauphin 2 (G-BTLC)	RN/Bond Helicopters, Plymouth
	ZJ165	AS365N-2 Dauphin 2 (G-NTOO)	RN/Bond Helicopters, Plymouth
	ZJ166	WAH-64 Apache AH1 (N9219G)	DPA/Westland Helicopters, Yeovil
	ZJ167	WAH-64 Apache AH1 (N3266B)	AAC No 651 Sqn, Middle Wallop
	ZJ168	WAH-64 Apache AH1 (N3123T)	AAC No 651 Sqn, Middle Wallop
	ZJ169	WAH-64 Apache AH1 (N3114H)	AAC No 651 Sqn, Middle Wallop
	ZJ170	WAH-64 Apache AH1 (N3065U)	DPA/Westland Helicopters, Yeovil
	ZJ171	WAH-64 Apache AH1 (N3266T)	DPA/AFD/QinetiQ, Boscombe Down
	ZJ172	WAH-64 Apache AH1	AAC No 651 Sqn, Middle Wallop
	ZJ173	WAH-64 Apache AH1 (N3266W)	DPA/Westland Helicopters, Yeovil
	ZJ174	WAH-64 Apache AH1	AAC No 651 Sqn, Middle Wallop
	ZJ175	WAH-64 Apache AH1 (N3218V)	AAC No 651 Sqn, Middle Wallop
	ZJ176	WAH-64 Apache AH1	AAC No 651 Sqn, Middle Wallop
	ZJ177	WAH-64 Apache AH1	AAC No 651 Sqn, Middle Wallop
	ZJ178	WAH-64 Apache AH1	AAC No 651 Sqn, Middle Wallop
	ZJ179	WAH-64 Apache AH1	AAC No 651 Sqn, Middle Wallop
	ZJ180	WAH-64 Apache AH1	AAC No 651 Sqn, Middle Wallop
	ZJ181	WAH-64 Apache AH1	AAC No 651 Sqn, Middle Wallop
	ZJ182	WAH-64 Apache AH1	AAC, stored Shawbury
	ZJ183	WAH-64 Apache AH1	AAC No 651 Sqn, Middle Wallop
	ZJ184	WAH-64 Apache AH1	DPA/Westland Helicopters, Yeovil
	ZJ185	WAH-64 Apache AH1	DPA/AFD/QinetiQ, Boscombe Down
	ZJ186	WAH-64 Apache AH1	DPA/Westland Helicopters, Yeovil
	ZJ187	WAH-64 Apache AH1	AAC, stored Shawbury
	ZJ188	WAH-64 Apache AH1	DPA/Westland Helicopters, Yeovil
	ZJ189	WAH-64 Apache AH1	DPA/Westland Helicopters, Yeovil
	ZJ190	WAH-64 Apache AH1	AAC, stored Shawbury
	ZJ191	WAH-64 Apache AH1	AAC, stored Shawbury
	ZJ192	WAH-64 Apache AH1	AAC, stored Shawbury
	ZJ193	WAH-64 Apache AH1	AAC, stored Shawbury
	ZJ194	WAH-64 Apache AH1	AAC, stored Shawbury
	ZJ195	WAH-64 Apache AH1	AAC, stored Shawbury
	ZJ196	WAH-64 Apache AH1	AAC, stored Shawbury
	ZJ197	WAH-64 Apache AH1	AAC, stored Shawbury
	ZJ198	WAH-64 Apache AH1	AAC, stored Shawbury
	ZJ199	WAH-64 Apache AH1	AAC, stored Shawbury
	ZJ200	WAH-64 Apache AH1	AAC, stored Shawbury
	ZJ202	WAH-64 Apache AH1	AAC, stored Shawbury
	ZJ203	WAH-64 Apache AH1	AAC, stored Shawbury
	ZJ204	WAH-64 Apache AH1	DPA/Westland Helicopters, Yeovil
	ZJ205	WAH-64 Apache AH1	DPA/Westland Helicopters, Yeovil
	ZJ206	WAH-64 Apache AH1	DPA/Westland Helicopters, Yeovil
	ZJ207	WAH-64 Apache AH1	DPA/Westland Helicopters, Yeovil
	ZJ208	WAH-64 Apache AH1	Westland Helicopters, for AAC
	ZJ209	WAH-64 Apache AH1	Westland Helicopters, for AAC
	ZJ210	WAH-64 Apache AH1	DPA/Westland Helicopters, Yeovil
	ZJ211	WAH-64 Apache AH1	DPA/Westland Helicopters, Yeovil
	ZJ212	WAH-64 Apache AH1	Westland Helicopters, for AAC
	ZJ213	WAH-64 Apache AH1	Westland Helicopters, for AAC
	ZJ214	WAH-64 Apache AH1	Westland Helicopters, for AAC
	ZJ215	WAH-64 Apache AH1	Westland Helicopters, for AAC
	ZJ216	WAH-64 Apache AH1	Westland Helicopters, for AAC
	ZJ217	WAH-64 Apache AH1	Westland Helicopters, for AAC
	ZJ218	WAH-64 Apache AH1	Westland Helicopters, for AAC
	ZJ219	WAH-64 Apache AH1	Westland Helicopters, for AAC
	ZJ220	WAH-64 Apache AH1	Westland Helicopters, for AAC
	ZJ221	WAH-64 Apache AH1	Westland Helicopters, for AAC
	ZJ222	WAH-64 Apache AH1	Westland Helicopters, for AAC
	ZJ223	WAH-64 Apache AH1	Westland Helicopters, for AAC

Serial	Type (other identity) [code]	Owner/operator, location or fate	Notes
ZJ224	WAH-64 Apache AH1	Westland Helicopters, for AAC	
ZJ225	WAH-64 Apache AH1	Westland Helicopters, for AAC	
ZJ226	WAH-64 Apache AH1	Westland Helicopters, for AAC	
ZJ227	WAH-64 Apache AH1	Westland Helicopters, for AAC	
ZJ228	WAH-64 Apache AH1	Westland Helicopters, for AAC	
ZJ229	WAH-64 Apache AH1	Westland Helicopters, for AAC	
ZJ230	WAH-64 Apache AH1	Westland Helicopters, for AAC	
ZJ231	WAH-64 Apache AH1	Westland Helicopters, for AAC	
ZJ232	WAH-64 Apache AH1	Westland Helicopters, for AAC	
ZJ233	WAH-64 Apache AH1	Westland Helicopters, for AAC	
ZJ234	Bell 412EP Griffin HT1 (G-BWZR) [S]	DHFS No 60(R) Sqn, RAF Shawbury	
ZJ235	Bell 412EP Griffin HT1 (G-BXBF) [I]	DHFS No 60(R) Sqn, RAF Shawbury	
ZJ236	Bell 412EP Griffin HT1 (G-BXBE) [X]	DHFS No 60(R) Sqn, RAF Shawbury	
ZJ237	Bell 412EP Griffin HT1 (G-BXFF) [T]	DHFS No 60(R) Sqn, RAF Shawbury	
ZJ238	Bell 412EP Griffin HT1 (G-BXHC) [Y]	DHFS No 60(R) Sqn, RAF Shawbury	
ZJ239	Bell 412EP Griffin HT1 (G-BXFH) [R]	DHFS No 60(R) Sqn, RAF Shawbury	
ZJ240	Bell 412EP Griffin HT1 (G-BXIR) [U]	DHFS No 60(R) Sqn/SARTU, RAF Valley	
ZJ241	Bell 412EP Griffin HT1 (G-BXIS) [L]	DHFS No 60(R) Sqn/SARTU, RAF Valley	
ZJ242	Bell 412EP Griffin HT1 (G-BXDK) [E]	DHFS No 60(R) Sqn/SARTU, RAF Valley	
ZJ243	AS350BA Squirrel HT2 (G-BWZS)	School of Army Aviation/No 670 Sqn, Middle Wallop	
ZJ244	AS350BA Squirrel HT2 (G-BXMD)	School of Army Aviation/No 670 Sqn, Middle Wallop	
ZJ245	AS350BA Squirrel HT2 (G-BXME)	School of Army Aviation/No 670 Sqn, Middle Wallop	
ZJ246	AS350BA Squirrel HT2 (G-BXMJ)	School of Army Aviation/No 670 Sqn, Middle Wallop	
ZJ247	AS350BA Squirrel HT2 (G-BXNB)	School of Army Aviation/No 670 Sqn, Middle Wallop	
ZJ248	AS350BA Squirrel HT2 (G-BXNE)	School of Army Aviation/No 670 Sqn, Middle Wallop	
ZJ249	AS350BA Squirrel HT2 (G-BXNJ)	School of Army Aviation/No 670 Sqn, Middle Wallop	
ZJ250	AS350BA Squirrel HT2 (G-BXNY)	School of Army Aviation/No 670 Sqn, Middle Wallop	
ZJ251	AS350BA Squirrel HT2 (G-BXOG)	School of Army Aviation/No 670 Sqn, Middle Wallop	
ZJ252	AS350BA Squirrel HT2 (G-BXOK)	School of Army Aviation/No 670 Sqn, Middle Wallop	
ZJ253	AS350BA Squirrel HT2 (G-BXPG)	School of Army Aviation/No 670 Sqn, Middle Wallop	
ZJ254	AS350BA Squirrel HT2 (G-BXPJ)	School of Army Aviation/No 670 Sqn, Middle Wallop	
ZJ255	AS350BB Squirrel HT1 (G-BXAG)	DHFS, RAF Shawbury	
ZJ256	AS350BB Squirrel HT1 (G-BXCE)	DHFS, RAF Shawbury	
ZJ257	AS350BB Squirrel HT1 (G-BXDJ)	DHFS, RAF Shawbury	
ZJ258	AS350BB Squirrel HT1 (G-BXEO)	DHFS, RAF Shawbury	
ZJ259	AS350BB Squirrel HT1 (G-BXFJ)	DHFS, RAF Shawbury	
ZJ260	AS350BB Squirrel HT1 (G-BXGB)	DHFS, RAF Shawbury	
ZJ261	AS350BB Squirrel HT1 (G-BXGJ)	DHFS, RAF Shawbury	
ZJ262	AS350BB Squirrel HT1 (G-BXHB)	DHFS, RAF Shawbury	
ZJ263	AS350BB Squirrel HT1 (G-BXHK)	DHFS, RAF Shawbury	
ZJ264	AS350BB Squirrel HT1 (G-BXHW)	DHFS, RAF Shawbury	
ZJ265	AS350BB Squirrel HT1 (G-BXHX)	DHFS, RAF Shawbury	
ZJ266	AS350BB Squirrel HT1 (G-BXIL)	DHFS, RAF Shawbury	
ZJ267	AS350BB Squirrel HT1 (G-BXIP)	DHFS, RAF Shawbury	
ZJ268	AS350BB Squirrel HT1 (G-BXJE)	DHFS, RAF Shawbury	
ZJ269	AS350BB Squirrel HT1 (G-BXJN)	DHFS, RAF Shawbury	
ZJ270	AS350BB Squirrel HT1 (G-BXJR)	DHFS, RAF Shawbury	
ZJ271	AS350BB Squirrel HT1 (G-BXKE)	DHFS, RAF Shawbury	
ZJ272	AS350BB Squirrel HT1 (G-BXKN)	DHFS, RAF Shawbury	
ZJ273	AS350BB Squirrel HT1 (G-BXKP)	DHFS, RAF Shawbury	
ZJ274	AS350BB Squirrel HT1 (G-BXKR)	DHFS, RAF Shawbury	
ZJ275	AS350BB Squirrel HT1 (G-BXLB)	DHFS, RAF Shawbury	

Notes	Serial	Type (other identity) [code]	Owner/operator, location or fate
	ZJ276	AS350BB Squirrel HT1 (G-BXLE)	DHFS, RAF Shawbury
	ZJ277	AS350BB Squirrel HT1 (G-BXLH)	DHFS, RAF Shawbury
	ZJ278	AS350BB Squirrel HT1 (G-BXMB)	DHFS, RAF Shawbury
	ZJ279	AS350BB Squirrel HT1 (G-BXMC)	DHFS, RAF Shawbury
	ZJ280	AS350BB Squirrel HT1 (G-BXMI)	DHFS, RAF Shawbury
	ZJ481	Northrop Chukar D1	For Navy
	ZJ514	BAE Systems Nimrod MRA4 (XV251) [PA-4]	DPA/BAE Systems, Woodford (conversion)
	ZJ515	BAE Systems Nimrod MRA4 (XV258) [PA-5]	DPA/BAE Systems, Woodford (conversion)
	ZJ516	BAE Systems Nimrod MRA4 (XV247) [PA-1]	DPA/BAE Systems, Woodford (conversion)
	ZJ517	BAE Systems Nimrod MRA4 (XV242) [PA-3]	DPA/BAE Systems, Woodford (conversion)
	ZJ518	BAE Systems Nimrod MRA4 (XV234) [PA-2]	DPA/BAE Systems, Woodford (conversion)
	ZJ519	BAE Systems Nimrod MRA4 (XZ284) [PA-6]	DPA/BAE Systems, Woodford (conversion)
	ZJ520	BAE Systems Nimrod MRA4 (XV233) [PA-7]	DPA/BAE Systems, Woodford (conversion)
	ZJ521	BAE Systems Nimrod MRA4	BAE Systems, for RAF
	ZJ522	BAE Systems Nimrod MRA4	BAE Systems, for RAF
	ZJ523	BAE Systems Nimrod MRA4	BAE Systems, for RAF
	ZJ524	BAE Systems Nimrod MRA4	BAE Systems, for RAF
	ZJ525	BAE Systems Nimrod MRA4	BAE Systems, for RAF
	ZJ526	BAE Systems Nimrod MRA4	BAE Systems, for RAF
	ZJ527	BAE Systems Nimrod MRA4	BAE Systems, for RAF
	ZJ528	BAE Systems Nimrod MRA4	BAE Systems, for RAF
	ZJ529	BAE Systems Nimrod MRA4	BAE Systems, for RAF
	ZJ530	BAE Systems Nimrod MRA4	BAE Systems, for RAF
	ZJ531	BAE Systems Nimrod MRA4	BAE Systems, for RAF
	ZJ532	BAE Systems Nimrod MRA4	*Cancelled*
	ZJ533	BAE Systems Nimrod MRA4	*Cancelled*
	ZJ534	BAE Systems Nimrod MRA4	*Cancelled*
	ZJ620	EHI-101 Merlin CDS <Sim>	For Navy
	ZJ621	EHI-101 Merlin CPT <Sim>	For Navy
	ZJ622	EHI-101 Merlin RCT <Sim>	For Navy
	ZJ623	EHI-101 Merlin RCT <Sim>	For Navy
	ZJ624	EHI-101 Merlin RCT <Sim>	For Navy
	ZJ625	EHI-101 Merlin MST <Sim>	For Navy
	ZJ626	EHI-101 Merlin WST <Sim>	For Navy
	ZJ635	AS355F-1 Twin Squirrel (G-NEXT)	DPA/ETPS, Boscombe Down
	ZJ645	D-BD Alpha Jet (98+62)	DPA/ETPS, Boscombe Down
	ZJ646	D-BD Alpha Jet (98+55)	DPA/AFD/QinetiQ, Llanbedr
	ZJ647	D-BD Alpha Jet (98+71)	DPA/ETPS, Boscombe Down
	ZJ648	D-BD Alpha Jet (98+09)	DPA/AFD/QinetiQ, Boscombe Down
	ZJ649	D-BD Alpha Jet (98+73)	DPA/AFD/QinetiQ, Llanbedr
	ZJ650	D-BD Alpha Jet (98+35)	DPA/AFD/QinetiQ, Boscombe Down
	ZJ651	D-BD Alpha Jet (41+42)	DPA/QinetiQ Boscombe Down, spares use
	ZJ652	D-BD Alpha Jet (41+09)	DPA/QinetiQ Boscombe Down, spares use
	ZJ653	D-BD Alpha Jet (40+22)	DPA/QinetiQ Boscombe Down, spares use
	ZJ654	D-BD Alpha Jet (41+02)	DPA/QinetiQ Boscombe Down, spares use
	ZJ655	D-BD Alpha Jet (41+19)	DPA/QinetiQ Boscombe Down, spares use
	ZJ656	D-BD Alpha Jet (41+40)	DPA/QinetiQ Boscombe Down, spares use
	ZJ690	Bombardier Global Express (C-GJRG)	Bombardier, for RAF
	ZJ691	Bombardier Global Express	Bombardier, for RAF
	ZJ692	Bombardier Global Express	Bombardier, for RAF
	ZJ693	Bombardier Global Express	Bombardier, for RAF
	ZJ694	Bombardier Global Express	Bombardier, for RAF
	ZJ695	Eurofighter Training Rig	RAF No 1 SoTT, Cosford
	ZJ696	Eurofighter Training Rig	RAF No 1 SoTT, Cosford
	ZJ697	Eurofighter Training Rig	RAF No 1 SoTT, Cosford
	ZJ698	Eurofighter Training Rig	RAF No 1 SoTT, Cosford
	ZJ699	Eurofighter Typhoon (PT001)	DPA/BAE Systems, Warton
	ZJ700	Eurofighter Typhoon (PS002)	DPA/BAE Systems, Warton
	ZJ701	WS Super Lynx Mk 88A	WHL, Yeovil, for German Navy as 83+03
	ZJ703	Bell 412EP Griffin HAR2 (G-CBST)	RAF No 84 Sqn, Akrotiri
	ZJ704	Bell 412EP Griffin HAR2 (G-CBWT)	RAF No 84 Sqn, Akrotiri
	ZJ705	Bell 412EP Griffin HAR2 (G-CBXL)	RAF No 84 Sqn, Akrotiri
	ZJ706	Bell 412EP Griffin HAR2 (G-CBYR)	RAF No 84 Sqn, Akrotiri
	ZJ707	Bell 412EP Griffin HT1 (G-CBUB)	Bell Helicopters, for RAF
	ZJ708	Bell 412EP Griffin HT1 (G-CBVP)	Bell Helicopters, for RAF

Serial	Type (other identity) [code]	Owner/operator, location or fate	Notes
ZJ710	BAE Systems Nimrod MRA4 (Sim)	DPA for RAF	
ZJ711	BAE Systems Nimrod MRA4 (Sim)	DPA for RAF	
ZJ712	BAE Systems Nimrod MRA4 (Sim)	DPA for RAF	
ZJ713	BAE Systems Nimrod MRA4 (Sim)	DPA for RAF	
ZJ714	BAE Systems Nimrod MRA4 (Sim)	DPA for RAF	
ZJ715	BAE Systems Nimrod MRA4 (Sim)	DPA for RAF	
ZJ716	BAE Systems Nimrod MRA4 (Sim)	DPA for RAF	
ZJ717	BAE Systems Nimrod MRA4 (Sim)	DPA for RAF	
ZJ718	BAE Systems Nimrod MRA4 (Sim)	DPA for RAF	
ZJ719	BAE Systems Nimrod MRA4 (Sim)	DPA for RAF	
ZJ720	BAE Systems Nimrod MRA4 (Sim)	DPA for RAF	
ZJ800	Eurofighter Typhoon (BT001)	DPA/BAE Systems, for RAF	
ZJ801	Eurofighter Typhoon (BT002)	DPA/BAE Systems, for RAF	
ZJ802	Eurofighter Typhoon (BT003)	DPA/BAE Systems, for RAF	
ZJ803	Eurofighter Typhoon (BT004)	DPA/BAE Systems, for RAF	
ZJ804	Eurofighter Typhoon (BT005)	DPA/BAE Systems, for RAF	
ZJ805	Eurofighter Typhoon (BT006)	DPA/BAE Systems, for RAF	
ZJ806	Eurofighter Typhoon (BT007)	DPA/BAE Systems, for RAF	
ZJ807	Eurofighter Typhoon (BT008)	DPA/BAE Systems, for RAF	
ZJ808	Eurofighter Typhoon (BT009)	DPA/BAE Systems, for RAF	
ZJ809	Eurofighter Typhoon (BT010)	DPA/BAE Systems, for RAF	
ZJ810	Eurofighter Typhoon (BT011)	DPA/BAE Systems, for RAF	
ZJ811	Eurofighter Typhoon (BT012)	DPA/BAE Systems, for RAF	
ZJ812	Eurofighter Typhoon (BT013)	DPA/BAE Systems, for RAF	
ZJ813	Eurofighter Typhoon (BT014)	DPA/BAE Systems, for RAF	
ZJ814	Eurofighter Typhoon (BT015)	DPA/BAE Systems, for RAF	
ZJ815	Eurofighter Typhoon (BT016)	DPA/BAE Systems, for RAF	
ZJ904	WS Lynx 100	Westland Helicopters, for R Malaysian Navy	
ZJ905	WS Lynx 100	Westland Helicopters, for R Malaysian Navy as M22	
ZJ906	WS Lynx 100	Westland Helicopters, for R Malaysian Navy as M23	
ZJ907	WS Lynx 100	Westland Helicopters, for R Malaysian Navy as M24	
ZJ908	WS Lynx 100	Westland Helicopters, for R Malaysian Navy	
ZJ909	WS Lynx 100	Westland Helicopters, for R Malaysian Navy	
ZJ910	Eurofighter Typhoon (BS0001)	DPA/BAE Systems, for RAF	
ZJ911	Eurofighter Typhoon (BS0002)	DPA/BAE Systems, for RAF	
ZJ912	Eurofighter Typhoon (BS0003)	DPA/BAE Systems, for RAF	
ZJ913	Eurofighter Typhoon (BS0004)	DPA/BAE Systems, for RAF	
ZJ914	Eurofighter Typhoon (BS0005)	DPA/BAE Systems, for RAF	
ZJ915	Eurofighter Typhoon (BS0006)	DPA/BAE Systems, for RAF	
ZJ916	Eurofighter Typhoon (BS0007)	DPA/BAE Systems, for RAF	
ZJ917	Eurofighter Typhoon (BS0008)	DPA/BAE Systems, for RAF	
ZJ918	Eurofighter Typhoon (BS0009)	DPA/BAE Systems, for RAF	
ZJ919	Eurofighter Typhoon (BS0010)	DPA/BAE Systems, for RAF	
ZJ920	Eurofighter Typhoon (BS0011)	DPA/BAE Systems, for RAF	
ZJ921	Eurofighter Typhoon (BS0012)	DPA/BAE Systems, for RAF	
ZJ922	Eurofighter Typhoon (BS0013)	DPA/BAE Systems, for RAF	
ZJ923	Eurofighter Typhoon (BS0014)	DPA/BAE Systems, for RAF	
ZJ924	Eurofighter Typhoon (BS0015)	DPA/BAE Systems, for RAF	
ZJ925	Eurofighter Typhoon (BS0016)	DPA/BAE Systems, for RAF	
ZJ926	Eurofighter Typhoon (BS0017)	DPA/BAE Systems, for RAF	
ZJ927	Eurofighter Typhoon (BS0018)	DPA/BAE Systems, for RAF	
ZJ928	Eurofighter Typhoon (BS0019)	DPA/BAE Systems, for RAF	
ZJ929	Eurofighter Typhoon (BS0020)	DPA/BAE Systems, for RAF	
ZJ930	Eurofighter Typhoon (BS0021)	DPA/BAE Systems, for RAF	
ZJ931	Eurofighter Typhoon (BS0022)	DPA/BAE Systems, for RAF	
ZJ932	Eurofighter Typhoon (BS0023)	DPA/BAE Systems, for RAF	

Notes	Serial	Type (other identity) [code]	Owner/operator, location or fate
	ZJ933	Eurofighter Typhoon (BS0024)	DPA/BAE Systems, for RAF
	ZJ934	Eurofighter Typhoon (BS0025)	DPA/BAE Systems, for RAF
	ZJ935	Eurofighter Typhoon (BS0026)	DPA/BAE Systems, for RAF
	ZJ936	Eurofighter Typhoon (BS0027)	DPA/BAE Systems, for RAF
	ZJ937	Eurofighter Typhoon (BS0028)	DPA/BAE Systems, for RAF
	ZJ938	Eurofighter Typhoon (BS0029)	DPA/BAE Systems, for RAF
	ZJ939	Eurofighter Typhoon (BS0030)	DPA/BAE Systems, for RAF
	ZJ940	Eurofighter Typhoon (BS0031)	DPA/BAE Systems, for RAF
	ZJ941	Eurofighter Typhoon (BS0032)	DPA/BAE Systems, for RAF
	ZJ942	Eurofighter Typhoon (BS0033)	DPA/BAE Systems, for RAF
	ZJ943	Eurofighter Typhoon (BS0034)	DPA/BAE Systems, for RAF
	ZJ944	Eurofighter Typhoon (BS0035)	DPA/BAE Systems, for RAF
	ZJ945	Eurofighter Typhoon (BS0036)	DPA/BAE Systems, for RAF
	ZJ951	BAE Systems Hawk 120D	BAE Systems, Warton
	ZJ952	BAE Systems Hawk 115	*To Canada as 155219, 23 August 2002*
	ZJ953	BAE Systems Hawk 115	*To Canada as 155220, 23 August 2002*
	ZJ954	SA330H Puma HC1	DPA/Eurocopter, for RAF
	ZJ955	SA330H Puma HC1	DPA/Eurocopter, for RAF
	ZJ956	SA330H Puma HC1	DPA/Eurocopter, for RAF
	ZJ957	SA330H Puma HC1	DPA/Eurocopter, for RAF
	ZJ958	SA330H Puma HC1	DPA/Eurocopter, for RAF
	ZJ959	SA330H Puma HC1	DPA/Eurocopter, for RAF
	ZJ960	Grob G109B Vigilant T1 (D-KSMU) [SH]	RAF CGMF, Syerston
	ZJ961	Grob G109B Vigilant T1 (D-KLCW) [SJ]	RAF CGMF, Syerston
	ZJ962	Grob G109B Vigilant T1 (D-KBEU) [SK]	RAF CGMF, Syerston
	ZJ963	Grob G109B Vigilant T1 (D-KMSN) [SL]	RAF CGMF, Syerston
	ZJ964	Bell 212 AH1 (G-BJGV/5N-ALT)	AAC BATSUB, Belize
	ZJ965	Bell 212 AH1 (G-BJGU/5N-ALS)	AAC BATSUB, Belize
	ZJ966	Bell 212 AH1 (G-BJJO/5N-BHM)	AAC BATSUB, Belize
	ZJ967	Grob G109B Vigilant T1 (G-DEWS)	RAF CGMF, Syerston
	ZJ968	Grob G109B Vigilant T1 (N109BT)	RAF CGMF, Syerston
	ZK531	BAe Hawk T53 (LL-5306)	BAE Systems, Warton
	ZK532	BAe Hawk T53 (LL-5315)	BAE Systems, Warton
	ZK533	BAe Hawk T53 (LL-5317)	BAE Systems, Warton
	ZK534	BAe Hawk T53 (LL-5319)	BAE Systems, Warton
	ZK535	BAe Hawk T53 (LL-5320)	BAE Systems, Warton
	ZT800	WS Super Lynx Mk 300	DPA/Westland Helicopters, Yeovil
	ZZ171	Boeing C-17A Globemaster III (00-201/N171UK)	RAF No 99 Sqn, Brize Norton
	ZZ172	Boeing C-17A Globemaster III (00-202/N172UK)	RAF No 99 Sqn, Brize Norton
	ZZ173	Boeing C-17A Globemaster III (00-203/N173UK)	RAF No 99 Sqn, Brize Norton
	ZZ174	Boeing C-17A Globemaster III (00-204/N174UK)	RAF No 99 Sqn, Brize Norton

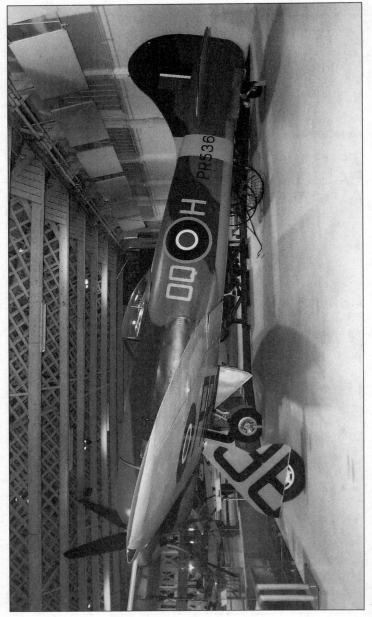

On display in the RAFM at Hendon, this former Indian Air Force Tempest II is painted in RAF markings as PR536. *PRM*

Painted in its original colours as Auster AOP10 VF516, this Beagle Terrier 2 conversion is privately owned. *PRM*

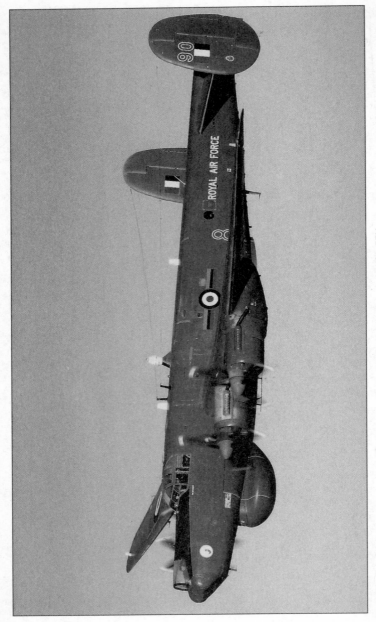

It is hoped that Avro Shackleton WL790 will return to Coventry this year after a protracted stay in the USA. *PRM*

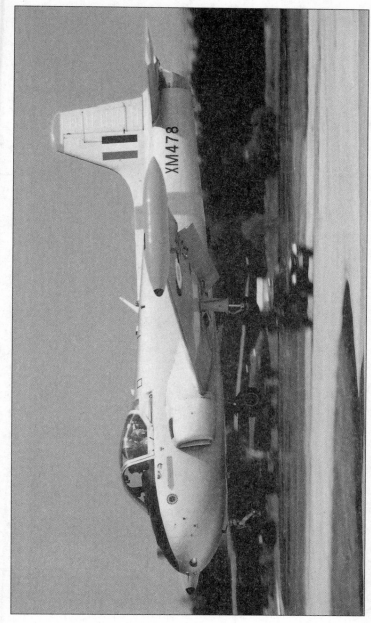

Hunting Jet Provost T3A XM478 is privately owned. *Daniel J March*

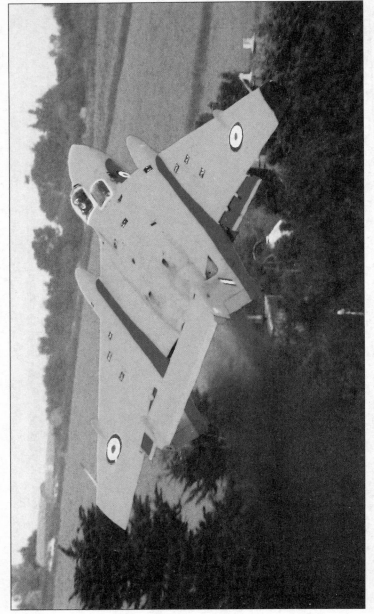

Colourful Sea Vixen D3 XP924 is a popular airshow performer. *PRM*

Kemble-based Gnat T1 XR538 is painted in No 4 FTS colours. *Daniel J March*

The first Wessex HC2 XR588, made the last RAF Wessex flight with No 84 Sqn in Cyprus, before retirement this year. *PRM*

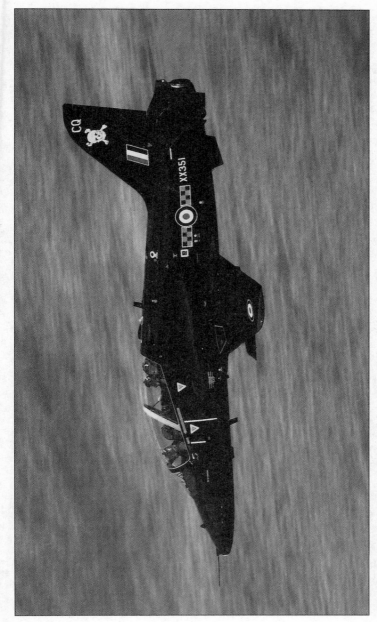

Low-flying Hawk T1A of No 100 Squadron based at RAF Leeming. *Chris Chambers*

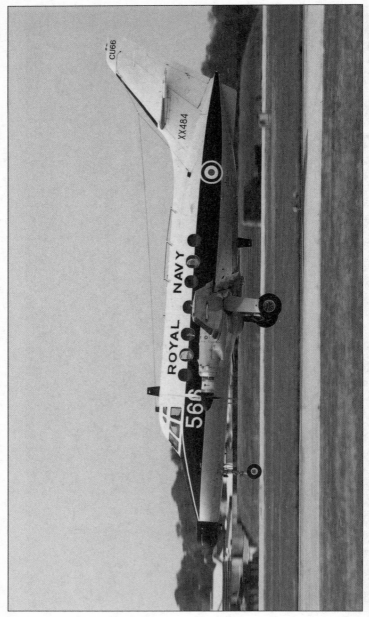

RNAS Culdrose-based Jetstream T2 XX484 is operated by 750 Naval Air Squadron. *PRM*

No 41 Squadron Jaguar GR3 XZ398 on a fast, low-level mission. *Chris Chambers*

Tornado GR4 ZA563 carries the markings of No 9 Squadron at RAF Marham. *Chris Chambers*

No 27 Squadron flies this Chinook HC2 ZA681 from RAF Odiham. *PRM*

In vertical landing phase, this Harrier GR7 ZD408 is in the colours of No 20 Squadron, the Harrier OCU. *PRM*

The Tornado F3 OCU, otherwise known as No 56 (R) Squadron, operates ZE250 in its fleet. *PRM*

Civil Registered Aircraft in UK Military Service

Serial	Type (other identity) [code]	Owner/operator, location or fate	Notes
G-BLVI	Slingsby T.67M Firefly 2	HCS/CFS, Cranwell	
G-BNSO	Slingsby T.67M Firefly 2	HCS/JEFTS, Barkston Heath	
G-BNSP	Slingsby T.67M Firefly 2	HCS/CFS, Cranwell	
G-BNSR	Slingsby T.67M Firefly 2	HCS/CFS, Cranwell	
G-BONT	Slingsby T.67M Firefly 2	HCS/CFS, Cranwell	
G-BUUA	Slingsby T.67M Firefly 2	HCS/JEFTS, Middle Wallop	
G-BUUB	Slingsby T.67M Firefly 2	HCS/JEFTS, Middle Wallop	
G-BUUC	Slingsby T.67M Firefly 2	HCS/JEFTS, Middle Wallop	
G-BUUD	Slingsby T.67M Firefly 2	HCS/JEFTS, Middle Wallop	
G-BUUE	Slingsby T.67M Firefly 2	HCS/JEFTS, Middle Wallop	
G-BUUF	Slingsby T.67M Firefly 2	HCS/JEFTS, Middle Wallop	
G-BUUG	Slingsby T.67M Firefly 2	HCS/JEFTS, Middle Wallop	
G-BUUI	Slingsby T.67M Firefly 2	HCS/JEFTS, Middle Wallop	
G-BUUJ	Slingsby T.67M Firefly 2	HCS/JEFTS, Middle Wallop	
G-BUUK	Slingsby T.67M Firefly 2	HCS/JEFTS, Middle Wallop	
G-BUUL	Slingsby T.67M Firefly 2	HCS/JEFTS, Middle Wallop	
G-BVHC	Grob G.115D-2 Heron	Shorts Bros/RN No 727 Sqn, Plymouth	
G-BVHD	Grob G.115D-2 Heron	Shorts Bros/RN No 727 Sqn, Plymouth	
G-BVHE	Grob G.115D-2 Heron	Shorts Bros/RN No 727 Sqn, Plymouth	
G-BVHF	Grob G.115D-2 Heron	Shorts Bros/RN No 727 Sqn, Plymouth	
G-BVHG	Grob G.115D-2 Heron	Shorts Bros/RN No 727 Sqn, Plymouth	
G-BWXA	Slingsby T.67M Firefly 260	HCS/JEFTS, Barkston Heath	
G-BWXB	Slingsby T.67M Firefly 260	HCS/JEFTS, Barkston Heath	
G-BWXC	Slingsby T.67M Firefly 260	HCS/JEFTS, Barkston Heath	
G-BWXD	Slingsby T.67M Firefly 260	HCS/JEFTS, Barkston Heath	
G-BWXE	Slingsby T.67M Firefly 260	HCS/JEFTS, Barkston Heath	
G-BWXF	Slingsby T.67M Firefly 260	HCS/JEFTS, Barkston Heath	
G-BWXG	Slingsby T.67M Firefly 260	HCS/JEFTS, Church Fenton	
G-BWXH	Slingsby T.67M Firefly 260	HCS/JEFTS, Barkston Heath	
G-BWXI	Slingsby T.67M Firefly 260	HCS/JEFTS, Barkston Heath	
G-BWXJ	Slingsby T.67M Firefly 260	HCS/JEFTS, Barkston Heath	
G-BWXK	Slingsby T.67M Firefly 260	HCS/JEFTS, Barkston Heath	
G-BWXL	Slingsby T.67M Firefly 260	HCS/JEFTS, Barkston Heath	
G-BWXM	Slingsby T.67M Firefly 260	HCS/JEFTS, Barkston Heath	
G-BWXN	Slingsby T.67M Firefly 260	HCS/JEFTS, Barkston Heath	
G-BWXO	Slingsby T.67M Firefly 260	HCS/JEFTS, Barkston Heath	
G-BWXP	Slingsby T.67M Firefly 260	HCS/JEFTS, Barkston Heath	
G-BWXR	Slingsby T.67M Firefly 260	HCS/JEFTS, Barkston Heath	
G-BWXS	Slingsby T.67M Firefly 260	HCS/JEFTS, Barkston Heath	
G-BWXT	Slingsby T.67M Firefly 260	HCS/JEFTS, Barkston Heath	
G-BWXU	Slingsby T.67M Firefly 260	HCS/JEFTS, Barkston Heath	
G-BWXV	Slingsby T.67M Firefly 260	HCS/JEFTS, Barkston Heath	
G-BWXW	Slingsby T.67M Firefly 260	HCS/JEFTS, Barkston Heath	
G-BWXX	Slingsby T.67M Firefly 260	HCS/JEFTS, Barkston Heath	
G-BWXY	Slingsby T.67M Firefly 260	HCS/JEFTS, Barkston Heath	
G-BWXZ	Slingsby T.67M Firefly 260 [6]	HCS/JEFTS, Barkston Heath	
G-BYOA	Slingsby T.67M Firefly 260	HCS/JEFTS, Barkston Heath	
G-BYOB	Slingsby T.67M Firefly 260	HCS/JEFTS, Barkston Heath	
G-BYUA	Grob G.115E Tutor	Bombardier/Cambridge UAS, Wyton	
G-BYUB	Grob G.115E Tutor	Bombardier/University of Wales AS, St Athan	
G-BYUC	Grob G.115E Tutor	Bombardier/CFS/East Midlands Universities AS, Cranwell	
G-BYUD	Grob G.115E Tutor	Bombardier/Northumbrian Universities AS, Leeming	
G-BYUE	Grob G.115E Tutor	Bombardier/CFS/East Midlands Universities AS, Cranwell	
G-BYUF	Grob G.115E Tutor	Bombardier/Cambridge UAS/University of London AS, Wyton	
G-BYUG	Grob G.115E Tutor	Bombardier/Universities of Glasgow & Strathclyde AS, Glasgow	
G-BYUH	Grob G.115E Tutor	Bombardier/Bristol UAS, Colerne	
G-BYUI	Grob G.115E Tutor	Bombardier/Liverpool UAS/Manchester and Salford Universities AS, Woodvale	
G-BYUJ	Grob G.115E Tutor	Bombardier/Northumbrian Universities AS, Leeming	
G-BYUK	Grob G.115E Tutor	Bombardier/Cambridge UAS, Wyton	

Civil Registered Aircraft in UK Military Service

Notes	Serial	Type (other identity) [code]	Owner/operator, location or fate
	G-BYUL	Grob G.115E Tutor	Bombardier/University of London AS, Wyton
	G-BYUM	Grob G.115E Tutor	Bombardier/Southampton UAS, Boscombe Down
	G-BYUN	Grob G.115E Tutor	Bombardier/Cambridge UAS/University of London AS, Wyton
	G-BYUO	Grob G.115E Tutor	Bombardier/University of London AS, Wyton
	G-BYUP	Grob G.115E Tutor	Bombardier/East Lowlands UAS/Aberdeen, Dundee & St Andrews UAS, Leuchars
	G-BYUR	Grob G.115E Tutor	Bombardier/East Lowlands UAS/Aberdeen, Dundee & St Andrews UAS, Leuchars
	G-BYUS	Grob G.115E Tutor	Bombardier/Oxford UAS, Benson
	G-BYUT	Grob G.115E Tutor	Bombardier/Oxford UAS, Benson
	G-BYUU	Grob G.115E Tutor	Bombardier/Universities of Glasgow & Strathclyde AS, Glasgow
	G-BYUV	Grob G.115E Tutor	Bombardier/Oxford UAS, Benson
	G-BYUW	Grob G.115E Tutor	Bombardier/East Lowlands UAS/Aberdeen, Dundee & St Andrews UAS, Leuchars
	G-BYUX	Grob G.115E Tutor	Bombardier/Liverpool UAS/Manchester and Salford Universities AS, Woodvale
	G-BYUY	Grob G.115E Tutor	Bombardier/East Lowlands UAS/Aberdeen, Dundee & St Andrews UAS, Leuchars
	G-BYUZ	Grob G.115E Tutor	Bombardier/Liverpool UAS/Manchester and Salford Universities AS, Woodvale
	G-BYVA	Grob G.115E Tutor	Bombardier/CFS/East Midlands Universities AS, Cranwell
	G-BYVB	Grob G.115E Tutor	Bombardier/Universities of Glasgow & Strathclyde AS, Glasgow
	G-BYVC	Grob G.115E Tutor	Bombardier/Bristol UAS, Colerne
	G-BYVD	Grob G.115E Tutor	Bombardier/Cambridge UAS/University of London AS, Wyton
	G-BYVE	Grob G.115E Tutor	Bombardier/Southampton UAS, Boscombe Down
	G-BYVF	Grob G.115E Tutor	Bombardier/Universities of Glasgow & Strathclyde AS, Glasgow
	G-BYVG	Grob G.115E Tutor	Bombardier/Yorkshire Universities AS, Church Fenton
	G-BYVH	Grob G.115E Tutor	Bombardier/East Lowlands UAS/Aberdeen, Dundee & St Andrews UAS, Leuchars
	G-BYVI	Grob G.115E Tutor	Bombardier/Universities of Glasgow & Strathclyde AS, Glasgow
	G-BYVJ	Grob G.115E Tutor	Bombardier/Northumbrian Universities AS, Leeming
	G-BYVK	Grob G.115E Tutor	Bombardier/East Lowlands UAS/Aberdeen, Dundee & St Andrews UAS, Leuchars
	G-BYVL	Grob G.115E Tutor	Bombardier/University of Wales AS, St Athan
	G-BYVM	Grob G.115E Tutor	Bombardier/East Lowlands UAS/Aberdeen, Dundee & St Andrews UAS, Leuchars
	G-BYVN	Grob G.115E Tutor	Bombardier/Bristol UAS, Colerne
	G-BYVO	Grob G.115E Tutor	Bombardier/University of Birmingham AS, Cosford
	G-BYVP	Grob G.115E Tutor	Bombardier/Oxford UAS, Benson
	G-BYVR	Grob G.115E Tutor	Bombardier/CFS/East Midlands Universities AS, Cranwell
	G-BYVS	Grob G.115E Tutor	Bombardier/Cambridge UAS/University of London AS, Wyton
	G-BYVT	Grob G.115E Tutor	Bombardier/Cambridge UAS/University of London AS, Wyton
	G-BYVU	Grob G.115E Tutor	Bombardier/Oxford UAS, Benson
	G-BYVV	Grob G.115E Tutor	Bombardier/Yorkshire Universities AS, Church Fenton
	G-BYVW	Grob G.115E Tutor	Bombardier/Yorkshire Universities AS, Church Fenton
	G-BYVX	Grob G.115E Tutor	Bombardier/Yorkshire Universities AS, Church Fenton
	G-BYVY	Grob G.115E Tutor	Bombardier/Yorkshire Universities AS, Church Fenton
	G-BYVZ	Grob G.115E Tutor	Bombardier/Yorkshire Universities AS, Church Fenton
	G-BYWA	Grob G.115E Tutor	Bombardier/University of Wales AS, St Athan

Serial	Type (other identity) [code]	Owner/operator, location or fate	Notes
G-BYWB	Grob G.115E Tutor	Bombardier/Bristol UAS, Colerne	
G-BYWC	Grob G.115E Tutor	Bombardier/Bristol UAS, Colerne	
G-BYWD	Grob G.115E Tutor	Bombardier/Liverpool UAS/Manchester and Salford Universities AS, Woodvale	
G-BYWE	Grob G.115E Tutor	Bombardier/Bristol UAS, Colerne	
G-BYWF	Grob G.115E Tutor	Bombardier/CFS/East Midlands Universities AS, Cranwell	
G-BYWG	Grob G.115E Tutor	Bombardier/Bristol UAS, Colerne	
G-BYWH	Grob G.115E Tutor	Bombardier/Northumbrian Universities AS, Leeming	
G-BYWI	Grob G.115E Tutor	Bombardier/Bristol UAS, Colerne	
G-BYWJ	Grob G.115E Tutor	Bombardier/Liverpool UAS/Manchester and Salford Universities AS, Woodvale	
G-BYWK	Grob G.115E Tutor	Grob/Bombardier for RAF	
G-BYWL	Grob G.115E Tutor	Bombardier/Liverpool UAS/Manchester and Salford Universities AS, Woodvale	
G-BYWM	Grob G.115E Tutor	Bombardier/CFS/East Midlands Universities AS, Cranwell	
G-BYWN	Grob G.115E Tutor	Bombardier/Liverpool UAS/Manchester and Salford Universities AS, Woodvale	
G-BYWO	Grob G.115E Tutor	Bombardier/University of Birmingham AS, Cosford	
G-BYWP	Grob G.115E Tutor	Bombardier/Yorkshire Universities AS, Church Fenton	
G-BYWR	Grob G.115E Tutor	Bombardier/Cambridge UAS/University of London AS, Wyton	
G-BYWS	Grob G.115E Tutor	Bombardier/Northumbrian Universities AS, Leeming	
G-BYWT	Grob G.115E Tutor	Bombardier/Northumbrian Universities AS, Leeming	
G-BYWU	Grob G.115E Tutor	Bombardier/Cambridge UAS/University of London AS, Wyton	
G-BYWV	Grob G.115E Tutor	Bombardier/University of Birmingham AS, Cosford	
G-BYWW	Grob G.115E Tutor	Bombardier/CFS/East Midlands Universities AS, Cranwell	
G-BYWX	Grob G.115E Tutor	Bombardier/Cambridge UAS/University of London AS, Wyton	
G-BYWY	Grob G.115E Tutor	Bombardier/CFS/East Midlands Universities AS, Cranwell	
G-BYWZ	Grob G.115E Tutor	Bombardier/CFS/East Midlands Universities AS, Cranwell	
G-BYXA	Grob G.115E Tutor	Bombardier/Liverpool UAS/Manchester and Salford Universities AS, Woodvale	
G-BYXB	Grob G.115E Tutor	Bombardier/Southampton UAS, Boscombe Down	
G-BYXC	Grob G.115E Tutor	Bombardier/CFS/East Midlands Universities AS, Cranwell	
G-BYXD	Grob G.115E Tutor	Bombardier/CFS/East Midlands Universities AS, Cranwell	
G-BYXE	Grob G.115E Tutor	Bombardier/Yorkshire Universities AS, Church Fenton	
G-BYXF	Grob G.115E Tutor	Bombardier/University of Birmingham AS, Cosford	
G-BYXG	Grob G.115E Tutor	Bombardier/University of Birmingham AS, Cosford	
G-BYXH	Grob G.115E Tutor	Bombardier/Cambridge UAS/University of London AS, Wyton	
G-BYXI	Grob G.115E Tutor	Bombardier/Liverpool UAS/Manchester and Salford Universities AS, Woodvale	
G-BYXJ	Grob G.115E Tutor	Bombardier/Southampton UAS, Boscombe Down	
G-BYXK	Grob G.115E Tutor	Bombardier/University of Wales AS, St Athan	
G-BYXL	Grob G.115E Tutor	Bombardier/University of Birmingham AS, Cosford	
G-BYXM	Grob G.115E Tutor	Bombardier/Southampton UAS, Boscombe Down	
G-BYXN	Grob G.115E Tutor	Bombardier/Southampton UAS, Boscombe Down	
G-BYXO	Grob G.115E Tutor	Bombardier/University of Birmingham AS, Cosford	

Civil Registered Aircraft in UK Military Service

Notes	Serial	Type (other identity) [code]	Owner/operator, location or fate
	G-BYXP	Grob G.115E Tutor	Bombardier/Cambridge UAS/University of London AS, Wyton
	G-BYXR	Grob G.115E Tutor	Bombardier/Oxford UAS, Benson
	G-BYXS	Grob G.115E Tutor	Bombardier/Oxford UAS, Benson
	G-BYXT	Grob G.115E Tutor	Bombardier/CFS/East Midlands Universities AS, Cranwell
	G-BYXX	Grob G.115E Tutor	Bombardier/Liverpool UAS/Manchester and Salford Universities AS, Woodvale
	G-BYXY	Grob G.115E Tutor	Bombardier/Northumbrian Universities AS, Leeming
	G-BYXZ	Grob G.115E Tutor	Bombardier/CFS/East Midlands Universities AS, Cranwell
	G-BYYA	Grob G.115E Tutor	Bombardier/CFS/East Midlands Universities AS, Cranwell
	G-BYYB	Grob G.115E Tutor	Bombardier/CFS/East Midlands Universities AS, Cranwell
	G-FFRA	Dassault Falcon 20DC (N902FR)	FR Aviation, Tees-side
	G-FRAF	Dassault Falcon 20E (N911FR)	FR Aviation, Bournemouth
	G-FRAH	Dassault Falcon 20DC (N900FR)	FR Aviation, Tees-side
	G-FRAI	Dassault Falcon 20E (N901FR)	FR Aviation, Tees-side
	G-FRAJ	Dassault Falcon 20E (N903FR)	FR Aviation, Tees-side
	G-FRAK	Dassault Falcon 20DC (N905FR)	FR Aviation, Bournemouth
	G-FRAL	Dassault Falcon 20DC (N904FR)	FR Aviation, Tees-side
	G-FRAM	Dassault Falcon 20DC (N907FR)	FR Aviation, Bournemouth
	G-FRAO	Dassault Falcon 20DC (N906FR)	FR Aviation, Bournemouth
	G-FRAP	Dassault Falcon 20DC (N908FR)	FR Aviation, Bournemouth
	G-FRAR	Dassault Falcon 20DC (N909FR)	FR Aviation, Bournemouth
	G-FRAS	Dassault Falcon 20C (117501)	FR Aviation, Tees-side
	G-FRAT	Dassault Falcon 20C (117502)	FR Aviation, Tees-side
	G-FRAU	Dassault Falcon 20C (117504)	FR Aviation, Tees-side
	G-FRAW	Dassault Falcon 20ECM (117507)	FR Aviation, Tees-side
	G-FRBA	Dassault Falcon 20C	FR Aviation, Bournemouth
	G-HONG	Slingsby T.67M Firefly 2	HCS/JEFTS, Middle Wallop
	G-KONG	Slingsby T.67M Firefly 2	HCS/JEFTS, Middle Wallop
	G-XXEA	Sikorsky S-76C+	Air Hanson/The Royal Flight, Blackbushe

Tucano T1 ZF293, one of the Linton-on-Ouse based trainers with No 1 FTS. *Chris Chambers*

RAF Maintenance Command/ Support Command/Logistics Command 'M' number Cross-reference

1764M/K4972
2015M/K5600
2292M/K8203
2361M/K6035
3118M/H5199/(BK892)
3858M/X7688
4354M/BL614
4552M/T5298
5377M/EP120
5405M/LF738
5466M/*BN230*/(LF751)
5690M/MK356
5718M/BM597
5758M/DG202
6457M/ML427
6490M/LA255
6640M/RM694
6850M/TE184
6946M/RW388
6948M/DE673
6960M/MT847
7008M/EE549
7014M/N6720
7015M/NL985
7035M/*K2567*/(DE306)
7060M/VF301
7090M/EE531
7118M/LA198
7119M/LA226
7150M/PK683
7154M/WB188
7174M/VX272
7175M/VV106
7200M/VT812
7241M/*MK178*(TE311)
7243M/TE462
7244M/*MK673*(TB382)
7246M/TD248
7256M/TB752
7257M/TB252
7279M/TB752
7281M/TB252
7288M/PK724
7293M/RW393
7323M/VV217
7325M/R5868
7326M/VN485
7362M/475081/(VP546)
7416M/WN907
7421M/WT660
7422M/WT684
7428M/WK198
7432M/WZ724
7438M/*18671*/(WP905)
7443M/WX853
7458M/WX905
7464M/XA564
7467M/WP978
7470M/XA553
7473M/XE946
7491M/WT569
7496M/WT612
7510M/WT694
7525M/WT619
7530M/WT648

7532M/WT651
7533M/WT680
7544M/WN904
7548M/PS915
7556M/WK584
7564M/XE982
7570M/XD674
7582M/WP190
7583M/WP185
7602M/WE600
7605M/WS692
7606M/WV562
7607M/TJ138
7615M/WV679
7616M/WW388
7618M/WW442
7622M/WV606
7631M/VX185
7641M/XA634
7645M/WD293
7646M/VX461
7648M/XF785
7659M/WH701
7673M/WV332
7688M/WW421
7693M/WV483
7694M/WV486
7696M/WV493
7698M/WV499
7704M/TW536
7705M/WL505
7706M/WB584
7709M/WT933
7711M/PS915
7712M/WK281
7715M/XK724
7716M/WS776
7718M/WA577
7719M/WK277
7729M/WB758
7734M/XD536
7737M/XD602
7741M/VZ477
7750M/*WK864*/(WL168)
7751M/WL131
7755M/WG760
7758M/PM651
7759M/PK664
7761M/XH318
7762M/XE670
7764M/XH318
7770M/*XF506*/(WT746)
7793M/XG523
7796M/WJ676
7798M/XH783
7806M/TA639
7809M/XA699
7816M/WG763
7817M/TX214
7825M/WK991
7827M/XA917
7829M/XH992
7839M/WV781
7841M/WV783
7851M/WZ706

7852M/XG506
7854M/XM191
7855M/XK416
7859M/XP283
7860M/XL738
7862M/XR246
7863M/*XP248*
7864M/XP244
7865M/TX226
7866M/XH278
7868M/WZ736
7869M/WK935
7872M/*WZ826*/(XD826)
7881M/WD413
7882M/XD525
7883M/XT150
7891M/XM693
7894M/XD818
7895M/WF784
7898M/XP854
7900M/WA576
7906M/WH132
7917M/WA591
7920M/WL360
7923M/XT133
7928M/XE849
7930M/WH301
7931M/RD253
7932M/WZ744
7933M/XR220
7937M/WS843
7938M/XH903
7939M/XD596
7940M/XL764
7955M/XH767
7957M/XF545
7959M/WS774
7960M/WS726
7961M/WS739
7964M/WS760
7965M/WS792
7967M/WS788
7970M/WP907
7971M/XK699
7973M/WS807
7976M/XK418
7979M/XM529
7980M/XM561
7982M/XH892
7983M/XD506
7984M/XN597
7986M/WG777
7988M/XL149
7990M/XD452
7997M/XG452
7998M/*XM515*/(XD515)
8005M/WG768
8009M/XG518
8010M/XG547
8012M/VS562
8017M/XL762
8018M/XN344
8019M/WZ869
8021M/XL824
8022M/XN341

8023M/XD463
8027M/XM5558032M/
    XH837
8033M/XD382
8034M/XL703
8041M/XF690
8043M/XF836
8046M/XL770
8049M/WE168
8050M/XG329
8052M/WH166
8054AM/XM410
8054BM/XM417
8055AM/XM402
8055BM/XM404
8056M/XG337
8057M/XR243
8063M/WT536
8070M/EP120
8072M/PK624
8073M/TB252
8078M/XM351
8079M/XN492
8080M/XM480
8081M/XM468
8082M/XM409
8086M/TB752
8092M/WK654
8094M/WT520
8101M/WH984
8102M/WT486
8103M/WR985
8106M/WR982
8108M/WV703
8113M/WV753
8114M/WL798
8117M/WR974
8118M/WZ549
8119M/WR971
8121M/XM474
8124M/WZ572
8128M/WH775
8131M/WT507
8140M/XJ571
8142M/XJ560
8147M/XR526
8151M/WV795
8153M/WV903
8154M/WV908
8155M/WV797
8156M/XE339
8158M/XE369
8159M/XD528
8160M/XD622
8161M/XE993
8162M/WM913
8163M/XP919
8164M/*WN105*/(WF299)
8165M/WH791
8169M/WH364
8173M/XN685
8176M/WH791
8177M/*WM311*/(WM224)
8179M/XN928
8183M/*XN972*/(XN962)

RAF Maintenance Cross-reference

8184M/WT520	8417M/XM144	8591M/XA813	8763M/WH665
8185M/WH946	8422M/XM169	8595M/XH278	8764M/XP344
8186M/WR977	8427M/XM172	8598M/WP270	8767M/XX635
8187M/WH791	8429M/XH592	8600M/XX761	8768M/A-522
8189M/*WD615* (WD646)	8434M/XM411	8602M/*PF179*/(XR541)	8769M/A-528
8190M/XJ918	8436M/XN554	8606M/XP530	8770M/XL623
8192M/XR658	8437M/WG362	8608M/XP540	8771M/XM602
8196M/XE920	8439M/WZ846	8610M/XL502	8772M/WR960
8198M/WT339	8440M/WD935	8611M/WF128	8777M/XX914
8203M/XD377	8442M/XP411	8618M/*XM693*/(XP504)	8778M/XM598
8205M/XN819	8453M/XP745	8620M/XP534	8779M/XM607
8206M/WG419	8457M/XS871	8621M/XR538	8780M/WK102
8207M/WD318	8458M/XP672	8624M/*XR991*/(XS102)	8781M/WE982
8208M/WG303	8459M/XR650	8627M/XP558	8782M/XH136
8209M/WG418	8460M/XP680	8628M/XJ380	8783M/XW272
8210M/WG471	8462M/XX477	8630M/WG362	8785M/XS642
8211M/WK570	8463M/XP355	8631M/XR574	8789M/XK970
8213M/WK626	8464M/XJ758	8633M/3W-17/MK732	8792M/XP345
8216M/WP927	8465M/W1048	8634M/WP314	8793M/XP346
8218M/WB645	8466M/L-866	8638M/XS101	8794M/XP398
8229M/XM355	8467M/WP912	8640M/XR977	8796M/XK943
8230M/XM362	8468M/MM5701/(BT474)	8642M/XR537	8797M/XX947
8231M/XM375	8470M/584219	8645M/XD163	8799M/WV787
8234M/XN458	8471M/701152	8648M/XK526	8800M/XG226
8235M/XN549	8472M/120227/(VN679)	8653M/XS120	8805M/XT772
8236M/XP573	8473M/WP190	8655M/XN126	8807M/XL587
8237M/XS179	8474M/494083	8656M/XP405	8810M/XJ825
8238M/XS180	8475M/360043/(PJ876)	8657M/VZ634	8814M/XM927
8344M/WH960	8476M/24	8661M/XJ727	8816M/XX734
8350M/WH840	8477M/4101/(DG200)	8662M/XR458	8818M/XK527
8352M/XN632	8478M/10639	8666M/XE793	8820M/VP952
8355M/*KG374*/(KN645)	8479M/730301	8668M/WJ821	8821M/XX115
8357M/WK576	8481M/191614	8671M/XJ435	8822M/VP957
8359M/WF825	8482M/112372/(VK893)	8672M/XP351	8828M/XS587
8361M/WB670	8483M/420430	8673M/XD165	8830M/XF515
8362M/WG477	8484M/5439	8676M/XL577	8831M/XG160
8364M/WG464	8485M/997	8679M/XF526	8832M/XG172
8365M/XK421	8486M/BAPC 99	8680M/XF527	8833M/XL569
8366M/XG454	8487M/J-1172	8681M/XG164	8834M/*XL571*
8367M/XG474	8488M/WL627	8682M/XP404	8836M/XL592
8368M/XF926	8491M/WJ880	8685M/XF516	8838M/*34037*/(429356)
8369M/WE139	8493M/XR571	8687M/XJ639	8839M/*69*/(XG194)
8370M/N1671	8494M/XP557	8693M/WH863	8840M/XG252
8371M/XA847	8495M/XR672	8696M/WH773	8841M/XE606
8372M/K8042	8501M/XP640	8700M/ZD234	8847M/XX344
8373M/P2617	8502M/XP686	8702M/XG196	8848M/XZ135
8375M/NX611	8507M/XS215	8703M/VW453	8851M/XT595
8376M/RF398	8508M/XS218	8706M/XF383	8852M/XV337
8377M/R9125	8509M/XT141	8708M/XF509	8853M/XT277
8378M/*T9707*	8514M/XS176	8709M/XG209	8855M/XT284
8379M/DG590	8535M/XN776	8710M/XG274	8857M/XW544
8380M/Z7197	8538M/XN781	8711M/XG290	8858M/XW541
8382M/VR930	8545M/XN726	8713M/XG225	8863M/XG154
8383M/K9942	8546M/XN728	8714M/XK149	8867M/XK532
8384M/X4590	8548M/WT507	8718M/XX396	8868M/WH775
8385M/N5912	8549M/WT534	8719M/XT257	8869M/WH957
8386M/NV778	8554M/TG511	8722M/WJ640	8870M/WH964
8387M/T6296	8561M/XS100	8724M/XW923	8871M/WJ565
8388M/XL993	8563M/*XX822*/(XW563)	8726M/XP299	8873M/XR453
8389M/VX573	8565M/*WT720*/(E-408)	8727M/XR486	8874M/XE597
8392M/SL674	8566M/XV279	8728M/WT532	8875M/XE624
8394M/WG422	8570M/XR954	8729M/WJ815	8876M/*VM791*/(XA312)
8395M/WF408	8573M/XM708	8733M/XL318	8879M/XX948
8396M/XK740	8575M/XP542	8736M/XF375	8880M/XF435
8399M/WR539	8576M/XP502	8739M/XH170	8881M/XG254
8401M/XP686	8578M/XR534	8740M/WE173	8883M/XX946
8406M/XP831	8582M/XE874	8741M/XW329	8884M/VX275
8407M/XP585	8583M/BAPC 94	8743M/WD790	8885M/XW922
8408M/XS186	8585M/XE670	8746M/XH171	8886M/XA243
8409M/XS209	8586M/XE643	8749M/XH537	8888M/XA231
8410M/XR662	8588M/XR681	8751M/XT255	8889M/XN239
8413M/XM192	8589M/XR700	8753M/WL795	8890M/WT532
8414M/XM173	8590M/XM191	8762M/WH740	8892M/XL618

8895M/XX746	9006M/XX967	9120M/XW419	9213M/N5182
8896M/XX821	9007M/XX968	9122M/XZ997	9215M/XL164
8897M/XX969	9008M/XX140	9123M/XT773	9216M/XL190
8898M/XX119	9009M/XX763	9124M/XW427	9217M/ZH257
8899M/XX756	9010M/XX764	9125M/XW410	9218M/XL563
8900M/XZ368	9011M/XM412	9126M/XW413	9219M/XZ971
8901M/XZ383	9012M/XN494	9127M/XW432	9220M/XZ995
8902M/XX739	9014M/XN584	9128M/XW292	9221M/XZ966
8903M/XX747	9015M/XW320	9129M/XW294	9222M/XZ968
8904M/XX966	9017M/ZE449	9130M/XW327	9224M/XL568
8905M/XX975	9018M/XW365	9131M/*DD931*	9225M/XX885
8906M/XX976	9019M/XX824	9132M/XX977	9226M/XV865
8907M/XZ371	9020M/XX825	9133M/*413573*	9227M/XB812
8908M/XZ382	9021M/XX826	9134M/XT288	9229M/ZA678
8909M/XV784	9022M/XX958	9136M/XT891	9230M/ZA676
8910M/XL160	9026M/XP629	9137M/XN579	9231M
8911M/XH673	9027M/XP556	9139M/XV863	9233M/XZ431
8917M/XM372	9028M/XP563	9140M/XZ287	9234M/XV864
8918M/XX109	9029M/XS217	9141M/XV118	9236M
8920M/XT469	9031M/XP688	9143M/XN589	9237M/XF445
8921M/XT466	9032M/XR673	9144M/XV353	9238M/ZA717
8922M/XT467	9033M/XS181	9145M/XV863	9239M/7198/18
8923M/XX819	9034M/XP638	9146M/XW299	9241M
8924M/XP701	9036M/XM350	9147M/XW301	9242M
8925M/XP706	9038M/XV810	9148M/XW436	9244M
8931M/XV779	9039M/XN586	9149M/XW375	9245M
8932M/XR718	9040M/XZ138	9150M/*FX760*	9246M/XS714
8934M/XR749	9041M/XW763	9151M/XT907	9247M/XV420
8935M/XR713	9042M/XL954	9152M/XV424	9248M/WB627
8937M/XX751	9044M/XS177	9153M/XW360	9249M/WV396
8938M/WV746	9045M/XN636	9154M/XW321	9250M/162068
8941M/XT456	9046M/XM349	9155M/WL679	9251M
8942M/XN185	9047M/XW409	9162M/XZ991	9252M
8943M/XE799	9048M/XM403	9163M/XV415	9253M/ZA254
8944M/WZ791	9049M/XW404	9165M/XV408	9254M
8945M/XX818	9050M/XG577	9166M/XW323	9255M/XZ375
8946M/XZ389	9052M/WJ717	9167M/XV744	9257M/XX962
8947M/XX726	9055M/XT770	9168M/XZ132	9258M
8948M/XX757	9056M/XS488	9169M/XW547	9259M/XS710
8949M/XX743	9059M/ZE360	9170M/XZ994	9260M/XS734
8950M/XX956	9060M/ZE356	9172M/XW304	9261M
8951M/XX727	9061M/XW335	9173M/XW418	9262M
8952M/XX730	9062M/XW351	9174M/XZ131	9263M
8953M/XX959	9066M/XV582	9175M/P1344	9264M
8954M/XZ384	9067M/XV586	9176M/XW430	9265M
8955M/XX110	9070M/XV581	9177M/XW328	9266M
8956M/XN577	9072M/XW768	9179M/XW309	9267M
8957M/XN582	9073M/XW924	9180M/XW311	9268M
8958M/XN501	9075M/XV753	9181M/XW358	9269M
8961M/XS925	9076M/XV808	9185M/XZ987	9270M
8967M/XV263	9078M/XV752	9187M/XW405	9272M/XS486
8969M/XR753	9079M/XZ130	9188M/XW364	9273M/XS726
8972M/XR754	9080M/ZE350	9189M/ZD350	9274M/XS738
8973M/XS922	9086M/ZE352	9190M/XW318	9275M/XS729
8974M/XM473	9087M/XX753	9191M/XW416	9276M/XS733
8975M/XW917	9090M/XW353	9192M/XW361	9277M/XT601
8976M/XZ630	9091M/XW434	9193M/XW367	9279M/XT681
8978M/XX837	9092M/XH669	9194M/XW420	9280M/XW804
8983M/XM478	9093M/WK124	9195M/XW330	9281M/XZ146
8984M/XN551	9095M/XW547	9196M/XW370	9282M/XZ101
8985M/WK127	9096M/WV322	9197M/*XX530*/(XX637)	9283M/XZ322
8986M/XV261	9097M/XW366	9198M/XS641	9284M/ZA267
8987M/XM358	9098M/XV406	9199M/XW290	9285M
8988M/XN593	9100M/XL188	9200M/XW425	9286M
8990M/XM419	9103M/XV411	9201M/ZD667	9287M
8995M/XM425	9109M/XW312	9203M/*3066*	9288M/XX520
8996M/XM414	9110M/XX736	9205M/*E449*	9289M
8997M/XX669	9111M/XW421	9206M/F6314	9290M/XX626
8998M/XT864	9113M/*XV498*	9207M/8417/18	9291M/XX686
9002M/XW763	9115M/XV863	9208M/F938	9292M/
9003M/XZ390	9117M/XV161	9210M/MF628	9293M/
9004M/XZ370	9118M/XV253	9211M/733682	9294M/
9005M/XZ374	9119M/XW303	9212M/*KL216*/(45-49295)	9295M/

RAF Maintenance Cross-reference

9296M/	9308M	9320M	9332M
9297M/	9309M	9321M	9333M
9298M/ZE340	9310M	9322M	9334M/ZA322
9299M	9311M	9323M	9335M/ZA375
9300M	9312M	9324M	9336M/ZA407
9301M	9313M	9325M	9337M
9302M	9314M	9326M	9338M
9303M	9315M	9327M	9339M
9304M	9316M	9328M	9340M
9305M	9317M	9329M	
9306M/XX979	9318M	9330M	
9307M	9319M	9331M	

A trio of Eurofighter Typhoons - all black ZH588 (DA2), two-seat ZH590 (DA4) along with EADS Manching's 98+29. *BAE Systems*

RAF Lyneham Transport Wing's C-130J-30 Hercules C4 ZH869. *PRM*

RN Landing Platform and Shore Station Code-letters

Code	Deck Letters	Vessel Name & Pennant No	Vessel Type & Unit
—	AS	RFA *Argus* (A135)	Aviation Training ship
365/6	AY	HMS *Argyll* (F231)	Type 23 (815 Sqn)
—	BD	RFA *Sir Bedivere* (L3004)	Landing ship
—	BV	RFA *Black Rover* (A273)	Fleet tanker
335	CF	HMS *Cardiff* (D108)	Type 42 (815 Sqn)
350/1	CL	HMS *Cumberland* (F85)	Type 22 (815 Sqn)
-	CM	HMS *Chatham* (F87)	Type 22
388	CT	HMS *Campbeltown* (F86)	Type 22 (815 Sqn)
—	CU	RNAS Culdrose (HMS *Seahawk*)	
336/7	CV	HMS *Coventry* (F98)	Type 22 (815 Sqn)
412/3	CW	HMS *Cornwall* (F99)	Type 22 (815 Sqn)
—	DC	HMS *Dumbarton Castle* (P265)	Fishery protection
—	DG	RFA *Diligence* (A132)	Maintenance
411	EB	HMS *Edinburgh* (D97)	Type 42 (815 Sqn)
434/5	EE	HMS *Endurance* (A171)	Ice Patrol (815 Sqn)
420	EX	HMS *Exeter* (D89)	Type 42 (815 Sqn)
—	FA	RFA *Fort Austin* (A386)	Support ship
—	FR	RFA *Fort Rosalie* (A385)	Support ship
—	FL	RNAY Fleetlands	
410	GC	HMS *Gloucester* (D96)	Type 42 (815 Sqn)
—	GD	RFA *Sir Galahad* (L3005)	Landing ship
—	GR	RFA *Sir Geraint* (L3027)	Landing ship
437	GT	HMS *Grafton* (F80)	Type 23 (815 Sqn)
—	GV	RFA *Gold Rover* (A271)	Fleet tanker
344	GW	HMS *Glasgow* (D88)	Type 42 (815 Sqn)
—	GY	RFA *Grey Rover* (A269)	Fleet tanker
—	HR	HMS *Herald* (H138)	Survey ship
—	ID	HMS *Intrepid* (L11)	Assault
404	IR	HMS *Iron Duke* (F234)	Type 23 (815 Sqn)
425	KT	HMS *Kent* (F78)	Type 23 (815 Sqn)
—	L	HMS *Illustrious* (R06)	Carrier
457	LA	HMS *Lancaster* (F229)	Type 23 (815 Sqn)
—	LC	HMS *Leeds Castle* (P258)	Fishery protection
332	LP	HMS *Liverpool* (D92)	Type 42 (815 Sqn)
363/4	MA	HMS *Marlborough* (F233)	Type 23 (815 Sqn)
360	MC	HMS *Manchester* (D95)	Type 42 (815 Sqn)
415	MM	HMS *Monmouth* (F235)	Type 23 (824 Sqn)
444	MR	HMS *Montrose* (F236)	Type 23 (815 Sqn)
—	N	HMS *Invincible* (R05)	Carrier
345	NC	HMS *Newcastle* (D87)	Type 42 (815 Sqn)
361/2	NF	HMS *Norfolk* (F230)	Type 23 (815 Sqn)
372	NL	HMS *Northumberland* (F238)	Type 23 (815 Sqn)
417	NM	HMS *Nottingham* (D91)	Type 42 (815 Sqn)
—	O	HMS *Ocean* (L12)	Helicopter carrier
—	ON	RFA *Olna* (A123)	Fleet tanker
—	OW	RFA *Olwen* (A122)	Fleet tanker
426	PD	HMS *Portland* (F79)	Type 23 (815 Sqn)
—	PV	RFA *Sir Percivale* (L3036)	Landing ship
—	R	HMS *Ark Royal* (R07)	Carrier
474	RM	HMS *Richmond* (F239)	Type 23 (815 Sqn)
355	SM	HMS *Somerset* (F82)	Type 23 (815 Sqn)
334	SN	HMS *Southampton* (D90)	Type 42 (815 Sqn)
422	SU	HMS *Sutherland* (F81)	Type 23 (815 Sqn)
—	TM	RFA *Sir Tristram* (L3055)	Landing ship
—	VL	RNAS Yeovilton (HMS *Heron*)	
462	WM	HMS *Westminster* (F237)	Type 23 (815 Sqn)
407	YK	HMS *York* (D98)	Type 42 (815 Sqn)
—	—	HMS *Albion* (L14)	Assault
—	—	HMS *Bulwark* (L15)	Assault
—	—	HMS *Daring* (D32)	Type 45

RN Landing Platforms

Code	Deck Letters	Vessel Name & Pennant No	Vessel Type & Unit
—	—	HMS *Dauntless* (D33)	Type 45
—	—	RFA *Fort Victoria* (A387)	Auxiliary Oiler
—	—	RFA *Fort George* (A388)	Auxiliary Oiler
—	—	HMS *St Albans* (F83)	Type 23
—	—	RFA *Wave Knight* (A389)	Auxiliary Oiler
—	—	RFA *Wave Ruler* (A390)	Fleet tanker

Civil-registered Grob Heron G-BVHE is flown from Plymouth by 727 Naval Air Squadron. *PRM*

The Joint Elementary Flying School at RAF Barkston Heath uses this civil-registered Firefly 260 G-BWXS. *PRM*

Ships' Numeric Code – Deck Letters Analysis

	0	1	2	3	4	5	6	7	8	9
33			LP		SN	CF				
34					GW	NC			CM	
35	CL	CL				SM				
36	MC	NF	NF	MA	MA	AY	AY			
37			NL							
38									CT	
40					IR			YK		
41	GC	EB	CW	CW		MM		NM		
42	EX		SU							
43					EE	EE		GT		
44					MR					
45								LA		
46			WM							
47					RM					

RN Code – Squadron – Base – Aircraft Cross-check

Deck/Base Code Numbers	Letters	Unit	Location	Aircraft Type(s)
000 — 006	L	801 Sqn	Yeovilton	Sea Harrier FA2
010 — 020	L	820 Sqn	Culdrose	Sea King HAS6
122 — 129	R	800 Sqn	Yeovilton	Sea Harrier FA2
180 — 182	CU	849 Sqn HQ Flt	Culdrose	Sea King AEW2
183 — 185	L	849 Sqn B Flt	Culdrose	Sea King AEW2
186 — 188	R	849 Sqn A Flt	Culdrose	Sea King AEW2
264 — 274	R	814 Sqn	Culdrose	Merlin HM1
300 — 308	PO	815 Sqn	Yeovilton	Lynx HAS3/HMA8
318 — 319	PO	815 Sqn OEU	Yeovilton	Lynx HMA8
332 — 479	*	815 Sqn	Yeovilton	Lynx HAS3/HMA8
535 — 541	CU	700M OEU	Culdrose	Merlin HM1
560 — 573	CU	750 Sqn	Culdrose	Jetstream T2
576 — 579	-	FONA	Yeovilton	Jetstream T3
580 — 585	CU	824 Sqn	Culdrose	Merlin HM1
630 — 648	PO	702 Sqn	Yeovilton	Lynx HAS3
670 — 676	PO	702 Sqn	Yeovilton	Lynx HMA8
710 — 719	VL	899 Sqn	Yeovilton	Sea Harrier FA2
720 — 724	VL	899 Sqn	Yeovilton	Harrier T8
730 — 731	VL	899 Sqn	Yeovilton	Sea Harrier FA2
820 — 827	CU	771 Sqn	Culdrose	Sea King HU5

*See foregoing separate ships' Deck Letter Analysis.
Note that only the 'last two' digits of the Code are worn by some aircraft types, especially helicopters.

Royal Air Force Squadron Markings

This table gives brief details of the markings worn by aircraft of RAF squadrons. While this may help to identify the operator of a particular machine, it may not always give the true picture. For example, from time to time aircraft are loaned to other units while others (such as those with No 4 FTS at Valley) wear squadron marks but are actually operated on a pool basis. Squadron badges are usually located on the front fuselage.

Squadron	Type(s) operated	Base(s)	Distinguishing marks & other comments
No 1 Sqn	Harrier GR7/T10	RAF Cottesmore	Badge: A red & white winged number 1 No 1 Sqn Harrier GR7/T10 RAF Cottesmore Badge: A red & white winged number 1 on a white diamond. Tail fin has a red stripe with the badge repeated on it.
No 2 Sqn	Tornado GR4A	RAF Marham	Badge: A wake knot on a white circular background flanked on either side by black and white triangles. Tail fin has a black stripe with white triangles and the badge repeated on it. Codes are single letters inside a white triangle on the tail.
No 3 Sqn	Harrier GR7/T10	RAF Cottesmore	Badge: A blue cockatrice on a white circular background flanked by two green bars edged with yellow. Tail fin has a green stripe edged with yellow.
No 4 Sqn	Harrier GR7/T10	RAF Cottesmore	Badge: A yellow lightning flash inside a red and black circle flanked by bars on either side repeating this design. Tail fin has a yellow lightning flash on a red and black stripe.
No 6 Sqn	Jaguar GR1A/GR3/T2A	RAF Coltishall	Badge: A red winged can opener inside a circle edged in red. Tail has a light blue bar with red diagonal lines. Aircraft are coded E*.
No 7 Sqn	Chinook HC2/ Gazelle HT3	RAF Odiham	Badge (on tail): A blue badge containing the seven stars of Ursa Major ('The Plough') in yellow. Aircraft are coded E*. Aircraft pooled with No 18 Sqn and No 27 Sqn.
No 8 Sqn	Sentry AEW1	RAF Waddington	Badge (on tail): A grey, sheathed, Arabian dagger. Aircraft pooled with No 23 Sqn.
No 9 Sqn	Tornado GR4	RAF Marham	Badge: A green bat on a black circular background, flanked by yellow and green horizontal stripes. The green bat also appears on the tail, edged in yellow. Aircraft are coded A*.
No 10 Sqn	VC10 C1K	RAF Brize Norton	Badge (on tail): A yellow arrow with red wings.
No 11 Sqn	Tornado F3	RAF Leeming	Roundel is superimposed over a yellow diamond on a black background. Badge (on tail): Two black eagles in flight. Aircraft are coded D*.
No 12 Sqn	Tornado GR4	RAF Lossiemouth	Roundel is superimposed on a green chevron. Tail fin has a black & white horizontal stripe with the squadron badge, a fox's head on a white circle, in the middle. Aircraft are coded F*.

Squadron	Type(s) operated	Base(s)	Distinguishing marks & other comments
No 13 Sqn	Tornado GR4/GR4A	RAF Marham	A yellow lightning flash on a green and blue background on the nose. Badge (on tail): A lynx's head over a dagger on a white shield.
No 14 Sqn	Tornado GR4	RAF Lossiemouth	Badge: A red cross on a white circle, with wings either side, flanked by blue diamonds on a white background. The blue diamonds are repeated horizontally across the tail. Aircraft are coded B*.
No 15(R) Sqn	Tornado GR4	RAF Lossiemouth	Roman numerals XV appear in white on the tail. Aircraft are either coded T* or TA*.
No 16(R) Sqn	Jaguar GR3/T2A/T4	RAF Coltishall	Badge: Two keys crossed on a black circle. On the tail is a black circle containing the 'Saint' emblem from the 60's TV series.
No 18 Sqn	Chinook HC2	RAF Odiham	Badge (on tail): A red winged horse on a black circle. Aircraft are coded B*. Aircraft pooled with No 7 Sqn and No 27 Sqn.
No 19(R) Sqn	Hawk T1/T1A/T1W	RAF Valley	Badge (on tail): A fish flanked by two wings on a yellow circle. Aircraft also carry black and white checks either side of the roundel on the fuselage. Aircraft pooled with No 208(R) Sqn; part of No 4 FTS.
No 20(R) Sqn [HOCU]	Harrier GR7/T10	RAF Wittering	Badge: An eagle in a white circle flanked by a white stripe on a blue background. On the tail is a stripe made up of black, yellow, green and red triangles.
No 22 Sqn	Sea King HAR3/HAR3A	A Flt: RMB Chivenor B Flt: Wattisham C Flt: RAF Valley	Badge: A black pi symbol in front of a white Maltese cross on a red circle.
No 23 Sqn	Sentry AEW1	RAF Waddington	Badge (on tail): A red eagle preying on a yellow falcon. Aircraft pooled with No 8 Sqn.
No 24 Sqn	Hercules C1/C3/C4/C5	RAF Lyneham	No squadron markings carried. Aircraft pooled with No 30 Sqn, No 47 Sqn, No 57(R) Sqn and No 70 Sqn.
No 25 Sqn	Tornado F3	RAF Leeming	Badge (on tail): A hawk on a gauntlet. Aircraft are coded F*.
No 27 Sqn	Chinook HC2	RAF Odiham	Badge (on tail): An dark green elephant on a green circle, flanked by green and dark green stripes. Aircraft pooled with No 7 Sqn and No 18 Sqn.
No 28 Sqn	Merlin HC3	RAF Benson	Badge: A winged horse above white two crosses on a red shield.
No 30 Sqn	Hercules C1/C3	RAF Lyneham	No squadron markings carried. Aircraft pooled with No 24 Sqn, No 47 Sqn, No 57(R) Sqn and No 70 Sqn.
No 31 Sqn	Tornado GR4	RAF Marham	Badge: A gold, five-pointed star on a yellow circle flanked by yellow and green checks. The star is repeated on the tail. Aircraft are coded D*.

RAF Squadron Markings

Squadron	Type(s) operated	Base(s)	Distinguishing marks & other comments
No 32 (The Royal) Sqn	125 CC3/146 CC2/ Twin Squirrel HCC1	RAF Northolt	No squadron markings carried but aircraft carry a distinctive livery with a blue flash along the middle of the fuselage and a red tail.
No 33 Sqn	Puma HC1	RAF Benson	Badge: A stag's head.
No 39 (1 PRU) Sqn	Canberra PR9/T4	RAF Marham	Badge (on tail): A winged bomb on a light blue circle. Aircraft are coded A*.
No 41 Sqn	Jaguar GR3/T4	RAF Coltishall	Badge: A red, double armed cross, flanked by red and white horizontal stipes. Stripes repeated on tail. Aircraft are coded F*.
No 42(R) Sqn	Nimrod MR2	RAF Kinloss	No squadron markings usually carried. Aircraft pooled with No 120 Sqn, No 201 Sqn and No 206 Sqn.
No 43 Sqn	Tornado F3	RAF Leuchars	Badge (on tail): A black and red gamecock flanked by a stripe of black and white checks. Aircraft are usually coded G*.
No 45(R) Sqn	Jetstream T1	RAF Cranwell	No squadron markings usually carried. Part of No 3 FTS.
No 47 Sqn	Hercules C1/C3	RAF Lyneham	No squadron markings usually carried. Aircraft pooled with No 24 Sqn, 30 Sqn, No 57(R) Sqn and No 70 Sqn.
No 51 Sqn	Nimrod R1	RAF Waddington	Badge (on tail): A red goose in flight.
No 54 Sqn	Jaguar GR3/GR3A/T2/T4	RAF Coltishall	Badge (on tail): A blue lion on a yellow shield, flanked by blue and yellow checks. A stripe of blue and yellow checks also appears on the tail. Aircraft are coded G*.
No 55(R) Sqn	Dominie T1	RAF Cranwell	Badge (on tail): A blue fist holding an arrow on a white circle.
No 56(R) Sqn [F3OCU]	Tornado F3	RAF Coningsby Moving to RAF Leuchars	Badge (on tail): A gold phoenix rising from red flames. The tail fin has a stripe made up of red and white checks. Aircraft are usually coded A*.
No 60(R) Sqn	Griffin HT1	RAF Shawbury [DHFS]	No squadron markings usually carried. & RAF Valley [SARTU]
No 70 Sqn	Hercules C1/C3/C4/C5	RAF Lyneham	No squadron markings usually carried. Aircraft pooled with No 24 Sqn, No 30 Sqn, No 47 Sqn and No 57(R) Sqn.
No 78 Sqn	Chinook HC2/ Sea King HAR3	RAF Mount Pleasant	Badge: A yellow, heraldic tiger with two tails, on a black circle. The badge appears on the tail of the Chinook and by the cockpit on the Sea King.
No 84 Sqn	Griffin HAR2	RAF Akrotiri	Badge: A black scorpion. Each aircraft has a different playing card symbol (diamonds, clubs etc). A vertical blue stripe (UN) through the roundel on the fuselage.
No 99 Sqn	Globemaster III	RAF Brize Norton	Badge (on tail): A black puma leaping.
No 100 Sqn	Hawk T1/T1A	RAF Leeming	Badge (on tail): A skull in front of two bones crossed. Aircraft are usually coded C*.

Squadron	Type(s) operated	Base(s)	Distinguishing marks & other comments
No 101 Sqn	VC10 K3/K4	RAF Brize Norton	Badge (on tail): A lion behind a castle turret.
No 111 Sqn	Tornado F3	RAF Leuchars	Badge (on tail): A cross in front of crossed swords on a light grey circle, flanked by a stripe of darker grey.
No 120 Sqn	Nimrod MR2	RAF Kinloss	No squadron markings usually carried. Aircraft pooled with No 42(R) Sqn, No 201 Sqn and No 206 Sqn.
No 201 Sqn	Nimrod MR2	RAF Kinloss	No squadron markings usually carried. Aircraft pooled with No 42(R) Sqn, No 120 Sqn and No 206 Sqn.
No 202 Sqn	Sea King HAR3	A Flt: RAF Boulmer D Flt: RAF Lossiemouth E Flt: RAF Leconfield	Badge: A mallard alighting on a white circle.
No 203(R) Sqn	Sea King HAR3	RAF St Mawgan RAF Akrotiri (Jan-April 03)	Badge: A green sea horse on a white circle.
No 206 Sqn	Nimrod MR2	RAF Kinloss	No squadron markings usually carried. Aircraft pooled with No 42(R) Sqn, No 120 Sqn and No 201 Sqn.
No 208(R) Sqn	Hawk T1/T1A/T1W	RAF Valley	Badge (on tail): A Sphinx inside a white circle, flanked by flashes of yellow. Aircraft also carry blue and yellow bars either side of the roundel on the fuselage and a blue and yellow chevron on the nose. Aircraft pooled with No 19(R) Sqn; part of No 4 FTS.
No 216 Sqn	TriStar K1/KC1/C2/C2A	RAF Brize Norton	Badge (on tail): An eagle in flight with a bomb in its claws.
No 230 Sqn	Puma HC1	RAF Aldergrove	Badge: A tiger in front of a palm tree on a black pentagon.
No 617 Sqn	Tornado GR4	RAF Lossiemouth	Badge: Dam breached, flanked on either side by red lightning flashes on a black background. Tail fin is black with a red lightning flash. Aircraft are coded AJ-*.
No 1435 Flt	Tornado F3	RAF Mount Pleasant	Badge (on tail): A red Maltese cross on a white circle, flanked by red and white horizontal bars.

University Air Squadrons/ Air Experience Flights

Now that the conversion to the Tutor has taken place, UAS aircraft have begun to carry squadron badges and markings, usually on the tail. Squadron crests all consist of a white circle surrounded by a blue circle, topped with a red crown and having a yellow scroll beneath. Each differs by the motto on the scroll, the UAS name running around the blue circle & by the contents at the centre and it is the latter which are described below. From April 1996 all AEFs have come under the administration of local UASs and these are listed here.

UAS	Base(s)	Marks
Aberdeen, Dundee & St Andrews UAS	RAF Leuchars	A red lion holding a stone turret between its paws above a crown.
University of Birmingham AS/ No 8 AEF	RAF Cosford	A blue griffon with two heads.
Bristol UAS/ No 3 AEF		RAF Colerne A sailing ship on water.
Cambridge UAS/ No 5 AEF		RAF Wyton A heraldic lion in front of a red badge.
East Lowlands UAS/ No 12 AEF	RAF Leuchars	An open book in front of a white diagonal cross edged in blue.
East Midlands Universities AS/ No 7 AEF	RAF Cranwell	A yellow quiver, full of arrows.
Universities of Glasgow and Strathclyde AS/ No 4 AEF	Glasgow	A bird of prey in flight, holding a branch in its beak, in front of an upright sword.
Liverpool UAS	RAF Woodvale	A bird atop an open book, holding a branch in its beak.
University of London AS/ No 6 AEF	RAF Wyton	A globe superimposed over an open book.
Manchester and Salford Universities AS/No 10 AEF	RAF Woodvale	A bird of prey with a green snake in its beak.
Northumbrian Universities AS/ No 11 AEF	RAF Leeming	A white cross on a blue background.
Oxford UAS	RAF Benson	An open book in front of crossed swords.
Southampton UAS/ No 2 AEF	Boscombe Down	A red stag in front of a stone pillar.
University of Wales AS/ No 1 AEF	DARA St Athan	A red Welsh dragon in front of an open book, clasping a sword. Some aircraft have the dragon in front of white and green squares.
Yorkshire Universities AS/ No 9 AEF	RAF Church Fenton	An open book in front of a Yorkshire rose with leaves.

Historic Aircraft in Overseas Markings

Some *historic, classic and warbird* aircraft carry the markings of overseas air arms and can be seen in the UK, mainly preserved in museums and collections or taking part in air shows.

Notes	Serial	Type (other identity)	Owner/operator, location
ARGENTINA			
0729	Beech T-34C Turbo Mentor		FAA Museum, stored RNAS Yeovilton
0767	Aermacchi MB339AA		Rolls-Royce Heritage Trust, stored Derby
A-515	FMA IA58 Pucara (ZD485)		RAF Museum, Cosford
A-517	FMA IA58 Pucara (G-BLRP)		Privately owned, Channel Islands
A-522	FMA IA58 Pucara (8768M)		FAA Museum, at NE Aircraft Museum, Usworth
A-528	FMA IA58 Pucara (8769M)		Norfolk & Suffolk Avn Museum, Flixton
A-533	FMA IA58 Pucara (ZD486) <ff>		Boscombe Down Museum
A-549	FMA IA58 Pucara (ZD487)		Imperial War Museum, Duxford
AE-409	Bell UH-1H Iroquois [656]		Museum of Army Flying, Middle Wallop
AE-422	Bell UH-1H Iroquois		FAA Museum, stored RNAS Yeovilton
AUSTRALIA			
A2-4	Supermarine Seagull V (VH-ALB)		RAF Museum, Hendon
A16-199	Lockheed Hudson IIIA (G-BEOX) [SF-R]		RAF Museum, Hendon
A17-48	DH82A Tiger Moth (G-BPHR)		Privately owned, Swindon
A19-144	Bristol 156 Beaufighter XIc (JM135/A8-324)		The Fighter Collection, Duxford
A79-808	DH115 Vampire T33		De Havilland Aviation, Swansea
A92-480	GAF Jindivik 4A (A92-LLAN-1)		QinetiQ Llanbedr, on display
A92-664	GAF Jindivik 4A		Privately owned, Llanbedr
A92-708	GAF Jindivik 4A		Bristol Aero Collection, stored Kemble
N6-766	DH115 Sea Vampire T22 (XG766/G-SPDR)		De Havilland Aviation, Swansea
BELGIUM			
FT-36	Lockheed T-33A		Dumfries & Galloway Avn Mus, Dumfries
H-50	Noorduyn AT-16 Harvard IIB (OO-DAF)		Privately owned, Brasschaat, Belgium
HD-75	Hanriot HD1 (G-AFDX)		RAF Museum, Hendon
IF-68	Hawker Hunter F6 <ff>		Privately owned, Welshpool
K-16	Douglas C-53D Skytrooper (OT-CWG/N49G)		Air Dakota, Brussels, Belgium
L-44	Piper L-18C Super Cub (OO-SPQ)		BSD Aeroclub FBA, Bierset, Belgium
L-47	Piper L-18C Super Cub (OO-SPG)		BSD Aeroclub FBA, Bierset, Belgium
L-57	Piper L-18C Super Cub (OO-GDH)		BSD Aeroclub FBA, Bierset, Belgium
L-156	Piper L-18C Super Cub (OO-LGB)		BSD Aeroclub FBA, Bierset, Belgium
V-18	Stampe SV-4B (OO-GWD)		Antwerp Stampe Centre, Antwerp-Deurne, Belgium
V-29	Stampe SV-4B (OO-GWB)		Antwerp Stampe Centre, Antwerp-Deurne, Belgium
BOLIVIA			
FAB184	SIAI-Marchetti SF.260W (G-SIAI)		Privately owned, Booker
BOTSWANA			
OJ1	BAC Strikemaster 83 (ZG805/G-BXFU)		Global Aviation, Humberside
OJ4	BAC Strikemaster 87 (G-AYHR/G-UNNY) [Z2]		Privately owned, Duxford
BRAZIL			
1317	Embraer T-27 Tucano		Shorts, Belfast (engine test bed)
BURKINA FASO			
BF-8431	SIAI-Marchetti SF.260 (G-NRRA) [31]		Privately owned, Elstree
CANADA			
622	Piasecki HUP-3 Retriever (51-16622/N6699D)		The Helicopter Museum, Weston-super-Mare
920	VS Stranraer (CF-BXO) [Q-N]		RAF Museum, Hendon

Historic Aircraft

Notes	Serial	Type (other identity)	Owner/operator, location
	3349	NA64 Yale (G-BYNF)	Privately owned, Duxford
	5450	Hawker Hurricane XII (G-TDTW)	Hawker Restorations Ltd, Milden
	5487	Hawker Hurricane II (G-CBOE)	Privately owned, Thruxton
9754		Consolidated PBY-5A Catalina (VP-BPS) [P]	Privately owned, Lee-on-Solent
	9893	Bristol 149 Bolingbroke IVT	Imperial War Museum store, Duxford
	9940	Bristol 149 Bolingbroke IVT	Royal Scottish Mus'm of Flight, E Fortune
	15195	Fairchild PT-19A Cornell	RAF Museum Restoration Centre, Cosford
16693		Auster J/1N Alpha (G-BLPG) [693]	Privately owned, Headcorn
18013		DHC1 Chipmunk 22 (G-TRIC) [013]	The Shuttleworth Collection, Old Warden
	18393	Avro Canada CF-100 Canuck 4B (G-BCYK)	Imperial War Museum, Duxford
18671		DHC1 Chipmunk 22 (WP905/ 7438M/G-BNZC) [671]	Privately owned, Wombleton
20310		CCF T-6J Harvard IV (G-BSBG) [310]	Privately owned, Liverpool
21261		Lockheed T-33A-N Silver Star (G-TBRD)	Golden Apple Operations/OFMC, Duxford
	21417	Canadair CT-133 Silver Star	Yorkshire Air Museum, Elvington
	23140	Canadair CL-13 Sabre [AX] <rf>	Midland Air Museum, Coventry
	23380	Canadair CL-13 Sabre <rf>	RAF Millom Museum, Haverigg
FJ777		Boeing-Stearman PT-13D Kaydet (42-17786/G-BRTK)	Privately owned, Swanton Morley

CHILE

Notes	Serial	Type (other identity)	Owner/operator, location
	H-171	Enstrom 280FX	Privately owned, Shoreham
	H-172	Enstrom 280FX	Privately owned, Shoreham
	H-178	Enstrom 280FX	Privately owned, Shoreham

CHINA

Notes	Serial	Type (other identity)	Owner/operator, location
	2632016	Nanchang CJ-6A Chujiao (G-BXZB) (also wears *2632019*)	Privately owned, Hibaldstow
	2751219	Nanchang CJ-6A Chujiao (G-BVVG) [China 1219]	Privately owned, Breighton

CZECH REPUBLIC

Notes	Serial	Type (other identity)	Owner/operator, location
	3677	Letov S-102 (MiG-15) (613677)	Royal Scottish Mus'm of Flight, E Fortune
	3794	Letov S-102 (MiG-15) (623794)	Imperial War Museum, stored Duxford
	9147	Mil Mi-4	The Helicopter Museum, Weston-super-Mare

DENMARK

Notes	Serial	Type (other identity)	Owner/operator, location
	A-011	SAAB A-35XD Draken	Privately owned, Grainthorpe, Lincs
	AR-107	SAAB S-35XD Draken	Newark Air Museum, Winthorpe
	E-402	Hawker Hunter F51	Privately owned, Farnborough
	E-419	Hawker Hunter F51	North-East Aircraft Museum, Usworth
	E-420	Hawker Hunter F51 (G-9-442)	Privately owned, Walton-on-Thames
	E-421	Hawker Hunter F51	Brooklands Museum, Weybridge
	E-423	Hawker Hunter F51 (G-9-444)	SWWAPS, Lasham
	E-424	Hawker Hunter F51 (G-9-445)	Aeroventure, Doncaster
	ET-272	Hawker Hunter T7 <ff>	Boulton Paul Association, Wolverhampton
	ET-273	Hawker Hunter T7 <ff>	Aeroventure, Doncaster
	K-682	Douglas C-47A Skytrain (OY-BPB)	Foreningen For Flyvende Mus, Vaerløse, Denmark
	L-866	Consolidated PBY-6A Catalina (8466M)	RAF Museum, Cosford
	R-756	Lockheed F-104G Starfighter	Midland Air Museum, Coventry
	S-881	Sikorsky S-55C	The Helicopter Museum, Weston-super-Mare
	S-882	Sikorsky S-55C	Paintball Adventure West, Lulsgate
	S-887	Sikorsky S-55C	Privately owned, Marksbury, Somerset

EGYPT

Notes	Serial	Type (other identity)	Owner/operator, location
	0446	Mikoyan MiG-21UM <ff>	Thameside Aviation Museum, Tilbury
	7907	Sukhoi Su-7 <ff>	Robertsbridge Aviation Society, Mayfield

FINLAND

Notes	Serial	Type (other identity)	Owner/operator, location
	VI-3	Valtion Viima 2 (OO-EBL)	Privately owned, Brasschaat, Belgium

FRANCE

Notes	Serial	Type (other identity)	Owner/operator, location
	3	Mudry/CAARP CAP-10B (G-BXRA)	Privately owned, Sedlescombe, Sussex
06		Dewoitine D27 (290/F-AZJD)	The Old Flying Machine Company, Duxford

Serial	Type (other identity)	Owner/operator, location	Notes
20	MH1521C1 Broussard (G-BWGG) [315-SQ]	Privately owned, Rednal	
37	Nord 3400 (G-ZARA) [MAB]	Privately owned, Boston	
57	Dassault Mystère IVA [8-MT]	Imperial War Museum, Duxford	
67	SNCAN 1101 Noralpha (F-GMCY) [CY]	Privately owned, la Ferté-Alais, France	
68	Nord 3400 [MHA]	Privately owned,	
70	Dassault Mystère IVA	Midland Air Museum, Coventry	
78	Nord 3202 (G-BIZK)	Privately owned, Swanton Morley	
79	Dassault Mystère IVA [2-EG]	Norfolk & Suffolk Avn Museum, Flixton	
83	Dassault Mystère IVA [8-MS]	Newark Air Museum, Winthorpe	
84	Dassault Mystère IVA [8-NF]	Lashenden Air Warfare Museum, Headcorn	
85	Dassault Mystère IVA [8-MV]	British Aviation Heritage, Bruntingthorpe	
100	Mudry/CAARP CAP-10B (G-BXRB)	Privately owned, Sedlescombe, Sussex	
101	Dassault Mystère IVA [8-MN]	Bomber County Aviation Museum, Hemswell	
104	MH1521M Broussard (F-GHFG) [307-FG]	Privately owned, France	
105	Nord N2501F Noratlas (F-AZVM) [62-SI]	Le Noratlas de Provence, Bretigny, France	
120	SNCAN Stampe SV4C (G-AZGC)	Privately owned, Reading	
121	Dassault Mystère IVA	City of Norwich Aviation Museum	
134	Mudry/CAARP CAP-10B (G-BXRC)	Privately owned, Sedlescombe, Sussex	
135	Mudry/CAARP CAP-10B (G-BXFE)	Privately owned, Sedlescombe, Sussex	
143	Morane-Saulnier MS733 Alcyon (G-MSAL)	The Squadron, North Weald	
FR145	SO1221 Djinn [CDL]	Privately owned, Luton	
146	Dassault Mystère IVA [8-MC]	North-East Aircraft Museum, Usworth	
185	MH1521M Broussard (G-BWLR)	Privately owned, Longhope	
282	Dassault MD311 Flamant (F-AZFX) [316-KY]	Memorial Flt Association, la Ferté-Alais, France	
316	MH1521M Broussard (F-GGKR) [315-SN]	The Old Flying Machine Company, Duxford	
318	Dassault Mystère IVA [8-NY]	Dumfries & Galloway Avn Mus, Dumfries	
319	Dassault Mystère IVA [8-ND]	Rebel Air Museum, Andrewsfield	
396	Stampe SV4A (G-BWRE)	Privately owned, stored Sandown	
538	Dassault Mirage IIIE [3-QH]	Yorkshire Air Museum, Elvington	
1058	SO1221 Djinn (FR108) [CDL]	The Helicopter Museum, Weston-super-Mare	
1417	SA.341G Gazelle I (G-BXJK)	Privately owned, Stapleford Tawney	
17473	Lockheed T-33A	Midland Air Museum, Coventry	
42157	NA F-100D Super Sabre [11-ML]	North-East Aviation Museum, Usworth	
63938	NA F-100F Super Sabre [11-MU]	Lashenden Air Warfare Museum, Headcorn	
121748	Grumman F8F-2P Bearcat (F-AZRJ) [5834/P]	Privately owned, Anemasse, France	
125716	Douglas AD-4N Skyraider (F-AZFN) [22-DG]	Privately owned, Etampes, France	
126965	Douglas AD-4NA Skyraider (OO-FOR)	Privately owned, Braaschaat, Belgium	
133704	CV F4U-7 Corsair (125541/ F-AZYS)	Privately owned, Cuers, France	
517545	NA T-28S Fennec (N14113) [CD-113]	Privately owned, Duxford	
517692	NA T-28S Fennec (F-AZFV/ G-TROY) [142]	Privately owned, Duxford	
56-5395	Piper L-18C Super Cub (52-2436/ G-CUBJ) [CDG]	Privately owned, Breighton	
C850	Salmson 2A2 <R>	Barton Aviation Heritage Society, Barton	
MS824	Morane-Saulnier Type N <R> (G-AWBU)	Privately owned, Booker	
TE184	VS361 Spitfire LF XVIE (6850M/ G-MXVI) [D]	De Cadenet Motor Racing, Halton	

GERMANY

-	Fieseler Fi103R-IV (V-1)) (BAPC 91)	Lashenden Air Warfare Museum, Headcorn	
-	Focke-Achgelis Fa330A-1 (8469M)	RAF Museum, Cosford	

Historic Aircraft

Notes	Serial	Type (other identity)	Owner/operator, location
	-	Fokker Dr1 Dreidekker <R> (G-BVGZ)	Privately owned, Breighton
	-	Fokker Dr1 Dreidekker <R> (BAPC 88)	FAA Museum, RNAS Yeovilton
	3	SNCAN 1101 Noralpha (G-BAYV)	Barton Aviation Heritage Society, Barton
	6	Messerschmitt Bf109G-2/Trop (10639/8478M/G-USTV)	RAF Museum, Hendon
	8	Focke Wulf Fw190 <R> (G-WULF)	The Real Aeroplane Company, Breighton
	14	Messerschmitt Bf109 <R> (BAPC 67)	Kent Battle of Britain Museum, Hawkinge
	14	SNCAN 1101 Noralpha (G-BSMD)	Privately owned, North Weald
	152/17	Fokker Dr1 Dreidekker <R> (G-ATJM)	Privately owned, East Garston, Bucks
	210/16	Fokker EIII (BAPC 56)	Science Museum, South Kensington
	214	SPP Yak C-11 (G-DYAK)	Classic Aviation Company, Hannover, Germany
	422/15	Fokker EIII <R> (G-AVJO)	Privately owned, Booker
	425/17	Fokker Dr1 Dreidekker <R> (BAPC 133)	Kent Battle of Britain Museum, Hawkinge
	626/8	Fokker DVII <R> (N6268)	Blue Max Movie Aircraft Museum, Booker
	764	Mikoyan MiG-21SPS <ff>	Privately owned, Booker
	959	Mikoyan MiG-21SPS	Midland Air Museum, Coventry
	1190	Messerschmitt Bf109E-3 [4]	Imperial War Museum, Duxford
	1480	Messerschmitt Bf109 <R> (BAPC 66) [6]	Kent Battle of Britain Museum, Hawkinge
	2100	Focke-Wulf Fw189A-1 (G-BZKY) [V7+1H]	Privately owned, W Sussex
	4101	Messerschmitt Bf109E-3 (DG200/8477M) [12]	RAF Museum, Hendon
	6357	Messerschmitt Bf109 <R> (BAPC 74) [6]	Kent Battle of Britain Museum, Hawkinge
	7198/18	LVG CVI (G-AANJ/9239M)	The Shuttleworth Collection, Old Warden
	7485	Messerschmitt Bf109F-4	Charleston Aviation Services, Colchester
	8147	Messerschmitt Bf109F-4	Charleston Aviation Services, Colchester
	8417/18	Fokker DVII (9207M)	RAF Museum, Hendon
	12802	Antonov An-2T (D-FOFM)	Privately owned, Lahr, Germany
	15458	Messerschmitt Bf109F-4	Charleston Aviation Services, Colchester
	100143	Focke-Achgelis Fa330A-1	Imperial War Museum, Duxford
	100502	Focke-Achgelis Fa330A-1	The Real Aeroplane Company, Breighton
	100509	Focke-Achgelis Fa330A-1	Science Museum, stored Wroughton
	100545	Focke-Achgelis Fa330A-1	Fleet Air Arm Museum, stored RNAS Yeovilton
	100549	Focke-Achgelis Fa330A-1	Lashenden Air Warfare Museum, Headcorn
	112372	Messerschmitt Me262A-2a (AM.51/VK893/8482M) [9K+XK]	RAF Museum, Cosford
	120227	Heinkel He162A-2 Salamander (VN679/AM.65/8472M) [2]	RAF Museum, Hendon
	120235	Heinkel He162A-1 Salamander (AM.68)	Imperial War Museum, Lambeth
	191316	Messerschmitt Me163B Komet	Science Museum, South Kensington
	191454	Messerschmitt Me163B Komet <R> (BAPC 271)	The Shuttleworth Collection, Old Warden
	191614	Messerschmitt Me163B Komet (8481M)	RAF Museum Restoration Centre, Cosford
	191659	Messerschmitt Me163B Komet (8480M) [15]	Royal Scottish Mus'm of Flight, E Fortune
	191660	Messerschmitt Me163B Komet (AM.214) [3]	Imperial War Museum, Duxford
	280020	Flettner Fl282/B-V20 Kolibri (frame only)	Midland Air Museum, Coventry
	360043	Junkers Ju88R-1 (PJ876/8475M) [D5+EV]	RAF Museum, Hendon
	420430	Messerschmitt Me410A-1/U2 (AM.72/8483M) [3U+CC]	RAF Museum, Cosford
	475081	Fieseler Fi156C-7 Storch (VP546/AM.101/7362M)[GM+AK]	RAF Museum, Cosford
	494083	Junkers Ju87D-3 (8474M) [RI+JK]	RAF Museum, Hendon
	584219	Focke Wulf Fw190F-8/U1 (AM.29/8470M) [38]	RAF Museum, Hendon
	701152	Heinkel He111H-23 (8471M) [NT+SL]	RAF Museum, Hendon

Serial	Type (other identity)	Owner/operator, location	Notes
730301	Messerschmitt Bf110G-4 (AM.34/ 8479M) [D5+RL]	RAF Museum, Hendon	
733682	Focke Wulf Fw190A-8/R7 (AM.75/ 9211M)	Imperial War Museum, Lambeth	
2+1	Focke Wulf Fw190 <R> (G-SYFW) [7334]	Privately owned, Guernsey, CI	
2E+RA	Fieseler Fi-156C-2 Storch (NX436FS)	Privately owned, North Weald	
4+1	Focke Wulf Fw190 <R> (G-BSLX)	Privately owned, Riseley	
4V+GH	Amiot AAC1/Ju52 (Port.AF 6316) [9]	Imperial War Museum, Duxford	
22+35	Lockheed F-104G Starfighter	SWWAPS, Lasham	
22+57	Lockheed F-104G Starfighter	Privately owned, Grainthorpe, Lincs	
58+89	Dornier Do28D-2 Skyservant (D-ICDY)	Moosreiner Consulting, Hamburg, Germany	
96+21	Mil Mi-24D (406)	Imperial War Museum, Duxford	
96+26	Mil Mi-24D (429)	The Helicopter Museum, Weston-super-Mare	
97+04	Putzer Elster B (G-APVF)	Privately owned, Breighton	
98+14	Sukhoi Su-22M-4	The Old Flying Machine Company, stored Scampton	
99+24	NA OV-10B Bronco (F-AZKM)	Privately owned, Montelimar, France	
99+26	NA OV-10B Bronco (G-BZGL)	Privately owned, Duxford	
99+32	NA OV-10B Bronco (G-BZGK)	Privately owned, Duxford	
BU+CC	CASA 1.131E Jungmann (G-BUCC)	Privately owned, Goodwood	
BU+CK	CASA 1.131E Jungmann (G-BUCK)	Privately owned, White Waltham	
CC+43	Pilatus P-2 (G-CJCI)	Privately owned, Norwich	
CF+HF	Morane-Saulnier MS502 (EI-AUY)	Imperial War Museum, Duxford	
CW+BG	CASA 1.131E Jungmann (G-BXBD) [483]	Privately owned, Kemble	
D5397/17	Albatros DVA <R> (G-BFXL)	FAA Museum, RNAS Yeovilton	
ES+BH	Messerschmitt Bf108B-2 (D-ESBH)	Messerschmitt Stiftung, Germany	
FI+S	Morane-Saulnier MS505 (G-BIRW)	Royal Scottish Mus'm of Flight, E Fortune	
FM+BB	Messerschmitt Bf109G-6 (D-FMBB)	Messerschmitt Stiftung, Germany	
JA+120	Canadair CL-13 Sabre 4 (MM19607)	Privately owned	
KG+EM	Nord 1002 (G-ETME)	Privately owned, Booker	
LG+01	Bücker Bü133C Jungmeister (G-AYSJ)	The Fighter Collection, Duxford	
LG+03	Bücker Bü133C Jungmeister (G-AEZX)	Privately owned, Milden	
NJ+C11	Nord 1002 (G-ATBG)	Privately owned, Sutton Bridge	
S4+A07	CASA 1.131E Jungmann (G-BWHP)	Privately owned, Yarcombe, Devon	
S5+B06	CASA 1.131E Jungmann 2000 (G-BSFB)	Privately owned, Stretton, Cheshire	
TA+RC	Morane-Saulnier MS505 (G-BPHZ)	Historic Aircraft Coll, Duxford	

GHANA

G-102	SA122 Bulldog	Privately owned, Hurstbourne Tarrant	
G-108	SA122 Bulldog (G-BCUP)	Privately owned, Hurstbourne Tarrant	

GREECE

51-6171	NA F-86D Sabre	North-East Aircraft Museum, Usworth	
52-6541	Republic F-84F Thunderflash [541]	North-East Aircraft Museum, Usworth	

HONG KONG

HKG-5	SA128 Bulldog (G-BULL)	Privately owned, Slinfold	
HKG-6	SA128 Bulldog (G-BPCL)	Privately owned, Elstree	
HKG-11	Slingsby T.67M Firefly 200 (G-BYRY)	Privately owned, Tibenham	
HKG-13	Slingsby T.67M Firefly 200 (G-BXKW)	Privately owned, Tibenham	

HUNGARY

501	Mikoyan MiG-21PF	Imperial War Museum, Duxford	

INDIA

Q497	EE Canberra T4 (WE191) (fuselage)	Dumfries & Galloway Avn Mus, Dumfries	

Historic Aircraft

Notes	Serial	Type (other identity)	Owner/operator, location
	INDONESIA		
	LL-5313	BAe Hawk T53	FR Aviation, stored Bournemouth
	IRAQ		
	333	DH115 Vampire T55 <ff>	Military Aircraft Pres'n Grp, Barton
	ITALY		
	MM5701	Fiat CR42 (BT474/8468M) [13-95]	RAF Museum, Hendon
	MM52801	Fiat G46-3B (G-BBII) [4-97]	Privately owned, Duxford
	MM53692	CCF T-6G Texan	RAeS Medway Branch, Rochester
	MM53774	Fiat G59-4B (I-MRSV) [181]	Privately owned, Parma, Italy
	MM54099	NA T-6G Texan (G-BRBC) [RR-56]	Privately owned, Chigwell
	MM54-2372	Piper L-21B Super Cub	Privately owned, Kesgrave, Suffolk
	W7	Avia FL3 (G-AGFT)	Privately owned, Leicester
	JAPAN		
	-	Yokosuka MXY 7 Ohka II (BAPC 159)	Defence School, Chattenden
	24	Kawasaki Ki100-1B (8476M/ BAPC 83)	RAF Museum, Cosford
	3685	Mitsubishi A6M3-2 Zero	Imperial War Museum, Duxford
	5439	Mitsubishi Ki46-III (8484M/ BAPC 84)	RAF Museum, Cosford
	15-1585	Yokosuka MXY 7 Ohka II (BAPC 58)	Science Museum, at FAA Museum, RNAS Yeovilton
	997	Yokosuka MXY 7 Ohka II (8485M/ BAPC 98)	Gr Manchester Mus of Science & Industry
	I-13	Yokosuka MXY 7 Ohka II (8486M/ BAPC 99)	RAF Museum, Cosford
	MYANMAR		
	UB424	VS361 Spitfire IX (UB425)	Historic Flying Ltd, Duxford
	UB441	VS361 Spitfire IX (ML119)	Privately owned, Rochester
	NETHERLANDS		
	174	Fokker S-11 Instructor (E-31/ G-BEPV)	Privately owned, Elstree
	204	Lockheed SP-2H Neptune [V]	RAF Museum, Cosford
	A-12	DH82A Tiger Moth (PH-TYG)	Privately owned, Gilze-Rijen, The Netherlands
	B-64	Noorduyn AT-16 Harvard IIB (PH-LSK)	Privately owned, Gilze-Rijen, The Netherlands
	B-71	Noorduyn AT-16 Harvard IIB (PH-MLM)	Privately owned, Gilze-Rijen, The Netherlands
	B-118	Noorduyn AT-16 Harvard IIB (PH-IIB)	Privately owned, Gilze-Rijen, The Netherlands
	E-14	Fokker S-11 Instructor (PH-AFS)	Privately owned, Lelystad, The Netherlands
	E-15	Fokker S-11 Instructor (G-BIYU)	Privately owned, White Waltham
	E-18	Fokker S-11 Instructor (PH-HTC)	Dukes of Brabant AF, Eindhoven, The Netherlands
	E-20	Fokker S-11 Instructor (PH-GRB)	Privately owned, Gilze-Rijen, The Netherlands
	E-27	Fokker S-11 Instructor (PH-HOL)	Privately owned, Lelystad, The Netherlands
	E-32	Fokker S-11 Instructor (PH-HOI)	Privately owned, Gilze-Rijen, The Netherlands
	E-36	Fokker S-11 Instructor (PH-ACG)	Privately owned, Lelystad, The Netherlands
	E-39	Fokker S-11 Instructor (PH-HOG)	Privately owned, Lelystad, The Netherlands
	G-29	Beech D18S (N5369X)	KLu Historic Flt, Gilze-Rijen, The Netherlands
	MK732	VS 361 Spitfire LF IXC (8633M/ PH-OUQ) [3W-17]	KLu Historic Flight, Lelystad, The Netherlands
	N-202	Hawker Hunter F6 [10] <ff>	Privately owned, Eaglescott
	N-250	Hawker Hunter F6 (G-9-185) <ff>	Imperial War Museum, Duxford
	N-268	Hawker Hunter FGA78 (Qatar QA-10)	Yorkshire Air Museum, Elvington
	N-315	Hawker Hunter T7 (XM121)	Jet Avn Preservation Grp, Long Marston
	N5-149	NA B-25J Mitchell (44-29507/ HD346/N320SQ) [232511]	Duke of Brabant AF, Eindhoven, The Netherlands

Serial	Type (other identity)	Owner/operator, location	Notes
R-55	Piper L-18C Super Cub (52-2466/ G-BLMI)	Privately owned, White Waltham	
R-109	Piper L-21B Super Cub (54-2337/ PH-GAZ)	Privately owned, Gilze-Rijen, The Netherlands	
R-122	Piper L-21B Super Cub (54-2412/ PH-PPW)	Privately owned, Gilze-Rijen, The Netherlands	
R-137	Piper L-21B Super Cub (54-2427/ PH-PSC)	Privately owned, Gilze-Rijen, The Netherlands	
R-151	Piper L-21B Super Cub (54-2441/ G-BIYR)	Privately owned, Dunkeswell	
R-156	Piper L-21B Super Cub (54-2446/ G-ROVE)	Privately owned, Headcorn	
R-163	Piper L-21B Super Cub (54-2453/ G-BIRH)	Privately owned, Lee-on-Solent	
R-167	Piper L-21B Super Cub (54-2457/ G-LION)	Privately owned, Turweston, Bucks	
R-177	Piper L-21B Super Cub (54-2467/ PH-KNR)	Privately owned, Gilze-Rijen, The Netherlands	
R-181	Piper L-21B Super Cub (54-2471/ PH-GAU)	Privately owned, Gilze-Rijen, The Netherlands	
R-345	Piper J-3C Cub (PH-UCS)	Privately owned, The Netherlands	
S-9	DHC2 L-20A Beaver (PH-DHC)	KLu Historic Flt, Gilze-Rijen, The Netherlands	
Y-74	Consolidated PBY-5A Catalina (2459/PH-PBY)	Neptune Association, Valkenburg, The Netherlands	

NEW ZEALAND

Serial	Type (other identity)	Owner/operator, location	Notes
NZ3909	WS Wasp HAS1 (XT782)	Kennet Aviation, North Weald, spares use	
NZ6361	BAC Strikemaster 87 (OJ5/ G-BXFP)	Privately owned, Chalgrove	

NORTH KOREA

Serial	Type (other identity)	Owner/operator, location	Notes
-	WSK Lim-2 (MiG-15) (01420/ G-BMZF)	FAA Museum, RNAS Yeovilton	

NORTH VIETNAM

Serial	Type (other identity)	Owner/operator, location	Notes
1211	WSK Lim-5 (MiG-17F) (G-BWUF)	Privately owned, Bournemouth	

NORWAY

Serial	Type (other identity)	Owner/operator, location	Notes
423/427	Gloster Gladiator I (L8032/ G-AMRK/*N2308*)	The Shuttleworth Collection, Old Warden	
848	Piper L-18C Super Cub (LN-ACL) [FA-N]	Privately owned, Norway	
56321	SAAB S91B Safir (G-BKPY) [U-AB]	Newark Air Museum, Winthorpe	

POLAND

Serial	Type (other identity)	Owner/operator, location	Notes
05	WSK SM-2 (Mi-2) (1005)	The Helicopter Museum, Weston-super-Mare	
309	WSK SBLim-2A (MiG-15UTI) <ff>	Royal Scottish Mus'm of Flight, E Fortune	
408	WSK-PZL Mielec TS-11 Iskra (1H-0408)	Privately owned, Coventry	
1018	WSK-PZL Mielec TS-11 Iskra (1H-1018/G-ISKA)	Privately owned, Bruntingthorpe	
1120	WSK Lim-2 (MiG-15bis)	RAF Museum, Cosford	

PORTUGAL

Serial	Type (other identity)	Owner/operator, location	Notes
85	Isaacs Fury II (G-BTPZ)	Privately owned, Ormskirk	
1360	OGMA/DHC1 Chipmunk T20 (fuselage) (G-BYYU)	Privately owned, Little Staughton	
1365	OGMA/DHC1 Chipmunk T20 (G-DHPM)	Privately owned, Spanhoe Lodge	
1372	OGMA/DHC1 Chipmunk T20 (HB-TUM)	Privately owned, Switzerland	
1377	DHC1 Chipmunk 22 (G-BARS)	Privately owned, Yeovilton	
1741	CCF Harvard IV (G-HRVD)	Air Atlantique Historic Flight, Coventry	
1747	CCF T-6J Harvard IV (*20385/* G-BGPB)	The Aircraft Restoration Co, Duxford	

QATAR

Serial	Type (other identity)	Owner/operator, location	Notes
QA12	Hawker Hunter FGA78 <ff>	The Planets Leisure Centre, Woking	
QP30	WS Lynx Mk 28 (G-BFDV/TD 013)	Army SEAE, Arborfield	
QP31	WS Lynx Mk 28	DARA Fleetlands Apprentice School	
QP32	WS Lynx Mk 28 (TD 016)	AAC Stockwell Hall, Middle Wallop	

Historic Aircraft

Notes	Serial	Type (other identity)	Owner/operator, location
		RUSSIA (& FORMER SOVIET UNION)	
	-	Mil Mi-24V (3532424810853)	Privately owned, Hawarden
1		SPP Yak C-11 (G-BZMY)	Privately owned, North Weald
01		Yakovlev Yak-18A (G-BVVX)	Privately owned, High Garrett
01		Yakovlev Yak-52 (9311709/ G-YKSZ)	Privately owned, Old Buckenham
02		Yakovlev Yak-52 (888615/G-CBLJ)	Privately owned, North Weald
2		Yakovlev Yak-18 (RA-02933)	Privately owned,
2		Yakovlev Yak-52 (9311708/ G-YAKS)	Privately owned, North Weald
03		Mil Mi-24D (3532461715415)	Privately owned, Hawarden
03		Yakovlev Yak-9UM (0470403/ F-AZYJ)	Privately owned, Dijon, France
03		Yakovlev Yak-52 (899803/ G-YAKR)	Privately owned, North Weald
04		Mikoyan MiG-23ML (024003607)	Newark Air Museum, Winthorpe
04		Yakovlev Yak-52 (9211612/ RA-22521)	Privately owned, Wellesbourne Mountford
05		Yakovlev Yak-50 (832507/YL-CBH)	Privately owned, Strathallan
06		Mil Mi-24D (3532464505029)	Privately owned, Hawarden
07		WSK SM-1 (Mi-1) (Czech. 2007)	The Helicopter Museum, Weston-super-Mare
07		Yakovlev Yak-18M (G-BMJY)	Privately owned, North Weald
09		Yakovlev Yak-52 (9411809/ G-BVMU)	Privately owned, Sandy, Beds
10		Yakovlev Yak-52 (9110580)	Privately owned, White Waltham
11		SPP Yak C-11 (G-YCII)	Privately owned, North Weald
12		LET L-29 Delfin (194555/ES-YLM/ G-DELF)	Privately owned, Manston
14		Yakovlev Yak-52 (899404/G-CCCP)	Privately owned, North Weald
18		LET L-29S Delfin (591771/YL-PAF)	Privately owned, Hawarden
19		Yakovlev Yak-52 (811202/YL-CBI)	Privately owned, Cumbernauld
20		Lavochkin La-11	The Fighter Collection, Duxford
20		Yakovlev Yak-52 (790404/YL-CBJ)	Privately owned, Strathallan
23		Mikoyan MiG-27D (83712515040)	Privately owned, Hawarden
26		Yakovlev Yak-52 (9111306/ G-BVXK)	Privately owned, White Waltham
27		SPP Yak C-11 (G-OYAK)	Privately owned, North Weald
31		Yakovlev Yak-52 (9111311/ RA-02209)	Privately owned, Rendcomb
35		Sukhoi Su-17M-3 (25102)	Privately owned, Hawarden
35		Yakovlev Yak-52 (9010508/ RA-02080)	Privately owned, White Waltham
36		LET/Yak C-11 (G-KYAK)	Privately owned, North Weald
36		SPP Yak C-11 (G-IYAK)	Privately owned, Earls Colne
42		Yakovlev Yak-52 (833901/G-LENA)	Privately owned, Old Sarum
49		Yakovlev Yak-55M (880606/ RA-44526)	Privately owned, White Waltham
50		Mikoyan MiG-23MF (023003508)	Privately owned, Hawarden
50		Yakovlev Yak-50 (812003/ RA-44549)	Privately owned, Little Gransden
50		Yakovlev Yak-50 (812101/ G-CBPM)	Privately owned, North Weald
50		Yakovlev Yak-50 (822305/ G-BXNO)	Privately owned, Denham
50		Yakovlev Yak-52 (9111415/ RA-44464)	Privately owned, White Waltham
51		LET L-29S Delfin (491273/YL-PAG)	Privately owned, Hawarden
52		Yakovlev Yak-52 (800708/ RA-44474)	Privately owned, Sherburn-in-Elmet
52		Yakovlev Yak-52 (878202/ G-BWVR)	Privately owned, Barton
54		Sukhoi Su-17M (69004)	Privately owned, Hawarden
55		Yakovlev Yak-52 (9111505/ G-BVOK)	Intrepid Aviation, North Weald
56		Yakovlev Yak-52 (811504)	Privately owned, Hawarden
56		Yakovlev Yak-52 (9111506/ RA-44516)	Privately owned, White Waltham
69		Hawker Hunter FGA9 (8839M/ XG194)	RAF North Luffenham Training Area
69		Yakovlev Yak-50 (801810/G-BTZB)	Privately owned, Audley End
69		Yakovlev Yak-52 (855509/LY-ALS)	Privately owned, Little Gransden

Serial	Type (other identity)	Owner/operator, location	Notes
69	Yakovlev Yak-52 (899413/ RA-44469)	Privately owned, Compton Abbas	
71	Mikoyan MiG-27M (61912507006)	Newark Air Museum, Winthorpe	
72	Yakovlev Yak-52 (9111608/ G-BXAV)	Privately owned, North Weald	
74	Yakovlev Yak-52 (877404/LY-AOK) [JA-74, IV-62]	Privately owned, Tollerton	
74	Yakovlev Yak-52 (888802/G-BXID)	Privately owned, Wellesbourne Mountford	
96	Yakovlev Yak-55 (901103/ RA-44525)	Privately owned, White Waltham	
98	Yakovlev Yak-52 (888911/G-CBRU/ RA-02042)	Privately owned, White Waltham	
100	Yakovlev Yak-52 (866904/G-YAKI)	Privately owned, Popham	
101	Yakovlev Yak-52 (866915/ RA-02705)	Privately owned, Rochester	
111	Aero L-39ZO Albatros (28+02/ G-OTAF)	The Old Flying Machine Company, Duxford	
112	Yakovlev Yak-52 (822610/LY-AFB)	Privately owned, Little Gransden	
139	Yakovlev Yak-52 (833810/ G-BWOD)	Privately owned, Sywell	
503	Mikoyan MiG-21SMT (G-BRAM)	Privately owned, Bournemouth	
1342	Yakovlev Yak-1 (G-BTZD)	Privately owned, Milden	
1-12	Yakovlev Yak-52 (9011013/ RA-02293)	Privately owned, Halfpenny Green	
1870710	Ilyushin Il-2 (G-BZVW)	Privately owned, Sandtoft	
1878576	Ilyushin Il-2 (G-BZVX)	Privately owned, Sandtoft	
BH328	Hawker Hurricane IIb	Privately owned, Isle of Wight	
PT879	VS361 Spitfire LF IX (G-BYDE)	Privately owned, Isle of Wight	
(RK858)	VS361 Spitfire LF IX	The Fighter Collection, Duxford	
(SM639)	VS361 Spitfire LF IX	Privately owned, Catfield	

SAUDI ARABIA

1104	BAC Strikemaster 80	Global Aviation, Humberside	
1107	BAC Strikemaster 80	Global Aviation, Humberside	
1108	BAC Strikemaster 80 (G-CBPB)	Privately owned, Shoreham	
1112	BAC Strikemaster 80 (G-FLYY)	Privately owned, Hawarden	
1114	BAC Strikemaster 80A (G-BZYH)	Privately owned, Sproughton	
1115	BAC Strikemaster 80A	Global Aviation, Humberside	
1120	BAC Strikemaster 80A	Global Aviation, Humberside	
1121	BAC Strikemaster 80A	Privately owned, North Weald	
1125	BAC Strikemaster 80A	Privately owned, Sproughton	
1129	BAC Strikemaster 80A	Global Aviation, Humberside	
1130	BAC Strikemaster 80A	Global Aviation, Humberside	
1133	BAC Strikemaster 80A (G-BESY)	Imperial War Museum, Duxford	
55-713	BAC Lightning T55 (ZF598)	Midland Air Museum, Coventry	

SLOVAKIA

7708	Mikoyan MiG-21MF	Boscombe Down Museum	

SOUTH AFRICA

92	Westland Wasp HAS1 (G-BYCX)	Privately owned, Bournemouth	
221	DH115 Vampire T55 <ff>	Privately owned, Hemel Mempstead	
6130	Lockheed Ventura II (AJ469)	RAF Museum, Cosford	
7429	NA AT-6D Harvard III (D-FASS)	Privately owned, Germany	

SOUTH VIETNAM

24550	Cessna L-19E Bird Dog (G-PDOG) [GP]	Privately owned, Lincs	

SPAIN

B.2I-27	CASA 2.111B (He111H-16) (B.2I-103)	Imperial War Museum, stored Duxford	
C.4E-88	Messerschmitt Bf109E	Privately owned, Hungerford	
C.4K-102	Hispano HA 1.112M1L Buchon (G-BWUE)	Privately owned, Breighton	
E.3B-114	CASA 1.131E Jungmann (G-BJAL)	Privately owned, Breighton	
E.3B-143	CASA 1.131E Jungmann (G-JUNG)	Privately owned, White Waltham	
E.3B-153	CASA 1.131E Jungmann (G-BPTS) [781-75]	Privately owned, Duxford	
E.3B-336	CASA 1.131E Jungmann (G-BUTA)	Privately owned, Breighton	
E.3B-350	CASA 1.131E Jungmann (G-BHPL) [05-97]	Privately owned, Kemble	

Historic Aircraft

Notes	Serial	Type (other identity)	Owner/operator, location
	(E.3B-369)	CASA 1.131E Jungmann (G-BPDM) [781-32]	Privately owned, Chilbolton
	E.3B-521	CASA 1.131E Jungmann [781-3]	RAF Museum, Hendon
EM-01		DH60G Moth (G-AAOR)	Privately owned, Rendcomb
	ES.1-16	CASA 1.133L Jungmeister	Privately owned, Stretton, Cheshire

SWEDEN

Notes	Serial	Type (other identity)	Owner/operator, location
081		CFM 01 Tummelisa <R> (SE-XIL)	Privately owned, Karlstad, Sweden
	05108	DH60 Moth	Privately owned, Langham
	17239	SAAB B-17A (SE-BYH) [7-J]	Flygvapenmuseum, Linköping, Sweden
	26158	NA P-51D Mustang (G-CBNM) [16-K]	The Fighter Collection, Duxford
28693		DH100 Vampire FB6 (J-1184/SE-DXY) [9-G]	Scandinavian Historic Flight, North Weald
	29640	SAAB J-29F [20-08]	Midland Air Museum, Coventry
	29670	SAAB J-29F (SE-DXB) [10-R]	Flygvapenmuseum/F10 Wing, Angelholm, Sweden
	32028	SAAB 32A Lansen (G-BMSG)	Privately owned, Cranfield
34066		Hawker Hunter F58 (J-4089/SE-DXA) [9-G]	Scandinavian Historic Flight, North Weald
	35075	SAAB J-35J Draken [40]	Imperial War Museum, Duxford
	A14	Thulin A/Bleriot XI (SE-XMC)	Privately owned, Karlstad, Sweden

SWITZERLAND

Notes	Serial	Type (other identity)	Owner/operator, location
A-10		CASA 1.131E Jungmann (G-BECW)	Privately owned, Denham
A-50		CASA 1.131E Jungmann (G-CBCE)	Privately owned, Breighton
A-57		CASA 1.131E Jungmann (G-BECT)	Privately owned, Goodwood
	A-125	Pilatus P-2 (G-BLKZ)	Privately owned, North Weald
	A-701	Junkers Ju52/3m (HB-HOS)	Ju-Air, Dubendorf, Switzerland
	A-702	Junkers Ju52/3m (HB-HOT)	Ju-Air, Dubendorf, Switzerland
	A-703	Junkers Ju52/3m (HB-HOP)	Ju-Air, Dubendorf, Switzerland
	A-806	Pilatus P3-03 (G-BTLL)	Privately owned, stored Headcorn
	C-552	EKW C-3605 (G-DORN)	Privately owned, Bournemouth
	C-558	EKW C-3605	Privately owned, Spanhoe
	J-1008	DH100 Vampire FB6	Mosquito Aircraft Museum, London Colney
	J-1149	DH100 Vampire FB6 (G-SWIS)	Privately owned, Bournemouth
	J-1172	DH100 Vampire FB6 (8487M)	RAF Museum Restoration Centre, Cosford
	J-1573	DH112 Venom FB50 (G-VICI)	Source Classic Jet Flight, Bournemouth
	J-1605	DH112 Venom FB50 (G-BLID)	Gatwick Aviation Museum, Charlwood, Surrey
	J-1629	DH112 Venom FB50	Source Classic Jet Flight, stored Bournemouth
	J-1632	DH112 Venom FB50 (G-VNOM)	Kennet Aviation, North Weald
	J-1649	DH112 Venom FB50	Source Classic Jet Flight, stored Bournemouth
	J-1704	DH112 Venom FB54	RAF Museum, Cosford
	J-1712	DH112 Venom FB54 <ff>	Botany Bay Village, Chorley, Lancs
	J-1758	DH112 Venom FB54 (N203DM)	Privately owned, stored North Weald
J-2001		Hawker Hunter F58 (J-4095/F-AZHS)	Privately owned, Cuers, France
J-4015		Hawker Hunter F58 (J-4040/HB-RVS)	Privately owned, Altenrhein, Switzerland
	J-4021	Hawker Hunter F58 (G-HHAC)	Historic Flying Ltd/OFMC, Scampton
	J-4031	Hawker Hunter F58 (G-BWFR)	The Old Flying Machine Company, Scampton
	J-4058	Hawker Hunter F58 (G-HHAD)	The Old Flying Machine Company, Scampton
	J-4066	Hawker Hunter F58 (G-HHAE)	The Old Flying Machine Company, Scampton
	J-4072	Hawker Hunter F58	Privately owned, Scampton
	J-4081	Hawker Hunter F58 (G-BWKB)	The Old Flying Machine Company, Scampton
	J-4083	Hawker Hunter F58 (G-EGHH)	Privately owned, Bournemouth
	J-4086	Hawker Hunter F58 (HB-RVU)	Privately owned, Altenrhein, Switzerland
	J-4090	Hawker Hunter F58 (G-SIAL)	The Old Flying Machine Company, Scampton
	J-4091	Hawker Hunter F58	British Aviation Heritage, Bruntingthorpe
	J-4201	Hawker Hunter T68 (HB-RVR)	Privately owned, Altenrhein, Switzerland
	J-4205	Hawker Hunter T68 (HB-RVP)	Privately owned, Altenrhein, Switzerland
	U-80	Bücker Bü133D Jungmeister (G-BUKK)	Privately owned, White Waltham

Serial	Type (other identity)	Owner/operator, location	Notes
U-99	Bücker Bü133C Jungmeister (G-AXMT)	Privately owned, Breighton	
U-110	Pilatus P-2 (G-PTWO)	Privately owned, Earls Colne	
U-142	Pilatus P-2 (G-BONE)	Privately owned, Hibaldstow	
V-54	SE3130 Alouette II (G-BVSD)	Privately owned, Staverton	
USA			
-	Noorduyn AT-16 Harvard IIB (KLu B-168)	American Air Museum, Duxford	
1	Spad XIII <R> (G-BFYO/*S3398*)	American Air Museum, Duxford	
14	Boeing-Stearman A75N-1 Kaydet (G-ISDN)	Privately owned, Rendcomb	
23	Fairchild PT-23 (N49272)	Privately owned, Halfpenny Green	
26	Boeing-Stearman A75N-1 Kaydet (G-BAVO)	Privately owned, Old Buckenham	
27	NA SNJ-7 Texan (90678/G-BRVG)	Privately owned, Goodwood	
33-K	PA-18 Super Cub 95 (51-15541/ G-BJLH)	Privately owned, Felthorpe	
43	Noorduyn AT-16 Harvard IIB (43-13064/G-AZSC) [SC]	Privately owned, North Weald	
44	Boeing-Stearman D75N-1 Kaydet (42-15852/G-RJAH)	Privately owned, Rendcomb	
44	Piper L-21B Super Cub (54-2405/ G-BWHH)	Privately owned, Felthorpe	
49	Curtiss P-40M Kittyhawk (43-5802/ G-KITT/*P8196*)	The Fighter Collection, Duxford	
57	WS55 Whirlwind HAS7 (XG592)	*Task Force* Adventure Park, Cowbridge, S Glam	
85	WAR P-47 Thunderbolt <R> (G-BTBI)	Privately owned, Carlisle	
88	Curtiss P-40E Kittyhawk (NZ3009/ ZK-RMH) [663]	The Old Flying Machine Company, Duxford	
112	Boeing-Stearman PT-13D Kaydet (42-17397/G-BSWC)	Privately owned, Staverton	
118	Boeing-Stearman PT-13A Kaydet (38-470/G-BSDS)	Privately owned, Swanton Morley	
379	Boeing-Stearman PT-13D Kaydet (42-14865/G-ILLE)	Privately owned, Oaksey Park	
441	Boeing-Stearman N2S-4 Kaydet (30010/G-BTFG)	Privately owned, Perth	
540	Piper L-4H Grasshopper (43-29877/G-BCNX)	Privately owned, Monewden	
578	Boeing-Stearman N2S-5 Kaydet (N1364V)	Privately owned, North Weald	
628	Beech D17S (44-67761/N18V)	Privately owned, stored North Weald	
718	Boeing-Stearman PT-13D Kaydet (42-17555/N5345N)	Privately owned, Tibenham	
744	Boeing-Stearman A75N-1 Kaydet (42-16532/OO-USN)	Privately owned, Wevelgem, Belgium	
817	Boeing-Stearman PT-17 Kaydet (N59269)	Privately owned, North Weald	
854	Ryan PT-22 Recruit (42-17378/ G-BTBH)	Privately owned, Wellesbourne Mountford	
855	Ryan PT-22 Recruit (41-15510/ N56421)	Privately owned, Halfpenny Green	
897	Aeronca 11AC Chief (G-BJEV) [E]	Privately owned, English Bicknor, Glos	
1102	Boeing-Stearman N2S-5 Kaydet (G-AZLE)	Privately owned, Tongham	
1164	Beech D18S (G-BKGL)	The Aircraft Restoration Co, Duxford	
1180	Boeing-Stearman N2S-3 Kaydet (3403/G-BRSK)	Privately owned, Tibenham	
2807	NA T-6G Texan (49-3072/G-BHTH) [V-103]	Northbrook College, Shoreham	
6136	Boeing-Stearman A75N-1 Kaydet (42-16136/G-BRUJ) [205]	Privately owned, Liverpool	
6771	Republic F-84F Thunderstreak (BAF FU-6)	RAF Museum, stored Cosford	
7797	Aeronca L-16A (47-0797/G-BFAF)	Privately owned, Finmere	
8178	NA F-86A Sabre (48-0178/ G-SABR) [FU-178]	Golden Apple Operations/ARC, Duxford	
8242	NA F-86A Sabre (48-0242) [FU-242]	American Air Museum, Duxford	
01532	Northrop F-5E Tiger II <R>	RAF Alconbury on display	

Historic Aircraft

Notes	Serial	Type (other identity)	Owner/operator, location
	02538	Fairchild PT-19B (N33870)	Privately owned, North Weald
	07539	Boeing-Stearman N2S-3 Kaydet (N63590) [143]	Privately owned, Tibenham
	14286	Lockheed T-33A (51-4286)	American Air Museum, Duxford
	O-14419	Lockheed T-33A (51-4419)	Midland Air Museum, Coventry
	14863	NA AT-6D Harvard III (41-33908/ G-BGOR)	Privately owned, Goudhurst, Kent
	15154	Bell OH-58A Kiowa (70-15154)	R. Military College of Science, Shrivenham
	15990	Bell AH-1F Hueycobra (67-15990)	Museum of Army Flying, Middle Wallop
	16445	Bell AH-1F Hueycobra (69-16445)	R. Military College of Science, Shrivenham
	16506	Hughes OH-6A Cayuse (67-16506)	The Helicopter Museum, Weston-super-Mare
	16579	Bell UH-1H Iroquois (66-16579)	The Helicopter Museum, Weston-super-Mare
	16718	Lockheed T-33A (51-6718)	City of Norwich Aviation Museum
	17962	Lockheed SR-71A (64-17962)	American Air Museum, Duxford
	18263	Boeing-Stearman PT-17 Kaydet (41-8263/N38940) [822]	Privately owned, Tibenham
	19252	Lockheed T-33A (51-9252)	Tangmere Military Aviation Museum
	20249	Noorduyn AT-16 Harvard IIB (PH-KLU) [XS-249]	Privately owned, Lelystad, The Netherlands
	21605	Bell UH-1H Iroquois (72-21605)	American Air Museum, Duxford
	21714	Grumman F8F-2P Bearcat (121714/G-RUMM) [201-B]	The Fighter Collection, Duxford
	24538	Kaman HH-43F Huskie (62-4535)	Midland Air Museum, Coventry
	24541	Cessna L-19E Bird Dog (F-GFVE)	Privately owned, Redhill
	24568	Cessna L-19E Bird Dog (LN-WNO)	Army Aviation Norway, Kjeller, Norway
	28521	CCF Harvard IV (G-TVIJ) [TA-521]	Privately owned, Woodchurch, Kent
	30861	NA TB-25J Mitchell (44-30861/ N9089Z)	Privately owned, North Weald
	31145	Piper L-4B Grasshopper (43-1145/ G-BBLH) [26-G]	Privately owned, Biggin Hill
	31171	NA B-25J Mitchell (44-31171/ N7614C)	American Air Museum, Duxford
	31952	Aeronca O-58B Defender (G-BRPR)	Privately owned, Earls Colne
	34037	NA TB-25N Mitchell (44-29366/ N9115Z/8838M)	RAF Museum, Hendon
	37414	McD F-4C Phantom (63-7414)	Midland Air Museum, Coventry
	39624	Wag Aero Sport Trainer (G-BVMH) [39-D]	Privately owned, Lincoln
	40467	Grumman F6F-5K Hellcat (80141/ G-BTCC) [19]	The Fighter Collection, Duxford
	41386	Thomas-Morse S4 Scout <R> (G-MJTD)	Privately owned, Hitchin
	42163	NA F-100D Super Sabre (54-2163) [HE]	Dumfries & Galloway Avn Mus, Dumfries
	42165	NA F-100D Super Sabre (54-2165) [VM]	American Air Museum, Duxford
	42174	NA F-100D Super Sabre (54-2174) [UH]	Midland Air Museum, Coventry
	42196	NA F-100D Super Sabre (54-2196) [LT]	Norfolk & Suffolk Avn Museum, Flixton
	46214	Grumman TBM-3E Avenger (69327/CF-KCG) [X-3]	American Air Museum, Duxford
	46867	Grumman FM-2 Wildcat (N909WJ)	Flying A Services, North Weald
	48846	Boeing B-17G Fortress (44-8846/ F-AZDX) [DS-M]	Assoc Fortresse Toujours Volant, Paris, France
	53319	Grumman TBM-3R Avenger (G-BTDP) [319-RB]	Privately owned, North Weald
	54137	CCF Harvard IV (MM54137/ G-CTKL) [69]	Privately owned, North Weald
	54433	Lockheed T-33A (55-4433)	Norfolk & Suffolk Avn Museum, Flixton
	54439	Lockheed T-33A (55-4439)	North-East Aircraft Museum, Usworth
	58811	NA B-25J Mitchell (45-8811/ F-AZID) [HD]	Privately owned, Athens, Greece
	60312	McD F-101F Voodoo (56-0312)	Midland Air Museum, Coventry
	60689	Boeing B-52D Stratofortress (56-0689)	American Air Museum, Duxford
	63000	NA F-100D Super Sabre (54-2212) [FW-000]	USAF Croughton, Oxon, at gate
	63319	NA F-100D Super Sabre (54-2269) [FW-319]	RAF Lakenheath, on display

Serial	Type (other identity)	Owner/operator, location	Notes
63428	Republic F-105G Thunderchief (62-4428)	USAF Croughton, Oxon, at gate	
66692	Lockheed U-2CT (56-6692)	American Air Museum, Duxford	
70270	McD F-101B Voodoo (57-270) (fuselage)	Midland Air Museum, Coventry	
80425	Grumman F7F-3P Tigercat (N7235C/G-RUMT) [WT-14]	The Fighter Collection, Duxford	
80480	Piper L-4J Grasshopper (44-80480/G-BECN) [44-E]	Privately owned, Kersey, Suffolk	
82062	DHC U-6A Beaver (58-2062)	Midland Air Museum, Coventry	
91822	Republic F-105D Thunderchief (59-1822)	American Air Museum, Duxford	
92844	Goodyear FG-1D Corsair (NZ5648/G-BXUL) [8]	The Old Flying Machine Company, Duxford	
93542	CCF Harvard IV (G-BRLV) [LTA-542]	Privately owned, North Weald	
96995	CV F4U-4 Corsair (OE-EAS) [BR-37]	Tyrolean Jet Services, Innsbruck, Austria	
97264	CV F4U-4 Corsair (F-AZVJ) [403]	Flying Legend, Dijon, France	
111836	NA AT-6C Harvard IIA (41-33262/G-TSIX) [JZ-6]	The Real Aeroplane Company, Breighton	
111989	Cessna L-19A Bird Dog (51-11989/N33600)	Museum of Army Flying, Middle Wallop	
115042	NA T-6G Texan (51-15042/G-BGHU) [TA-042]	Privately owned, Headcorn	
115227	NA T-6G Texan (51-15227/G-BKRA)	Privately owned, Sandown	
115302	Piper L-18C Super Cub (51-15302/G-BJTP) [TP]	Privately owned, Bidford	
115684	Piper L-21A Super Cub (51-15684/G-BKVM) [DC]	Privately owned, North Coates	
124143	Douglas AD-4NA Skyraider (F-AZDP) [205-RM]	Amicale J-B Salis, la Ferté-Alais, France	
124485	Boeing B-17G Fortress (44-85784/G-BEDF) [DF-A]	B-17 Preservation Ltd, Duxford	
124724	CV F4U-5NL Corsair (F-AZEG) [22]	Amicale J-B Salis, la Ferté-Alais, France	
126922	Douglas AD-4NA Skyraider (G-RAID) [402-AK]	The Fighter Collection, Duxford	
126956	Douglas AD-4NA Skyraider (F-AZDQ) [3-RM]	Aéro Retro, St Rambert d'Albon, France	
127002	Douglas AD-4NA Skyraider (F-AZHK) [618-G]	Privately owned, Cuers, France	
138179	NA T-28A Trojan (OE-ESA) [BA]	Tyrolean Jet Services, Innsbruck, Austria	
140547	NA T-28C Trojan (N2800Q)	Privately owned	
146289	NA T-28C Trojan (N99153) [2W]	Norfolk & Suffolk Aviation Museum, Flixton	
150225	WS58 Wessex 60 (G-AWOX) [123]	Privately owned, Lulsgate	
151632	NA TB-25N Mitchell (44-30925/G-BWGR)	Privately owned, Sandtoft	
155529	McD F-4S Phantom (ZE359) [AJ-114]	American Air Museum, Duxford	
155848	McD F-4S Phantom [WT-11]	Royal Scottish Mus'm of Flight, E Fortune	
159233	HS AV-8A Harrier [CG-33]	Imperial War Museum North, Salford Quays	
162068	McD AV-8B Harrier II (9250M) (fuselage)	RAF Cottesmore BDRT	
162071	McD AV-8B Harrier II (fuselage)	Rolls-Royce, Filton	
162730	McD AV-8B Harrier II (fuselage)	RAF, Wyton	
162958	McD AV-8B Harrier II (fuselage)	QinetiQ, Boscombe Down	
211072	Boeing-Stearman PT-17 Kaydet (N50755)	Privately owned, Swanton Morley	
217786	Boeing-Stearman PT-17 Kaydet (41-8169/CF-EQS) [25]	American Air Museum, Duxford	
219993	Bell P-39Q Airacobra (42-19993/N139DP)	The Fighter Collection	
226413	Republic P-47D Thunderbolt (45-49192/N47DD) [ZU-N]	American Air Museum, Duxford	
226671	Republic P-47M Thunderbolt (G-THUN) [MX-X]	The Fighter Collection, Duxford	
231983	Boeing B-17G Fortress (44-83735/F-BDRS) [IY-G]	American Air Museum, Duxford	
234539	Fairchild PT-19B Cornell (42-34539/N50429) [63]	Privately owned, Dunkeswell	
237123	Waco CG-4A Hadrian (BAPC 157) (fuselage)	Yorkshire Air Museum, Elvington	

Historic Aircraft

Notes	Serial	Type (other identity)	Owner/operator, location
	238410	Piper L-4A Grasshopper (42-38410/G-BHPK) [44-A]	Privately owned, Tibenham
	243809	Waco CG-4A Hadrian (BAPC 185)	Museum of Army Flying, Middle Wallop
	252983	Schweizer TG-3A (42-52983/ N66630)	American Air Museum, Duxford
	314887	Fairchild Argus III (43-14887/) G-AJPI	Privately owned, Felthorpe
	315211	Douglas C-47A (43-15211/ N1944A) [J8-Z]	Privately owned, Booker
	315509	Douglas C-47A (43-15509/ G-BHUB) [W7-S]	American Air Museum, Duxford
	329405	Piper L-4H Grasshopper (43-29405/G-BCOB) [23-A]	Privately owned, South Walsham
	329417	Piper L-4A Grasshopper (42-38400/G-BDHK)	Privately owned, Coleford
	329471	Piper L-4H Grasshopper (43-29471/G-BGXA) [44-F]	Privately owned, Martley, Worcs
	329601	Piper L-4H Grasshopper (43-29601/G-AXHR) [44-D]	Privately owned, Nayland
	329854	Piper L-4H Grasshopper (43-29854/G-BMKC) [44-R]	Privately owned, Newtownards
	329934	Piper L-4H Grasshopper (43-29934/G-BCPH) [72-B]	Privately owned, White Waltham
	330238	Piper L-4H Grasshopper (43-30238/G-LIVH) [24-A]	Privately owned, Barton
	330485	Piper L-4H Grasshopper (43-30485/G-AJES) [44-C]	Privately owned, Shifnal
	343251	Boeing-Stearman N2S-5 Kaydet (43517/G-NZSS) [27]	Privately owned, Swanton Morley
	411622	NA P-51D Mustang (44-74427/ F-AZSB) [G4-C]	Privately owned, Nimes, France
	413573	NA P-51D Mustang (44-73415/ 9133M/N6526D) [B6-V]	RAF Museum, Hendon
	413704	NA P-51D Mustang (44-73149/ G-BTCD) [B7-H]	The Old Flying Machine Company, Duxford
	414151	NA P-51D Mustang (44-73140/ NL314BG) [HO-M]	Flying A Services, North Weald
	414419	NA P-51D Mustang (45-15118/ G-MSTG) [LH-F]	Privately owned, Norwich
	414450	NA P-51D Mustang (44-73877/ N167F) [B6-S]	Scandinavian Historic Flight, North Weald
	434602	Douglas A-26B Invader (44-34602/ N167B) [BC-602]	Scandinavian Historic Flight, North Weald
	435710	Douglas A-26C Invader (44-35710/ OO-INV)	Historic Invader Avn, Schiphol, The Netherlands
	442268	Noorduyn AT-16 Harvard IIB (KF568/LN-TEX) [TA-268]	Scandinavian Historic Flight, Oslo, Norway
	454467	Piper L-4J Grasshopper (45-4467/ G-BILI) [44-J]	Privately owned, White Waltham
	454537	Piper L-4J Grasshopper (45-4537/ G-BFDL) [04-J]	Privately owned, Shempston Farm, Lossiemouth
	461748	Boeing B-29A Superfortress (44-61748/G-BHDK) [Y]	American Air Museum, Duxford
	463209	NA P-51D Mustang <R> (BAPC 255) [WZ-S]	American Air Museum, Duxford
	472035	NA P-51D Mustang (44-72035/ F-AZMU)	Aéro Retro, St Rambert d'Albon, France
	472216	NA P-51D Mustang (44-72216/ G-BIXL) [HO-M]	Privately owned, East Garston, Bucks
	472218	CAC-18 Mustang 22 (A68-192/ G-HAEC) [WZ-I]	Privately owned, Woodchurch, Kent
	472218	NA P-51D Mustang (44-73979) [WZ-I]	Imperial War Museum, Lambeth
	472773	NA P-51D Mustang (44-72773/ G-SUSY) [QP-M]	Privately owned, Sywell
	474008	NA P-51D Mustang (44-73339/ G-SIRR) [VF-R]	Privately owned, Duxford
	474425	NA P-51D Mustang (44-74425/ NL11T) [OC-G]	Dutch Mustang Flt, Lelystad, The Netherlands
	474923	NA P-51D Mustang (44-74923/ N6395)	Privately owned, Lelystad, The Netherlands
	479744	Piper L-4H Grasshopper (44-79744/G-BGPD) [49-M]	Privately owned, Marsh, Bucks

Serial	Type (other identity)	Owner/operator, location	Notes
479766	Piper L-4H Grasshopper (44-79766/G-BKHG) [63-D]	Privately owned, Goldcliff, Gwent	
480015	Piper L-4H Grasshopper (44-80015/G-AKIB) [44-M]	Privately owned, Bodmin	
480133	Piper L-4J Grasshopper (44-80133/G-BDCD) [44-B]	Privately owned, Slinfold	
480321	Piper L-4J Grasshopper (44-80321/G-FRAN) [44-H]	Privately owned, Rayne, Essex	
480551	Piper L-4J Grasshopper (44-80551/LN-KLT) [43-S]	Scandinavian Historic Flight, Oslo, Norway	
480636	Piper L-4J Grasshopper (44-80636/G-AXHP) [58-A]	Privately owned, Southend	
480723	Piper L-4J Grasshopper (44-80723/G-BFZB) [E5-J]	Privately owned, Egginton	
480752	Piper L-4J Grasshopper (44-80752/G-BCXJ) [39-E]	Privately owned, Old Sarum	
483868	Boeing B-17G Fortress (44-83868/N5237V) [A-N]	RAF Museum, Hendon	
486893	NA B-25J Mitchell (N6123C)	Tyrolean Jet Services, Innsbruck, Austria	
493209	NA T-6G Texan (49-3209/ G-DDMV/41)	Privately owned, Duxford	
511701A	Beech C-45H (51-11701/ G-BSZC) [AF258]	Privately owned, Bryngwyn Bach	
607327	PA-18 Super Cub 95 (G-ARAO) [09-L]	Privately owned, Denham	
2106449	NA P-51C Mustang (43-25147/ N51PR/G-PSIC) [HO-W]	The Fighter Collection, Duxford	
2-134	NA T-6G Texan (114700)	Privately owned, North Weald	
3-1923	Aeronca O-58B Defender (43-1923/G-BRHP)	Privately owned, Chiseldon	
18-2001	Piper L-18C Super Cub (52-2401/ G-BIZV)	Privately owned, Oxenhope	
39-139	Beech YC-43 Traveler (N295BS)	Dukes of Brabant AF, Eindhoven, The Netherlands	
40-1766	Boeing-Stearman PT-17 Kaydet	Privately owned, Swanton Morley	
41-33275	NA AT-6C Texan (G-BICE) [CE]	Privately owned, Ipswich	
42-12417	Noorduyn AT-16 Harvard IIB (Klu. B-163)	Covert Forces Museum, Harrington, Northants	
42-40557	Consolidated B-24D Liberator <ff>	American Air Museum, Duxford	
42-58678	Taylorcraft DF-65 (G-BRIY) [IY]	Privately owned, North Weald	
42-78044	Aeronca 11AC Chief (G-BRXL)	Privately owned, High Cross, Herts	
42-84555	NA AT-6D Harvard III (FAP.1662/ G-ELMH) [EP-H]	Privately owned, Hardwick, Norfolk	
42-93510	Douglas C-47A Skytrain [CM] <ff>	Privately owned, Kew	
43-9628	Douglas A-20G Havoc <ff>	Privately owned, Hinckley, Leics	
43-35943	Beech C-45G (51-11665/G-BKRG)	Privately owned, Bruntingthorpe	
44-13954	NA P-51D Mustang	Privately owned, Coventry	
44-14574	NA P-51D Mustang (fuselage)	East Essex Aviation Museum, Clacton	
44-51228	Consolidated B-24M Liberator [RE-N]	American Air Museum, Duxford	
44-79609	Piper L-4H Grasshopper (G-BHXY) [PR]	Privately owned, Bodmin	
44-80594	Piper L-4J Grasshopper (G-BEDJ)	Privately owned, White Waltham	
44-80647	Piper L-4J Grasshopper (D-EGAF)	The Vintage Aircraft Co, Fürstenwalde, Germany	
44-83184	Fairchild UC-61K Argus III (G-RGUS)	Privately owned, Sturgate, Lincs	
51-9036	Lockheed T-33A	Newark Air Museum, Winthorpe	
54-223	NA F-100D Super Sabre (54-2223)	Newark Air Museum, Winthorpe	
54-2447	Piper L-21B Super Cub (G-SCUB)	Privately owned, Anwick	
63-699	McD F-4C Phantom (63-7699) [CG]	Midland Air Museum, Coventry	
64-17657	Douglas A-26A Invader (N99218) <ff>	Tower Museum, Ludham, Norfolk	
65-777	McD F-4C Phantom (63-7419) [LN]	RAF Lakenheath, on display	
67-120	GD F-111E Aardvark (67-0120) [UH]	American Air Museum, Duxford	
68-0060	GD F-111F Aardvark <ff>	Dumfries & Galloway Avn Mus, Dumfries	
72-1447	GD F-111F Aardvark <ff>	American Air Museum, Duxford	
72-448	GD F-111E Aardvark (68-0011) [LN]	RAF Lakenheath, on display	
76-020	McD F-15A Eagle (76-0020) [BT]	American Air Museum, Duxford	
76-124	McD F-15B Eagle (76-0124) [LN]	RAF Lakenheath, instructional use	

Historic Aircraft

Notes	Serial	Type (other identity)	Owner/operator, location
	77-259	Fairchild A-10A Thunderbolt (77-0259) [AR]	American Air Museum, Duxford
	80-219	Fairchild GA-10A Thunderbolt (80-0219) [AR]	RAF Alconbury, on display
	92-048	McD F-15A Eagle (74-0131) [LN]	RAF Lakenheath, on display
	146-11042	Wolf WII <R> (G-BMZX) [7]	Privately owned, Haverfordwest
	146-11083	Wolf WII <R> (G-BNAI) [5]	Privately owned, Haverfordwest
	998-8888	Bell UH-1H Iroquois (Arg. AE-406)	RAF Valley, instructional use
	H-57	Piper L-4A Grasshopper (42-36375/G-AKAZ)	Privately owned, Duxford

YUGOSLAVIA

Notes	Serial	Type (other identity)	Owner/operator, location
	23194	Soko G-2A Galeb (YU-YAG)	Privately owned, Biggin Hill
	23196	Soko G-2A Galeb (YU-YAC)	Privately owned, Biggin Hill
	30139	Soko P-2 Kraguj [139]	Privately owned, Biggin Hill
	30140	Soko P-2 Kraguj (G-RADA) [140]	Privately owned, Biggin Hill
	30146	Soko P-2 Kraguj (G-BSXD) [146]	Privately owned, Elstree
	30149	Soko P-2 Kraguj (G-SOKO) [149]	Privately owned, Bournemouth
	30151	Soko P-2 Kraguj [151]	D-Day Aviation Museum, Shoreham
	51182	UTVA-66 (YU-DMN)	Privately owned, Biggin Hill
	51183	UTVA-66 (YU-DMT)	Privately owned, Biggin Hill

Former Czech Air Force Mil Mi-4 9147 is on display at The Helicopter Museum at Weston-super-Mare.
PRM

The Shuttleworth Collection's Gladiator I is painted in Norwegian Air Force colours. *PRM*

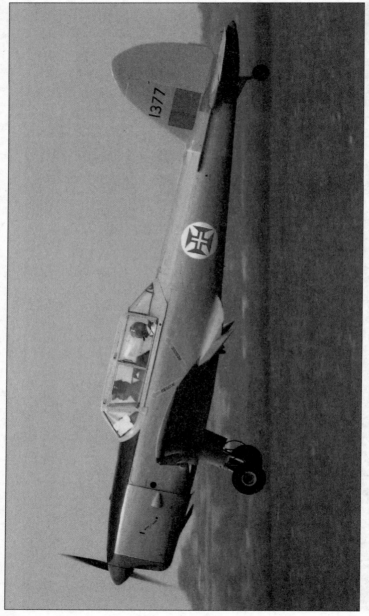

This Chipmunk 22 (G-BARS) is painted in Portuguese Air Force markings and serial 1377. *PRM*

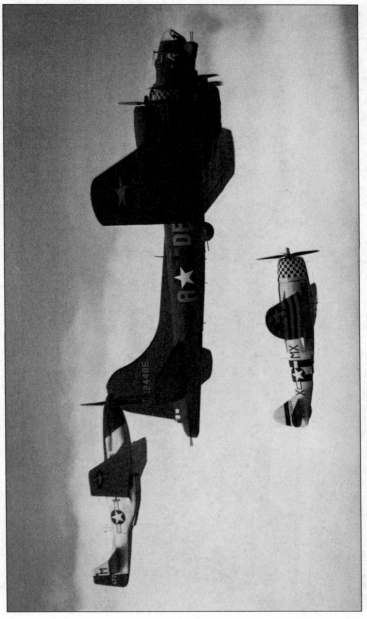

Duxford-based B-17G Sally B flying with TFC's P-47 Thunderbolt and privately owned P-51D 472216. *PRM*

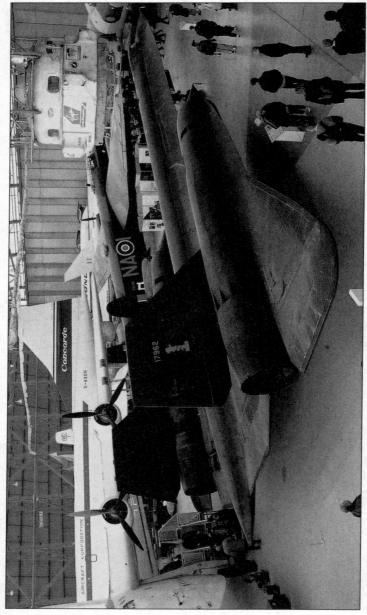

The SR-71A Blackbird 17962 photographed at Duxford before it was moved into the American Air Museum. *PRM*

Irish Military Aircraft Markings

Serial	Type (other identity)	Owner/operator, location	Notes
34	Miles M14A Magister (N5392)	IAC stored, Baldonnel	
141	Avro 652A Anson C19	IAC stored, Baldonnel	
161	VS509 Spitfire T9 (G-TRIX/PV202)	Historic Flying Ltd, Duxford	
164	DHC1 Chipmunk T20	IAC stored, Baldonnel	
168	DHC1 Chipmunk T20	IAC No 1 Operations Wing, Baldonnel	
172	DHC1 Chipmunk T20	IAC stored, Baldonnel	
173	DHC1 Chipmunk T20	South East Aviation Enthusiasts, Dromod	
176	DH104 Dove 4 (VP-YKF)	South East Aviation Enthusiasts, Waterford	
177	Percival P56 Provost T51 (G-BLIW)	Privately owned, Shoreham	
181	Percival P56 Provost T51	Privately owned, Thatcham	
183	Percival P56 Provost T51	IAC stored, Baldonnel	
184	Percival P56 Provost T51	South East Aviation Enthusiasts, Waterford	
187	DH115 Vampire T55	South East Aviation Enthusiasts, Waterford	
189	Percival P56 Provost T51 (comp XF846)	IAC Baldonnel Fire Section	
191	DH115 Vampire T55	IAC Museum, Baldonnel	
192	DH115 Vampire T55	South East Aviation Enthusiasts, Waterford	
195	Sud SA316 Alouette III	IAC No 302 Sqn/3 Operations Wing, Baldonnel	
196	Sud SA316 Alouette III	IAC No 302 Sqn/3 Operations Wing, Baldonnel	
197	Sud SA316 Alouette III	IAC No 302 Sqn/3 Operations Wing, Baldonnel	
198	DH115 Vampire T11 (XE977)	IAC stored, Baldonnel	
199	DHC1 Chipmunk T22	IAC stored, Baldonnel	
203	Reims-Cessna FR172H	IAC No 104 Sqn/1 Operations Wing, Baldonnel	
205	Reims-Cessna FR172H	IAC No 104 Sqn/1 Operations Wing, Baldonnel	
206	Reims-Cessna FR172H	IAC No 104 Sqn/1 Operations Wing, Baldonnel	
207	Reims-Cessna FR172H	IAC, stored, Waterford	
208	Reims-Cessna FR172H	IAC No 104 Sqn/1 Operations Wing, Baldonnel	
210	Reims-Cessna FR172H	IAC No 104 Sqn/1 Operations Wing, Baldonnel	
211	Sud SA316 Alouette III	IAC No 302 Sqn/3 Operations Wing, Baldonnel	
212	Sud SA316 Alouette III	IAC No 302 Sqn/3 Operations Wing, Baldonnel	
213	Sud SA316 Alouette III	IAC No 302 Sqn/3 Operations Wing, Baldonnel	
214	Sud SA316 Alouette III	IAC No 302 Sqn/3 Operations Wing, Baldonnel	
215	Fouga CM170 Super Magister	IAC, stored Baldonnel	
216	Fouga CM170 Super Magister	IAC Technical Training School, Baldonnel	
217	Fouga CM170 Super Magister	IAC, stored Baldonnel	
218	Fouga CM170 Super Magister	IAC, stored Baldonnel	
219	Fouga CM170 Super Magister	IAC, stored Baldonnel	
220	Fouga CM170 Super Magister	Carlow Institute of Technology, instructional use	
222	SIAI SF-260WE Warrior	IAC Flying Training School, Baldonnel	
225	SIAI SF-260WE Warrior	IAC Flying Training School, Baldonnel	
226	SIAI SF-260WE Warrior	IAC Flying Training School, Baldonnel	
227	SIAI SF-260WE Warrior	IAC Flying Training School, Baldonnel	
229	SIAI SF-260WE Warrior	IAC Flying Training School, Baldonnel	
230	SIAI SF-260WE Warrior	IAC Flying Training School, Baldonnel	
231	SIAI SF-260WE Warrior	IAC Flying Training School, Baldonnel	
240	Beech Super King Air 200MR	IAC No 102 Sqn/1 Operations Wing, Baldonnel	
241	Aérospatiale SA342L Gazelle	IAC No 303 Sqn/3 Operations Wing, Baldonnel	
243	Reims-Cessna FR172K	IAC No 104 Sqn/1 Operations Wing, Baldonnel	
244	Aérospatiale SA365F Dauphin II	IAC No 301 Sqn/3 Operations Wing, Baldonnel	
245	Aérospatiale SA365F Dauphin II	IAC No 301 Sqn/3 Operations Wing, Baldonnel	

Irish Military Aircraft Markings

Notes	Serial	Type (other identity)	Owner/operator, location
	246	Aérospatiale SA365F Dauphin II	IAC No 301 Sqn/3 Operations Wing, Baldonnel
	247	Aérospatiale SA365F Dauphin II	IAC No 301 Sqn/3 Operations Wing, Baldonnel
	251	Grumman G1159C Gulfstream IV	IAC No 102 Sqn/1 Operations Wing, Baldonnel
	252	Airtech CN.235 MPA Persuader	IAC No 101 Sqn/1 Operations Wing, Baldonnel
	253	Airtech CN.235 MPA Persuader	IAC No 101 Sqn/1 Operations Wing, Baldonnel
	254	PBN-2T Defender 4000 (G-BWPN)	IAC No 106 Sqn/1 Operations Wing, Baldonnel
	255	AS355N Twin Squirrel (G-BXEV)	IAC No 106 Sqn/1 Operations Wing, Baldonnel
	256	Eurocopter EC135T-1	IAC No 106 Sqn/1 Operations Wing, Baldonnel

Canadian Forces Airbus A310-304F Polaris 15004 is a regular visitor to the UK. *PRM*

Overseas Military Aircraft Markings

Aircraft included in this section are a selection of those likely to be seen visiting UK civil and military airfields on transport flights, exchange visits, exercises and for air shows. It is not a comprehensive list of *all* aircraft operated by the air arms concerned.

ALGERIA
Force Aérienne Algérienne/ Al Quwwat al Jawwiya al Jaza'eriya

Lockheed C-130H Hercules
7T-WHE	(4935)
7T-WHF	(4934)
7T-WHI	(4930)
7T-WHJ	(4928)
7T-WHQ	(4926)
7T-WHR	(4924)
7T-WHS	(4912)
7T-WHT	(4911)
7T-WHY	(4913)
7T-WHZ	(4914)

Lockheed C-130H 30 Hercules
7T-WHA	(4997)
7T-WHB	(5224)
7T-WHD	(4987)
7T-WHL	(4989)
7T-WHM	(4919)
7T-WHN	(4894)
7T-WHO	(4897)
7T-WHP	(4921)

Grumman G.1159A Gulfstream III/ G.1159C Gulfstream IV/ G.1159C Gulfstream IVSP
Ministry of Defence, Boufarik
7T-VPC	(1418)	
		Gulfstream IV
7T-VPM	(1421)	
		Gulfstream IV
7T-VPR	(1288)	
		Gulfstream IVSP
7T-VPS	(1291)	
		Gulfstream IVSP
7T-VRD	(399)	
		Gulfstream III

Gulfstream Aerospace Gulfstream V
Ministry of Defence, Boufarik
7T-VPG	(617)

AUSTRALIA
Royal Australian Air Force

Boeing 707-338C/368C*
33 Sqn, Amberley
A20-261*
A20-623
A20-624
A20-629

Boeing 737-7DT
34 Sqn, Canberra
A36-001
A36-002

Canadair CL.604 Challenger
34 Sqn, Canberra
A37-001
A37-002
A37-003

Lockheed C-130H Hercules
36 Sqn, Richmond, NSW
A97-001
A97-002
A97-003
A97-004
A97-005
A97-006
A97-007
A97-008
A97-009
A97-010
A97-011
A97-012

Lockheed C-130J-30 Hercules
37 Sqn, Richmond, NSW
A97-440
A97-441
A97-442
A97-447
A97-448
A97-449
A97-450
A97-464
A97-465
A97-466
A97-467
A97-468

Lockheed P-3 Orion
10/11 Sqns, Maritime Patrol Group, Edinburgh, NSW
A9-656	P-3W	10 Sqn
A9-657	P-3W	11 Sqn
A9-658	P-3W	11 Sqn
A9-659	P-3W	11 Sqn
A9-660	P-3W	11 Sqn
A9-661	P-3W	11 Sqn
A9-662	P-3W	11 Sqn
A9-663	P-3W	11 Sqn
A9-664	P-3W	11 Sqn
A9-665	P-3W	10 Sqn
A9-751	P-3C	11 Sqn
A9-752	P-3C	10 Sqn
A9-753	P-3C	10 Sqn
A9-755	P-3C	11 Sqn
A9-756	P-3C	11 Sqn
A9-757	P-3C	10 Sqn
A9-758	P-3C	10 Sqn
A9-759	AP-3C	10 Sqn
A9-760	AP-3C	10 Sqn

AUSTRIA
Öesterreichische Luftstreitkräfte

SAAB 35ÖE Draken
Fliegerregiment II
1 Staffel/Uberwg, Zeltweg;
2 Staffel/Uberwg, Graz
01	(351401)	1 Staffel
02	(351402)	1 Staffel
03	(351403)	1 Staffel
04	(351404)	1 Staffel
05	(351405)	1 Staffel
06	(351406)	1 Staffel
07	(351407)	1 Staffel
08	(351408)	1 Staffel
09	(351409)	1 Staffel
10	(351410)	1 Staffel
11	(351411)	1 Staffel
12	(351412)	1 Staffel
13	(351413)	2 Staffel
14	(351414)	2 Staffel
15	(351415)	2 Staffel
16	(351416)	2 Staffel
18	(351418)	2 Staffel
19	(351419)	2 Staffel
20	(351420)	2 Staffel
21	(351421)	2 Staffel
22	(351422)	2 Staffel
23	(351423)	2 Staffel
24	(351424)	2 Staffel

SAAB 105ÖE
Fliegerregiment III
Dusenstaffel, Linz
(yellow)
B	(105402)
D	(105404)
E	(105405)
F	(105406)
G	(105407)
I	(105409)
J	(105410)

(green)
A	(105411)
B	(105412)
D	(105414)
GF-16	(105416)
GG-17	(105417)

(red)
B	(105422)
C	(105423)
D	(105424)
E	(105425)
F	(105426)
G	(105427)
H	(105428)
I	(105429)
J	(105430)

(blue)
A	(105431)

B	(105432)
C	(105433)
D	(105434)
E	(105435)
F	(105436)
G	(105437)
I	(105439)
J	(105440)

Short SC7 Skyvan 3M
Fliegerregiment I
Flachenstaffel, Tulln
5S-TA
5S-TB

BAHRAIN
BAE RJ.100
Bahrain Defence Force
A9C-BDF

Boeing 747SP-21
Bahrain Amiri Flt
A9C-HHH

Boeing 747-4P8
Bahrain Amiri Flt
A9C-HMK

Grumman
G.1159 Gulfstream IITT/
G.1159C Gulfstream IV
Govt of Bahrain
A9C-BAH Gulfstream IV
A9C-BG Gulfstream IITT

BELGIUM
Belgische Luchtmacht
D-BD Alpha Jet E
7/11 Smaldeel (1 Wg),
Bevekom
AT-01
AT-02
AT-03
AT-05
AT-06
AT-08
AT-10
AT-11
AT-12
AT-13
AT-14
AT-15
AT-17
AT-18
AT-19
AT-20
AT-21
AT-22
AT-23
AT-24
AT-25
AT-26
AT-27
AT-28
AT-29
AT-30
AT-31
AT-32
AT-33

Airbus A.310-322
21 Smaldeel (15 Wg),
Melsbroek
CA-01
CA-02

Dassault Falcon 900B
21 Smaldeel (15 Wg),
Melsbroek
CD-01

Embraer ERJ.135LR/
ERJ.145LR*
21 Smaldeel (15 Wg),
Melsbroek
CE-01
CE-02
CE-03*
CE-04*

Lockheed C-130H Hercules
20 Smaldeel (15 Wg),
Melsbroek
CH-01
CH-02
CH-03
CH-04
CH-05
CH-07
CH-08
CH-09
CH-10
CH-11
CH-12

Dassault Falcon 20E
21 Smaldeel (15 Wg),
Melsbroek
CM-01
CM-02

General Dynamics F-16
(MLU aircraft are marked
with a *)
1,350 Smaldeel (2 Wg),
Florennes [FS];
31,349 Smaldeel, OCU
(10 Wg), Kleine-Brogel
[BL]

FA-27	F-16A(R)	2 Wg
FA-46	F-16A	10 Wg
FA-47	F-16A	2 Wg
FA-48	F-16A*	2 Wg
FA-49	F-16A(R)	2 Wg
FA-50	F-16A(R)	2 Wg
FA-53	F-16A(R)	2 Wg
FA-55	F-16A(R)	2 Wg
FA-56	F-16A*	10 Wg
FA-57	F-16A*	2 Wg
FA-58	F-16A*	2 Wg
FA-60	F-16A*	10 Wg
FA-61	F-16A*	10 Wg
FA-65	F-16A*	10 Wg
FA-66	F-16A*	2 Wg
FA-67	F-16A*	2 Wg
FA-68	F-16A*	10 Wg
FA-69	F-16A	2 Wg
FA-70	F-16A*	10 Wg
FA-71	F-16A*	2 Wg
FA-72	F-16A*	2 Wg
FA-73	F-16A*	10 Wg
FA-74	F-16A*	10 Wg
FA-75	F-16A*	2 Wg
FA-76	F-16A*	10 Wg
FA-77	F-16A*	10 Wg
FA-78	F-16A*	10 Wg
FA-81	F-16A*	10 Wg
FA-82	F-16A*	10 Wg
FA-83	F-16A*	2 Wg
FA-84	F-16A*	2 Wg
FA-86	F-16A*	10 Wg
FA-87	F-16A*	2 Wg
FA-88	F-16A*	2 Wg
FA-89	F-16A*	2 Wg
FA-90	F-16A*	10 Wg
FA-91	F-16A*	10 Wg
FA-92	F-16A*	2 Wg
FA-93	F-16A*	10 Wg
FA-94	F-16A*	2 Wg
FA-95	F-16A*	10 Wg
FA-97	F-16A*	2 Wg
FA-98	F-16A*	10 Wg
FA-99	F-16A*	10 Wg
FA-100	F-16A*	10 Wg
FA-101	F-16A*	10 Wg
FA-102	F-16A*	10 Wg
FA-103	F-16A	349 Sm
FA-104	F-16A*	10 Wg
FA-106	F-16A*	10 Wg
FA-107	F-16A	2 Wg
FA-108	F-16A*	2 Wg
FA-109	F-16A	10 Wg
FA-110	F-16A*	10 Wg
FA-111	F-16A*	10 Wg
FA-112	F-16A*	10 Wg
FA-114	F-16A*	10 Wg
FA-115	F-16A*	2 Wg
FA-116	F-16A*	10 Wg
FA-117	F-16A*	2 Wg
FA-118	F-16A	2 Wg
FA-119	F-16A*	10 Wg
FA-120	F-16A*	2 Wg
FA-121	F-16A	2 Wg
FA-122	F-16A*	10 Wg
FA-123	F-16A*	10 Wg
FA-124	F-16A*	10 Wg
FA-125	F-16A	2 Wg
FA-126	F-16A*	10 Wg
FA-127	F-16A	2 Wg
FA-128	F-16A	2 Wg
FA-129	F-16A	10 Wg
FA-130	F-16A*	10 Wg
FA-131	F-16A	2 Wg
FA-132	F-16A	2 Wg
FA-133	F-16A	2 Wg
FA-134	F-16A*	10 Wg
FA-135	F-16A	2 Wg
FA-136	F-16A*	10 Wg
FB-01	F-16B*	10 Wg
FB-02	F-16B	OCU
FB-04	F-16B	2 Wg
FB-05	F-16B	2 Wg
FB-07	F-16B*	10 Wg
FB-08	F-16B	10 Wg
FB-09	F-16B	2 Wg
FB-10	F-16B	10 Wg
FB-12	F-16B	2 Wg
FB-14	F-16B*	10 Wg
FB-15	F-16B*	OCU
FB-17	F-16B*	OCU
FB-18	F-16B*	10 Wg
FB-20	F-16B*	2 Wg
FB-21	F-16B*	2 Wg
FB-22	F-16B*	OCU
FB-23	F-16B*	10 Wg
FB-24	F-16B*	OCU

Fouga CM170 Magister
Fouga Flight/7 Smaldeel
(1 Wg), Bevekom
MT-04
MT-13
MT-14
MT-26

MT-34
MT-35
MT-37
MT-40
MT-44
MT-48

Westland Sea King Mk48/48A*
40 Smaldeel, Koksijde
RS-01
RS-02
RS-03*
RS-04
RS-05

SIAI Marchetti SF260M/SF260D*
Ecole de Pilotage Elementaire (5 Sm/1 Wg), Bevekom
ST-02
ST-03
ST-04
ST-06
ST-10
ST-12
ST-15
ST-16
ST-17
ST-18
ST-19
ST-20
ST-22
ST-23
ST-24
ST-25
ST-26
ST-27
ST-30
ST-31
ST-32
ST-34
ST-35
ST-36
ST-40*
ST-41*
ST-42*
ST-43*
ST-44*
ST-45*
ST-46*
ST-47*
ST-48*

Aviation Légère de la Force Terrestre/Belgische Landmacht
Sud SA318C/SE3130* Alouette II
16 BnHLn, Bierset;
SLV, Brasschaat

A-22*	16 BnHLn
A-40	SLV
A-41	SLV
A-43	SLV
A-44	SLV
A-46	SLV
A-47	16 BnHLn
A-49	16 BnHLn
A-50	16 BnHLn
A-53	16 BnHLn
A-54	SLV
A-55	16 BnHLn
A-57	16 BnHLn
A-59	16 BnHLn
A-61	SLV
A-62	16 BnHLn
A-64	SLV
A-65	SLV
A-66	SLV
A-68	16 BnHLn
A-69	16 BnHLn
A-70	SLV
A-72	16 BnHLn
A-73	16 BnHLn
A-74	16 BnHLn
A-75	16 BnHLn
A-77	16 BnHLn
A-78	16 BnHLn
A-79	SLV
A-80	16 BnHLn

Britten-Norman BN-2A/BN-2B-21* Islander
16 BnHLn, Bierset;
SLV, Brasschaat

B-01	LA	SLV
B-02*	LB	SLV
B-03*	LC	SLV
B-04*	LD	SLV
B-07*	LG	16 BnHLn
B-08*	LH	16 BnHLn
B-09*	LI	16 BnHLn
B-10*	LJ	16 BnHLn
B-11*	LK	SLV
B-12	LL	SLV

Agusta A109HA/HO*
17 BnHATk, Bierset;
18 BnHATk, Bierset;
SLV, Brasschaat

H-01*	SLV
H-02*	SLV
H-03*	SLV
H-04*	SLV
H-05*	17 BnHATk
H-06*	17 BnHATk
H-07*	17 BnHATk
H-08*	18 BnHATk
H-09*	18 BnHATk
H-10*	18 BnHATk
H-11*	SLV
H-12*	SLV
H-13*	SLV
H-14*	SLV
H-15*	SLV
H-16*	18 BnHATk
H-17*	17 BnHATk
H-18*	18 BnHATk
H-20	18 BnHATk
H-21	18 BnHATk
H-22	17 BnHATk
H-23	17 BnHATk
H-24	17 BnHATk
H-25	18 BnHATk
H-26	18 BnHATk
H-27	18 BnHATk
H-28	18 BnHATk
H-29	18 BnHATk
H-30	18 BnHATk
H-31	18 BnHATk
H-32	18 BnHATk
H-33	18 BnHATk
H-34	SLV
H-35	17 BnHATk
H-36	17 BnHATk
H-37	17 BnHATk
H-38	17 BnHATk
H-39	18 BnHATk
H-40	SLV
H-41	17 BnHATk
H-42	SLV
H-43	17 BnHATk
H-44	17 BnHATk
H-45	17 BnHATk
H-46	17 BnHATk

Force Navale Belge/Belgische Zeemacht
Sud SA316B Alouette III
Koksijde Heli Flight

M-1	(OT-ZPA)
M-2	(OT-ZPB)
M-3	(OT-ZPC)

Gendarmerie/Rijkswacht
Cessna 182 Skylane
Luchsteundetachment, Melsbroek

G-01	C.182Q
G-03	C.182R
G-04	C.182R

MDH MD.520N
Luchsteundetachment, Melsbroek
G-14
G-15

MDH MD.900 Explorer
Luchsteundetachment, Melsbroek
G-10
G-11
G-12

BOTSWANA
Botswana Defence Force
Grumman G.1159C Gulfstream IV
OK-1

Lockheed C-130B Hercules
OM-1
OM-2
OM-3

BRAZIL
Força Aérea Brasileira
Boeing KC-137
2° GT 2° Esq, Galeão;
2401
2402
2403
2404

Lockheed C-130 Hercules
1° GT, 1° Esq, Galeão;
1° GTT, 1° Esq, Afonsos

2451	C-130E	1° GTT
2453	C-130E	1° GTT
2454	C-130E	1° GTT
2456	C-130E	1° GTT
2458	SC-130E	1° GT
2459	SC-130E	1° GT
2461	KC-130H	1° GT
2462	KC-130H	1° GT
2463	C-130H	1° GT
2464	C-130H	1° GT
2465	C-130H	1° GT
2467	C-130H	1° GT

Brunei – Czech Republic

BRUNEI
Airbus A.340-212
Brunei Govt, Bandar Seri
Bergawan
V8-BKH

Boeing 747-430
Brunei Govt, Bandar Seri
Bergawan
V8-ALI

Boeing 767-27GER
Brunei Govt, Bandar Seri
Bergawan
V8-MHB

Gulfstream Aerospace
Gulfstream V
Brunei Govt, Bandar Seri
Bergawan
055
V8-007

BULGARIA
Bulgarsky Voenno-Vazdushni
Sily
  Antonov An-30
  16 TAP, Sofia/Dobroslavtzi
  055

Bulgarian Govt
  Dassault Falcon 2000
  Bulgarian Govt, Sofia
  LZ-OOI

  Tupolev Tu-134A-3
  Bulgarian Govt, Sofia
  LZ-TUG

  Tupolev Tu-154M
  Bulgarian Govt, Sofia
  LZ-BTQ
  LZ-BTZ

BURKINA FASO
  Boeing 727-14
  Govt of Burkina Faso,
    Ouagadougou
  XT-BBE

CAMEROON
  Grumman
  G.1159A Gulfstream III
  Govt of Cameroon, Yaounde
  TJ-AAW

CANADA
Canadian Forces
  Lockheed CC-130 Hercules
  CC-130E/CC-130E(SAR)*
  413 Sqn, Greenwood (SAR)
    (14 Wing);
  424 Sqn, Trenton (SAR)
    (8 Wing);
  426 Sqn, Trenton (8 Wing);
  429 Sqn, Trenton (8 Wing);
  435 Sqn, Winnipeg (17 Wing);
  436 Sqn, Trenton (8 Wing)

130305*	8 Wing
130306*	14 Wing
130307	8 Wing
130308*	8 Wing
130310*	8 Wing
130311*	8 Wing
130313	8 Wing
130314*	14 Wing
130315*	14 Wing
130316	8 Wing
130317	8 Wing
130319	8 Wing
130320	8 Wing
130323	8 Wing
130324*	8 Wing
130325	8 Wing
130326	8 Wing
130327	8 Wing
130328	8 Wing

CC-130H/CC-130H(T)*
130332	17 Wing
130333	17 Wing
130334	8 Wing
130335	8 Wing
130336	17 Wing
130337	8 Wing
130338*	17 Wing
130339*	17 Wing
130340*	17 Wing
130341*	17 Wing
130342*	17 Wing

CC-130H-30
130343	8 Wing
130344	8 Wing

  Lockheed CP-140 Aurora/
  CP-140A Arcturus*
  404/405/415 Sqns,
    Greenwood (14 Wing);
  407 Sqn, Comox (19 Wing)
140101	14 Wing
140102	14 Wing
140103	407 Sqn
140104	14 Wing
140105	407 Sqn
140106	14 Wing
140107	14 Wing
140108	14 Wing
140109	407 Sqn
140110	14 Wing
140111	14 Wing
140112	14 Wing
140113	14 Wing
140114	14 Wing
140115	14 Wing
140116	407 Sqn
140117	14 Wing
140118	407 Sqn
140119*	14 Wing
140120*	14 Wing
140121*	14 Wing

  De Havilland Canada CT-142
  402 Sqn, Winnipeg (17 Wing)
142803	CT-142
142804	CT-142
142805	CT-142
142806	CT-142

  Canadair CC-144 Challenger
  412 Sqn, Ottawa (8 Wing)
144601	CC-144A
144602	CC-144A
144604	CC-144A
144614	CC-144B
144615	CC-144B
144616	CC-144B

  Airbus CC-150 Polaris
  (A310-304/A310-304F*)
  437 Sqn, Trenton (8 Wing)

15001	991
15002*	992
15003*	993
15004*	994
15005*	995

CHILE
Fuerza Aérea de Chile
  Boeing 707
  Grupo 10, Santiago
902	707-351C
903	707-330B
904	707-358C

  Boeing 737
  Grupo 10, Santiago
921	737-58N
922	737-330

  Extra EA-300
  Los Halcones
021	[1]
022	[7]
024	[2]
025	[3]
027	[4]
028	[5]
029	[6]

  Grumman
  G.1159C Gulfstream IV
  Grupo 10, Santiago
  911

  Lockheed C-130B/H
  Hercules
  Grupo 10, Santiago
994	C-130B
995	C-130H
996	C-130H
997	C-130B
998	C-130B

CROATIA
  Canadair CL.601 Challenger
  Croatian Govt, Zagreb
  9A-CRO
  9A-CRT

CZECH REPUBLIC
Ceske Vojenske Letectvo
  Aero L-39/L-59 Albatros
  42 slt/4 zTL, Cáslav;
  321 tpzlt & 322 tlt/32 zTL,
    Námĕst;
  341 vlt/34 zSL, Pardubice;
  LZO, Praha/Kbely
0001	L-39MS	LZO
0103	L-39C	341 vlt/34 zSL
0105	L-39C	341 vlt/34 zSL
0106	L-39C	341 vlt/34 zSL
0107	L-39C	341 vlt/34 zSL
0108	L-39C	341 vlt/34 zSL
0113	L-39C	341 vlt/34 zSL
0115	L-39C	341 vlt/34 ZSL
0440	L-39C	341 vlt/34 zSL
0441	L-39C	341 vlt/34 zSL
0444	L-39C	341 vlt/34 zSL
0445	L-39C	341 vlt/34 zSL
0448	L-39C	341 vlt/34 zSL
2341	L-39ZA	42 slt/4 zTL
2344	L-39ZA	42 slt/4 zTL
2347	L-39ZA	42 slt/4 zTL
2350	L-39ZA	42 slt/4 zTL

2415	L-39ZA	42 slt/4 zTL
2418	L-39ZA	42 slt/4 zTL
2421	L-39ZA	42 slt/4 zTL
2424	L-39ZA	32 zTL
2427	L-39ZA	42 slt/4 zTL
2430	L-39ZA	42 slt/4 zTL
2433	L-39ZA	42 slt/4 zTL
2436	L-39ZA	42 slt/4 zTL
3903	L-39ZA	32 zTL
4605	L-39C	341 vlt/34 ZSL
4606	L-39C	341 vlt/34 ZSL
5013	L-39ZA	32 zTL
5015	L-39ZA	32 zTL
5017	L-39ZA	32 zTL
5019	L-39ZA	32 zTL

Aero L-159 ALCA/L-159T*
42 slt/4 zTL, Cáslav;
322 tlt/32 zTL, Náměšt;
LZO, Praha/Kbely

5831*	LZO
5832	LZO
6001	4 zTL
6002	4 zTL
6003	4 zTL
6004	
6005	4 zTL
6006	4 zTL
6007	4 zTL
6008	4 zTL
6009	4 zTL
6010	4 zTL
6011	4 zTL
6012	4 zTL
6013	4 zTL
6014	4 zTL
6015	4 zTL
6016	4 zTL
6017	4 zTL
6018	4 zTL
6019	32 zTL
6020	32 zTL
6021	32 zTL
6022	32 zTL
6023	32 zTL
6024	32 zTL
6025	32 zTL
6026	4 zTL
6027	4 zTL
6028	32 zTL
6029	32 zTL
6030	32 zTL
6031	32 zTL
6032	32 zTL
6033	32 zTL
6034	32 zTL
6035	32 zTL
6036	32 zTL
6037	32 zTL
6038	32 zTL
6039	32 zTL
6040	32 zTL
6041	32 zTL
6042	32 zTL

Antonov An-24V
61 dlt/6 zDL, Praha/Kbely
7109
7110

**Antonov An-26/
An-26Z-1M***
61 dlt/6 zDL, Praha/Kbely
2408

2409
2507
3209*
4201

Antonov An-30FG
344 pzdlt/34 zSL, Pardubice
1107

**Canadair CL.601-3A
Challenger**
61 dlt/6 zDL, Praha/Kbely
5105

LET 410 Turbolet
61 dlt/6 zDL, Praha/Kbely;
344 pzdlt/34 zSL, Pardubice

0503	L-410MA	
		344 pzdlt/34 zSL
0712	L-410UVP-S	
		344 pzdlt/34 zSL
0731	L-410UVP	
		61 dlt/6 zDL
0926	L-410UVP-T	
		61 dlt/6 zDL [4]
0928	L-410UVP-T	
		61 dlt/6 zDL
0929	L-410UVP-T	
		61 dlt/6 zDL [2]
1132	L-410UVP-T	
		61 dlt/6 zDL [3]
1134	L-410UVP	
		61 dlt/6 zDL
1504	L-410UVP	
		61 dlt/6 zDL
1523	L-410FG	
		344 pzdlt/34 zSL
1525	L-410FG	
		344 pzdlt/34 zSL
1526	L-410FG	
		344 pzdlt/34 zSL
2312	L-410UVP-E	
		61 dlt/6 zDL
2601	L-410UVP-E	
		61 dlt/6 zDL
2602	L-410UVP-E	
		61 dlt/6 zDL
2710	L-410UVP-E	
		61 dlt/6 zDL

LET 610M
61 dlt/6 zDL, Praha/Kbely;
LZO, Praha/Kbely
0003 1 dlt/6 zDL
0005 LZO

**Mikoyan MiG-21MF/
MiG-21UM***
41 slt/4 zTL, Cáslav;
LZO, Ceske Budejovice

2205	41 slt/4 zTL
2500	41 slt/4 zTL
2614	41 slt/4 zTL
3186*	41 slt/4 zTL
3746*	41 slt/4 zTL
4003	41 slt/4 zTL
4017	41 slt/4 zTL
4175	41 slt/4 zTL
4307	LZO
4405	41 slt/4 zTL
5031*	41 slt/4 zTL
5201	41 slt/4 zTL
5203	LZO
5210	41 slt/4 zTL
5212	41 slt/4 zTL
5213	41 slt/4 zTL
5214	41 slt/4 zTL
5301	41 slt/4 zTL
5302	41 slt/4 zTL
5303	41 slt/4 zTL
5304	41 slt/4 zTL
5305	41 slt/4 zTL
5508	41 slt/4 zTL
5512	41 slt/4 zTL
5581	41 slt/4 zTL
5603	41 slt/4 zTL
7701	41 slt/4 zTL
7802	41 slt/4 zTL
9011*	41 slt/4 zTL
9332*	41 slt/4 zTL
9333*	41 slt/4 zTL
9341*	41 slt/4 zTL
9399*	41 slt/4 zTL
9410	41 slt/4 zTL
9414	41 slt/4 zTL
9707	41 slt/4 zTL
9711	41 slt/4 zTL
9801	41 slt/4 zTL
9802	LZO
9804	41 slt/4 zTL
9805	41 slt/4 zTL

Mil Mi-24
331 ltBVr/33 zVrL, Přerov

0103	Mi-24D
0140	Mi-24D
0142	Mi-24D
0146	Mi-24D
0151	Mi-24D
0214	Mi-24D
0216	Mi-24D
0217	Mi-24D
0218	Mi-24D
0219	Mi-24D
0220	Mi-24D
0701	Mi-24V1
0702	Mi-24V1
0703	Mi-24V1
0705	Mi-24V1
0709	Mi-24V1
0710	Mi-24V1
0788	Mi-24V1
0789	Mi-24V1
0790	Mi-24V1
0812	Mi-24V1
0815	Mi-24V1
0816	Mi-24V1
0834	Mi-24V2
0835	Mi-24V2
0836	Mi-24V2
0837	Mi-24V2
0838	Mi-24V2
0839	Mi-24V2
4010	Mi-24D
4011	Mi-24D
6050	Mi-24DU

Tupolev Tu-154
61 dlt/6 zDL, Praha/Kbely
0601 Tu-154B-2
1003 Tu-154M
1016 Tu-154M

Yakovlev Yak-40
61 dlt/6 zDL, Praha/Kbely
0260 Yak-40
1257 Yak-40K

Denmark – Egypt

DENMARK
Flyvevåbnet

Lockheed C-130H Hercules
Eskadrille 721, Vaerløse
B-678
B-679
B-680

Canadair CL.604 Challenger
Eskadrille 721, Vaerløse
C-080
C-168
C-172

General Dynamics F-16
(MLU aircraft are marked
with a *)
Eskadrille 726, Aalborg;
Eskadrille 727, Skrydstrup;
Eskadrille 730, Skrydstrup

E-004	F-16A*	Esk 726
E-005	F-16A*	Esk 726
E-007	F-16A*	Esk 726
E-008	F-16A*	Esk 726
E-011	F-16A	Esk 726
E-016	F-16A	Esk 726
E-017	F-16A*	Esk 730
E-018	F-16A*	Esk 726
E-024	F-16A	Esk 730
E-074	F-16A	Esk 730
E-075	F-16A	Esk 730
E-107	F-16A*	Esk 726
E-174	F-16A	Esk 727
E-176	F-16A	Esk 726
E-177	F-16A*	Esk 727
E-180	F-16A*	Esk 730
E-181	F-16A	Esk 727
E-182	F-16A	Esk 730
E-183	F-16A	Esk 727
E-184	F-16A	Esk 727
E-187	F-16A*	Esk 730
E-188	F-16A	Esk 727
E-190	F-16A	Esk 730
E-191	F-16A	Esk 730
E-192	F-16A*	Esk 730
E-193	F-16A	Esk 727
E-194	F-16A*	Esk 730
E-195	F-16A	Esk 730
E-196	F-16A	Esk 727
E-197	F-16A	Esk 727
E-198	F-16A	Esk 726
E-199	F-16A*	Esk 730
E-200	F-16A	Esk 727
E-202	F-16A*	Esk 730
E-203	F-16A*	Esk 730
E-596	F-16A*	Esk 730
E-597	F-16A*	Esk 730
E-598	F-16A*	Esk 726
E-599	F-16A*	Esk 727
E-600	F-16A*	Esk 726
E-601	F-16A*	Esk 730
E-602	F-16A*	Esk 730
E-603	F-16A*	Esk 730
E-604	F-16A*	Esk 726
E-605	F-16A*	Esk 730
E-606	F-16A*	Esk 730
E-607	F-16A*	Esk 730
E-608	F-16A*	Esk 726
E-609	F-16A*	Esk 726
E-610	F-16A*	Esk 730
E-611	F-16A	Esk 726
ET-022	F-16B	Esk 727
ET-197	F-16B	Esk 727
ET-198	F-16B*	Esk 727
ET-199	F-16B*	Esk 730
ET-204	F-16B*	Esk 726
ET-206	F-16B*	Esk 730
ET-207	F-16B*	Esk 730
ET-208	F-16B	Esk 730
ET-210	F-16B	Esk 727
ET-612	F-16B*	Esk 727
ET-613	F-16B*	Esk 726
ET-614	F-16B*	Esk 727
ET-615	F-16B*	Esk 726
ET-626	F-16B	Esk 727

Grumman G.1159A Gulfstream III
Eskadrille 721, Vaerløse
F-249
F-313

SAAB T-17 Supporter
Eskadrille 721, Vaerløse;
Flyveskolen, Karup (FLSK)

T-401	FLSK
T-402	FLSK
T-403	FLSK
T-404	FLSK
T-405	FLSK
T-407	Esk 721
T-408	FLSK
T-409	FLSK
T-410	FLSK
T-411	FLSK
T-412	FLSK
T-413	FLSK
T-414	FLSK
T-415	FLSK
T-417	FLSK
T-418	Esk 721
T-419	FLSK
T-420	Esk 721
T-421	FLSK
T-423	FLSK
T-425	FLSK
T-426	FLSK
T-427	FLSK
T-428	FLSK
T-429	FLSK
T-430	FLSK
T-431	Esk 721
T-432	FLSK

Sikorsky S-61A Sea King
Eskadrille 722, Vaerløse
Detachments at:
Aalborg, Ronne, Skrydstrup
U-240
U-275
U-276
U-277
U-278
U-279
U-280
U-481

Søvaernets Flyvetjaeneste (Navy)
Westland Lynx Mk 80/90/90B
Eskadrille 728, Karup

S-134	Mk 80
S-142	Mk 80
S-170	Mk 90B
S-175	Mk 80
S-181	Mk 90B
S-191	Mk 90B
S-249	Mk 90
S-256	Mk 90

Haerens Flyvetjaeneste (Army)
Hughes 500M
OVH Kmp, Vandel;
PVH Kmp, Vandel
H-201
H-202
H-203
H-205
H-206
H-207
H-209
H-211
H-213
H-244
H-245
H-246

Aérospatiale AS.550C-2 Fennec
PVH Kmp, Vandel
P-090
P-234
P-254
P-275
P-276
P-287
P-288
P-319
P-320
P-339
P-352
P-369

EGYPT
Al Quwwat al-Jawwiya il Misriya
Lockheed C-130H/ C-130H-30* Hercules
16 Sqn, Cairo West
1271/SU-BAB
1272/SU-BAC
1273/SU-BAD
1274/SU-BAE
1275/SU-BAF
1277/SU-BAI
1278/SU-BAJ
1279/SU-BAK
1280/SU-BAL
1281/SU-BAM
1282/SU-BAN
1283/SU-BAP
1284/SU-BAQ
1285/SU-BAR
1286/SU-BAS
1287/SU-BAT
1288/SU-BAU
1289/SU-BAV
1290/SU-BAW
1291/SU-BAX
1292/SU-BAY
1293/SU-BKS*
1294/SU-BKT*
1295/SU-BKU*

Egyptian Govt
Airbus A.340-211
Egyptian Govt, Cairo
SU-GGG

Boeing 707-366C
Egyptian Govt, Cairo
SU-AXJ

Grumman
G.1159A Gulfstream III/
G.1159C Gulfstream IV
Egyptian Air Force/Govt,
  Cairo

SU-BGM	Gulfstream IV
SU-BGU	Gulfstream III
SU-BGV	Gulfstream III
SU-BNC	Gulfstream IV
SU-BND	Gulfstream IV

FINLAND
Suomen Ilmavoimat
Fokker F.27 Friendship
Tukilentolaivue,
  Jyväskylä/Tikkakoski

FF-1	F.27-100
FF-2	F.27-100
FF-3	F.27-400M

McDonnell Douglas
F-18 Hornet
Hävittäjälentolaivue 11,
  Roveniemi;
Hävittäjälentolaivue 21,
  Tampere/Pirkkala;
Hävittäjälentolaivue 31,
  Kuopio/Rissala;
Koelentokeskus, Halli
F-18C Hornet

HN-401	HavLLv 31
HN-402	HavLLv 21
HN-403	HavLLv 31
HN-404	HavLLv 11
HN-405	HavLLv 21
HN-406	HavLLv 21
HN-407	HavLLv 31
HN-408	HavLLv 31
HN-409	HavLLv 21
HN-410	KoelntK
HN-411	HavLLv 11
HN-412	HavLLv 21
HN-413	HavLLv 21
HN-414	KoelntK
HN-415	HavLLv 31
HN-416	HavLLv 11
HN-417	HavLLv 21
HN-418	HavLLv 31
HN-419	HavLLv 11
HN-420	HavLLv 11
HN-421	HavLLv 21
HN-422	
HN-423	HavLLv 31
HN-424	HavLLv 31
HN-425	HavLLv 21
HN-426	HavLLv 21
HN-427	HavLLv 21
HN-428	
HN-429	HavLLv 11
HN-431	HavLLv 31
HN-432	HavLLv 31
HN-433	HavLLv 21
HN-434	HavLLv 21
HN-435	HavLLv 31
HN-436	HavLLv 21
HN-437	
HN-438	HavLLv 31
HN-439	HavLLv 21
HN-440	HavLLv 11
HN-441	HavLLv 21

HN-442	HavLLv 31
HN-443	
HN-444	HavLLv 31
HN-445	HavLLv 21
HN-446	HavLLv 31
HN-447	HavLLv 11
HN-448	
HN-449	HavLLv 21
HN-450	
HN-451	HavLLv 21
HN-452	HavLLv 21
HN-453	HavLLv 21
HN-454	
HN-455	HavLLv 21
HN-456	HavLLv 11
HN-457	HavLLv 11

F-18D Hornet

HN-461	KoelntK
HN-462	HavLLv 21
HN-463	HavLLv 21
HN-464	HavLLv 11
HN-465	HavLLv 21
HN-466	HavLLv 11
HN-467	HavLLv 31

FRANCE
Armée de l'Air
Aérospatiale SN601
Corvette
CEV, Cazaux

1	MV
2	MW
10	MX

Aérospatiale TB-30 Epsilon
Cartouche Dorée,
(EPAA 00.315) Cognac;
EPAA 00.315, Cognac;
SOCATA, Tarbes
Please note: A large number
of these machines are kept
in temporary storage at
Chateaudun

1	315-UA
2	315-UB
3	FZ SOCATA
4	315-UC
5	315-UD
6	315-UE
7	315-UF
8	315-UG
9	315-UH
10	315-UI
12	315-UK
13	315-UL
14	315-UM
15	315-UN
16	315-UO
17	315-UP
19	315-UR
20	315-US
21	315-UT
23	315-UV
24	315-UW
25	315-UX
26	315-UY
27	315-UZ
28	315-VA
29	315-VB
30	315-VC
31	315-VD
32	315-VE
33	315-VF
34	315-VG

35	315-VH
36	315-VI
37	315-VJ
38	315-VK
39	315-VL
40	315-VM
41	315-VN
42	315-VO
43	315-VP
44	315-VQ
45	315-VR
46	315-VS
47	315-VT
48	315-VU
49	315-VV
50	315-VW
52	315-VX
53	315-VY
54	315-VZ
56	315-WA
57	F-ZVLB
61	315-WD
62	315-WE
63	315-WF
64	315-WG
65	315-WH
66	315-WI
67	315-WJ
68	315-WK
69	315-WL
70	315-WM
72	315-WO
73	315-WP
74	315-WQ
75	315-WR
76	315-WS
77	315-WT
78	315-WU
79	315-WV
80	315-WW
81	315-WX
82	315-WY
83	315-WZ
84	315-XA
85	315-XB
86	315-XC
87	315-XD
88	315-XE
89	315-XF
90	315-XG
91	315-XH
92	F-SEXI [1]*
93	315-XJ
94	315-XK
95	315-XL
96	315-XM
97	315-XN
98	315-XO
99	315-XP
100	F-SEXQ [2]*
101	315-XR
102	315-XS
103	315-XT
104	315-XU
105	F-SEXV [4]*
106	315-XW
107	315-XX
108	315-XY
109	315-XZ
110	315-YA
111	315-YB
112	315-YC
113	315-YD
114	315-YE

115	315-YF	
116	315-YG	
117	F-SEYH [3]*	
118	315-YI	
119	315-YJ	
120	315-YK	
121	315-YL	
122	315-YM	
123	315-YN	
124	315-YO	
125	315-YP	
126	315-YQ	
127	315-YR	
128	315-YS	
129	315-YT	
130	315-YU	
131	315-YV	
132	315-YW	
133	315-YX	
134	315-YY	
135	315-YZ	
136	315-ZA	
137	315-ZB	
138	315-ZC	
139	315-ZD	
140	315-ZE	
141	315-ZF	
142	315-ZG	
143	315-ZH	
144	315-ZI	
145	315-ZJ	
146	315-ZK	
149	315-ZM	
150	315-ZN	
152	315-ZO	
153	315-ZP	
154	315-ZQ	
155	315-ZR	
158	315-ZS	
159	315-ZT	

Airbus A.310-304
ET 03.060 *Esterel*, Paris/ Charles de Gaulle

418	F-RADC
421	F-RADA
422	F-RADB

Airbus A.319CJ-115
ETEC 00.065, Villacoublay

1485	F-RBFA
1556	F-RBFB

Airtech CN-235M-200
ETE 00.042 *Ventoux*, Mont-de-Marsan
ETL 01.062 *Vercors*, Creil;
ETOM 00.052 *La Tontouta*, Noumea;
ETOM 00.082 *Maine*, Faaa-Tahiti

043	62-IA	01.062
045	62-IB	01.062
065	82-IC	00.082
066	52-ID	00.052
071	62-IE	01.062
072	82-IF	00.082
105	62-IG	01.062
107	52-IH	00.052
111	62-II	01.062
114	62-IJ	01.062
123	62-IM	01.062
128	62-IK	00.042
129	62-IL	01.062
137	62-IN	01.062
141	62-IO	01.062

Boeing C-135 Stratotanker
ERV 00.093 *Bretagne*, Istres

470	C-135FR	93-CA
471	C-135FR	93-CB
472	C-135FR	93-CC
474	C-135FR	93-CE
475	C-135FR	93-CF
497	KC-135R	93-CM
525	KC-135R	93-CN
574	KC-135R	93-CP
735	C-135FR	93-CG
736	C-135FR	93-CH
737	C-135FR	93-CI
738	C-135FR	93-CJ
739	C-135FR	93-CK
740	C-135FR	93-CL

Boeing E-3F Sentry
EDCA 00.036, Avord

201	36-CA
202	36-CB
203	36-CC
204	36-CD

CASA 212-300 Aviocar
CEV, Cazaux & Istres

377	MO
378	MP
386	MQ
388	MS

Cessna 310
CEV, Cazaux & Istres

046	310L	wfu
185	310N	AU
187	310N	BJ
188	310N	BK
190	310N	BL
192	310N	BM
193	310N	BG
194	310N	BH
242	310K	AW
244	310K	AX
513	310N	BI
693	310N	BI
820	310Q	CL
981	310Q	BF

D-BD Alpha Jet
AMD-BA, Istres;
CEAM (EC 02.330), Mont-de-Marsan;
CEV, Cazaux & Istres;
CITac 00.339 *Aquitaine*, Luxeuil;
EAC 00.314, Tours;
EC 01.002 *Cicogne*, Dijon;
EC 01.007 *Provence* & EC 02.007 *Argonne*, St Dizier;
EPNER, Istres;
ERS 01.091 *Gascogne*, Mont-de-Marsan;
ETO 01.008 *Saintonge* & ETO 02.008 *Nice*, Cazaux;
GI 00.312, Salon de Provence;
Patrouille de France (PDF) (EPAA 20.300), Salon de Provence

01	F-ZJTS	CEV
E1	CEV	
E3	314-LV	00.314
E4	CEV	
E5	339-WH	00.339
E7	314-LJ	00.314
E8	CEV	
E9	8-MJ	01.008
E10	314-LK	00.314
E11	8-MW	01.008
E12	CEV	
E13	8-NM	02.008
E14	8-NX	02.008
E15	8-NO	02.008
E17	314-TE	00.314
E18	8-NN	02.008
E19	330-AH	CEAM
E20	339-DI	00.339
E21	330-AL	CEAM
E22	314-UB	00.314
E23	314-UG	00.314
E24	314-TJ	00.314
E25	314-UK	00.314
E26	314-LS	00.314
E28	8-NK	02.008
E29	314-TM	00.314
E30	314-TD	00.314
E31	314-TY	00.314
E32	314-LF	00.314
E33	8-MZ	01.008
E34	8-MF	01.008
E35	314-UF	00.314
E36	2-EF	01.002
E37	8-NI	02.008
E38	339-DG	00.339
E41	F-TERA	*PDF* [3]
E42	7-PX	2.007
E43	314-LI	00.314
E44	314-LP	00.314
E45		
E46	8-NL	02.008
E47	7-PJ	2.007
E48	8-MH	01.008
E49	314-TA	00.314
E51	314-TH	00.314
E52		
E53	314-TC	00.314
E55	314-UC	00.314
E58		
E59	314-LY	00.314
E60	EPNER	
E61		
E63	314-LN	00.314
E64	314-TL	00.314
E65	8-MD	01.008
E66	8-ME	01.008
E67	314-TB	00.314
E68		
E69	314-TO	00.314
E72	314-LA	00.314
E73	8-ND	02.008
E74	8-MS	01.008
E75	F-TERW	*PDF* [6]
E76	8-MR	01.008
E79	8-MI	01.008
E80	CEV	
E81	314-LX	00.314
E82	8-NB	02.008
E83	2-EI	01.002
E84		
E85	314-LF	00.314
E86	8-NS	02.008
E87		
E88	314-LL	00.314
E89	314-TQ	00.314

E90		
E91	2-EL	01.002
E92	330-AK	CEAM
E93	314-LD	00.314
E94	314-UM	00.314
E95		
E96	8-MT	01.008
E97	314-UN	00.314
E98	314-TT	00.314
E99	8-NF	02.008
E100	EPNER	
E101		
E102		
E103	314-UA	00.314
E104	314-TG	00.314
E105	314-LE	00.314
E106	8-NA	02.008
E107	312-RT	00.312
E108		
E109	8-NJ	02.008
E110	8-NG	02.008
E112	DA	01.091
E113	312-RU	00.312
E114	314-TU	00.314
E115	8-NW	02.008
E116	8-MG	01.008
E117	314-LU	00.314
E118	314-LM	00.314
E119	7-PZ	02.007
E120	F-TERG	PDF [1]
E121	F-TERK	PDF
E122	F-TERD	PDF [5]
E123	8-ML	01.008
E124	312-RS	00.312
E125	314-LI	00.314
E126	314-LI	00.314
E127		
E128	F-TERN	PDF [4]
E129	314-TO	00.314
E130	314-LQ	00.314
E131	312-RV	00.312
E132	314-TR	00.314
E133	8-NE	02.008
E134	7-PX	02.007
E135	F-TERX	PDF [2]
E136	314-TN	00.314
E137	339-DE	00.339
E138		
E139	330-AH	CEAM
E140	314-UH	00.314
E141	314-LC	00.314
E142	314-LB	00.314
E143	8-MM	01.008
E144	314-LO	00.314
E145	314-LZ	00.314
E146		
E147	8-NH	02.008
E148	8-NP	02.008
E149	8-MO	01.008
E150	8-NC	02.008
E151	8-MC	01.008
E152	339-DH	00.339
E153	F-TERH	PDF
E154	339-DF	00.339
E155	314-TP	00.314
E156	314-TI	00.314
E157	314-LG	00.314
E158	F-TERG	PDF [9]
E159	7-PP	02.007
E160	F-TERC	PDF [0]
E161	8-MK	01.008
E162	314-TZ	00.314
E163	F-TERB	PDF [8]

E164	8-MB	01.008
E165	F-TER.	PDF
E166	314-TX	00.314
E167		
E168	314-TS	00.314
E169	F-TERQ	PDF [7]
E170	7-PQ	02.007
E171	314-LR	00.314
E173	314-LH	00.314
E176	8-MA	01.008

Dassault Falcon 20
CEV, Cazaux & Istres;
CITac 00.339 Aquitaine, Luxeuil;
EAM 09.120, Cazaux;
ETEC 00.065, Villacoublay

22	CS	CEV
49	120-FA	09.120
79	CT	CEV
86	CG	CEV
93	F-RAED	00.065
96	CB	CEV
104	CW	CEV
124	CC	CEV
131	CD	CEV
138	CR	CEV
167	(F-RAEB)	00.065
182	339-JA	00.339
188	CX	CEV
238	F-RAEE	00.065
252	CA	CEV
260	F-RAEA	00.065
263	CY	CEV
268	F-RAEF	00.065
288	CV	CEV
291	65-EG	00.065
342	F-RAEC	00.065
375	CZ	CEV
422	65-EH	00.065
451	339-JC	00.339
483	339-JI	00.339

Dassault Falcon 50
ETEC 00.065, Villacoublay

5	F-RAFI	
27	(F-RAFK)	
34	(F-RAFL)	
78	F-RAFJ	

Dassault Falcon 900
ETEC 00.065, Villacoublay

2	(F-RAFP)	
4	(F-RAFQ)	

Dassault Mirage IVP
ERS 01.091 Gascogne, Mont-de-Marsan

25	AX	
36	BI	
53	BZ	
59	CF	
61	CH	

Dassault Mirage F.1
CEAM (EC 02.330), Mont-de-Marsan;
CEV, Cazaux & Istres;
EC 01.030 Alsace &
EC 02.030 Normandie Niemen, Colmar;
ER 01.033 Belfort,
ER 02.033 Savoie &
EC 03.033 Lorraine, Reims;
EC 04.033 Vexin, Djibouti

Mirage F.1C/F.1CT*

5	33-FC	03.033
24		
31		
32		
52	33-FB	03.033
62	33-FK	03.033
64		
76	33-FI	03.033
77	33-FR	03.033
80	33-FP	03.033
81	33-LJ	04.033
83	33-FO	03.033
84		
85		
87	33-FS	03.033
90	33-FE	03.033
100	33-LA	04.033
103	33-FU	03.033
201	33-FJ	03.033
202	33-FN	03.033
203	33-LB	04.033
205		
206	33-FN	03.033
207*	330-AO	CEAM
210	33-LC	04.033
211	33-FQ	03.033
213	33-FW	03.033
214		
218	33-LC	04.033
219*	30-SN	01.030
220*	330-AJ	CEAM
221*	30-SY	01.030
223*	30-QX	02.030
224	33-LG	04.033
225*	30-QE	02.030
226*	30-QU	02.030
227*	330-AP	CEAM
228*	30-QT	02.030
229*	30-QC	02.030
230*		
231*	30-SA	01.030
232*	30-QW	02.030
233*	30-QG	02.030
234*	30-SI	01.030
235*	30-SK	01.030
236*	30-SB	01.030
237*	30-SM	01.030
238*	30-QN	02.030
239*	30-QD	02.030
241*	30-QA	02.030
242*		
243*	30-QJ	02.030
244*	30-QH	02.030
245*	30-SX	01.030
246*	30-ST	01.030
247*	30-QP	02.030
248*	330-AI	CEAM
251*	30-SM	01.030
252*	30-QO	02.030
253*	30-SJ	01.030
254*		
255*		
256*	30-QK	02.030
257*	30-SF	01.030
258*	30-SZ	01.030
259*	30-QZ	02.030
260*		

France

261*	30-QB	02.030	651	33-NB	02.033	11	5-NJ	01.005
262*	30-SE	01.030	653	33-NV	02.033	12	5-NV	01.005
264*	30-SW	01.030	654	33-CL	01.033	13	5-NM	01.005
265*	30-SH	01.030	655	330-AT	CEAM	14	5-NW	01.005
267*			656	33-NK	02.033	15	5-NA	01.005
268*	30-SR	01.030	657	33-CV	01.033	16	5-NE	01.005
271*	30-QQ	02.030	658	33-CW	01.033	17	5-NR	01.005
272*	30-QL	02.030	659			18	5-NP	01.005
273*			660	33-CY	01.033	19	5-OB	02.005
274*			661	33-CX	01.033	20	5-NB	01.005
275*	30-QM	02.030	662	33-NA	02.033	21	5-NG	01.005
278*	30-QY	02.030				22	5-ND	01.005
279*	30-SC	01.030				25	5-OF	02.005
280*	30-SD	01.030				27	5-NT	01.005
281*						28	5-NN	01.005
283*	30-SV	01.030				29	5-NO	01.005

Mirage F.1B

501		
502		
503	33-FG	03.033
504	33-FV	03.033
505		
507	33-FA	03.033
509	33-FX	03.033
510	33-FI	03.033
511	33-FT	03.033
512	33-FL	03.033
513	330-AD	CEAM
514	33-FZ	03.033
516	33-FH	03.033
517	33-FB	03.033
518	33-FF	03.033
519	33-FM	03.033
520	33-FJ	03.033

Mirage F.1CR

602		CEV
603	33-CB	01.033
604	33-NU	02.033
605	33-CO	01.033
606	33-NP	02.033
607	33-ND	02.033
608	33-NG	02.033
610	33-NQ	02.033
611	33-NN	02.033
612	33-NJ	02.033
613	330-AF	CEAM
614	33-CN	01.033
615	33-NZ	02.033
616	33-NM	02.033
617	33-NO	02.033
620	33-CT	01.033
622	33-NH	02.033
623	33-CA	01.033
624	33-NY	02.033
627	33-CF	01.033
628	33-NB	02.033
630	33-CU	01.033
631	33-NS	02.033
632	33-NE	02.033
634	33-CK	01.033
635	33-NX	02.033
636	33-CG	01.033
637	33-CP	01.033
638	33-CI	01.033
640	33-CH	01.033
641	33-CD	01.033
642	33-NC	02.033
643	33-NR	02.033
645	33-CC	01.033
646	33-NW	02.033
647	33-CQ	01.033
648	33-CE	01.033
649	33-CZ	01.033
650	33-CJ	01.033

Dassault Mirage 2000B/2000-5F*

AMD-BA, Istres;
CEAM (EC 02.330), Mont-de-Marsan,
CEV, Cazaux & Istres;
EC 02.002 Côte d'Or, Dijon;
EC 01.005 Vendée &
  EC 02.005 Ile de France, Orange;
EC 01.012 Cambrésis &
  EC 02.012 Picardie, Cambrai

501*	(BX1)	CEV
502	5-OH	02.005
504*		CEV
505	5-OY	02.005
506	5-OD	02.005
507	5-OX	02.005
508	5-OT	02.005
509	5-OP	02.005
510	5-OQ	02.005
512	5-OU	02.005
513	5-OI	02.005
514	5-OE	02.005
515	5-OG	02.005
516	5-OL	02.005
518	5-OM	02.005
519	5-OW	02.005
520		
521	5-ON	02.005
522	5-OV	02.005
523	12-KA	02.012
524	330-AZ	CEAM
525	12-YP	01.012
526		
527	12-KM	02.012
528	330-AN	CEAM
529	12-KJ	02.012
530		

Dassault Mirage 2000C/2000-5F*

CEAM (EC 02.330), Mont-de-Marsan;
CEV, Istres;
EC 01.002 Cicogne &
  EC 02.002 Côte d'Or, Dijon;
EC 01.005 Vendée &
  EC 02.005 Ile de France, Orange;
EC 01.012 Cambrésis &
  EC 02.012 Picardie, Cambrai;
EC 04.033 Vexin, Djibouti

1		
2		CEV
3	5-OR	02.005
4	5-NB	01.005
5	5-NI	01.005
8	5-OA	02.005
9	5-OJ	02.005

30	5-OZ	02.005
32	5-NQ	01.005
34	5-NH	01.005
35	5-NL	01.005
36	5-OC	02.005
37	5-NF	01.005
38*	2-FK	02.002
40*	2-FG	01.002
41*	2-EJ	01.002
42*	2-FH	02.002
43*	2-FB	02.002
44*	2-EQ	01.002
45*		
46*	2-EN	01.002
47*	2-EP	01.002
48*	2-ER	01.002
49*	2-FF	02.002
51*	330-AS	CEAM
52*	2-FC	02.002
53*	330-AM	CEAM
54*	2-EA	01.002
55*	2-FA	02.002
56*	2-EG	01.002
57*	2-ET	01.002
58*	2-FO	02.002
59*	2-EV	01.002
61*	2-EM	01.002
62*	2-ED	01.002
63*	2-FQ	02.002
64	330-AQ	CEAM
65*		
66*	2-FD	02.002
67*	2-FL	02.002
68*	2-FM	02.002
69*	2-FE	02.002
70*	2-EC	01.002
71*	2-EH	01.002
72*	2-FR	02.002
73*	2-ES	01.002
74*	2-EU	01.002
76*	2-EB	01.002
77*	330-AX	CEAM
78*	2-FZ	02.002
79	12-YF	01.012
80	12-YJ	01.012
81		
82	12-KV	02.012
83	12-YL	01.012
85	12-KC	02.012
86	12-KL	02.012
87	12-YQ	01.012
88	12-YR	01.012
89	12-KU	02.012
90	12-YS	01.012
91	12-YO	01.012
92	330-AW	CEAM
93	12-KK	02.012
94	12-YI	01.012

95	12-KM	02.012
96		
97	12-YT	01.012
98	12-KH	01.012
99		
100	12-YG	01.012
101	12-KI	02.012
102	12-KO	02.012
103	12-YN	01.012
104	12-YK	01.012
105	12-YL	01.012
106		
107	12-KQ	02.012
108	12-KE	02.012
109	12-KR	02.012
111	12-KI	02.012
112	12-YC	01.012
113	12-KN	02.012
114	12-YK	01.012
115		
116	12-KF	02.012
117	12-YH	01.012
118	12-YE	01.012
119	12-KD	02.012
120		
121	12-YD	01.012
122	12-YU	01.012
123	12-YA	01.012
124	12-KB	02.012
X7		CEV

Dassault Mirage 2000D
AMD-BA, Istres;
CEAM (EC 02.330),
  Mont-de-Marsan;
CEV, Istres;
EC 01.003 Navarre,
  EC 02.003 Champagne &
  EC 03.003 Ardennes,
  Nancy

601	3-IA	01.003
602		
603	330-AA	CEAM
604	3-IN	01.003
605	3-IE	01.003
606	3-XX	03.003
607		CEV
609		
610	3-II	01.003
611		
612	3-IL	01.003
613		
614	330-A.	CEAM
615	3-JA	02.003
616	3-JS	02.003
617	3-XA	03.003
618	3-JF	02.003
619	3-JE	02.003
620	3-IM	01.003
621		
622	3-IW	01.003
623	3-IB	01.003
624		
625	3-JC	02.003
626	3-XH	03.003
627	3-JG	02.003
628	3-XF	03.003
629	3-XJ	03.003
630	3-XD	03.003
631	3-XI	03.003
632	3-XJ	03.003
634	3-JD	02.003
635	3-XP	03.003
636	3-JJ	02.003
637	3-XC	03.003
638	3-IJ	01.003
639	3-XQ	03.003
640	3-IR	01.003
641	3-XG	03.003
642	3-JB	02.003
643	330-AG	CEAM
644	3-IU	01.003
645	3-JO	02.003
646	3-IC	01.003
647		
648	3-XT	03.003
649	3-JW	02.003
650		
651		
652	3-XN	03.003
653	3-JK	02.003
654	3-IT	01.003
655	3-XE	03.003
656	3-JL	02.003
657	3-JM	02.003
658	3-JN	02.003
659	3-XR	03.003
660	3-IO	01.003
661	3-IH	01.003
662	3-IP	01.003
663	3-XS	03.003
664	3-JU	02.003
665	3-XV	03.003
666	3-IK	01.003
667	3-JX	02.003
668	330-AR	CEAM
669	3-JZ	02.003
670	3-IQ	01.003
671	3-XK	03.003
672	3-JQ	02.003
673	3-XA	03.003
674	3-XL	03.003
675	3-JI	02.003
676		CEV
677	3-XY	03.003
678	3-IC	01.003
679	3-IP	01.003
680	3-XM	03.003
681	3-IG	01.003
682	3-JR	02.003
683	3-JT	02.003
684	3-IF	01.003
685	3-XZ	03.003
686	3-JH	02.003

Dassault Mirage 2000N
CEAM (EC 02.330),
  Mont-de-Marsan;
CEV, Istres;
EC 01.004 Dauphiné &
  EC 02.004 Lafayette,
  Luxeuil;
EC 03.004 Limousin, Istres

301		CEV
303	4-CL	03.004
304	4-CK	03.004
305	4-CS	03.004
306	4-BL	02.004
307	4-CH	03.004
309	4-AO	01.004
310	4-CE	03.004
311	4-BT	02.004
312	4-CN	03.004
313	4-CR	03.004
314	4-AX	01.004
315	4-BF	02.004
316	4-BH	02.004
317	4-CR	03.004
318	4-BP	02.004
319	4-AC	01.004
320	4-CD	03.004
322		
323	4-CV	03.004
324	4-CX	03.004
325	4-CC	03.004
326	4-CM	03.004
327	4-CJ	03.004
329	4-AU	01.004
330	4-AT	01.004
331	4-CQ	03.004
332	4-BN	02.004
333	4-AB	01.004
334	330-AV	CEAM
335	4-CI	03.004
336	4-BI	02.004
337	4-AK	01.004
338		
339	4-AD	01.004
340	4-AA	01.004
341	4-AF	01.004
342	4-BA	02.004
343	4-AH	01.004
344	4-AJ	01.004
345	4-BU	02.004
348	4-AL	01.004
349	4-BM	02.004
350	4-BV	02.004
351	4-AQ	01.004
353	4-BD	02.004
354	4-BJ	02.004
355	4-AE	01.004
356	4-AN	01.004
357	4-CO	03.004
358	4-AM	01.004
359	4-BG	02.004
360	4-CB	03.004
361	4-CL	03.004
362	4-CU	03.004
363	4-BK	02.004
364	4-BB	02.004
365	4-BE	02.004
366	4-BO	02.004
367	4-AS	01.004
368	4-AR	01.004
369	4-BQ	02.004
370	4-CA	03.004
371	4-AV	01.004
372	4-BR	02.004
373	4-CF	03.004
374	4-BS	02.004
375	4-BC	02.004

Dassault Rafale-B
AMD-BA, Istres;
CEV, Istres

B01		CEV
B1		AMD-BA
301		AMD-BA
302		AMD-BA

Dassault Rafale-C
AMD-BA, Istres

C01		AMD-BA

DHC-6 Twin Otter 200/300*
ET 00.042 Ventoux,
  Mont-de-Marsan;
GAM 00.056
Vaucluse, Evreux

292	CC	00.056
298	CD	00.056
300	CE	00.056

730*	CA	00.042
742*	CB	00.042
745*	CV	00.042
786*	CT	00.042
790*	CW	00.042

Douglas DC-8-72CF
EE 00.051 *Aubrac*, Evreux;
ET 03.060 *Esterel*,
   Paris/Charles de Gaulle

46013	F-RAFG	03.060
46043		00.051
46130	F-RAFF	03.060

Embraer EMB.121AA/AN*
Xingu
EAT 00.319, Avord

054	YX
055*	YZ
064	YY
66*	
69*	
70*	
072	YA
073	YB
075	YC
076	YD
77*	
078	YE
080	YF
082	YG
083*	ZE
084	YH
086	YI
089	YJ
090*	ZF
091	YK
092	YL
095	YM
096	YN
098	YO
099	YP
101	YR
102	YS
103	YT
105	YU
107	YV
108	YW
111	YQ

Embraer EMB.312F Tucano
GI 00.312, Salon de
   Provence

438	312-UW
439	312-UY
456	312-JA
457	312-JB
458	312-JC
459	312-JD
460	312-JE
461	312-JF
462	312-JG
463	312-JH
464	312-JI
466	312-JK
467	312-JL
468	312-JM
469	312-JN
470	312-JO
471	312-JP
472	312-JQ
473	312-JR
474	312-JS
475	312-JT
477	312-JU

478	312-JV
479	312-JX
480	312-JY
481	312-JZ
483	312-UB
484	312-UC
485	312-UD
486	312-UE
487	312-UF
488	312-UG
489	312-UH
490	312-UI
491	312-UJ
492	312-UK
493	312-UL
494	312-UM
495	312-UN
496	312-UO
497	312-UP
498	312-UQ
499	312-UR
500	312-US
501	312-UT
502	312-UU
503	312-UV
504	312-UX

Eurocopter AS.332 Super
Puma/AS.532 Cougar
EH 03.067 *Parisis*,
   Villacoublay;
EH 05.067 *Alpilles*,
   Aix-en-Provence;
ETOM 00.082 *Maine*,
   Faaa-Tahiti;
GAM 00.056 *Vaucluse*,
   Evreux

2014	AS.332C	PN	
			05.067
2057	AS.332C	PO	
			00.082
2093	AS.332L	F-ZKCM	
2233	AS.332L-1	67-FY	
			03.067
2235	AS.332L-1	67-FZ	
			03.067
2244	AS.332C	PM	
			00.082
2342	AS.532UL	FX	
			00.056
2369	AS.532UL	FW	
			00.056
2375	AS.532UL	FV	
			00.056
2377	AS.332L-1	67-FU	
			03.067

Lockheed C-130H/
C-130H-30* Hercules
ET 02.061 *Franche-Comté*,
   Orléans

4588	61-PM
4589	61-PN
5114	61-PA
5116	61-PB
5119	61-PC
5140	61-PD
5142*	61-PE
5144*	61-PF
5150*	61-PG
5151*	61-PH
5152*	61-PI
5153*	61-PJ
5226*	61-PK
5227*	61-PL

Morane Saulnier
MS.760 Paris
CEV, Istres

115	OV
119	NL

Nord 262A/262D* Frégate
CEV, Istres;
EPNER, Istres;
ETE 00.041 *Verdun*, Metz;
ET 00.042 *Ventoux*,
   Mont-de-Marsan;
ETE 00.043 *Médoc*,
   Bordeaux;
ETE 00.044 *Mistral*,
   Villacoublay;
ETEC 00.065, Villacoublay

58	MJ	EPNER
67	MI	CEV
77*	AK	00.044
80*	AW	00.065
81*	AH	00.041
88*	AL	00.042
89*	AZ	00.041
91*	AT	00.042
93*	AP	00.065
95*	AR	00.065
105*	AE	00.065
106*	AY	00.041
107*	AX	00.065
108*	AG	00.041
109*	AM	00.043
110*	AS	00.065

SEPECAT Jaguar
CEV, Cazaux & Istres;
CEAM (EC 02.330),
   Mont-de-Marsan;
CITac 00.339 *Aquitaine*,
   Luxeuil;
EC 01.007 *Provence*,
   St Dizier

Jaguar A

A99	7-HC	01.007
A101	7-HB	01.007
A104	7-HM	01.007
A113	7-HT	01.007
A120	7-HL	01.007
A122	7-HA	01.007
A124	7-HD	01.007
A128	7-HP	01.007
A131	7-HF	01.007
A135	7-HK	01.007
A137	7-HQ	01.007
A138	7-HV	01.007
A139	7-HU	01.007
A140	7-HI	01.007
A145	7-HG	01.007
A148	7-HN	01.007
A151	7-HE	01.007
A154	7-HO	01.007
A157	7-HH	01.007
A159	7-HJ	01.007
A160	7-HS	01.007

Jaguar E

E3	339-WF	00.339
E6	7-HR	01.007
E10	339-WL	00.339
E12	339-WI	00.339
E19	339-WG	00.339
E29	339-WJ	00.339
E35	7-HY	01.007
E37	7-HZ	01.007
E40	7-HX	01.007

SOCATA TBM 700

CEV, Cazaux & Istres;
ETE 00.041 *Verdun*, Metz;
ETE 00.043 *Médoc*, Bordeaux;
ETE 00.044 *Mistral*, Villacoublay;
ETEC 00.065, Villacoublay;
EdC 00.070, Chateaudun

33	XA	00.043
35	XB	00.043
70	XC	00.043
77	XD	00.041
78	65-XE	00.044
80	41-XF	00.041
93	XL	00.043
94	65-XG	00.070
95	65-XH	00.065
103	41-XI	00.041
104	XJ	00.070
105	XK	00.065
106	MN	CEV
110	XP	00.041
111	XM	00.065
117	XN	00.044
125	65-XO	00.065
131	XQ	00.065
146	XR	00.065
147	XS	00.065

Transall C-160F/C-160NG GABRIEL*/C-160R

CEAM (EET 06.330), Mont-de-Marsan;
CEV, Cazaux & Istres;
EET 01.054 *Dunkerque*, Metz;
ET 01.061 *Touraine* & ET 03.061 *Poitou*, Orléans;
ET 01.064 *Béarn* & ET 02.064 *Anjou*, Evreux;
ETOM 00.050 *Réunion*, St Denis;
ETOM 00.055 *Ouessant*, Dakar;
ETOM 00.058 *Guadeloupe*, Pointe-à-Pitre;
ETOM 00.088 *Larzac*, Djibouti

RA02	C-160R	61-MI	01.061
RA04	C-160R	61-MS	01.061
RA06	C-160R	61-ZB	03.061
R1	C-160R	61-MA	01.061
R2	C-160R	61-MB	01.061
R3	C-160R	61-MC	00.058
R4	C-160R	61-MD	01.061
R5	C-160R	61-ME	01.061
R11	C-160R	61-MF	01.061
R12	C-160R	61-MG	01.061
R13	C-160R	61-MH	00.050
R15	C-160R	61-MJ	01.061
R17	C-160R	61-ML	01.061
R18	C-160R	61-MM	01.061
R42	C-160R	61-MN	01.061
R43	C-160R	61-MO	01.061
R44	C-160R	61-MP	01.061
R45	C-160R	61-MQ	01.061
R46	C-160R	61-MR	01.061
R48	C-160R	61-MT	01.061
F49	C-160F	59-MU	CEV
R51	C-160R	61-MW	01.061
R52	C-160R	61-MX	01.061
R53	C-160R	61-MY	01.061
R54	C-160R	61-MZ	01.061
R55	C-160R	61-ZC	03.061
R86	C-160R	61-ZD	03.061
R87	C-160R	61-ZE	00.050
R88	C-160R	61-ZF	03.061
R89	C-160R	61-ZG	03.061
R90	C-160R	61-ZH	03.061
R91	C-160R	61-ZI	03.061
R92	C-160R	61-ZJ	03.061
R93	C-160R	61-ZK	03.061
R94	C-160R	61-ZL	03.061
R95	C-160R	61-ZM	03.061
R96	C-160R	61-ZN	03.061
R97	C-160R	61-ZO	03.061
R98	C-160R	61-ZP	03.061
R99	C-160R	61-ZQ	03.061
R100	C-160R	61-ZR	03.061
R153	C-160R	61-ZS	03.061
R154	C-160R	61-ZT	03.061
R157	C-160R	61-ZW	03.061
R158	C-160R	61-ZX	03.061
R159	C-160R	61-ZY	03.061
R160	C-160R	61-ZZ	03.061
R201	C-160R	64-GA	01.064
R202	C-160R	64-GB	02.064
R203	C-160R	64-GC	01.064
R204	C-160R	64-GD	02.064
R205	C-160R	64-GE	01.064
R206	C-160R	64-GF	02.064
R207	C-160R	64-GG	01.064
R208	C-160R	64-GH	02.064
R210	C-160R	64-GJ	02.064
R211	C-160R	64-GK	01.064
R212	C-160R	64-GL	02.064
R213	C-160R	64-GM	01.064
R214	C-160R	64-GN	02.064
R215	C-160R	64-GO	01.064
F216	C-160NG*	54-GT	01.054
R217	C-160R	64-GQ	01.064
R218	C-160R	64-GR	02.064
F221	C-160NG*	61-GS	01.061
R223	C-160R	64-GW	01.064
R224	C-160R	64-GX	02.064
R225	C-160R	64-GY	01.064
R226	C-160R	64-GZ	02.064

Aéronavale/Marine

Aérospatiale SA.321G Super Frelon

32 Flottille, Hyères & Lanvéoc/Poulmic

101
106
118
134
137
144
148
160
162
163
165

Dassault-Breguet Atlantique 2

21 Flottille, Nimes/Garons;
23 Flottille, Lorient/ Lann Bihoué

1	21F
2	21F
3	23F
4	21F
5	21F
6	21F
7	21F
8	23F
9	21F
10	23F
11	23F

France

12	21F
13	21F
14	21F
15	21F
16	21F
17	23F
18	21F
19	23F
20	21F
21	21F
22	21F
23	21F
24	21F
25	21F
26	23F
27	23F
28	21F
29	
30	

Dassault Falcon 10(MER)
ES 57, Landivisiau

32	
101	
129	
133	
143	
185	

Dassault Falcon 20G Guardian
25 Flottille, Papeete & Tontouta

48	
65	
72	
77	
80	

Dassault Falcon 50 SURMAR
24 Flottille, Lorient/ Lann Bihoué

7	
30	
36	
132	

Dassault Rafale-M
AMD-BA, Istres;
CEV, Istres

M01	AMD-BA
M02	AMD-BA
1	CEV
2	12F
3	
4	12F
5	
6	12F
7	12F
8	12F
9	12F
10	12F

Dassault Super Etendard
11 Flottille, Landivisiau;
17 Flottille, Landivisiau;
CEV, Cazaux & Istres

1	11F
2	11F
3	11F
4	11F
6	11F
8	17F

10	11F
11	17F
12	17F
13	17F
14	17F
15	17F
16	11F
17	11F
18	11F
19	11F
23	11F
24	11F
25	17F
26	17F
28	17F
30	11F
31	11F
32	11F
33	11F
35	CEV
37	11F
38	11F
39	11F
41	11F
43	17F
44	17F
45	11F
46	17F
47	11F
48	17F
49	11F
50	11F
51	11F
52	11F
55	11F
57	11F
59	11F
60	11F
61	17F
62	11F
64	11F
65	11F
66	11F
68	CEV
69	11F
71	17F

Embraer EMB.121AN Xingu
24 Flottille, Lorient/ Lann Bihoué;
28 Flottille, Hyères;
ES 2, Lorient/Lann Bihoué

30	24F
47	2S
65	2S
67	2S
68	2S
71	28F
74	2S
79	2S
81	2S
85	28F
87	2S

Eurocopter SA.365/ AS.565 Panther
35 Flottille, Hyères, (with detachments at Cherbourg, La Rochelle & Le Touquet);
36 Flottille, Hyères

17	SA.365N	35F
19	SA.365N	35F
24	SA.365N	35F

81	SA.365N	35F
91	SA.365N	35F
313	SA.365F1	35F
318	SA.365F1	35F
322	SA.365F1	35F
355	AS.565MA	36F
362	AS.565MA	36F
436	AS.565MA	36F
452	AS.565MA	36F
453	AS.565MA	36F
466	AS.565MA	36F
482	AS.565MA	36F
486	AS.565MA	36F
503	AS.565MA	36F
505	AS.565MA	36F
506	AS.565MA	36F
507	AS.565MA	36F
511	AS.565MA	36F
519	AS.565MA	36F
522	AS.565MA	36F

Nord 262E Frégate
28 Flottille, Hyères;
ERCE, Hyères;
ES 2, Lorient/Lann Bihoué;
ES 55, Aspretto

45	28F
46	28F
51	2S
53	28F
60	28F
63	28F
69	28F
70	28F
71	28F
72	28F
73	28F
75	28F
79	28F
100	2S

Northrop Grumman E-2C Hawkeye
4 Flottille, Lorient/ Lann Bihoué

1	(165455)
2	(165456)

Westland Lynx HAS2(FN)/ HAS4(FN)*
31 Flottille, Hyères;
34 Flottille, Lanvéoc/Poulmic;
CEPA, Hyères;

260	
262	34F
263	34F
264	34F
265	34F
266	31F
267	31F
268	
269	34F
270	31F
271	34F
272	34F
273	34F
274	34F
275	34F
276	34F
620	34F
621	34F
622	34F
623	34F
624	31F

625	31F
627	34F
801*	31F
802*	34F
804*	31F
806*	34F
807*	34F
808*	34F
810*	34F
811*	31F
812*	31F
813*	34F
814*	31F

Aviation Legère de l'Armée de Terre (ALAT)
Cessna F.406 Caravan II
EAAT, Rennes

0008	ABM
0010	ABN

SOCATA TBM 700
EAAT, Rennes

99	ABO
100	ABP
115	ABQ
136	ABR
139	ABS
156	ABT
159	ABU
160	ABV

French Govt
Aérospatiale AS.355F-1 Twin Ecureuil
Douanes Francaises

F-ZBAC	(5026)
F-ZBEF	(5236)
F-ZBEJ	(5003)
F-ZBEK	(5298)
F-ZBEL	(5299)

Beech Super King Air B200
Sécurité Civile

F-ZBEM	
F-ZBFJ	98
F-ZBFK	96

Cessna F.406 Caravan II
Douanes Francaises

F-ZBAB	(0025)
F-ZBBB	(0039)
F-ZBCE	(0042)
F-ZBCF	(0077)
F-ZBCG	(0066)
F-ZBCH	(0075)
F-ZBCI	(0070)
F-ZBCJ	(0074)
F-ZBEP	(0006)
F-ZBES	(0017)
F-ZBFA	(0001)
F-ZBGA	(0086)

Dassault Falcon 20
AVDEF, Nimes/Garons

F-GPAA	Falcon 20ECM
F-GPAB	Falcon 20E
F-GPAD	Falcon 20E

Fokker F-27-600
Sécurité Civile

F-ZBFF	71	(10432)
F-ZBFG	72	(10440)

GERMANY
Luftwaffe, Marineflieger
Airbus A.310-304/MRTT*
1/FBS, Köln-Bonn

10+21
10+22
10+23
10+24*
10+25*
10+26*
10+27*

Canadair CL601-1A Challenger
3/FBS, Köln-Bonn

12+02
12+03
12+04
12+05
12+06
12+07

McD F-4F Phantom
Flugleherzentrum F-4F, Hopsten;
JG-71 *Richthoven*, Wittmundhaven;
JG-74 *Molders*, Neuburg/Donau;
TsLw-1, Kaufbeuren;
WTD-61, Ingolstadt

37+01	FlZ F-4F
37+03	JG-71
37+04	TsLw-1
37+09	FlZ F-4F
37+10	FlZ F-4F
37+11	FlZ F-4F
37+12	FlZ F-4F
37+13	JG-74
37+14	TsLw-1
37+15	WTD-61
37+16	WTD-61
37+17	JG-74
37+22	JG-71
37+26	JG-71
37+28	JG-71
37+29	FlZ F-4F
37+31	FlZ F-4F
37+32	JG-71
37+33	JG-74
37+34	FlZ F-4F
37+35	FlZ F-4F
37+36	JG-74
37+37	FlZ F-4F
37+38	FlZ F-4F
37+39	JG-71
37+43	FlZ F-4F
37+44	FlZ F-4F
37+45	FlZ F-4F
37+48	JG-74
37+55	JG-71
37+58	FlZ F-4F
37+61	JG-74
37+63	JG-71
37+71	JG-74
37+75	FlZ F-4F
37+76	JG-71
37+77	JG-71
37+78	JG-71
37+79	JG-71
37+81	JG-74
37+82	JG-71
37+83	JG-71

37+84	JG-74
37+85	JG-71
37+86	JG-71
37+88	FlZ F-4F
37+89	JG-71
37+92	JG-74
37+93	FlZ F-4F
37+94	JG-74
37+96	FlZ F-4F
37+97	JG-74
37+98	JG-71
38+00	JG-74
38+01	JG-71
38+02	JG-74
38+03	FlZ F-4F
38+05	FlZ F-4F
38+06	JG-74
38+07	JG-71
38+09	JG-74
38+10	JG-74
38+12	JG-71
38+13	WTD-61
38+14	JG-71
38+16	JG-74
38+17	JG-74
38+18	JG-74
38+20	FlZ F-4F
38+24	JG-74
38+25	JG-74
38+26	JG-74
38+27	FlZ F-4F
38+28	JG-74
38+29	JG-74
38+30	JG-71
38+31	FlZ F-4F
38+32	FlZ F-4F
38+33	JG-74
38+36	JG-71
38+37	FlZ F-4F
38+39	JG-74
38+40	JG-71
38+42	
38+43	FlZ F-4F
38+44	JG-71
38+45	JG-71
38+46	JG-71
38+48	JG-74
38+49	JG-71
38+50	FlZ F-4F
38+53	JG-74
38+54	JG-71
38+55	JG-71
38+56	
38+57	JG-74
38+58	JG-71
38+60	JG-74
38+61	JG-71
38+62	FlZ F-4F
38+64	FlZ F-4F
38+66	JG-74
38+67	JG-74
38+68	JG-74
38+69	JG-74
38+70	JG-74
38+73	FlZ F-4F
38+74	JG-74
38+75	JG-71

Panavia Tornado Strike/Trainer[1]/ECR[2]
AkG-51 *Immelmann*, Schleswig/Jagel;
EADS, Manching;
JbG-31 *Boelcke*, Nörvenich;

Germany

JbG-32, Lechfeld;
JbG-33, Büchel;
JbG-34 *Algau*, Memmingen;
JbG-38 *Ostfriesland*, Jever;
MFG-2, Eggebek;
TsLw-1, Kaufbeuren;
WTD-61, Ingolstadt

Reg.	Unit	Reg.	Unit	Reg.	Unit
43+01[1]	JbG-31	43+96	AkG-51	45+00	JbG-38
43+02[1]	JbG-38	43+98	AkG-51	45+02	MFG-2
43+03[1]	JbG-38	44+00	JbG-31	45+04	JbG-33
43+04[1]	JbG-38	44+04	AkG-51	45+06	AkG-51
43+05[1]	JbG-38	44+06	JbG-34	45+07	JbG-33
43+06[1]	JbG-38	44+07	JbG-32	45+08	JbG-33
43+07[1]	JbG-38	44+08	JbG-31	45+12[1]	MFG-2
43+08[1]	JbG-32	44+09	JbG-33	45+13[1]	MFG-2
43+09[1]	JbG-38	44+10[1]	JbG-32	45+14[1]	JbG-38
43+10[1]	JbG-38	44+11	JbG-33	45+15[1]	MFG-2
43+11[1]	JbG-38	44+13	TsLw-1	45+16[1]	JbG-38
43+13	EADS	44+15	AkG-51	45+17	JbG-33
43+15[1]	JbG-38	44+16[1]	JbG-31	45+18	JbG-33
43+16[1]	JbG-38	44+17	AkG-51	45+19	JbG-33
43+17[1]	JbG-38	44+19	JbG-31	45+20	AkG-51
43+20	JbG-31	44+21	JbG-34	45+21	JbG-33
43+23[1]	JbG-38	44+23	JbG-33	45+22	JbG-33
43+25	JbG-31	44+24	AkG-51	45+23	JbG-31
43+27	JbG-31	44+25[1]	JbG-38	45+24	JbG-33
43+29[1]	JbG-31	44+26	JbG-34	45+25	AkG-51
43+30	JbG-38	44+27	JbG-33	45+27	MFG-2
43+31[1]	JbG-31	44+29	JbG-31	45+28	MFG-2
43+32	JbG-31	44+30	JbG-31	45+29	WTD-61
43+33[1]	JbG-33	44+31	JbG-31	45+30	MFG-2
43+34	TsLw-1	44+32	JbG-38	45+31	MFG-2
43+35[1]	AkG-51	44+33	JbG-33	45+33	MFG-2
43+37[1]	JbG-32	44+34	AkG-51	45+34	MFG-2
43+38	JbG-34	44+35	JbG-31	45+35	MFG-2
43+40	JbG-33	44+37[1]	JbG-38	45+36	MFG-2
43+41	JbG-31	44+40	JbG-33	45+37	MFG-2
43+43[1]	AkG-51	44+41	JbG-31	45+38	MFG-2
43+46	AkG-51	44+42	AkG-51	45+39	MFG-2
43+47	AkG-51	44+43	JbG-34	45+40	MFG-2
43+48	AkG-51	44+44	JbG-31	45+41	MFG-2
43+50	AkG-51	44+46	JbG-34	45+42	MFG-2
43+52	JbG-38	44+48	JbG-33	45+43	MFG-2
43+53	JbG-33	44+50	AkG-51	45+44	MFG-2
43+54	JbG-31	44+52	JbG-31	45+45	MFG-2
43+55	MFG-2	44+53	AkG-51	45+46	MFG-2
43+58	JbG-33	44+54	JbG-33	45+47	MFG-2
43+59	TsLw-1	44+55	JbG-38	45+49	MFG-2
43+60	JbG-34	44+56	JbG-34	45+50	MFG-2
43+61	TsLw-1	44+57	JbG-31	45+51	AkG-51
43+62	JbG-34	44+58	JbG-31	45+52	MFG-2
43+63	JbG-34	44+61	AkG-51	45+53	MFG-2
43+64	JbG-33	44+62	JbG-32	45+54	MFG-2
43+65	JbG-38	44+63	AkG-51	45+55	MFG-2
43+67	JbG-34	44+64	AkG-51	45+56	MFG-2
43+68	JbG-32	44+65	AkG-51	45+57	JbG-34
43+69	JbG-31	44+66	JbG-34	45+59	MFG-2
43+70	JbG-33	44+68	AkG-51	45+64	TsLw-1
43+71	JbG-38	44+69	AkG-51	45+66	MFG-2
43+72	JbG-38	44+70	JbG-31	45+67	AkG-51
43+73	AkG-51	44+71	JbG-31	45+68	MFG-2
43+76	JbG-38	44+72[1]	JbG-33	45+69	MFG-2
43+77	JbG-34	44+75[1]	JbG-33	45+70[1]	JbG-33
43+78	JbG-34	44+76	JbG-31	45+71	MFG-2
43+79	AkG-51	44+78	JbG-31	45+72	MFG-2
43+80	AkG-51	44+79	JbG-33	45+73[1]	JbG-31
43+81	AkG-51	44+80	JbG-31	45+74	MFG-2
43+82	AkG-51	44+83	JbG-33	45+76	JbG-38
43+85	JbG-33	44+84	JbG-33	45+77[1]	JbG-33
43+86	JbG-34	44+85	JbG-33	45+78	JbG-33
43+87	MFG-2	44+86	AkG-51	45+79	JbG-31
43+90[1]	JbG-38	44+87	AkG-51	45+81	JbG-31
43+92[1]	JbG-31	44+88	AkG-51	45+82	JbG-31
43+94[1]	JbG-34	44+89	JbG-33	45+84	AkG-51
		44+90	JbG-33	45+85	AkG-51
		44+91	JbG-33	45+86	JbG-33
		44+92	JbG-31	45+87	JbG-34
		44+94	JbG-33	45+88	JbG-33
		44+95	JbG-38	45+89	JbG-34
		44+96	JbG-31	45+90	JbG-31
		44+97	JbG-38	45+91	AkG-51

45+92	JbG-31	50+35	LTG-62	51+13	LTG-61		
45+93	AkG-51	50+36	LTG-62	51+14	LTG-63		
45+94	JbG-33	50+37	LTG-62	51+15	LTG-61		
45+95	JbG-31	50+38	LTG-62				

45+99[1] AkG-51

Dornier Do.228/Do.228LM*
MFG-3, Nordholz;
WTD-61, Ingolstadt

46+01	JbG-32	50+40	LTG-61	57+01*	MFG-3
46+02	JbG-33	50+41	LTG-62	57+02*	MFG-3

46+04[1] JbG-32 — 50+42 LTG-63 — 57+03 MFG-3
46+05[1] MFG-2 — 50+44 LTG-61 — 57+04* MFG-3
46+07[1] JbG-34 — 50+45 LTG-63 — 98+78 WTD-61

46+10	WTD-61	50+46	LTG-62
46+11	MFG-2	50+47	LTG-61
46+12	MFG-2	50+48	LTG-61
46+13	JbG-34	50+49	LTG-63
46+14	JbG-34	50+50	LTG-62
46+15	MFG-2	50+51	LTG-61
46+18	MFG-2	50+52	LTG-62
46+19	MFG-2	50+53	LTG-61
46+20	MFG-2	50+54	LTG-63
46+21	MFG-2	50+55	LTG-62
46+22	MFG-2	50+56	LTG-63

Breguet Br.1150 Atlantic *Elint
MFG-3, Nordholz

61+03*
61+04
61+05
61+06*
61+08
61+09

46+23[2]	JbG-32	50+57	WTD-61
46+24[2]	JbG-32	50+58	LTG-62
46+25[2]	JbG-32	50+59	LTG-63
46+26[2]	JbG-32	50+60	LTG-62
46+27[2]	JbG-32	50+61	LTG-63
46+28[2]	JbG-32	50+62	LTG-62
46+29[2]	JbG-32	50+64	LTG-61
46+30[2]	JbG-32	50+65	LTG-62
46+31[2]	JbG-32	50+66	LTG-61
46+32[2]	JbG-32	50+67	LTG-63
46+33[2]	JbG-32	50+68	LTG-61
46+34[2]	JbG-32	50+69	LTG-63
46+35[2]	JbG-32	50+70	LTG-63
46+36[2]	JbG-32	50+71	LTG-63
46+37[2]	JbG-32	50+72	LTG-63
46+38[2]	JbG-32	50+73	LTG-63
46+39[2]	JbG-32	50+74	LTG-61
46+40[2]	WTD-61	50+75	LTG-63
46+41[2]	JbG-32	50+76	LTG-63
46+42[2]	JbG-32	50+77	LTG-63
46+43[2]	JbG-32	50+78	LTG-62
46+44[2]	JbG-32	50+79	LTG-63
46+45[2]	JbG-32	50+81	LTG-62
46+46[2]	JbG-32	50+82	LTG-63
46+47[2]	JbG-32	50+83	LTG-62
46+48[2]	JbG-32	50+84	LTG-61
46+49[2]	JbG-32	50+85	LTG-63
46+50[2]	JbG-32	50+86	LTG-61
46+51[2]	JbG-32	50+87	LTG-63
46+52[2]	JbG-32	50+88	LTG-61
46+53[2]	JbG-32	50+89	LTG-62
46+54[2]	JbG-32	50+90	LTG-62
46+55[2]	JbG-32	50+91	LTG-62
46+56[2]	JbG-32	50+92	LTG-61
46+57[2]	JbG-32	50+93	LTG-61
98+59	WTD-61	50+94	LTG-63
98+60	WTD-61	50+95	LTG-63
98+79[2]	WTD-61	50+96	LTG-61

61+10
61+11
61+12
61+13
61+14
61+15
61+16
61+17
61+18*
61+19*
61+20

Eurocopter AS.532U-2 Cougar
3/FBS, Berlin-Tegel
82+01
82+02
82+03

Transall C-160D
LTG-61, Landsberg;
LTG-62, Wunstorf;
LTG-63, Hohn;
WTD-61, Ingolstadt

50+06	LTG-63	50+97	LTG-62
50+07	LTG-61	50+98	LTG-61
50+08	LTG-63	50+99	LTG-61
50+09	LTG-62	51+00	LTG-62
50+10	LTG-62	51+01	LTG-62
50+17	LTG-62	51+02	LTG-63
50+29	LTG-62	51+03	LTG-62
50+33	LTG-61	51+04	LTG-61
50+34	LTG-63	51+05	LTG-62

Westland Lynx Mk88/ Super Lynx Mk88A*
MFG-3, Nordholz
83+02
83+03*
83+04
83+05
83+06*
83+07
83+09
83+10
83+11

51+06	LTG-63
51+07	LTG-62
51+08	WTD-61
51+09	LTG-63
51+10	LTG-61
51+11	LTG-62
51+12	LTG-63

83+12
83+13
83+15
83+17
83+18
83+19*
83+20*
83+21*
83+22*
83+23*
83+24*
83+25*
83+26*

Westland Sea King HAS41
MFG-5, Kiel-Holtenau
89+50
89+51
89+52
89+53
89+54

Germany

89+55		
89+56		
89+57		
89+58		
89+60		
89+61		
89+62		
89+63		
89+64		
89+65		
89+66		
89+67		
89+68		
89+69		
89+70		
89+71		

**Eurofighter EF.2000/
EF.2000T* Typhoon**
EADS, Manching;
WTD-61, Ingolstadt

98+03*	EADS
98+29	WTD-61
98+30	WTD-61

NH Industries NH.90

98+90

Heeresfliegertruppe
Eurocopter EC.135P-1
HFWS, Bückeburg

82+51		
82+52		
82+53		
82+54		
82+55		
82+56		
82+57		
82+58		
82+59		
82+60		
82+61		
82+62		
82+63		
82+64		
82+65		

MBB Bo.105
HFR-15, Rheine-Bentlage;
HFR-25, Laupheim;
HFR-26, Roth;
HFR-35, Mendig;
HFR-36, Fritzlar;
HFS-400, Cottbus;
HFVS-910, Bückeburg;
HFWS, Bückeburg;
TsLw-3, Fassberg;
WTD-61, Ingolstadt

80+01	Bo.105M	HFR-35
80+02	Bo.105M	HFWS
80+03	Bo.105M	HFWS
80+05	Bo.105M	HFR-35
80+07	Bo.105M	HFWS
80+08	Bo.105M	HFR-25
80+09	Bo.105M	HFR-35
80+10	Bo.105M	HFR-25
80+11	Bo.105M	HFWS
80+12	Bo.105M	HFWS
80+14	Bo.105M	HFWS
80+15	Bo.105M	HFR-15
80+16	Bo.105M	HFR-15
80+18	Bo.105M	HFR-15
80+19	Bo.105M	HFR-15
80+21	Bo.105M	HFR-15
80+25	Bo.105M	HFR-35
80+26	Bo.105M	HFR-35
80+27	Bo.105M	HFR-35
80+28	Bo.105M	TsLw-3
80+29	Bo.105M	HFR-35
80+30	Bo.105M	HFR-35
80+31	Bo.105M	HFR-35
80+33	Bo.105M	HFR-35
80+34	Bo.105M	HFR-25
80+36	Bo.105M	HFR-25
80+38	Bo.105M	HFR-25
80+39	Bo.105M	HFR-25
80+40	Bo.105M	HFR-25
80+41	Bo.105M	HFR-25
80+42	Bo.105M	HFR-25
80+43	Bo.105M	HFR-25
80+44	Bo.105M	HFR-25
80+46	Bo.105M	TsLw-3
80+47	Bo.105M	HFR-26
80+48	Bo.105M	HFR-25
80+49	Bo.105M	HFS-400
80+51	Bo.105M	HFR-15
80+54	Bo.105M	HFR-15
80+56	Bo.105M	HFS-400
80+57	Bo.105M	HFR-35
80+58	Bo.105M	HFR-35
80+59	Bo.105M	HFR-35
80+60	Bo.105M	HFR-35
80+61	Bo.105M	HFS-400
80+62	Bo.105M	HFR-35
80+64	Bo.105M	HFR-35
80+66	Bo.105M	HFR-15
80+67	Bo.105M	HFR-15
80+68	Bo.105M	HFR-15
80+69	Bo.105M	HFR-15
80+71	Bo.105M	HFR-15
80+72	Bo.105M	HFR-15
80+73	Bo.105M	HFR-15
80+74	Bo.105M	HFR-15
80+76	Bo.105M	HFR-15
80+77	Bo.105M	HFR-35
80+78	Bo.105M	HFR-35
80+79	Bo.105M	HFR-35
80+80	Bo.105M	HFS-400
80+81	Bo.105M	HFR-26
80+82	Bo.105M	HFR-25
80+83	Bo.105M	HFR-25
80+84	Bo.105M	HFR-25
80+85	Bo.105M	HFR-25
80+86	Bo.105M	HFS-400
80+87	Bo.105M	HFR-25
80+88	Bo.105M	HFS-400
80+89	Bo.105M	HFS-400
80+90	Bo.105M	HFS-400
80+91	Bo.105M	HFR-35
80+92	Bo.105M	HFR-35
80+93	Bo.105M	HFS-400
80+94	Bo.105M	HFR-25
80+96	Bo.105M	HFR-25
80+97	Bo.105M	HFR-35
80+98	Bo.105M	HFR-25
80+99	Bo.105M	HFR-25
81+00	Bo.105M	HFR-25
86+01	Bo.105P	
86+02	Bo.105P	HFWS
86+03	Bo.105P	HFWS
86+04	Bo.105P	HFR-36
86+05	Bo.105P	HFWS
86+06	Bo.105P	HFWS
86+07	Bo.105P	HFWS
86+08	Bo.105P	HFWS
86+09	Bo.105P	HFWS
86+10	Bo.105P	
86+11	Bo.105P	HFR-35
86+12	Bo.105P	HFWS
86+13	Bo.105P	HFWS
86+14	Bo.105P	
86+15	Bo.105P	
86+16	Bo.105P	HFWS
86+17	Bo.105P	HFVS-910
86+18	Bo.105P	HFR-26
86+19	Bo.105P	HFR-26
86+20	Bo.105P	HFWS
86+21	Bo.105P	HFR-36
86+22	Bo.105P	HFWS
86+23	Bo.105P	HFWS
86+24	Bo.105P	HFVS-910
86+25	Bo.105P	
86+26	Bo.105P	HFS-400
86+27	Bo.105P	HFR-26
86+28	Bo.105P	HFWS
86+29	Bo.105P	
86+30	Bo.105P	HFR-26
86+31	Bo.105P	
86+32	Bo.105P	HFR-26
86+33	Bo.105P	HFR-26
86+34	Bo.105P	HFR-26
86+35	Bo.105P	HFR-26
86+36	Bo.105P	HFR-36
86+37	Bo.105P	
86+38	Bo.105P	HFR-36
86+39	Bo.105P	
86+41	Bo.105P	
86+42	Bo.105P	HFR-26
86+43	Bo.105P	
86+44	Bo.105P	HFR-26
86+45	Bo.105P	HFVS-910
86+46	Bo.105P	HFR-26
86+47	Bo.105P	
86+48	Bo.105P	
86+49	Bo.105P	HFR-26
86+50	Bo.105P	
86+51	Bo.105P	HFR-36
86+52	Bo.105P	
86+53	Bo.105P	HFR-26
86+54	Bo.105P	
86+55	Bo.105P	
86+56	Bo.105P	HFR-36
86+57	Bo.105P	
86+58	Bo.105P	HFR-36
86+59	Bo.105P	
86+60	Bo.105P	
86+61	Bo.105P	HFR-26
86+62	Bo.105P	HFVS-910
86+63	Bo.105P	HFR-26
86+64	Bo.105P	HFR-26
86+65	Bo.105P	HFR-26
86+66	Bo.105P	HFVS-910
86+67	Bo.105P	HFR-26
86+68	Bo.105P	HFR-36
86+69	Bo.105P	HFR-26
86+70	Bo.105P	
86+71	Bo.105P	HFR-36
86+72	Bo.105P	HFR-36
86+73	Bo.105P	HFWS
86+74	Bo.105P	
86+75	Bo.105P	HFR-36
86+76	Bo.105P	HFR-26
86+77	Bo.105P	
86+78	Bo.105P	HFR-26
86+80	Bo.105P	
86+81	Bo.105P	
86+83	Bo.105P	
86+84	Bo.105P	
86+85	Bo.105P	
86+86	Bo.105P	
86+87	Bo.105P	
86+88	Bo.105P	

86+89	Bo.105P		87+65	Bo.105P	HFR-36	84+22	HFR-15	
86+90	Bo.105P	HFR-26	87+66	Bo.105P	TsLw-3	84+23	HFR-35	
86+91	Bo.105P	HFR-26	87+67	Bo.105P	HFWS	84+24	HFR-35	
86+92	Bo.105P	HFR-36	87+68	Bo.105P	HFWS	84+25*	HFR-35	
86+93	Bo.105P	HFVS-910	87+69	Bo.105P	HFR-26	84+26	HFR-35	
86+94	Bo.105P	HFWS	87+70	Bo.105P	HFR-35	84+27	HFR-35	
86+95	Bo.105P		87+71	Bo.105P	HFR-26	84+28	HFR-25	
86+96	Bo.105P	HFR-26	87+72	Bo.105P	HFR-15	84+29	HFR-35	
86+97	Bo.105P	HFR-36	87+73	Bo.105P	HFWS	84+30	HFR-35	
86+98	Bo.105P	HFR-35	87+74	Bo.105P	HFVS-910	84+31	HFR-35	
86+99	Bo.105P	HFR-26	87+75	Bo.105P		84+32	HFR-35	
87+00	Bo.105P	HFR-26	87+76	Bo.105P	HFR-15	84+33	HFR-35	
87+01	Bo.105P	HFR-26	87+77	Bo.105P		84+34	HFR-35	
87+02	Bo.105P	HFR-26	87+78	Bo.105P		84+35	HFR-35	
87+03	Bo.105P	HFR-26	87+79	Bo.105P		84+36	HFR-35	
87+04	Bo.105P	HFR-35	87+80	Bo.105P		84+37	HFWS	
87+05	Bo.105P	HFR-26	87+81	Bo.105P		84+38	HFR-35	
87+06	Bo.105P	HFR-36	87+82	Bo.105P		84+39	HFR-35	
87+07	Bo.105P	HFR-26	87+83	Bo.105P		84+40	HFR-25	
87+08	Bo.105P	HFWS	87+84	Bo.105P	HFVS-910	84+41	HFWS	
87+09	Bo.105P	HFR-36	87+85	Bo.105P	HFR-35	84+42	HFR-25	
87+10	Bo.105P	HFR-26	87+86	Bo.105P	HFR-26	84+43	HFR-25	
87+11	Bo.105P		87+87	Bo.105P	HFR-35	84+44	HFR-25	
87+12	Bo.105P	HFR-36	87+88	Bo.105P	HFR-26	84+45*	HFR-25	
87+13	Bo.105P	HFR-36	87+89	Bo.105P	HFR-26	84+46	HFR-35	
87+14	Bo.105P	HFR-36	87+90	Bo.105P	HFWS	84+47	HFR-25	
87+15	Bo.105P	HFR-36	87+91	Bo.105P	HFR-35	84+48	HFR-25	
87+16	Bo.105P	HFR-36	87+92	Bo.105P	HFR-26	84+49	HFWS	
87+17	Bo.105P	HFR-26	87+93	Bo.105P	HFR-26	84+50	HFR-25	
87+18	Bo.105P	HFWS	87+94	Bo.105P	HFR-26	84+51	HFR-25	
87+19	Bo.105P	HFR-36	87+95	Bo.105P	HFR-26	84+52*	HFR-25	
87+20	Bo.105P	HFR-26	87+96	Bo.105P	HFR-26	84+53	HFR-25	
87+21	Bo.105P	HFWS	87+97	Bo.105P	HFR-36	84+54	HFR-25	
87+22	Bo.105P		87+98	Bo.105P	HFR-26	84+55	HFR-25	
87+23	Bo.105P	HFR-36	87+99	Bo.105P	HFR-36	84+56	HFR-35	
87+24	Bo.105P		88+01	Bo.105P	HFR-26	84+57	HFR-25	
87+25	Bo.105P	HFR-26	88+02	Bo.105P	HFR-36	84+58	HFR-25	
87+26	Bo.105P		88+03	Bo.105P	HFR-36	84+59	HFR-25	
87+27	Bo.105P		88+04	Bo.105P	HFR-36	84+60	HFR-25	
87+28	Bo.105P		88+05	Bo.105P	HFVS-910	84+62	HFR-25	
87+29	Bo.105P	HFVS-910	88+06	Bo.105P	HFR-36	84+63	HFR-25	
87+30	Bo.105P		88+07	Bo.105P	HFR-36	84+64	HFR-35	
87+31	Bo.105P		88+08	Bo.105P	HFR-36	84+65	HFR-35	
87+32	Bo.105P	HFWS	88+09	Bo.105P	HFR-35	84+66	HFR-35	
87+33	Bo.105P	HFR-26	88+10	Bo.105P	HFWS	84+67	HFR-35	
87+34	Bo.105P	HFR-26	88+11	Bo.105P	HFR-36	84+68	HFWS	
87+35	Bo.105P	HFR-26	88+12	Bo.105P	HFR-36	84+69	HFR-15	
87+36	Bo.105P	HFR-26	98+28	Bo.105C	WTD-61	84+70	HFR-15	
87+37	Bo.105P	HFR-26				84+71	HFR-15	
87+38	Bo.105P	HFR-36	**Sikorsky/VFW**			84+72	HFR-15	
87+39	Bo.105P	HFR-36	**CH-53G/CH-53GS***			84+73	HFR-15	
87+41	Bo.105P		HFR-15, Rheine-Bentlage;			84+74	HFR-15	
87+42	Bo.105P	HFR-36	HFR-25, Laupheim;			84+75	HFR-35	
87+43	Bo.105P	HFR-36	HFR-35, Mendig;			84+76	HFR-35	
87+44	Bo.105P	HFR-36	HFWS, Bückeburg;			84+77	HFR-15	
87+45	Bo.105P	HFR-16	TsLw-3, Fassberg;			84+78	HFR-15	
87+46	Bo.105P		WTD-61, Ingolstadt			84+79*	HFR-15	
87+47	Bo.105P	HFR-15	84+01*	WTD-61		84+80	HFR-15	
87+48	Bo.105P		84+02	WTD-61		84+82	HFR-35	
87+49	Bo.105P		84+03	HFR-15		84+83	HFR-15	
87+50	Bo.105P	HFR-26	84+05	HFR-35		84+84	HFR-15	
87+51	Bo.105P		84+06	HFR-15		84+85	HFR-15	
87+52	Bo.105P		84+09	HFR-25		84+86	HFR-15	
87+53	Bo.105P	HFR-26	84+10	HFWS		84+87	HFR-15	
87+55	Bo.105P	HFVS-910	84+11	HFWS		84+88	HFR-15	
87+56	Bo.105P	HFR-26	84+12	HFR-15		84+89	HFR-35	
87+57	Bo.105P	HFR-26	84+13	HFWS		84+90	HFR-15	
87+58	Bo.105P	HFWS	84+14	HFWS		84+91	HFR-15	
87+59	Bo.105P	HFR-36	84+15*	HFR-25		84+93	HFR-35	
87+60	Bo.105P	HFR-36	84+16	HFWS		84+94	HFR-35	
87+61	Bo.105P	HFR-35	84+17	HFR-25		84+95	HFR-25	
87+62	Bo.105P	HFR-36	84+18	HFWS		84+96	HFR-25	
87+63	Bo.105P	HFWS	84+19	HFWS		84+97	HFR-25	
87+64	Bo.105P	HFR-36	84+21	HFWS		84+98	HFWS	

84+99	HFR-15
85+00*	HFWS
85+01	HFR-35
85+02	HFR-35
85+03	HFR-35
85+04	HFR-25
85+05	HFR-25
85+06	HFR-25
85+07	HFR-15
85+08	HFR-15
85+09*	HFR-15
85+10	HFR-35
85+11	HFR-25
85+12*	HFR-15

Eurocopter AS.665 Tiger
WTD-61, Ingolstadt
98+23
98+25
98+26

GHANA
Ghana Air Force
Fokker F-28 Fellowship 3000
VIP Flight, Accra
G-530

Grumman G.1159A
Gulfstream III
VIP Flight, Accra
G-540

GREECE
Ellinikí Polemikí Aeroporía
Embraer ERJ.135EW*/
ERJ.135LR
356 MTM/112 PM, Elefsís;
380 Mira/112 PM, Elefsís

145-209	356 MTM
145-374*	380 Mira
145-484	356 MTM

Lockheed C-130H Hercules
356 MTM/112 PM, Elefsís
*ECM
741*
742
743
744
745
746
747*
749
751
752

Lockheed F-16C/F-16D*
Fighting Falcon
330 Mira/111 PM,
  Nea Ankhialos;
341 Mira/111 PM,
  Nea Ankhialos;
346 MAPK/110 PM, Larissa;
347 Mira/111 PM,
  Nea Ankhialos

046	341 Mira
047	347 Mira
048	341 Mira
049	347 Mira
050	341 Mira
051	347 Mira
052	341 Mira
053	347 Mira
054	341 Mira

055	347 Mira
056	341 Mira
057	347 Mira
058	341 Mira
059	347 Mira
060	341 Mira
061	347 Mira
062	341 Mira
063	347 Mira
064	341 Mira
065	347 Mira
066	341 Mira
067	347 Mira
068	341 Mira
069	347 Mira
070	341 Mira
071	347 Mira
072	341 Mira
073	347 Mira
074	341 Mira
075	341 Mira
076	341 Mira
077*	341 Mira
078*	341 Mira
079*	347 Mira
080*	341 Mira
081*	341 Mira
082*	341 Mira
083*	347 Mira
084*	341 Mira
110	330 Mira
111	330 Mira
112	346 MAPK
113	330 Mira
114	346 MAPK
115	330 Mira
116	330 Mira
117	330 Mira
118	346 MAPK
119	330 Mira
120	330 Mira
121	330 Mira
122	346 MAPK
124	330 Mira
125	330 Mira
126	346 MAPK
127	330 Mira
128	346 MAPK
129	330 Mira
130	346 MAPK
132	346 MAPK
133	330 Mira
134	346 MAPK
136	346 MAPK
138	346 MAPK
139	330 Mira
140	346 MAPK
141	330 Mira
143	346 MAPK
144*	330 Mira
145*	330 Mira
146*	346 MAPK
147*	330 Mira
148*	346 MAPK
149*	330 Mira
600*	

SAAB SF.340AEW&C
380 Mira/112 PM, Elefsis
004

Greek Govt
  Dassault Falcon 900
  Greek Govt/Olympic
    Airways, Athens
  SX-ECH

HUNGARY
Magyar Honvédseg Repülö
Csapatai
Antonov An-26
89 VSD, Szolnok

405	(03405)
406	(03406)
407	(03407)
603	(03603)

Mikoyan MiG-29/29UB*
59 HRO, Kecskemét
01
02
03
04
05
06
07
08
09
10
11
12
14
15
16
18
19
20
21
23
24*
25*
26*
27*
28*
29*

ISRAEL
Heyl ha'Avir
Boeing 707
120 Sqn, Tel Aviv

120	RC-707
128	RC-707
137	RC-707
140	KC-707
242	VC-707
248	KC-707
250	KC-707
255	EC-707
260	KC-707
264	RC-707
272	VC-707
275	KC-707
290	VC-707

Lockheed C-130 Hercules
103 Sqn & 131 Sqn, Tel Aviv

102	C-130H
106	C-130H
208	C-130E
305	C-130E
309	C-130E
310	C-130E
313	C-130E
314	C-130E
316	C-130E

420	KC-130H
427	C-130H
428	C-130H
435	C-130H
436	C-130H
522	KC-130H
545	KC-130H

Israeli Govt
Hawker 800XP
Israeli Govt, Tel Aviv
4X-COV

ITALY
Aeronautica Militare Italiana
9ª Brigata Aerea,
  Pratica di Mare:
    8° Gruppo & 71° Gruppo;
46ª Brigata Aerea, Pisa:
  2° Gruppo & 98° Gruppo;
RSV, Pratica di Mare

G222AAA

CSX62144	46-98	RSV

G222RM

MM62139	14-20	8
MM62140	14-21	8
MM62141	14-22	8

G222TCM

MM62111	46-83	98
MM62117	46-25	2
MM62121	46-21	2
MM62124	46-88	98
MM62125	14-24	8
MM62136	46-97	98
MM62137	46-95	98
MM62153X	RS-46	RSV
MM62154	46-54	8

G222VS

MM62107		71

C-27J

CSX62127		Alenia

Aeritalia-EMB AMX/AMX-T*
2° Stormo, Rivolto:
  14° Gruppo;
32° Stormo, Amendola:
  13° Gruppo &
  101° Gruppo;
51° Stormo, Istrana:
  103° Gruppo &
  132° Gruppo;
RSV, Pratica di Mare

MMX595		Alenia
MMX596		Alenia
MMX597		Alenia
MMX599		Alenia
MM7089		
MM7090		
MM7091	32-64	101
MM7092	RS-14	RSV
MM7093		
MM7094	3-37	
MM7095		103
MM7096		
MM7097		3-36
MM7098	3-35	
MM7099		
MM7100	32-66	101
MM7101	51-25	103
MM7102	2-03	14
MM7103		
MM7104	51-26	103
MM7106	3-25	
MM7107		
MM7110		
MM7111		
MM7112		
MM7115	2-12	14
MM7116	32-11	13
MM7117	3-34	
MM7118	2-11	14
MM7119		
MM7120		
MM7122	3-32	
MM7123		
MM7124	51-15	103
MM7125	RS-11	RSV
MM7126		
MM7127	3-24	
MM7128		
MM7129	2-03	14
MM7130		
MM7131	2-19	
MM7132	51-14	103
MM7133	2-18	14
MM7134	51-34	132
MM7135		
MM7138		
MM7139		
MM7140	51-26	103
MM7141		
MM7142	51-37	132
MM7143	51-20	103
MM7144	51-41	132
MM7145	51-44	132
MM7146	51-21	103
MM7147	32-04	13
MM7148	51-22	103
MM7149		
MM7150	32-65	101
MM7151	2-14	14
MM7152	51-53	132
MM7153		
MM7154	51-54	132
MM7155	32-05	13
MM7156	32-10	13
MM7157	32-07	13
CSX7158	RS-12	RSV
MM7159	51-11	103
MM7160	32-14	13
MM7161	2-21	14
MM7162	51-01	103
MM7163	2-25	
MM7164	51-30	132
MM7165	51-13	103
MM7166	32-02	13
MM7167	2-01	14
MM7168	2-04	14
MM7169	2-06	14
MM7170	2-23	14
MM7171		
MM7172	51-37	132
MM7173	2-16	14
MM7174	51-04	103
MM7175	51-43	132
MM7176	2-20	14
MM7177	2-22	14
MM7178	2-24	14
MM7179		
MM7180		
MM7182	51-16	103
MM7183		
MM7184	51-33	132
MM7185	2-02	14
MM7186	51-05	103
MM7189	51-03	103
MM7190	32-17	13
MM7191	32-01	13
MM7192	51-06	103
MM7193	51-07	103
MM7194	32-07	13
MM7195		
MM7196	32-13	13
MM7197	32-21	13
MM7198	32-03	13
MM55024*	15	RSV
MM55025*	RS-16	RSV
MM55026*	32-43	101
MM55027*		
MM55029*	3-55	
MM55030*	32-41	101
MM55031*	32-40	101
MM55034*	18	RSV
MM55035*	32-50	101
MM55036*	32-51	101
MM55037*	32-64	101
MM55038*	32-53	101
MM55039*	32-54	101
MM55040*	32-52	101
MM55041*	32-55	101
MM55042*	32-56	101
MM55043*	32-65	101
MM55044*	32-57	101
MM55046*	32-47	101
MM55047*	32-45	101
MM55048*	32-44	101
MM55049*	32-46	101
MM55050*	32-43	101
MM55051*	32-42	101

Aermacchi MB339A/
MB339CD*
61° Stormo, Lecce:
  212° Gruppo &
  213° Gruppo;
Aermacchi, Venegono;
Frecce Tricolori [FT]
  (313° Gruppo), Rivolto
  (MB339A/PAN);
RSV, Pratica di Mare

MMX606*		RSV
MM54438	61-93	
MM54440	61-00	
MM54441	61-71	
MM54442	61-95	
MM54443	61-50	
MM54445	61-25	
MM54446	61-01	
MM54447	61-02	
MM54449	61-04	
MM54450	61-94	
MM54451	61-116	
MM54452		
MM54453	61-05	
MM54454	61-06	
MM54455	61-07	
MM54456	61-10	
MM54457	61-11	
MM54458	61-12	
MM54459	61-13	
MM54460	61-14	
MM54461		
MM54462	61-16	
MM54463	61-17	
MM54467	61-23	
MM54468	61-24	
MM54471	61-27	
MM54472	61-30	
MM54473	8	[FT]
MM54475		[FT]
MM54477	9	[FT]

Italy

MM54478		[FT]
MM54479	1	[FT]
MM54480	7	[FT]
MM54482		[FT]
MM54483	61-102	
MM54484	61-101	
MM54485	12	[FT]
MM54487	61-31	
MM54488	61-32	
MM54489	61-33	
MM54490	61-34	
MM54491	61-35	
MM54492	61-36	
MM54493	61-37	
MM54494	61-40	
MM54496	61-42	
MM54497	10	[FT]
MM54498	61-44	
MM54499	61-45	
MM54500		[FT]
MM54503	61-51	
MM54504	61-52	
MM54505	0	[FT]
MM54506	61-54	
MM54507	61-55	
MM54508	61-56	
MM54509	61-57	
MM54510	61-60	
MM54511	61-61	
MM54512	61-62	
MM54513	61-63	
MM54514	61-64	
MM54515	61-65	
MM54516	61-66	
MM54517	3	[FT]
MM54518	61-70	
MM54532		
MM54533	61-72	
MM54534	61-73	
MM54535	61-74	
MM54536	5	[FT]
MM54537		
MM54538	61-75	
MM54539	61-76	
MM54541	61-100	
MM54542	6	[FT]
MM54543		[FT]
MM54544*	(Aermacchi)	
MM54545	61-84	
MM54546		[FT]
MM54547	4	[FT]
MM54548	61-90	
MM54549	61-107	
MM54550	61-110	
MM54551	2	[FT]
MM55052	61-96	
MM55053	61-97	
MM55054	61-15	
MM55055	61-20	
MM55058	61-41	
MM55059	61-26	
MM55062*	RS-26	RSV
MM55063*	RS-27	RSV
MM55064*	61-130	
MM55065*	61-131	
MM55066*	61-132	
MM55067*	61-133	
MM55068*	61-134	
MM55069*	61-135	
MM55070*	61-136	
MM55072*	61-140	
MM55073*	61-141	
MM55074*	61-142	
MM55075*	61-143	

MM55076*	61-144

Airbus A.319CJ-115
31° Stormo, Roma-Ciampino:
  306° Gruppo

MM62173	
MM62174	
MM62 . . .	

Boeing 707-328B/-3F5C*
9ª Brigata Aerea,
  Pratica di Mare:
  8° Gruppo;

MM62148	14-01
MM62149	14-02
MM62150*	14-03
MM62151*	14-04

Breguet Br.1150 Atlantic
30° Stormo, Cagliari:
  86° Gruppo;
41° Stormo, Catania:
  88° Gruppo

MM40108	41-70
MM40109	30-71
MM40110	41-72
MM40111	41-73
MM40112	30-74
MM40113	30-75
MM40114	41-76
MM40115	41-77
MM40116	30-01
MM40117	41-02
MM40118	30-03
MM40119	30-04
MM40120	41-05
MM40121	41-06
MM40122	30-07
MM40123	30-10
MM40124	41-11
MM40125	41-12

Dassault Falcon 50
31° Stormo, Roma-Ciampino:
  93° Gruppo

MM62020	
MM62021	
MM62026	
MM62029	

Dassault Falcon 900EX
31° Stormo, Roma-Ciampino:
  93° Gruppo

MM62171	
MM62172	

Eurofighter EF.2000/
EF.2000T* Typhoon
Alenia, Torino/Caselle;
RSV, Pratica di Mare

MMX602	RS-01	RSV
MMX603	(Alenia)	
MMX614*	(Alenia)	

Grumman G.1159A
Gulfstream III
31° Stormo, Roma-Ciampino:
  306° Gruppo

MM62025	

Lockheed C-130H Hercules
46ª Brigata Aerea, Pisa:
  50° Gruppo

MM61988	46-02
MM61989	46-03
MM61990	46-04
MM61991	46-05
MM61992	46-06
MM61993	46-07
MM61994	46-08
MM61995	46-09
MM61997	46-11
MM61998	46-12

Lockheed C-130J/
C-130J-30 Hercules II
46ª Brigata Aerea, Pisa:
  2° Gruppo & 50° Gruppo

C-130J

MM62175	46-40	2
MM62176	46-41	2
MM62177	46-42	2
MM62178	46-43	2
MM62179	46-44	2
MM62180	46-45	2
MM62181	46-46	50
MM62182	46-47	50
MM62183	46-48	50
MM62184	46-49	50

C-130J-30

MM62185		
MM62186	46-52	
MM62187	46-53	
MM62188	46-54	
MM62189		
MM62190		
MM62191		
MM62192		
MM62193		
MM62194		
MM62195		
MM62196		

Lockheed F-104 Starfighter
4° Stormo, Grosseto:
  9° Gruppo & 20° Gruppo;
5° Stormo, Cervia:
  23° Gruppo;
9° Stormo, Grazzanise:
  10° Gruppo;
37° Stormo, Trapani:
  18° Gruppo;
RSV, Pratica di Mare

F-104S-ASA/F-104ASA-M*

MM6704*	9-52	10
MM6710		
MM6714		
MM6716*	5-30	23
MM6717*	5-41	23
MM6719*	5-35	23
MM6720*	9-51	10
MM6722*	5-31	23
MM6731*	37-03	18
MM6732*	37-04	18
MM6733*	4-51	20
MM6734*	4-11	9
MM6736		
MM6737*	5-46	23

Serial	Code	Unit
MM6739*	5-47	23
MM6740*	4-56	20
MM6748		
MM6756*	5-42	23
MM6759*	37-20	18
MM6762*	37-02	18
MM6763*	9-33	10
MM6764*	37-11	18
MM6767*	37-05	18
MM6770*	9-35	10
MM6771*		
MM6772*	37-11	18
MM6773		
MM6776*	9-46	10
MM6787*	4-50	20
MM6812*	9-41	10
MM6818		
MM6823		
MM6838*	4-58	20
MM6839		
MM6841		
MM6848*		
MM6849*	4-10	9
MM6850*	37-24	18
MM6870*	5-45	23
MM6872*	37-23	18
MM6873*	4-7	9
MM6876*	37-11	18
MM6879*	4-15	9
MM6881*	4-59	20
MM6886		
MM6887*	5-33	23
MM6890*	37-25	18
MM6912*	9-42	10
MM6914*	37-01	18
MM6923*	4-2	9
MM6924		
MM6925*	37-15	18
MM6926*	4-12	9
MM6930*	9-53	10
MM6932*	4-54	20
MM6934*	9-31	10
MM6935*	9-32	10
MM6936*	9-41	10
MM6939*	4-52	20
MM6942		
MM6943		

TF-104G/TF-104G-M*

Serial	Code	Unit
MM54226*	4-23	20
MM54228*	4-26	20
MM54232*	4-29	20
MM54233	RS-09	RSV
MM54237*	4-32	20
MM54250*	4-33	20
MM54251*	4-34	20
MM54253*	4-35	20
MM54255	4-37	20
MM54256	4-38	20
MM54258	4-40	20
MM54260*	4-41	20
MM54261*	4-42	20
MM54554*	4-48	20
MM54555*	4-45	20
MM54556*	4-47	20

Panavia Tornado ADV/Trainer[1]
36° Stormo, Gioia del Colle:
  12° Gruppo

MM7202	36-33	(ZE832)
MM7203	36-02	(ZE761)
MM7204	36-05	(ZE730)
MM7205	36-06	(ZE787)
MM7206	36-26	(ZE760)
MM7207	36-27	(ZE762)
MM7208	36-32	(ZE811)
MM7209	36-25	(ZE835)
MM7210	36-14	(ZE836)
MM7211	36-16	(ZE792)
MM7225	36-04	(ZE252)
MM7226	36-21	(ZE911)
MM7227	36-22	(ZG732)
MM7228	36-34	(ZG733)
MM7229	36-07	(ZG728)
MM7230	36-11	(ZG730)
MM7231	36-12	(ZG734)
MM7232	36-10	(ZG735)
MM7233	36-23	(ZG768)
MM7234	36-24	(ZE167)
MM55056[1]	36-01	(ZE202)
MM55057[1]	36-03	(ZE837)
MM55060[1]	36-30	(ZE208)
MM55061[1]	36-20	(ZE205)

Panavia Tornado Strike/Trainer[1]/ECR[2]
6° Stormo, Ghedi:
  102° Gruppo &
  154° Gruppo;
50° Stormo, Piacenza:
  155° Gruppo;
156° Gruppo Autonomo,
  Gioia del Colle;
RSV, Pratica di Mare

Serial	Code	Unit
MM7002	6-10	154
MM7003	6-23	154
MM7004	36-46	156
MM7005[2]	50-05	155
MM7006	6-16	154
MM7007	36-37	156
MM7008		
MM7009	6-09	154
MM7011	6-04	154
MM7013	36-40	156
MM7014		
MM7015	50-53	155
MM7016		
MM7018	6-46	102
MM7019[2]	50-19	155
MM7020[2]	50-21	155
MM7021[2]	50-01	155
MM7022	6-02	154
MM7023	6-13	154
MM7025	6-43	102
MM7026	6-44	102
MM7027[2]	50-51	155
MM7028		
MM7029	6-22	154
MM7030		
MM7031	6-21	154
MM7033	50-50	155
MM7034	6-30	154
MM7035	36-47	156
MM7036[2]	50-..	155
MM7037	6-47	102
MM7038	36-41	156
MM7039	50-03	155
CMX7040	RS-01	RSV
MM7041	36-54	156
MM7042	6-31	102
MM7043		
MM7044	6-20	154
MM7046[2]	6-06	154
MM7047[2]	50-43	155
MM7048	36-54	Alenia
MM7049	6-34	102
MM7050	36-44	156
MM7051	50-45	155
MM7052		
MM7053[2]	50-07	155
MM7054[2]	50-40	155
MM7055	50-42	155
MM7056	50-47	155
MM7057	6-12	154
MM7058	6-36	102
MM7059	50-47	155
MM7060	36-36	156
MM7061	6-01	154
MM7062[2]	50-44	155
MM7063	36-42	156
MM7064	6-26	154
MM7065	6-25	154
MM7066		
MM7067	67	156
CSX7068[2]		Alenia
MM7070[2]	50-46	155
MM7071	6-35	102
MM7072	36-57	156
MM7073[2]		Alenia
MM7075		
MM7078	50-02	155
CMX7079[2]		Alenia
MM7080	6-33	102
MM7081	6-11	154
MM7082[2]	6-14	154
MM7083	6-37	102
MM7084	6-36	102
CMX7085	36-50	Alenia
MM7086		
MM7087	36-35	156
MM7088	6-18	154
MM55000[1]	6-51	102
MM55001[1]	6-42	102
MM55002[1]	6-52	102
MM55003[1]	6-..	154
MM55004[1]	6-53	102
MM55005[1]	6-40	102
MM55006[1]	6-44	102
MM55007[1]	36-55	156
MM55008[1]	6-45	102
MM55009[1]	36-56	156
MM55010[1]	6-42	102
MM55011[1]		

Piaggio P-180AM Avanti
9ª Brigata Aerea,
  Pratica di Mare:
  71° Gruppo;
36° Stormo, Gioia del Colle:
  636ª SC;
RSV, Pratica di Mare

Serial	Code	Unit
MM62159		636
MM62160	54	RSV
MM62161		71
MM62162		71
MM62163		71
CSX62164		RSV
MM62199		71
MM62201		71
MM62202		71

Piaggio-Douglas PD-808-GE/PD-808-RM/PD-808-TA
9ª Brigata Aerea,
  Pratica di Mare:
  8° Gruppo &
  71° Gruppo;
RSV, Pratica di Mare

Serial	Code	Unit
MM61952	GE	71
MM61954	TA	71
MM61955	GE	71

MM61960	GE	71
MM61962	GE	71
MM62014	RM	8

Guardia di Finanza
Aérospatiale
ATR.42-400MP
2° Gruppo EM,
Pratica di Mare

MM62165	GF-13
MM62166	GF-14

Marina Militare Italiana
McDonnell Douglas
AV-8B/TAV-8B Harrier II+
Gruppo Aerei Imbarcarti,
Taranto/Grottaglie
AV-8B

MM7199	1-03
MM7200	1-04
MM7201	1-05
MM7212	1-06
MM7213	1-07
MM7214	1-08
MM7215	1-09
MM7217	1-11
MM7218	1-12
MM7219	1-13
MM7220	1-14
MM7221	1-15
MM7222	1-16
MM7223	1-18
MM7224	1-19

TAV-8B

MM55032	1-01
MM55033	1-02

Italian Govt
Dassault Falcon 200
Italian Govt/Soc. CAI,
Roma/Ciampino
I-CNEF
I-SOBE

Dassault Falcon 900
Italian Govt/Soc. CAI,
Roma/Ciampino
I-DIES
I-FICV
I-NUMI

IVORY COAST
Grumman G.1159C
Gulfstream IV
Ivory Coast Govt, Abidjan
TU-VAD

JAPAN
Japan Air Self Defence Force
Boeing 747-47C
701st Flight Sqn, Chitose
20-1101
20-1102

JORDAN
Al Quwwat al Jawwiya
al Malakiya al Urduniya
Extra EA-300S
Royal Jordanian Falcons,
Amman
JY-RNA
JY-RNC
JY-RND
JY-RNE

JY-RNG
JY-RNL

Lockheed C-130H Hercules
3 Sqn, Al Matar AB/Amman
344
345
346
347

Jordanian Govt
Airbus A.340-211
Jordanian Govt, Amman
JY-ABH

Canadair CL.604 Challenger
Jordanian Govt, Amman
JY-ONE
JY-TWO

Lockheed L.1011 TriStar 500
Jordanian Govt, Amman
JY-HKJ

KAZAKHSTAN
Boeing 757-2M6
Govt of Kazakhstan, Almaty
P4-NSN

Tupolev Tu-134A-3
Govt of Kazakhstan, Almaty
UN-65799

KENYA
Kenyan Air Force
Fokker 70ER
308

KUWAIT
Al Quwwat al Jawwiya
al Kuwaitiya
Lockheed L100-30 Hercules
41 Sqn, Kuwait International
KAF 323
KAF 324
KAF 325

Kuwaiti Govt
Airbus A.300C4-620
Kuwaiti Govt, Safat
9K-AHI

Airbus A.310-308
Kuwaiti Govt, Safat
9K-ALD

Grumman
G.1159C Gulfstream IV
Kuwaiti Govt/Kuwait
Airways, Safat
9K-AJA
9K-AJB

Gulfstream Aerospace
Gulfstream V
Kuwaiti Govt/Kuwait
Airways, Safat
9K-AJD
9K-AJE
9K-AJF

KYRGYZSTAN
Tupolev Tu-134A-3
Govt of Kyrgyzstan, Bishkek

EX-65119

Tupolev Tu-154B/Tu-154M
Govt of Kyrgyzstan, Bishkek
EX-85294 Tu-154B
EX-85718 Tu-154M
EX-85762 Tu-154M

LITHUANIA
Karines Oro Pajegos
LET 410 Turbolet
I Transporto Eskadrile,
Zokniai
01
02

Lithuanian Govt
Lockheed L.1329 Jetstar 731
Lithuanian Govt, Vilnius
LY-AMB

LUXEMBOURG
NATO
Boeing 707-307C/329C*
NAEWF, Geilenkirchen
LX-N19997
LX-N19999
LX-N20000
LX-N20199*

Boeing E-3A
NAEWF, Geilenkirchen
LX-N90442
LX-N90443
LX-N90444
LX-N90445
LX-N90446
LX-N90447
LX-N90448
LX-N90449
LX-N90450
LX-N90451
LX-N90452
LX-N90453
LX-N90454
LX-N90455
LX-N90456
LX-N90458
LX-N90459

MALAYSIA
Royal Malaysian Air Force/
Tentera Udara Diraja
Malaysia
Bombardier BD.700-1A10
Global Express
2 Sqn, Simpang
M48-01
M48-02

Lockheed C-130 Hercules
4 Sqn, Subang;
14 Sqn, Labuan;
20 Sqn, Subang

M30-01	C-130H(MP)	4 Sqn
M30-02	C-130H	14 Sqn
M30-03	C-130H	14 Sqn
M30-04	C-130H-30	20 Sqn
M30-05	C-130H	14 Sqn
M30-06	C-130H	14 Sqn
M30-07	C-130T	20 Sqn
M30-08	C-130H(MP)	20 Sqn
M30-09	C-130H(MP)	20 Sqn
M30-10	C-130H-30	20 Sqn

M30-11	C-130H-30	20 Sqn
M30-12	C-130H-30	20 Sqn
M30-14	C-130H-30	20 Sqn
M30-15	C-130H-30	20 Sqn
M30-16	C-130H-30	20 Sqn

MEXICO
Fuerza Aérea Mexicana
  Boeing 757-225
  8° Grupo Aéreo, Mexico City
  TP-01 (XC-UJM)

MOROCCO
Force Aérienne Royaume
  Marocaine/ Al Quwwat al
  Jawwiya al Malakiya
  Marakishiya
  Airtech CN.235M-100
  Escadrille de Transport,
  Rabat

023	CNA-MA
024	CNA-MB
025	CNA-MC
026	CNA-MD
027	CNA-ME
028	CNA-MF
031	CNA-MG

  CAP-231/CAP-232
  Marche Verte
  CAP-231

09	CN-ABL
22	CN-ABM
23	CN-ABN
24	CN-ABO

  CAP-232

28	CNA-BP
29	CNA-BQ
31	CNA-BR
36	CNA-BS
37	CNA-BT

  Lockheed C-130H Hercules
  Escadrille de Transport,
  Rabat

4535	CN-AOA
4551	CN-AOC
4575	CN-AOD
4581	CN-AOE
4583	CN-AOF
4713	CN-AOG
4717	CN-AOH
4733	CN-AOI
4738	CN-AOJ
4739	CN-AOK
4742	CN-AOL
4875	CN-AOM
4876	CN-AON
4877	CN-AOO
4888	CN-AOP
4892	CN-AOQ
4907	CN-AOR
4909	CN-AOS
4940	CN-AOT

Govt of Morocco
  Boeing 707-138B
  Govt of Morocco, Rabat
  CNA-NS

  Cessna 560 Citation V
  Govt of Morocco, Rabat
  CNA-NW

Dassault Falcon 50
Govt of Morocco, Rabat
CN-ANO

Grumman
G.1159 Gulfstream IITT/
G.1159A Gulfstream III
Govt of Morocco, Rabat

CNA-NL	Gulfstream IITT
CNA-NU	Gulfstream III
CNA-NV	Gulfstream III

NAMIBIA
  Dassault Falcon 900B
  Namibian Govt, Windhoek
  V5-NAM

NETHERLANDS
Koninklijke Luchtmacht
  Agusta-Bell AB.412SP
  303 Sqn, Leeuwarden
  R-01
  R-02
  R-03

  Boeing-Vertol
  CH-47D Chinook
  298 Sqn, Soesterberg
  D-101
  D-102
  D-103
  D-104
  D-105
  D-106
  D-661
  D-662
  D-663
  D-664
  D-665
  D-666
  D-667

  Eurocopter
  AS.532U-2 Cougar
  300 Sqn, Gilze-Rijen
  S-400
  S-419
  S-433
  S-438
  S-440
  S-441
  S-442
  S-444
  S-445
  S-447
  S-450
  S-453
  S-454
  S-456
  S-457
  S-458
  S-459

  Fokker 50
  334 Sqn, Eindhoven
  U-05
  U-06

  Fokker 60UTA-N
  334 Sqn, Eindhoven
  U-01
  U-02
  U-03
  U-04

General Dynamics F-16
(MLU aircraft are marked
with a *)
TGp/306/311/312 Sqns,
  Volkel;
313/315 Sqns, Twenthe;
322/323 Sqns, Leeuwarden

J-001	F-16A*	322 Sqn
J-002	F-16A*	322 Sqn
J-003	F-16A*	322 Sqn
J-004	F-16A*	322 Sqn
J-005	F-16A*	322 Sqn
J-006	F-16A*	322 Sqn
J-008	F-16A*	322 Sqn
J-009	F-16A*	322 Sqn
J-010	F-16A*	323 Sqn
J-011	F-16A*	322 Sqn
J-013	F-16A*	322 Sqn
J-014	F-16A*	322 Sqn
J-015	F-16A*	315 Sqn
J-016	F-16A*	312 Sqn
J-017	F-16A*	312 Sqn
J-018	F-16A*	313 Sqn
J-019	F-16A*	323 Sqn
J-020	F-16A*	315 Sqn
J-021	F-16A*	311 Sqn
J-055	F-16A*	322 Sqn
J-057	F-16A*	323 Sqn
J-058	F-16A*	315 Sqn
J-060	F-16A*	315 Sqn
J-061	F-16A*	322 Sqn
J-062	F-16A*	322 Sqn
J-063	F-16A*	322 Sqn
J-064	F-16B*	322 Sqn
J-065	F-16B*	313 Sqn
J-066	F-16B*	TGp
J-067	F-16B*	315 Sqn
J-068	F-16B*	322 Sqn
J-135	F-16A*	311 Sqn
J-136	F-16A*	315 Sqn
J-137	F-16A*	322 Sqn
J-138	F-16A*	315 Sqn
J-139	F-16A	312 Sqn
J-141	F-16A*	315 Sqn
J-142	F-16A*	323 Sqn
J-143	F-16A*	315 Sqn
J-144	F-16A*	315 Sqn
J-145	F-16A*	313 Sqn
J-146	F-16A*	313 Sqn
J-192	F-16A*	311 Sqn
J-193	F-16A*	312 Sqn
J-194	F-16A*	312 Sqn
J-196	F-16A	312 Sqn
J-197	F-16A*	315 Sqn
J-198	F-16A*	315 Sqn
J-199	F-16A*	312 Sqn
J-201	F-16A*	312 Sqn
J-202	F-16A*	312 Sqn
J-203	F-16A*	311 Sqn
J-204	F-16A*	323 Sqn
J-205	F-16A*	322 Sqn
J-207	F-16A*	312 Sqn
J-208	F-16B*	312 Sqn
J-209	F-16B*	315 Sqn
J-210	F-16B*	312 Sqn
J-211	F-16B*	322 Sqn
J-243	F-16A	306 Sqn
J-251	F-16A*	306 Sqn
J-253	F-16A*	306 Sqn
J-254	F-16A*	306 Sqn
J-255	F-16A*	306 Sqn
J-257	F-16A*	306 Sqn
J-267	F-16B*	306 Sqn

Netherlands – New Zealand

J-269	F-16B*	312 Sqn
J-270	F-16B*	306 Sqn
J-360	F-16A*	323 Sqn
J-362	F-16A*	315 Sqn
J-363	F-16A*	323 Sqn
J-364	F-16A	312 Sqn
J-365	F-16A*	313 Sqn
J-366	F-16A*	315 Sqn
J-367	F-16A*	322 Sqn
J-368	F-16B*	311 Sqn
J-369	F-16B*	315 Sqn
J-508	F-16A*	315 Sqn
J-509	F-16A*	315 Sqn
J-510	F-16A*	312 Sqn
J-511	F-16A*	315 Sqn
J-512	F-16A*	313 Sqn
J-513	F-16A*	323 Sqn
J-514	F-16A*	315 Sqn
J-515	F-16A*	322 Sqn
J-516	F-16A*	311 Sqn
J-616	F-16A*	315 Sqn
J-617	F-16A*	313 Sqn
J-619	F-16A*	313 Sqn
J-620	F-16A*	315 Sqn
J-622	F-16A*	323 Sqn
J-623	F-16A	306 Sqn
J-624	F-16A*	306 Sqn
J-627	F-16A*	306 Sqn
J-628	F-16A*	315 Sqn
J-630	F-16A*	311 Sqn
J-631	F-16A*	311 Sqn
J-632	F-16A*	311 Sqn
J-633	F-16A*	312 Sqn
J-635	F-16A*	312 Sqn
J-636	F-16A*	311 Sqn
J-637	F-16A*	312 Sqn
J-638	F-16A*	312 Sqn
J-640	F-16A*	312 Sqn
J-641	F-16A*	311 Sqn
J-642	F-16A*	312 Sqn
J-643	F-16A*	322 Sqn
J-644	F-16A*	313 Sqn
J-646	F-16A*	306 Sqn
J-647	F-16A*	311 Sqn
J-648	F-16A*	312 Sqn
J-649	F-16B	306 Sqn
J-650	F-16B*	323 Sqn
J-652	F-16B*	313 Sqn
J-653	F-16B*	TGp
J-654	F-16B*	311 Sqn
J-655	F-16B*	306 Sqn
J-656	F-16B*	313 Sqn
J-657	F-16B*	313 Sqn
J-864	F-16A*	315 Sqn
J-866	F-16A*	312 Sqn
J-867	F-16A*	313 Sqn
J-868	F-16A*	311 Sqn
J-869	F-16A*	306 Sqn
J-870	F-16A*	313 Sqn
J-871	F-16A*	312 Sqn
J-872	F-16A*	312 Sqn
J-873	F-16A*	315 Sqn
J-874	F-16A*	306 Sqn
J-875	F-16A*	313 Sqn
J-876	F-16A*	311 Sqn
J-877	F-16A*	311 Sqn
J-878	F-16A*	313 Sqn
J-879	F-16A*	313 Sqn
J-881	F-16A*	323 Sqn
J-882	F-16B*	306 Sqn
J-884	F-16B*	311 Sqn
J-885	F-16B*	323 Sqn

Grumman G-1159C Gulfstream IV
334 Sqn, Eindhoven
V-11

Lockheed C-130H-30 Hercules
334 Sqn, Eindhoven
G-273
G-275

MBB Bo.105CB/ Bo.105CB-4*
931 Sqn, Gilze-Rijen
B-39*
B-40*
B-41*
B-44
B-47
B-48
B-63
B-64
B-66
B-68
B-69
B-75
B-76
B-80

MDH AH-64DN Apache Longbow
301 Sqn, Gilze-Rijen;
302 Sqn, Gilze-Rijen

Q-01	302 Sqn
Q-02	302 Sqn
Q-03	302 Sqn
Q-04	301 Sqn
Q-05	302 Sqn
Q-06	302 Sqn
Q-07	302 Sqn
Q-08	302 Sqn
Q-09	301 Sqn
Q-10	301 Sqn
Q-11	
Q-12	
Q-13	302 Sqn
Q-14	302 Sqn
Q-15	301 Sqn
Q-16	301 Sqn
Q-17	302 Sqn
Q-18	301 Sqn
Q-19	301 Sqn
Q-20	301 Sqn
Q-21	302 Sqn
Q-22	302 Sqn
Q-23	302 Sqn
Q-24	301 Sqn
Q-25	302 Sqn
Q-26	302 Sqn
Q-27	
Q-28	
Q-29	301 Sqn
Q-30	302 Sqn

McDonnell Douglas KDC-10
334 Sqn, Eindhoven
T-235
T-264

Pilatus PC-7
131 EMVO Sqn, Woensdrecht
L-01

L-02
L-03
L-04
L-05
L-06
L-07
L-08
L-09
L-10
L-11
L-12
L-13

Sud Alouette III
300 Sqn, Soesterberg
A-247
A-275
A-292
A-301

Marine Luchtvaart Dienst Beech Super King Air 200
OVALK, Valkenburg
PH-SBK

Lockheed P-3C Orion
MARPAT (320 Sqn & 321 Sqn), Valkenburg and Keflavik
300
301
302
303
304
305
306
307
308
309
310
311
312

Westland SH-14D Lynx
HELIGRP (7 Sqn & 860 Sqn), De Kooij
(7 Sqn operates 860 Sqn aircraft on loan)
261
262
264
265
267
268
269
270
271
276
277
280
281
283

Netherlands Govt Fokker 70
Dutch Royal Flight, Schiphol
PH-KBX

NEW ZEALAND
Royal New Zealand Air Force Boeing 727-22C
40 Sqn, Whenuapai
NZ7271
NZ7272

Lockheed C-130H Hercules		
40 Sqn, Whenuapai		
NZ7001		
NZ7002		
NZ7003		
NZ7004		
NZ7005		

Lockheed P-3K Orion
5 Sqn, Whenuapai
NZ4201
NZ4202
NZ4203
NZ4204
NZ4205
NZ4206

NIGERIA
Federal Nigerian Air Force
Lockheed C-130H/
C-130H-30* Hercules
88th MAG, Lagos
NAF-910
NAF-912
NAF-913
NAF-915
NAF-917*
NAF-918*

Nigerian Govt
Boeing 727-2N6
Federal Govt of Nigeria,
  Lagos
5N-FGN   [001]

Dassault Falcon 900
Federal Govt of Nigeria,
  Lagos
5N-FGE
5N-FGO

Grumman
G.1159 Gulfstream II/
G.1159A Gulfstream III
Federal Govt of Nigeria,
  Lagos
5N-AGV   Gulfstream II
5N-FGP   Gulfstream III

Gulfstream Aerospace
Gulfstream V
Federal Govt of Nigeria,
  Lagos
5N-FGS

Hawker 1000
Federal Govt of Nigeria,
  Lagos
5N-FGR

NORWAY
Kongelige Norske Luftforsvaret
Bell 412SP
339 Skv, Bardufoss;
720 Skv, Rygge
139   339 Skv
140   339 Skv
141   720 Skv
142   720 Skv
143   339 Skv
144   339 Skv
145   720 Skv
146   339 Skv
147   720 Skv

148   339 Skv
149   339 Skv
161   339 Skv
162   339 Skv
163   720 Skv
164   720 Skv
165   720 Skv
166   720 Skv
167   720 Skv
194   720 Skv

Dassault Falcon 20 ECM
717 Skv, Rygge
041
053
0125

General Dynamics F-16
(MLU aircraft are marked
with a *)
331 Skv, Bodø (r/w/bl);
332 Skv, Rygge (y/bk);
338 Skv, Ørland
272   F-16A*   332 Skv
273   F-16A   332 Skv
275   F-16A*   331 Skv
276   F-16A   338 Skv
277   F-16A*   332 Skv
279   F-16A*   332 Skv
281   F-16A   332 Skv
282   F-16A*   338 Skv
284   F-16A*   332 Skv
285   F-16A*   338 Skv
286   F-16A*   338 Skv
288   F-16A*   338 Skv
289   F-16A*   338 Skv
291   F-16A*   338 Skv
292   F-16A*   338 Skv
293   F-16A*   332 Skv
295   F-16A*   338 Skv
297   F-16A*   332 Skv
298   F-16A   338 Skv
299   F-16A*   332 Skv
302   F-16B*   332 Skv
304   F-16B*   338 Skv
305   F-16B*   332 Skv
306   F-16B*   332 Skv
658   F-16A*
659   F-16A*
660   F-16A*   331 Skv
661   F-16A*   338 Skv
662   F-16A*
663   F-16A
664   F-16A*   331 Skv
665   F-16A*
666   F-16A*
667   F-16A*   331 Skv
668   F-16A*   331 Skv
669   F-16A*   331 Skv
670   F-16A   332 Skv
671   F-16A*   338 Skv
672   F-16A
673   F-16A*   331 Skv
674   F-16A   331 Skv
675   F-16A   331 Skv
677   F-16A*   331 Skv
678   F-16A*   331 Skv
680   F-16A*   338 Skv
681   F-16A*   338 Skv
682   F-16A*   331 Skv
683   F-16A
686   F-16A*   331 Skv
687   F-16A*   331 Skv
688   F-16A*   331 Skv

689   F-16B*   332 Skv
690   F-16B*   338 Skv
691   F-16B
692   F-16B*   332 Skv
693   F-16B*   338 Skv
711   F-16B*   331 Skv

Lockheed C-130H Hercules
335 Skv, Gardermoen
952
953
954
955
956
957

Lockheed P-3C Orion
333 Skv, Andøya
3296
3297
3298
3299

Lockheed P-3N Orion
333 Skv, Andøya
4576
6603

Northrop F-5A
Eye of the Tiger Project,
  Rygge
128
130
131
133
134
896
902

Northrop F-5B
Eye of the Tiger Project,
  Rygge
136
243
244
387
906
907
908
909

Westland Sea King Mk 43/
Mk 43A/Mk 43B
330 Skv:
  A Flt, Bodø;
  B Flt, Banak;
  C Flt, Ørland;
  D Flt, Sola
060   Mk 43
062   Mk 43
066   Mk 43
069   Mk 43
070   Mk 43
071   Mk 43B
072   Mk 43
073   Mk 43
074   Mk 43
189   Mk 43A
322   Mk 43B
329   Mk 43B
330   Mk 43B

Norway – Portugal

Kystvakt (Coast Guard)
Westland Lynx Mk86
337 Skv, Bardufoss
207
216
228
232
237
350

OMAN
Royal Air Force of Oman
BAC 1-11/485GD
4 Sqn, Seeb
551
552
553

Lockheed C-130H Hercules
4 Sqn, Seeb
501
502
503

Omani Govt
Boeing 747SP-27
Govt of Oman, Seeb
A4O-SO
A4O-SP

Grumman G.1159C
Gulfstream IV
Govt of Oman, Seeb
A4O-AB
A4O-AC

PAKISTAN
Pakistan Fiza'ya
Boeing 707-340C
68-19635 12 Sqn
68-19866 12 Sqn

Pakistani Govt
Boeing 737-33A
Govt of Pakistan, Karachi
AP-BEH

PERU
Fuerza Aérea Peruana
Douglas DC-8-62AF
370 (OB-1372)
371 (OB-1373)

POLAND
Polskie Wojska Lotnicze
Antonov An-26
13 ELTR, Krakow/Balice
1307
1310
1402
1403
1406
1407
1508
1509
1602
1603
1604

Mikoyan MiG-29A/UB*
1 ELT, Minsk/Mazowiecki;
41 ELT, Malbork
01   41 ELT
02   41 ELT

04*   41 ELT
06   41 ELT
08   41 ELT
10   41 ELT
11   41 ELT
13   41 ELT
15*   1 ELT
18   41 ELT
19   41 ELT
24   41 ELT
26*   41 ELT
28*   1 ELT
32   41 ELT
38   1 ELT
40   1 ELT
42*   1 ELT
48*   41 ELT
54   1 ELT
56   1 ELT
59   1 ELT
64*   1 ELT
65   1 ELT
66   1 ELT
67   1 ELT
70   1 ELT
77   1 ELT
83   1 ELT
86   1 ELT
92   1 ELT
105   1 ELT
108   1 ELT
111   1 ELT
114   1 ELT
115   1 ELT
128   41 ELT
300   41 ELT
310   41 ELT
314   41 ELT
315   41 ELT
408*   41 ELT
800   41 ELT
5115   41 ELT

PZL M28 Bryza
13 ELTr, Balice;
LGPR, Bydgoszcz
0203   M28B-1   13 ELTr
0204   M28B-1   13 ELTr
0723   M28RL   LGPR
1003   M28TD   13 ELTr

Tupolev Tu-154M
36 SPLT, Warszawa
101
102

Yakovlev Yak-40
36 SPLT, Warszawa
032
034
036
037
038
039
040
041
042
043
044
045
047
048

Lotnictwo Marynarki Wojennej
PZL M28 Bryza
1 DLMW, Gydnia/Babie Doly;
3 DLMW, Cewice/Siemirowice
0404   M28B-E   1 DLMW
0405   M28B-E   1 DLMW
0810   M28B-1R   PZL
1006   M28B-1R   3 DLMW
1007   M28B-1   1 DLMW
1008   M28B-1R   3 DLMW
1017   M28B-1R   3 DLMW
1022   M28B-1R   3 DLMW
1114   M28B-1R   3 DLMW
1115   M28B-1R   3 DLMW
1116   M28B-1R   3 DLMW
1117   M28B-1   1 DLMW
1118   M28B-1   1 DLMW

PORTUGAL
Força Aérea Portuguesa
Aérospatiale SA.330C Puma
Esq 711, Lajes;
Esq 751, Montijo
19502   Esq 751
19503   Esq 751
19504   Esq 751
19505   Esq 751
19506   Esq 711
19508   Esq 711
19509   Esq 751
19511   Esq 711
19512   Esq 751
19513   Esq 711

CASA 212A/212ECM*
Aviocar
Esq 401, Sintra;
Esq 501, Sintra;
Esq 502, Sintra;
Esq 711, Lajes
16501*   Esq 501
16502*   Esq 501
16503   Esq 501
16504   Esq 501
16505   Esq 502
16506   Esq 502
16507   Esq 502
16508   Esq 502
16509   Esq 501
16510   Esq 401
16511   Esq 502
16512   Esq 401
16513   Esq 711
16514   Esq 711
16515   Esq 711
16517   Esq 711
16519   Esq 401
16520   Esq 711
16521*   Esq 401
16522*   Esq 401
16523*   Esq 401
16524*   Esq 401

CASA 212-300 Aviocar
Esq 401, Sintra
17201
17202

D-BD Alpha Jet
Esq 103, Beja;
Esq 301, Beja
15201
15202
15204
15205
15206
15208
15209
15210
15211
15213
15214
15215
15216
15217
15218
15219
15220
15221
15222
15223
15224
15225
15226
15227
15228
15229
15230
15231
15232
15233
15234
15235
15236
15237
15238
15239
15240
15241
15242
15243
15244
15246
15247
15250

Dassault Falcon 20DC
Esq 504, Lisbon/Montijo
17103

Dassault Falcon 50
Esq 504, Lisbon/Montijo
17401
17402
17403

**Lockheed C-130H/
C-130H-30* Hercules**
Esq 501, Lisbon/Montijo
16801*
16802*
16803
16804
16805
16806*

**Lockheed (GD)
F-16A/F-16B***
Esq 201, Monte Real;
Esq 304, Monte Real
15101   Esq 201
15102   Esq 201

15103	Esq 201
15104	Esq 201
15105	Esq 201
15106	Esq 201
15107	Esq 201
15108	Esq 201
15109	Esq 201
15110	Esq 201
15112	Esq 201
15113	Esq 201
15114	Esq 201
15115	Esq 201
15116	Esq 201
15117	Esq 201
15118*	Esq 201
15119*	Esq 201
15120*	Esq 201
15121	Esq 304
15122	Esq 304
15123	Esq 304
15124	Esq 304
15125	Esq 304
15126	Esq 304
15127	Esq 304
15128	Esq 304
15129	Esq 304
15130	Esq 304
15131	Esq 304
15132	Esq 304
15133	Esq 304
15134	Esq 304
15135	Esq 304
15136	Esq 304
15137	Esq 304
15138	Esq 304
15139*	Esq 304
15140*	Esq 304
15141*	Esq 304

Lockheed P-3P Orion
Esq 601, Lisbon/Montijo
14801
14802
14803
14804
14805
14806

**Marinha
Westland Super Lynx Mk 95**
Esq de Helicopteros,
Lisbon/Montijo
19201
19202
19203
19204
19205

**QATAR
Airbus A.310-304**
Qatari Govt, Doha
A7-AAF

Airbus A.319CJ-133
Qatari Govt, Doha
A7-HHJ

Airbus A.320-232
Qatari Govt, Doha
A7-AAG

Airbus A.340-211
Qatari Govt, Doha
A7-HHK

**ROMANIA
Fortele Aeriene Romania
Lockheed C-130B Hercules**
19 FMT, Bucharest/Otapeni
5927
5930
6150
6166

**RUSSIA
Voenno-Vozdushniye Sily
Rossioki Federatsii (Russian
Air Force)
Sukhoi Su-27**
TsAGI, Gromov Flight
Institute, Zhukhovsky
595   Su-27P
597   Su-30
598   Su-27P

**Russian Govt
Ilyushin Il-62M**
Russian Govt, Moscow
RA-86466
RA-86467
RA-86468
RA-86536
RA-86537
RA-86540
RA-86553
RA-86554
RA-86559
RA-86561
RA-86710
RA-86711
RA-86712

Ilyushin Il-96-300
Russian Govt, Moscow
RA-96012

Tupolev Tu-134A
Russian Govt, Moscow
RA-65904

Tupolev Tu-154B-2
Russian Govt, Moscow
RA-85426
RA-85594

Tupolev Tu-154M
Russian Govt, Moscow;
Open Skies*
RA-85629
RA-85630
RA-85631
RA-85645
RA-85651
RA-85653
RA-85655*
RA-85658
RA-85659
RA-85666
RA-85675
RA-85676
RA-85843

**SAUDI ARABIA
Al Quwwat al Jawwiya
as Sa'udiya
BAe 125-800/-800B***
1 Sqn, Riyadh
HZ-105

Saudi Arabia – Slovakia

HZ-109*
HZ-110*

Boeing E-3A/KE-3A* Sentry
18 Sqn, Riyadh;
19 Sqn, Riyadh
1801
1802
1803
1804
1805
1811*
1812*
1813*
1814*
1815*
1816*
1818*
1901*

Grumman G.1159A
Gulfstream III/G.1159C
Gulfstream IV
1 Sqn, Riyadh
HZ-103   Gulfstream IV
HZ-108   Gulfstream III

Lockheed C-130/L.100
Hercules
1 Sqn, Prince Sultan AB;
4 Sqn, Jeddah;
16 Sqn, Prince Sultan AB;
32 Sqn, Prince Sultan AB

111	VC-130H	1 Sqn
112	VC-130H	1 Sqn
451	C-130E	4 Sqn
452	C-130H	4 Sqn
455	C-130E	4 Sqn
461	C-130H	4 Sqn
462	C-130H	4 Sqn
463	C-130H	4 Sqn
464	C-130H	4 Sqn
465	C-130H	4 Sqn
466	C-130H	4 Sqn
467	C-130H	4 Sqn
468	C-130H	4 Sqn
471	C-130H-30	4 Sqn
472	C-130H	4 Sqn
473	C-130H	4 Sqn
474	C-130H	4 Sqn
475	C-130H	4 Sqn
476	C-130H	4 Sqn
477	C-130H	4 Sqn
478	C-130H	4 Sqn
479	C-130H	4 Sqn
1601	C-130H	16 Sqn
1602	C-130H	16 Sqn
1603	C-130H	16 Sqn
1604	C-130H	16 Sqn
1605	C-130E	16 Sqn
1606	C-130E	16 Sqn
1607	C-130E	16 Sqn
1608	C-130E	16 Sqn
1609	C-130E	16 Sqn
1610	C-130E	16 Sqn
1611	C-130E	16 Sqn
1612	C-130H	16 Sqn
1613	C-130H	16 Sqn
1614	C-130H	16 Sqn
1615	C-130H	16 Sqn
1618	C-130H	16 Sqn
1619	C-130H	16 Sqn
1622	C-130H-30	16 Sqn
1623	C-130H-30	16 Sqn

1624	C-130H	16 Sqn
1625	C-130H	16 Sqn
1626	C-130H	16 Sqn
3201	KC-130H	32 Sqn
3202	KC-130H	32 Sqn
3203	KC-130H	32 Sqn
3204	KC-130H	32 Sqn
3205	KC-130H	32 Sqn
3206	KC-130H	32 Sqn
3207	KC-130H	32 Sqn
3208	KC-130H	32 Sqn
HZ-114	VC-130H	1 Sqn
HZ-115	VC-130H	1 Sqn
HZ-116	VC-130H	1 Sqn
HZ-117	L.100-30	1 Sqn
HZ-128	L.100-30	1 Sqn
HZ-129	L.100-30	1 Sqn

Saudi Govt
Airbus A.340-211
Royal Embassy of Saudi
  Arabia, Riyadh
HZ-124

Boeing 737-268
Saudi Royal Flight, Jeddah
HZ-HM4

Boeing 747-3G1
Saudi Royal Flight, Jeddah
HZ-HM1A

Boeing 747SP-68
Saudi Govt, Jeddah;
Saudi Royal Flight, Jeddah
HZ-AIF   Govt
HZ-AIJ   Royal Flight
HZ-HM1B   Royal Flight

Boeing MD-11
Saudi Royal Flight, Jeddah
HZ-AFA1
HZ-HM7

Canadair CL.604
Challenger
Saudi Royal Flight, Jeddah
HZ-AFA2

Dassault Falcon 900
Saudi Govt, Jeddah
HZ-AFT
HZ-AFZ

Grumman G.1159A
Gulfstream III
Armed Forces Medical
  Services, Riyadh;
Saudi Govt, Jeddah
HZ-AFN   Govt
HZ-AFR   Govt
HZ-MS3   AFMS

Grumman G.1159C
Gulfstream IV
Armed Forces Medical
  Services, Riyadh;
Saudi Govt, Jeddah
HZ-AFU   Govt
HZ-AFV   Govt
HZ-AFW   Govt
HZ-AFX   Govt
HZ-AFY   Govt
HZ-MS4   AFMS

Gulfstream Aerospace
Gulfstream V
Armed Forces Medical
  Services, Riyadh
HZ-MS5
HZ-MS5A

Lockheed C-130H/
L.100 Hercules
Armed Forces Medical
  Services, Riyadh
HZ-MS6   L.100-30
HZ-MS7   C-130H
HZ-MS8   C-130H-30
HZ-MS09   L.100-30
HZ-MS019 C-130H

Lockheed L.1011
TriStar 500
Saudi Royal Flight, Jeddah
HZ-HM5
HZ-HM6

SINGAPORE
Republic of Singapore Air Force
Boeing KC-135R
Stratotanker
122 Sqn, Paya Labar
750
751
752
753

Lockheed C-130 Hercules
122 Sqn, Paya Labar

720	KC-130B
721	KC-130B
724	KC-130B
725	KC-130B
730	C-130H
731	C-130H
732	C-130H
733	C-130H
734	KC-130H
735	C-130H

SLOVAKIA
Slovenské Vojenske Letectvo
Aero L-39 Albatros
31 SLK/3 Letka, Sliač [SL];
VSL, Koštice;
White Albatroses,
  Koštice (*WA*)

0101	L-39C	WA [4]
0102	L-39C	WA [6]
0103	L-39C	VSL
0111	L-39C	WA [5]
0112	L-39C	WA [1]
0442	L-39C	WA [2]
0443	L-39C	WA [7]
0730	L-39V	VSL
0745	L-39V	VSL
1701	L-39ZA	31 SLK
1725	L-39ZA	31 SLK
1730	L-39ZA	31 SLK
4701	L-39ZA	31 SLK
4703	L-39ZA	31 SLK
4707	L-39ZA	31 SLK
4711	L-39ZA	31 SLK

Antonov An-24V
32 ZmDK/1 Letka, Piešťany
2903
5605

Antonov An-26
32 ZmDK/1 Letka, Piešťany
2506
3208

LET 410 Turbolet
31 SLK/4 Letka, Sliač [SL];
32 ZmDK/1 Letka, Piešťany;
VSL, Košice

0730	L-410UVP	32 ZmDK
0927	L-410T	31 SLK
0930	L-410T	32 ZmDK
1133	L-410T	VSL
1203	L-410FG	32 ZmDK
1521	L-410FG	32 ZmDK
2311	L-410UVP	32 ZmDK

Mikoyan MiG-29A/UB*
31 SLK/1 & 2 Letka,
Sliač [SL]
0619
0820
0921
1303*
2123
3709
3911
4401*
5113
5304*
5515
5817
6124
6425
6526
6627
6728
7501
8003
8605
9308

Sukhoi Su-25K/UBK*
33 SBoLK/2 Letka, Malacky
1006
1007
1008
1027
3237*
5033
5036
6017
6018
8072
8073
8074
8075

Slovak Govt
Tupolev Tu-154M
Slovak Govt,
Bratislava/Ivanka
OM-BYO
OM-BYR

Yakovlev Yak-40
Slovak Govt,
Bratislava/Ivanka
OM-BYE
OM-BYL

SLOVENIA
Slovene Army
LET 410UVP-E
15 Brigada, Ljubljana
L4-01

Pilatus PC-9
15 Brigada, Ljubljana
L9-51
L9-52
L9-53
L9-54
L9-55
L9-56
L9-57
L9-58
L9-59
L9-60
L9-61
L9-62
L9-63
L9-64
L9-65
L9-66
L9-67
L9-68
L9-69

Slovenian Govt
Gates LearJet
Slovenian Govt, Ljubljana
S5-BAA   LearJet 35A
S5-BAB   LearJet 24D

SOUTH AFRICA
South African Air Force/
Suid Afrikaanse Lugmag
Boeing 707
60 Sqn, Waterkloof
1415   328C
1417   328C
1419   328C
1423   344C

Boeing 737-7ED
21 Sqn, Waterkloof
ZS-RSA

Dassault Falcon 900
21 Sqn, Waterkloof
ZS-NAN

Lockheed C-130B/
C-130BZ* Hercules
28 Sqn, Waterkloof
401
402
403
404
405
406
407*
408*
409*

SPAIN
Ejército del Aire
Airtech
CN.235M-10 (T.19A)/
CN.235M-100 (T.19B)
Ala 35, Getafe

T.19A-01	35-60
T.19A-02	35-61
T.19B-03	35-21
T.19B-04	35-22
T.19B-05	35-23
T.19B-06	35-24
T.19B-07	35-25
T.19B-08	35-26
T.19B-09	35-27
T.19B-10	35-28
T.19B-11	35-29
T.19B-12	35-30
T.19B-13	35-31
T.19B-14	35-32
T.19B-15	35-33
T.19B-16	35-34
T.19B-17	35-35
T.19B-18	35-36
T.19B-19	35-37
T.19B-20	35-38

Boeing 707
408 Esc, Torrejón;
Grupo 45, Torrejón

T.17-1	331B	45-10
T.17-2	331B	45-11
T.17-3	368C	45-12
TM.17-4	351C	408-21

CASA 101EB Aviojet
Grupo 54, Torrejón;
Grupo de Escuelas de
Matacán (74);
AGA, San Javier (79);
Patrulla Aguila, San Javier*

E.25-01	79-01	
E.25-05	79-05	
E.25-06	79-06	[2]*
E.25-07	79-07	[7]*
E.25-08	79-08	[1]*
E.25-09	79-09	
E.25-10	79-10	
E.25-11	79-11	
E.25-12	79-12	
E.25-13	79-13	
E.25-14	79-14	
E.25-15	79-15	
E.25-16	79-16	
E.25-17	74-40	
E.25-18	74-42	
E.25-19	79-19	
E.25-20	79-20	
E.25-21	79-21	
E.25-22	79-22	
E.25-23	79-23	[4]*
E.25-24	79-24	
E.25-25	79-25	
E.25-26	79-26	[3]*
E.25-27	79-27	
E.25-28	79-28	
E.25-29	74-45	
E.25-31	79-31	
E.25-33	74-02	
E.25-34	79-34	
E.25-35	54-20	
E.25-37	79-37	
E.25-38	79-38	
E.25-40	79-40	
E.25-41	74-41	
E.25-43	74-43	
E.25-44	79-44	
E.25-45	79-45	
E.25-46	79-46	
E.25-47	79-47	
E.25-48	79-48	
E.25-49	79-49	
E.25-50	79-33	

Spain

E.25-51	74-07		T.12B-15	37-02		TR.20-02	403-12	
E.25-52	79-34	[6]*	T.12B-16	74-71				
E.25-53	74-09		T.12B-17	37-03		**Dassault Falcon 20D/E/F**		
E.25-54	79-35		T.12B-18	46-31		Grupo 45, Torrejón;		
E.25-55	44-05		T.12B-19	46-32		408 Esc, Torrejón		
E.25-56	74-11		T.12B-20	37-04		TM.11-1	20E	45-02
E.25-57	74-12		T.12B-21	37-05		TM.11-2	20D	45-03
E.25-59	74-13		T.12B-22	37-06		TM.11-3	20D	408-11
E.25-61	54-22		T.12B-23	72-01		TM.11-4	20E	408-12
E.25-62	79-17		T.12B-24	54-12		T.11-5	20F	45-05
E.25-63	74-17		T.12B-25	74-72				
E.25-64	74-18		T.12B-26	72-02		**Dassault Falcon 50**		
E.25-65	79-95		T.12B-27	46-33		Grupo 45, Torrejón		
E.25-66	74-20		T.12B-28	72-03		T.16-1	45-20	
E.25-67	74-21		T.12B-29	37-08				
E.25-68	74-22		T.12B-30	74-73		**Dassault Falcon 900**		
E.25-69	79-97		T.12B-31	46-34		Grupo 45, Torrejón		
E.25-71	74-25		T.12B-33	72-04		T.18-1	45-40	
E.25-72	74-26		T.12B-34	74-74		T.18-2	45-41	
E.25-73	79-98		T.12B-35	37-09				
E.25-74	74-28		T.12B-36	37-10		**Eurofighter EF2000T**		
E.25-75	74-29		T.12B-37	72-05		**Typhoon**		
E.25-76	74-30		T.12B-39	74-75		CASA, Getafe		
E.25-78	79-02		TE.12B-40	79-93		CE.16-02		
E.25-79	79-39		TE.12B-41	79-94				
E.25-80	79-03		T.12C-43	46-50		**Fokker F.27M**		
E.25-81	74-34		T.12C-44	37-50		**Friendship 400MPA**		
E.25-83	74-35		T.12B-46	74-76		802 Esc, Gando,		
E.25-84	79-04		T.12B-47	72-06		Las Palmas		
E.25-86	79-32	[5]*	T.12B-48	37-11		D.2-01	802-10	
E.25-87	79-29		T.12B-49	72-07		D.2-02	802-11	
E.25-88	74-39		T.12B-52	46-35		D.2-03	802-12	
			T.12B-53	46-36				

CASA 212 Aviocar
212 (XT.12)/
212A (T.12B)/
212B (TR.12A)/
212D (TE.12B)/
212DE (TM.12D)/
212E (T.12C)/
212S (D.3A)/
212S1 (D.3B)/
212-200 (T.12D)/
212-200 (TR.12D)
Ala 37, Villanubla;
Ala 46, Gando, Las Palmas;
CLAEX, Torrejón (54);
Ala 72, Alcantarilla;
Grupo Esc, Matacán (74);
AGA (Ala 79), San Javier;
403 Esc, Getafe;
408 Esc, Torrejón;
801 Esc, Palma/
  Son San Juan;
803 Esc, Cuatro Vientos;
INTA, Torrejón

D.3A-1	(801 Esc)
D.3A-2	(803 Esc)
D.3B-3	(803 Esc)
D.3B-4	(801 Esc)
D.3B-5	(801 Esc)
D.3B-6	(801 Esc)
D.3B-7	(803 Esc)
D.3B-8	(801 Esc)
XT.12A-1	54-10
TR.12A-4	403-02
TR.12A-5	403-03
TR.12A-6	403-04
TR.12A-8	403-06
T.12B-9	74-83
TE.12B-10	79-92
T.12B-12	74-82
T.12B-13	74-70
T.12B-14	37-01

T.12B-54	46-37
T.12B-55	46-38
T.12B-56	74-79
T.12B-57	72-08
T.12C-59	37-51
T.12C-60	37-52
T.12C-61	37-53
T.12B-63	37-14
T.12B-64	46-40
T.12B-65	74-80
T.12B-66	72-09
T.12B-67	74-81
T.12B-68	37-15
T.12B-69	37-16
T.12B-70	37-17
T.12B-71	37-18
TM.12D-72	408-01
TM.12D-74	54-11
T.12D-75	403-07
TR.12D-76	37-60
TR.12D-77	37-61
TR.12D-78	37-62
TR.12D-79	37-63
TR.12D-80	37-64
TR.12D-81	37-65

CASA 295
Ala 35, Getafe;

T.21-01	35-39
T.21-02	35-40
T.21-03	35-41
T.21-04	35-42
T.21-05	
T.21-06	
T.21-07	
T.21-08	
T.21-09	

Cessna 560 Citation VI
403 Esc, Getafe

TR.20-01	403-11

Lockheed C-130H/
C-130H-30/KC-130H
Hercules
311 Esc/312 Esc (Ala 31),
Zaragoza

TL.10-01	C-130H-30	31-01
T.10-02	C-130H	31-02
T.10-03	C-130H	31-03
T.10-04	C-130H	31-04
TK.10-5	KC-130H	31-50
TK.10-6	KC-130H	31-51
TK.10-7	KC-130H	31-52
T.10-8	C-130H	31-05
T.10-9	C-130H	31-06
T.10-10	C-130H	31-07
TK.10-11	KC-130H	31-53
TK.10-12	KC-130H	31-54

Lockheed P-3A/P-3B*
Orion
Grupo 22, Morón

P.3-01	22-21
P.3-03	22-22
P.3-08	22-31*
P.3-09	22-32*
P.3-10	22-33*
P.3-11	22-34*
P.3-12	22-35*

McDonnell Douglas
F-18 Hornet
Ala 11, Morón;
Ala 12, Torrejón;
Ala 15, Zaragoza;
Esc 462, Gran Canaria
EF-18A/EF-18B* Hornet

CE.15-1	15-70*
CE.15-2	15-71*
CE.15-3	15-72*
CE.15-4	15-73*
CE.15-5	15-74*

CE.15-6	15-75*
CE.15-7	15-76*
CE.15-8	12-71*
CE.15-9	15-77*
CE.15-10	12-73*
CE.15-11	12-74*
CE.15-12	12-75*
C.15-13	12-01
C.15-14	15-01
C.15-15	15-02
C.15-16	15-03
C.15-18	15-05
C.15-20	15-07
C.15-21	15-08
C.15-22	15-09
C.15-23	15-10
C.15-24	15-11
C.15-25	15-12
C.15-26	15-13
C.15-27	15-14
C.15-28	15-15
C.15-29	15-16
C.15-30	15-17
C.15-31	15-18
C.15-32	15-19
C.15-33	15-20
C.15-34	15-21
C.15-35	15-22
C.15-36	15-23
C.15-37	15-24
C.15-38	15-25
C.15-39	15-26
C.15-40	15-27
C.15-41	15-28
C.15-43	15-30
C.15-44	12-02
C.15-45	12-03
C.15-46	12-04
C.15-47	15-31
C.15-48	12-06
C.15-49	12-07
C.15-50	12-08
C.15-51	12-09
C.15-52	12-10
C.15-53	12-11
C.15-54	12-12
C.15-55	12-13
C.15-56	12-14
C.15-57	12-15
C.15-58	12-16
C.15-59	12-17
C.15-60	12-18
C.15-61	12-19
C.15-62	12-20
C.15-64	12-22
C.15-65	12-23
C.15-66	12-24
C.15-67	15-33
C.15-68	12-26
C.15-69	12-27
C.15-70	12-28
C.15-72	12-30

F/A-18A Hornet

C.15-73	11-01
C.15-74	46-02
C.15-75	46-03
C.15-76	21-04
C.15-77	21-05
C.15-78	46-06
C.15-79	11-07
C.15-80	21-08
C.15-81	11-09
C.15-82	46-10

C.15-83	46-11
C.15-84	46-12
C.15-85	46-13
C.15-86	11-14
C.15-87	46-15
C.15-88	11-16
C.15-89	21-17
C.15-90	11-18
C.15-91	46-19
C.15-92	46-20
C.15-93	46-21
C.15-94	46-22
C.15-95	46-23
C.15-96	46-24

Arma Aérea de l'Armada Española
BAe/McDonnell Douglas EAV-8B/EAV-8B+/ TAV-8B Harrier II
Esc 009, Rota
EAV-8B

VA.1A-15	01-903
VA.1A-18	01-906
VA.1A-19	01-907
VA.1A-21	01-909
VA.1A-22	01-910
VA.1A-23	01-911
VA.1A-24	01-912

EAV-8B+

VA.1B-25	01-914
VA.1B-26	01-915
VA.1B-27	01-916
VA.1B-28	01-917
VA.1B-29	01-918
VA.1B-30	01-919
VA.1B-31	01-920
VA.1B-32	01-921
VA.1B-34	01-923
VA.1B-35	01-924

TAV-8B

VAE.1A-33	01-922

Cessna 550 Citation 2
Esc 004, Rota

U.20-1	01-405
U.20-2	01-406
U.20-3	01-407

SWEDEN
Svenska Flygvapnet
Beechcraft Super King Air (Tp.101)
Flottiljer 7, Såtenäs;
Flottiljer 17, Ronneby/
Kallinge;
Flottiljer 21, Luleå/
Kallax

101002	012	F21
101003	013	F17
101004	014	F7

Grumman G.1159C Gulfstream 4 (Tp.102A/S.102B Korpen/ Tp.102C)
Flottiljer 16M,
Stockholm/Bromma &
Uppsala
Tp.102A

102001	021

S.102B Korpen

102002	022
102003	023

Tp.102C

102004	024

Lockheed C-130 Hercules (Tp.84)
Flottiljer 7, Såtenäs

84001	841	C-130E
84002	842	C-130E
84003	843	C-130H
84004	844	C-130H
84005	845	C-130H
84006	846	C-130H
84007	847	C-130H
84008	848	C-130H

Rockwell Sabreliner-40 (Tp.86)
FMV, Malmslätt

86001	861
86002	862

SAAB 37 Viggen
Flottiljer 4, Östersund/
Frösön;
Flottiljer 16, Uppsala;
Flottiljer 21, Luleå/
Kallax;
FMV, Malmslätt
JA 37/JA 37D[D]/JA 37DI[I]

37311	03	F21
37317	06	F21
37318	58	F16
37319	59	F16
37320	60	F16
37322	62	F16
37325	25	F4
37326[I]	26	FMV
37327	08	F16
37330	30	F16
37331	31	F4
37336	04	F4
37341	41	F4
37343	43	F4
37350	50	F21
37353	33	F21
37357	57	F4
37363	10	F21
37364	11	F21
37365	12	F21
37366	13	F16
37367	14	F16
37369	16	F21
37370	17	F21
37371	18	F21
37375	25	
37376	36	F4
37377	37	F4
37379	15	F21
37380	50	F4
37382	52	F4
37385	55	F4
37386[D]	46	
37388	58	F4
37389[D]	59	
37390	60	F4
37393	63	F4
37394	47	
37395	65	
37397[I]	20	F4
37398[I]	08	
37400	50	F16
37401[I]	01	F4
37402[D]	02	
37403	23	F21

Sweden

37404^D	24		37974	64	F21		39165	165	F21
37405	25	F21	37976	66	F21		39166	66	F7
37406	26	F4					39167	67	F10
37407	27	F21	**SAAB JAS 39 Gripen**				39168	168	F10
37408	28	F16	Flottiljer 7, Såtenäs [G];				39169	169	F7
37409	29	F21	Flottiljer 10, Angelholm;				39170	170	F10
37410	10	F16	Flottiljer 17, Ronneby/				39171	171	F10
37411	11	F16	Kallinge;				39172	172	F21
37412^D	12		Flottiljer 21, Luleå/Kallax				39173	173	F10
37413^D	13	F21	FMV, Malmslätt				39174	174	F10
37414^I	14	F4	**JAS 39**				39175	175	F10
37415^I	15	F16	39-5	55	FMV		39176	176	F10
37418^D	18	F21	**JAS 39A**				39177	177	FMV
37420	20	F16	39101	51	FMV		39178	178	F10
37421^I	21	F4	39103	103	FMV		39179	179	F17
37422^I	22	F4	39104	04	F7		39180	180	F10
37423	23	F16	39105	105	F10		39181	181	F7
37424^I	24	F21	39106	106	F10		39182	182	F7
37426^I	26		39107	07	F7		39183	183	F10
37427^I	27	F4	39108	108	F7		39184	184	F10
37428^I	28	F16	39109	09	F7		39185	185	FMV
37429^D	29	F4	39110	10	F7		39186	186	F7
37431^D	31		39111	11	F7		39187	187	F21
37432	32	F16	39112	112	F7		39188	188	F7
37433	33	F16	39113	13	F7		39189	189	FMV
37434	34	F16	39114	14	F7		39190	190	F21
37435^D	35	F4	39115	15	F7		39191	191	F10
37436^I	32	F16	39116	16	SAAB		39192	192	F7
37437^I	37		39117	17	F7		39193	193	FMV
37438^D	38	F4	39118	18	SAAB		39194	194	FMV
37439	01	F4	39119	19	F7		39195		
37440^I	40	F4	39120	120	F7		39196	196	FMV
37441	41		39121	21	F7		39197	197	FMV
37442^I	52		39122	122	F7		39198	198	FMV
37443^D	43	F21	39123	23	F7		39199	198	SAAB
37444^I	04		39124	124	F17		39200		
37445^D	45		39125	125	F7		39201		
37446^I	06	F4	39126	26	F17		39202		
37447	35	F16	39127	27	F7		39203	203	SAAB
37449^I	49	F4	39128	28	F7		39204		
Sk 37/Sk 37E*			39129	29	F7		39205	205	F21
37801	80	F4	39131	31	F7		39206	206	
37802	81	F4	39132	132	F10		39208	208	F17
37804	83	F4	39133	33	F7		39209		
37807*	70	F4	39134	134	F10		39210		
37808*	71	F4	39135	135	F10		39211		
37809*	72	F4	39136	36	F21		39212		
37811*	74	F4	39137	137	F10		39213		
37813*	75	F4	39138	138	F17		39214		
37814*	76	F4	39139	39	F10		39215		
37815*	77	F4	39140	40	F10		39216		
37816*	78	F4	39141	41	F7		39217		
37817*	79	F4	39142	42	F7		39218		
AJSH 37			39143	43	F10		39219		
37901	51	F21	39144	44	F10		39220		
37903	05	F21	39145	45	F10		39221		
37911	33	F21	39146	46	F17		39222		
37913			39147	47	F10		39223		
37914	61	F21	39148	48	F10		39224		
37915	69	F21	39149	49	F21		39225		
37916	37	FMV	39150	50	F10		39226		
37918	71	F21	39151	51	F7		39227		
37922	61	F21	39152	52	F7		**JAS 39B**		
37925	75	F21	39153	53	F10		39800	56	FMV
AJSF 37			39154	54	F7		39801	70	F7
37950	48	F21	39155	55	F7		39802	802	FMV
37951	50	F21	39157	57	F7		39803	803	F7
37952	52	F21	39158	58	F7		39804	804	F7
37954	54	F21	39159	59	F7		39805	805	F7
37957	56	F21	39160	60	F7		39806	806	FMV
37958	58	F21	39161	61	F7		39807	807	F7
37960	60	F21	39162	162	F10		39808	808	FMV
37971	62	F21	39163	163	F17		39809	809	SAAB
			39164	64	F10		39810		

39811		
39812		
39813	813	SAAB
39814	814	SAAB

JAS 39C

39-6		FMV
39228		
39229		
39230		
39231		
39232		
39233		
39234		
39235		
39236		
39237		
39238		
39239		
39240		

SAAB SF.340AEW&C (S.100B) Argus
Flottiljer 16M, Uppsala

100002	002
100005	005
100006	006
100007	007

Förvarsmaktens Helikopterflottilj

Aérospatiale AS.332M-1 Super Puma (Hkp.10)
1.HkpBat, Lycksele & Östersund/Frösön;
2.HkpBat, Ronneby/Kallinge, Såtenäs, Sundsvall, Uppsala & Visby;

10401	91	2.HkpBat
10402	92	2.HkpBat
10403	93	1.HkpBat
10405	95	2.HkpBat
10406	96	2.HkpBat
10407	97	1.HkpBat
10408	98	2.HkpBat
10409	99	2.HkpBat
10410	90	2.HkpBat
10411	88	1.HkpBat
10412	89	1.HkpBat

Agusta-Bell AB.412HP (Hkp.11)
1.HkpBat, Boden;
4.HkpBat, Malmslätt

11331	31	4.HkpBat
11332	32	
11333	33	1.HkpBat
11334	34	1.HkpBat
11335	35	1.HkpBat
11336	36	
11337	37	
11338	38	
11339	39	
11340	40	
11341	41	
11342	42	

MBB Bo.105CBS (Hkp.9A)
1.HkpBat, Boden;
4.HkpBat, Malmslätt;
FMV (Flygvapnet), Malmslätt

09201	01	4.HkpBat
09202	02	1.HkpBat
09203	03	4.HkpBat
09204	04	4.HkpBat
09205	05	1.HkpBat
09206	06	1.HkpBat
09207	07	1.HkpBat
09208	08	1.HkpBat
09209	09	4.HkpBat
09210	10	1.HkpBat
09211	11	1.HkpBat
09212	12	1.HkpBat
09213	13	4.HkpBat
09214	14	4.HkpBat
09215	15	4.HkpBat
09216	16	4.HkpBat
09217	17	4.HkpBat
09218	18	4.HkpBat
09219	19	1.HkpBat
09220	20	4.HkpBat
09221	90	FMV

Vertol/Kawasaki-Vertol 107
2.HkpBat, Berga, Goteborg/ Säve, & Ronneby/Kallinge;
FMV (Flygvapnet), Malmslätt

Vertol 107-II-15 (Hkp.4B)

04061	61	2.HkpBat
04063	63	2.HkpBat
04064	64	2.HkpBat

Kawasaki-Vertol KV.107-II-16 (Hkp.4C)

04065	65	2.HkpBat
04067	67	2.HkpBat
04068	68	2.HkpBat
04069	69	2.HkpBat
04070	70	2.HkpBat
04071	71	2.HkpBat
04072	72	FMV

Vertol 107-II-15 (Hkp.4D)

04073	73	2.HkpBat
04074	74	2.HkpBat
04075	75	2.HkpBat
04076	76	2.HkpBat

SWITZERLAND
Schweizerische Flugwaffe
(Most aircraft are pooled centrally. Some carry unit badges but these rarely indicate actual operators.)

Aérospatiale AS.332M-1/ AS.532UL Super Puma
Leichte Flieger Staffel 5 (LtSt 5), Interlaken;
Leichte Flieger Staffel 6 (LtSt 6), Alpnach;
Leichte Flieger Staffel 8 (LtSt 8), Ulrichen;
Detachments at Alpnach, Emmen, Meiringen, Payerne & Sion

AS.332M-1

T-311
T-312
T-313
T-314
T-315
T-316
T-317
T-318
T-319
T-320
T-321
T-322
T-323
T-324
T-325

AS.532UL

T-331
T-332
T-333
T-334
T-335
T-336
T-337
T-338
T-339
T-340
T-341
T-342

Beechcraft Super King Air 350C
Flugswaffenbrigade 31, Dübendorf

HB-GII

Dassault Falcon 50
VIP Flight, Dübendorf

T-783

Dassault Mirage III
Flieger Staffel 3 (FlSt 3), Sion;
Flieger Staffel 4 (FlSt 4), Payerne;
Flieger Staffel 10 (FlSt 10), Buochs;
Gruppe fur Rustunggdienste (GRD), Emmen;
Instrumentation Flieger Staffel 14 (InstruFlSt 14), Payerne

Mirage IIIBS

J-2001	InstruFlSt 14
U-2004	InstruFlSt 14

Mirage IIIUDS

J-2011	InstruFlSt 14
J-2012	InstruFlSt 14

Mirage IIIRS

R-2102
R-2103
R-2104
R-2105
R-2106
R-2107
R-2108
R-2109
R-2110
R-2111
R-2112
R-2113
R-2114
R-2115
R-2116
R-2117
R-2118

Gates LearJet 35A
VIP Flight, Dübendorf

T-781

McDonnell Douglas F/A-18 Hornet
Flieger Staffel 11 (FlSt 11), Meiringen;
Flieger Staffel 17 (FlSt 17), Payerne;
Flieger Staffel 18 (FlSt 18), Payerne

Switzerland – Turkey

F/A-18C	J-3027	**SYRIA**
J-5001	J-3029	**Tupolev Tu-134A**
J-5002	J-3030	Govt of Syria, Damascus
J-5003	J-3033	YK-AYA
J-5004	J-3034	
J-5005	J-3036	
J-5006	J-3037	**TUNISIA**
J-5007	J-3038	**Boeing 737-7HJ**
J-5008	J-3041	Govt of Tunisia, Tunis
J-5009	J-3043	TS-IOO
J-5010	J-3044	
J-5011	J-3046	**TURKEY**
J-5012	J-3047	**Türk Hava Kuvvetleri**
J-5013	J-3049	**Boeing KC-135R**
J-5014	J-3051	**Stratotanker**
J-5015	J-3052	101 Filo, Incirlik
J-5016	J-3053	00325
J-5017	J-3054	00326
J-5018	J-3055	23539
J-5019	J-3056	23563
J-5020	J-3057	23567
J-5021	J-3058	72609
J-5022	J-3060	80110
J-5023	J-3061	
J-5024	J-3062	**Cessna 650 Citation VII**
J-5025	J-3063	224 Filo, Ankara/Etimes ut
J-5026	J-3065	004
F/A-18D	J-3066	005
J-5232	J-3067	
J-5233	J-3068	**Grumman G.1159C**
J-5234	J-3069	**Gulfstream 4**
J-5235	J-3070	224 Filo, Ankara/Etimes ut
J-5236	J-3071	001
J-5237	J-3072	002
J-5238	J-3073	003
	J-3074	
	J-3075	**Lockheed C-130B Hercules**
Northrop F-5 Tiger II	J-3076	222 Filo, Erkilet
Flieger Staffel 1 (FlSt 1),	J-3077	3496 (23496)
Turtman;	J-3079	10960
Flieger Staffel 6 (FlSt 6),	J-3080 *P. Suisse*	10963
Sion;	J-3081 *P. Suisse*	70527
Flieger Staffel 8 (FlSt 8),	J-3082 *P. Suisse*	80736
Meiringen;	J-3083 *P. Suisse*	
Flieger Staffel 11 (FlSt 11),	J-3084 *P. Suisse*	**Lockheed C-130E Hercules**
Meiringen;	J-3085 *P. Suisse*	222 Filo, Erkilet
Flieger Staffel 13 (FlSt 13),	J-3086 *P. Suisse*	01468 12-468
Meiringen;	J-3087 *P. Suisse*	01947
Flieger Staffel 18 (FlSt 18),	J-3088 *P. Suisse*	13186 12-186
Payerne;	J-3089	13187
Flieger Staffel 19 (FlSt 19),	J-3090 *P. Suisse*	13188 12-188
Mollis;	J-3091 *P. Suisse*	13189
Gruppe fur Rustunggdienste	J-3092	73-991
(GRD), Emmen;	J-3093	
Instrumentation Flieger	J-3094	**Transall C-160D**
Staffel 14 (InstruFlSt 14),	J-3095	221 Filo, Erkilet
Dübendorf;	J-3096	019
Patrouille Suisse, Emmen	J-3097 GRD	68-020
(*P. Suisse*)	J-3098	021
F-5E	**F-5F**	022
J-3001	J-3201	023
J-3002	J-3202	024
J-3004	J-3203	025 12-025
J-3005	J-3204 GRD	69-026
J-3006	J-3205	027
J-3007	J-3206	69-028 12-028
J-3008 InstruFlSt 14	J-3207	029
J-3009	J-3208	69-031
J-3010	J-3209	032
J-3011	J-3210	69-033
J-3014	J-3211	034
J-3015	J-3212	035
J-3016		036
J-3024		037 12-037
J-3025		038

178

039			89-0036	162 Filo		92-0022*	181 Filo	
69-040			89-0037	162 Filo		92-0023*	181 Filo	
			89-0038	162 Filo		92-0024*	182 Filo	
TUSAS-GD F-16C/F-16D*			89-0039	162 Filo		93-0001	181 Filo	
Fighting Falcon			89-0040	162 Filo		93-0002	181 Filo	
4 AJÜ, Mürted:			89-0041	162 Filo		93-0003	181 Filo	
141 Filo, 142 Filo &			89-0042*	141 Filo		93-0004	181 Filo	
Öncel Filo;			89-0043*	162 Filo		93-0005	181 Filo	
5 AJÜ, Merzifon:			89-0044*	162 Filo		93-0006	181 Filo	
151 Filo & 152 Filo;			89-0045*	182 Filo		93-0007	181 Filo	
6 AJÜ, Bandirma:			90-0001	162 Filo		93-0008	181 Filo	
161 Filo & 162 Filo;			90-0004	162 Filo		93-0009	181 Filo	
8 AJÜ, Diyarbakir:			90-0005	162 Filo		93-0010	181 Filo	
181 Filo & 182 Filo;			90-0006	162 Filo		93-0011	181 Filo	
9 AJÜ, Balikesir:			90-0007	162 Filo		93-0012	181 Filo	
191 Filo & 192 Filo			90-0008	162 Filo		93-0013	181 Filo	
86-0066	Öncel Filo		90-0009	162 Filo		93-0014	181 Filo	
86-0068	Öncel Filo		90-0010	162 Filo		93-0657	141 Filo	
86-0069	Öncel Filo		90-0011	162 Filo		93-0658		
86-0070	Öncel Filo		90-0012	161 Filo		93-0659		
86-0071	Öncel Filo		90-0013	161 Filo		93-0660	151 Filo	
86-0072	Öncel Filo		90-0014	161 Filo		93-0661	151 Filo	
86-0191*	Öncel Filo		90-0015	161 Filo		93-0662	151 Filo	
86-0192*	Öncel Filo		90-0016	161 Filo		93-0663	151 Filo	
86-0193*	Öncel Filo		90-0017	161 Filo		93-0664		
86-0194*	Öncel Filo		90-0018	161 Filo		93-0665		
86-0195*	Öncel Filo		90-0019	161 Filo		93-0666		
86-0196*	Öncel Filo		90-0020	162 Filo		93-0667	151 Filo	
87-0002*	Öncel Filo		90-0021	161 Filo		93-0668		
87-0003*	Öncel Filo		90-0022*	161 Filo		93-0669	152 Filo	
87-0009	Öncel Filo		90-0023*	161 Filo		93-0670		
87-0010	Öncel Filo		90-0024*	161 Filo		93-0671		
87-0011	Öncel Filo		91-0001	161 Filo		93-0672	152 Filo	
87-0013	Öncel Filo		91-0002	161 Filo		93-0673	Öncel Filo	
87-0014	Öncel Filo		91-0003	161 Filo		93-0674	192 Filo	
87-0015	Öncel Filo		91-0004	161 Filo		93-0675	192 Filo	
87-0016	Öncel Filo		91-0005	161 Filo		93-0676	192 Filo	
87-0017	Öncel Filo		91-0006	161 Filo		93-0677	192 Filo	
87-0018	Öncel Filo		91-0007	161 Filo		93-0678	192 Filo	
87-0019	Öncel Filo		91-0008	141 Filo		93-0679	192 Filo	
87-0020	Öncel Filo		91-0010	141 Filo		93-0680	192 Filo	
87-0021	Öncel Filo		91-0011	141 Filo		93-0681	192 Filo	
88-0013*	Öncel Filo		91-0012	141 Filo		93-0682	192 Filo	
88-0014*	141 Filo		91-0013	192 Filo		93-0683	192 Filo	
88-0015*	141 Filo		91-0014	141 Filo		93-0684	192 Filo	
88-0019	Öncel Filo		91-0015	182 Filo		93-0685	192 Filo	
88-0020	Öncel Filo		91-0016	182 Filo		93-0686	192 Filo	
88-0021	Öncel Filo		91-0017	182 Filo		93-0687	192 Filo	
88-0024	142 Filo		91-0018	182 Filo		93-0688	192 Filo	
88-0025	141 Filo		91-0019	182 Filo		93-0689	Öncel Filo	
88-0026	142 Filo		91-0020	182 Filo		93-0690	192 Filo	
88-0027*	Öncel Filo		91-0022*	141 Filo		93-0691*		
88-0028	191 Filo		91-0024*	141 Filo		93-0692*	152 Filo	
88-0029	142 Filo		92-0001	182 Filo		93-0693*	Öncel Filo	
88-0030	191 Filo		92-0002	182 Filo		93-0694*		
88-0031	Öncel Filo		92-0003	162 Filo		93-0695*	192 Filo	
88-0032	Öncel Filo		92-0004	182 Filo		93-0696*	192 Filo	
88-0033	141 Filo		92-0005	191 Filo		94-0071	192 Filo	
88-0034	141 Filo		92-0006	182 Filo		94-0072	191 Filo	
88-0035	141 Filo		92-0007	182 Filo		94-0073	191 Filo	
88-0036	141 Filo		92-0008	191 Filo		94-0074	191 Filo	
88-0037	141 Filo		92-0009	191 Filo		94-0075	191 Filo	
89-0022	141 Filo		92-0010	182 Filo		94-0076	191 Filo	
89-0023	141 Filo		92-0011	182 Filo		94-0077	191 Filo	
89-0024	141 Filo		92-0012	182 Filo		94-0078	191 Filo	
89-0025	141 Filo		92-0013	182 Filo		94-0079	191 Filo	
89-0026	141 Filo		92-0014	182 Filo		94-0080	191 Filo	
89-0027	141 Filo		92-0015	182 Filo		94-0081	191 Filo	
89-0028	141 Filo		92-0016	182 Filo		94-0082	191 Filo	
89-0030	141 Filo		92-0017	182 Filo		94-0083	191 Filo	
89-0031	141 Filo		92-0018	182 Filo		94-0084	191 Filo	
89-0032	141 Filo		92-0019	181 Filo		94-0085	191 Filo	
89-0034	162 Filo		92-0020	181 Filo		94-0086	191 Filo	
89-0035	162 Filo		92-0021	181 Filo		94-0087	191 Filo	

94-0088	
94-0089	
94-0090	
94-0091	152 Filo
94-0092	
94-0093	
94-0094	Öncel Filo
94-0095	
94-0096	
94-0105*	191 Filo
94-0106*	191 Filo
94-0107*	191 Filo
94-0108*	151 Filo
94-0109*	
94-0110*	
94-1557*	
94-1558*	Öncel Filo
94-1559*	152 Filo
94-1560*	151 Filo
94-1561*	191 Filo
94-1562*	192 Filo
94-1563*	192 Filo
94-1564*	191 Filo

TURKMENISTAN
BAe 1000B
Govt of Turkmenistan,
    Ashkhabad
EZ-B021

Boeing 757-23A
Govt of Turkmenistan,
    Ashkhabad
EZ-A010

UGANDA
Grumman G.1159C
Gulfstream IV
Govt of Uganda, Entebbe
5X-UEF

UKRAINE
Ukrainian Air Force
Ilyushin Il-76MD
321 TAP, Uzin
78820
UR-76413
UR-76537

UR-76624
UR-76677
UR-76687
UR-76697
UR-76699
Ilyushin Il-62M
Govt of Ukraine, Kiev
UR-86527
UR-86528

Tupolev Tu-134
Govt of Ukraine, Kiev
UR-63982

UNITED ARAB EMIRATES
United Arab Emirates Air Force
Abu Dhabi
Lockheed C-130H/
L.100-30* Hercules
1211
1212
1213
1214
1215*

Dubai
311*
312*

UAE Govt
Airbus A.300B4-620
Govt of Abu Dhabi
A6-PFD
A6-SHZ

Airbus A.319CJ-113X
Dubai Air Wing
A6-ESH

Boeing 737-7F0/
7Z5/8EC
Govt of Abu Dhabi;
Govt of Dubai

A6-AIN	7Z5	Abu Dhabi
A6-DAS	7Z5	Abu Dhabi
A6-HRS	7F0	Dubai
A6-LIW	7Z5	Dubai
A6-MRM	8EC	Dubai

A6-SIR	7Z5	Dubai

Boeing 747SP-31/
747SP-Z5*
Govt of Dubai
A6-SMM
A6-SMR
A6-ZSN*

Boeing 747-2B4BF/
747-4F6*
Dubai Air Wing;
Govt of Abu Dhabi

A6-GDP	Dubai
A6-YAS*	Abu Dhabi

Boeing 767-341ER
Govt of Abu Dhabi
A6-SUL

Dassault Falcon 900
Govt of Abu Dhabi
A6-AUH

Grumman G.1159C
Gulfstream IV
Dubai Air Wing
A6-HHH

YEMEN
Boeing 747SP-27
Govt of Yemen, Sana'a
7O-YMN

YUGOSLAVIA
Dassault Falcon 50
Govt of Yugoslavia,
    Belgrade
YU-BNA
YU-BPZ

Gates LearJet 25B/
LearJet 25D*
Govt of Yugoslavia,
    Belgrade
YU-BJG
YU-BKR*

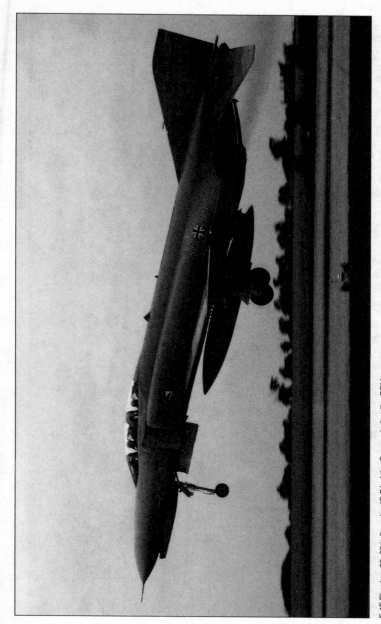

F-4F Phantom 38+00 is flown by JG-74 of the German Luftwaffe. *PRM*

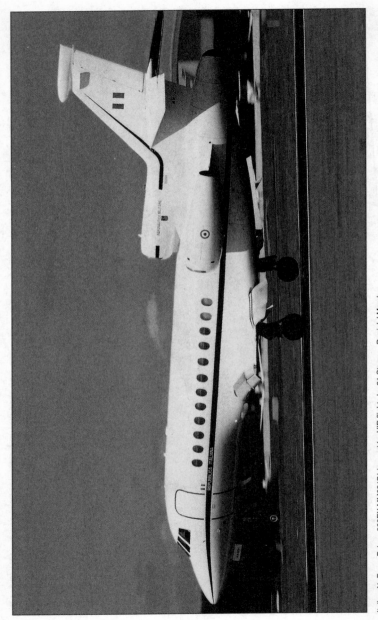

Italian Air Force Falcon 900EX MM62171 is used for VIP flights by 31 Stormo. *Daniel J March*

A Portuguese Air Force Alpha Jet (15234) from the training wing at Beja. *PRM*

One of 15 Brigada's Pilatus PC-9s, L9-68 is based at Ljubljana in Slovenia. *PRM*

Swedish Air Force JAS 39A Gripen 39149 operated by Flottiljer 21 at Lulea. *SAAB*

US Military Aircraft Markings

All USAF aircraft have been allocated a fiscal year (FY) number since 1921. Individual aircraft are given a serial according to the fiscal year in which they are ordered. The numbers commence at 0001 and are prefixed with the year of allocation. For example F-15C Eagle 84-0001 was the first aircraft ordered in 1984. The fiscal year (FY) serial is carried on the technical data block which is usually stencilled on the left-hand side of the aircraft just below the cockpit. The number displayed on the fin is a corruption of the FY serial. Most tactical aircraft carry the fiscal year in small figures followed by the last three or four digits of the serial in large figures. Large transport and tanker aircraft such as C-130s and KC-135s sometimes display a five-figure number commencing with the last digit of the appropriate fiscal year and four figures of the production number. An example of this is KC-135R 58-0128 which displays 80128 on its fin.

USN serials follow a straightforward numerical sequence which commenced, for the present series, with the allocation of 00001 to an SB2C Helldiver by the Bureau of Aeronautics in 1940. Numbers in the 165000 series are presently being issued. They are usually carried in full on the rear fuselage of the aircraft.

UK-based USAF Aircraft

The following aircraft are normally based in the UK. They are listed in numerical order of type with individual aircraft in serial number order. Where it is possible to identify the allocation of aircraft to individual squadrons by means of colours carried on fin or cockpit edge, this is also provided.

Notes	Type				Notes	Type			
	McDonnell Douglas F-15C Eagle/					91-0301	F-15E	bl	
	F-15D Eagle/ F-15E Strike Eagle					91-0302	F-15E	bl	
	LN: 48th FW, RAF Lakenheath:					91-0303	F-15E	bl	
	492nd FS blue/white					91-0304	F-15E	bl	
	493rd FS black/yellow					91-0305	F-15E	bl	
	494th FS red/white					91-0306	F-15E	r	
	83-0018	F-15C	y			91-0307	F-15E	bl	
	84-0001	F-15C	y			91-0308	F-15E	bl	
	84-0004	F-15C	y			91-0309	F-15E	bl	
	84-0009	F-15C	y			91-0310	F-15E	r	
	84-0010	F-15C	y			91-0311	F-15E	bl	
	84-0014	F-15C	y			91-0312	F-15E	bl	
	84-0015	F-15C	y			91-0313	F-15E	m	[48th OG]
	84-0019	F-15C	y			91-0314	F-15E	r	[494th FS]
	84-0027	F-15C	y			91-0315	F-15E	r	
	84-0044	F-15D	y			91-0316	F-15E	r	
	86-0147	F-15C	y			91-0317	F-15E	r	
	86-0154	F-15C	y			91-0318	F-15E	r	
	86-0156	F-15C	y			91-0319	F-15E	r	
	86-0159	F-15C	y			91-0320	F-15E	r	
	86-0160	F-15C	y			91-0321	F-15E	r	
	86-0163	F-15C	y			91-0322	F-15E	r	
	86-0164	F-15C	y	[493rd FS]		91-0323	F-15E	r	
	86-0165	F-15C	y			91-0324	F-15E	r	
	86-0166	F-15C	y			91-0326	F-15E	r	
	86-0167	F-15C	y			91-0328	F-15E	r	
	86-0171	F-15C	y			91-0329	F-15E	bl	
	86-0172	F-15C	y			91-0330	F-15E	r	
	86-0174	F-15C	y			91-0331	F-15E	r	
	86-0175	F-15C	y			91-0332	F-15E	bl	
	86-0176	F-15C	y			91-0333	F-15E	r	
	86-0178	F-15C	y			91-0334	F-15E	r	
	86-0182	F-15D	y			91-0335	F-15E	r	
	91-0300	F-15E	r			91-0601	F-15E	r	
						91-0602	F-15E	r	

Type			Notes	Type			Notes
91-0603	F-15E	r		**Lockheed C-130 Hercules**			
91-0604	F-15E	r		352nd SOG, RAF Mildenhall:			
91-0605	F-15E	bl		7th SOS* & 67th SOS,			
92-0364	F-15E	r		37814	(FY63)	C-130E	
96-0201	F-15E	bl		61699	(FY86)	MC-130H*	
96-0202	F-15E	bl		70023	(FY87)	MC-130H*	
96-0204	F-15E	bl		80193	(FY88)	MC-130H*	
96-0205	F-15E	bl		80194	(FY88)	MC-130H*	
97-0217	F-15E	bl	[48th OSS]	90280	(FY89)	MC-130H*	
97-0218	F-15E	m	[48th FW]	95823	(FY69)	MC-130P	
97-0219	F-15E	bl		95826	(FY69)	MC-130P	
97-0220	F-15E	bl		95828	(FY69)	MC-130P	
97-0221	F-15E	bl	[492nd FS]	95831	(FY69)	MC-130P	
97-0222	F-15E	bl		95832	(FY69)	MC-130P	
98-0131	F-15E	bl					
98-0132	F-15E	bl		**Boeing KC-135R Stratotanker**			
98-0133	F-15E	bl		351st ARS/100th ARW,			
98-0134	F-15E	bl		Mildenhall [D] (r/w/bl)			
98-0135	F-15E	bl		00313	(FY60)		
00-3000	F-15E	r		10302	(FY61)		
00-3001	F-15E	r		14829	(FY64)		
				14830	(FY64)		
Sikorsky MH-53M				14835	(FY64)		
21st SOS/352nd SOG, RAF Mildenhall				23538	(FY62)		
01625	(FY70)			23551	(FY62)		
01630	(FY70)			37978	(FY63)		
14994	(FY67)			37980	(FY63)		
31649	(FY73)			38008	(FY63)		
31652	(FY73)			38025	(FY63)		
95784	(FY69)			38879	(FY63)		
95795	(FY69)			38884	(FY63)		
95796	(FY69)			72605	(FY57)		
				91459	(FY59)		

UK-based US Navy Aircraft

Beech UC-12M Super King Air
Naval Air Facility, Mildenhall
3836 (163836) [7C]
3843 (163843)

These aircraft are normally based in Western Europe with the USAFE. They are shown in numerical order of type designation, with individual aircraft in serial number order as carried on the aircraft. Fiscal year (FY) details are also provided if necessary. The unit allocation and operating bases are given for most aircraft.

Notes	Type			Notes	Type		
	Lockheed U-2S					22nd FS red/white	
	OL-FR/9th RW, Istres, France [BB]					23rd FS blue/white	
	01081	(FY80)			87-0350	AV gn	
	01082	(FY80)			87-0351	AV m	[31st OSS]
	01083	(FY80)			87-0355	AV pr	
					87-0359	AV gn	
	McDonnell Douglas				88-0413	AV pr	[510th FS]
	C-9A Nightingale				88-0425	AV gn	
	86th AW, Ramstein, Germany:				88-0435	AV gn	
	75th AS & 76th AS[1]				88-0443	AV pr	
	FY71				88-0444	AV pr	
	10876[1] (VIP)				88-0446	AV pr	
	10879				88-0491	AV pr	
	10880				88-0525	AV pr	
	10881				88-0526	AV gn	
	10882				88-0529	AV pr	
	FY67				88-0532	AV gn	
	22585				88-0535	AV gn	[555th FS]
					88-0541	AV pr	
	Fairchild A-10A Thunderbolt II				89-2001	AV m	[31st FW]
	SP: 52nd FW, Spangdahlem,				89-2009	AV gn	
	Germany: 81st FS black/yellow				89-2011	AV pr	
	80-0281	bk	[81st FS]		89-2016	AV gn	[16th AF]
	81-0948	bk			89-2018	AV gn	
	81-0951	bk			89-2023	AV gn	
	81-0952	m	[52nd FW]		89-2024	AV gn	
	81-0954	bk	[81st FS]		89-2026	AV gn	
	81-0956	bk			89-2029	AV pr	
	81-0962	bk			89-2030	AV pr	
	81-0963	bk			89-2035	AV gn	
	81-0966	bk			89-2038	AV gn	
	81-0976	bk			89-2039	AV gn	
	81-0978	bk			89-2044	AV gn	
	81-0980	bk			89-2046	AV pr	
	81-0983	bk			89-2047	AV pr	
	81-0984	bk			89-2049	AV pr	
	81-0985	bk			89-2057	AV gn	
	81-0988	bk			89-2068	AV gn	
	81-0991	bk			89-2102	AV gn	
	81-0992	m	[52nd OG]		89-2137	AV pr	[31st OG]
	82-0649	bk			89-2178*	AV pr	
	82-0650	bk			90-0709	AV pr	
	82-0654	bk			90-0772	AV gn	
	82-0656	bk			90-0773	AV gn	
					90-0795*	AV gn	
	Beech C-12C/C-12D/C-12F				90-0796*	AV pr	
	JUSMG, Ankara, Turkey;				90-0800*	AV gn	
	US Embassy Flight, Budapest,				90-0813	SP r	
	Hungary				90-0818	SP r	
	FY83				90-0827	SP r	
	30495	C-12D	Budapest		90-0828	SP r	
	FY73				90-0829	SP r	[22nd FS]
	31216	C-12C	Ankara		90-0831	SP r	
					90-0833	SP r	
	Lockheed (GD) F-16C/F-16D*				90-0843*	SP r	
	AV: 31st FW, Aviano, Italy:				90-0846*	SP bl	
	510th FS purple/white				91-0336	SP r	
	555th FS green/yellow				91-0337	SP r	
	SP: 52nd FW, Spangdahlem,				91-0338	SP r	
	Germany:				91-0339	SP r	[22nd FS]

Type		Notes	Type		Notes
91-0340	SP r		40082*		
91-0341	SP r		40083*		
91-0342	SP r		40084		
91-0343	SP r		40085		
91-0344	SP r		40086		
91-0351	SP r		40087		
91-0352	SP m	[52nd FW]	40108		
91-0391	SP bl		40109		
91-0402	SP bl		40110		
91-0403	SP bl		40111		
91-0405	SP bl		40112		
91-0406	SP bl				
91-0407	SP bl		**Gulfstream Aerospace C-37A**		
91-0408	SP bl		**Gulfstream V**		
91-0409	SP bl		309th AS/86th AW, Chievres,		
91-0410	SP bl		Belgium		
91-0412	SP bl		FY01		
91-0414	SP bl		10076		
91-0416	SP bl	[52nd OG]			
91-0417	SP bl		**Sikorsky HH-60G Blackhawk**		
91-0418	SP bl		56th RQS/85th Wing, Keflavik,		
91-0419	SP bl		Iceland [IS]		
91-0420	SP bl		26109	(FY88)	
91-0421	SP bl		26205	(FY89)	
91-0464*	SP r		26206	(FY89)	
91-0472*	SP bl		26208	(FY89)	
91-0474*	SP bl		26212	(FY89)	
91-0481*	SP bl				
92-3915	SP bl		**Lockheed C-130E Hercules**		
92-3918	SP bl		37th AS/86th AW, Ramstein,		
96-0080	SP bl	[23rd FS]	Germany [RS] (bl/w)		
96-0081	SP bl		01260	(FY70)	
96-0082	SP m	[52nd FW]	01264	(FY70)	[86th AW]
96-0083	SP bl		01271	(FY70)	
			01274	(FY70)	[86th AW]
Grumman C-20H Gulfstream IV			10935	(FY68)	
76th AS/86th AW, Ramstein,			10938	(FY68)	
Germany			10943	(FY68)	[86th OG]
FY90			10947	(FY68)	
00300			17681	(FY64)	
FY92			18240	(FY64)	
20375			37885	(FY63)	
			37887	(FY63)	
Gates C-21A Learjet			40502	(FY64)	
76th AS/86th AW, Ramstein,			40527	(FY64)	
Germany;			40533	(FY64)	
*7005th ABS/HQ USEUCOM,			40550	(FY64)	
Stuttgart, Germany			96566	(FY69)	[37th AS]
FY84			96582	(FY69)	
40068*			96583	(FY69)	
40081*					

European-based US Navy Aircraft

Notes	Type			Notes	Type		
	Lockheed P-3 Orion				**Fairchild C-26D**		
	CinCUSNFE				NAF Naples, Italy;		
	NAF Sigonella, Italy;				NAF Sigonella, Italy		
	NAF Keflavik, Iceland;				900528	Sigonella	
	VQ-2, NAF Rota, Spain				900530	Sigonella	
	150495	UP-3A	NAF Keflavik		900531	Naples	
	150496	VP-3A	CinCUSNFE		910502	Naples	
	156519	[21]	EP-3E VQ-2				
	156525	[11]	P-3C VQ-2		**Sikorsky MH-53E Sea Stallion**		
	156529	[24]	EP-3E VQ-2		HC-4, NAF Sigonella, Italy		
	157316	[23]	EP-3E VQ-2		162505	[HC-47]	
	157325	[25]	EP-3E VQ-2		162509	[HC-49]	
	157326	[22]	EP-3E VQ-2		162516	[HC-46]	
	159886	[09]	P-3C VQ-2		163053	[HC-44]	
	161121	[15]	P-3C VQ-2		163055	[HC-45]	
					163057	[HC-41]	
	Beech UC-12M Super King Air				163065	[HC-43]	
	NAF Rota, Spain				163068	[HC-42]	
	3839	(163839)	Rota		164864	[HC-48]	
	3842	(163842)	Rota				

European-based US Army Aircraft

Notes	Type			Notes	Type		
	Bell UH-1H Iroquois				1st Military Intelligence Btn,		
	LANDSOUTHEAST, Cigli, Turkey;				Wiesbaden;		
	'B' Co, 2nd Btn, 502nd Avn Reg't,				214th Avn Reg't, Wiesbaden		
	Coleman Barracks;				*FY84*		
	7th Army Training Center, Grafenwöhr;				40144	C-12F	214th Avn
	Combat Manoeuvre Training Centre,				40152	C-12F	214th Avn
	Hohenfels;				40153	C-12F	1st MIB
	6th Avn Co, Vicenza, Italy				40155	C-12F	214th Avn
	FY68				40156	C-12F	214th Avn
	16341	LANDSOUTHEAST			40157	C-12F	214th Avn
	16662	LANDSOUTHEAST			40158	C-12F	HQ/USEUCOM
	FY72				40160	C-12F	214th Avn
	21569	CMTC			40161	C-12F	6th Avn Co
	21632	CMTC			40162	C-12F	214th Avn
	21636	CMTC			40164	C-12F	214th Avn
	FY73				40165	C-12F	214th Avn
	21668	CMTC			*FY94*		
	21725	7th ATC			40315	C-12R	A/2-228th Avn
	21786	CMTC			40316	C-12R	A/2-228th Avn
	21806	LANDSOUTHEAST			40318	C-12R	A/2-228th Avn
	21824	7th ATC			40319	C-12R	A/2-228th Avn
	22127	B/2-502nd Avn			*FY85*		
	FY74				50147	RC-12K	1st MIB
	22303	CMTC			50148	RC-12K	1st MIB
	22318	6th Avn Co			50149	RC-12K	1st MIB
	22330	CMTC			50150	RC-12K	1st MIB
	22347	CMTC			50152	RC-12K	1st MIB
	22355	CMTC			50153	RC-12K	1st MIB
	22370	CMTC			50155	RC-12K	1st MIB
	22410	CMTC					
	22448	CMTC					
	22465	CMTC			**Beech C-12J**		
	22504	7th ATC			HQ/USEUCOM, Stuttgart		
					FY86		
	Beech C-12 Super King Air				60079		
	'A' Co, 2nd Btn, 228th Avn Reg't,						
	Heidelberg;				**Cessna UC-35A Citation V**		
	'B' Co, 2nd Btn, 228th Avn Reg't,				214th Avn Reg't, Wiesbaden		
	Heidelberg;				*FY95*		
	HQ/USEUCOM, Stuttgart;				50123		
	6th Avn Co, Vicenza, Italy;				50124		

Type	Notes
FY97	
70101	
70102	
70105	
FY99	
90102	

Boeing-Vertol CH-47D Chinook
'F' Co, 159th Avn Reg't Giebelstadt

Type	Notes
FY87	
70072	
70073	
FY88	
80098	
80099	
80100	
80101	
80102	
80103	
80104	
80106	
FY89	
90138	
90139	
90140	
90141	
90142	
90143	
90144	
90145	

Bell OH-58D(I) Kiowa Warrior
1st Btn, 1st Cavalry Reg't, Budingen;
1st Btn, 4th Cavalry Reg't, Schweinfurt

Type	Notes
FY90	
00348	1-1st Cav
00371	1-1st Cav
00373	1-4th Cav
FY91	
10540	1-1st Cav
10544	1-1st Cav
10564	1-1st Cav
FY92	
20520	1-1st Cav
20529	1-1st Cav
20545	1-1st Cav
FY93	
30971	1-4th Cav
30996	1-4th Cav
30998	1-4th Cav
31002	1-4th Cav
31005	1-4th Cav
31006	1-4th Cav
31007	1-4th Cav
31008	1-4th Cav
FY94	
40149	1-4th Cav
40150	1-4th Cav
40151	1-4th Cav
40152	1-1st Cav
40153	1-4th Cav
40154	1-4th Cav
40174	1-4th Cav
40175	1-1st Cav
40176	1-4th Cav
40178	1-1st Cav
40179	1-1st Cav
40180	1-1st Cav
FY89	
90114	1-1st Cav
90116	1-1st Cav
90117	1-1st Cav

Sikorsky H-60 Black Hawk
2nd Btn, 1st Avn Reg't, Ansbach;
45th Medical Co, Ansbach;
'B' Co, 5th Btn, 158th Avn Reg't, Aviano;
'A' Co, 127th Divisional Avn Support Btn, Bad Kreuznach;
357th Avn Det/SHAPE, Chievres;
'B' Co, 70th Transportation Reg't, Coleman Barracks;
214th Avn Reg't, Coleman Barracks;
'C' Co, 3rd Btn, 158th Avn Reg't, Giebelstadt;
'D' Co, 3rd Btn, 158th Avn Reg't, Giebelstadt;
'A' Co, 5th Btn, 158th Avn Reg't, Giebelstadt;
'C' Co, 5th Btn, 158th Avn Reg't, Giebelstadt;
2nd Btn, 501st Avn Reg't, Hanau;
'B' Co, 7th Btn, 159th AVIM, Illesheim;
236th Medical Co (HA), Landstuhl;
6th Avn Co, Vicenza, Italy;
159th Medical Co, Wiesbaden

Type		Notes
FY82		
23675	UH-60A	45th Med Co
23685	UH-60A	159th Med Co
23692	UH-60A	C/3-158th Avn
23693	UH-60A	45th Med Co
23727	UH-60A	159th Med Co
23729	UH-60A	45th Med Co
23735	UH-60A	159th Med Co
23736	UH-60A	236th Med Co
23737	UH-60A	236th Med Co
23738	UH-60A	
23745	UH-60A	236th Med Co
23749	UH-60A	236th Med Co
23750	UH-60A	159th Med Co
23751	UH-60A	45th Med Co
23752	UH-60A	236th Med Co
23753	UH-60A	159th Med Co
23754	UH-60A	45th Med Co
23755	UH-60A	236th Med Co
23756	UH-60A	236th Med Co
23757	UH-60A	214th Avn
FY83		
23854	UH-60A	357th Avn Det
23855	UH-60A	214th Avn
23868	UH-60A	214th Avn
23869	UH-60A	214th Avn
FY84		
23951	UH-60A	159th Med Co
23970	UH-60A	C/5-158th Avn
23975	UH-60A	C/5-158th Avn
24019	EH-60A	2-1st Avn
FY85		
24391	UH-60A	45th Med Co
24467	EH-60A	2-1st Avn
24475	EH-60A	2-1st Avn
24478	EH-60A	2-1st Avn
FY86		
24498	UH-60A	2-501st Avn
24530	UH-60A	2-501st Avn
24531	UH-60A	45th Med Co
24532	UH-60A	45th Med Co
24538	UH-60A	214th Avn
24550	UH-60A	236th Med Co
24551	UH-60A	236th Med Co
24552	UH-60A	159th Med Co
24554	UH-60A	C/5-158th Avn
24555	UH-60A	
24566	EH-60C	2-501st Avn

US Army Europe

Type		
FY87		
24579	UH-60A	A/5-158th Avn
24581	UH-60A	159th Med Co
24583	UH-60A	357th Avn Det
24584	UH-60A	357th Avn Det
24589	UH-60A	214th Avn
24621	UH-60A	214th Avn
24628	UH-60A	159th Med Co
24634	UH-60A	159th Med Co
24642	UH-60A	214th Avn
24644	UH-60A	45th Med Co
24645	UH-60A	45th Med Co
24647	UH-60A	214th Avn
24650	UH-60A	
24656	UH-60A	159th Med Co
24660	EH-60C	2-501st Avn
24664	EH-60A	2-501st Avn
26001	UH-60A	45th Med Co
26002	UH-60A	159th Med Co
26003	UH-60A	B/5-158th Avn
FY88		
26019	UH-60A	214th Avn
26020	UH-60A	236th Med Co
26023	UH-60A	236th Med Co
26025	UH-60A	214th Avn
26026	UH-60A	B/5-158th Avn
26027	UH-60A	214th Avn
26028	UH-60A	C/5-158th Avn
26031	UH-60A	236th Med Co
26034	UH-60A	159th Med Co
26037	UH-60A	B/7-159th AVIM
26038	UH-60A	A/5-158th Avn
26039	UH-60A	45th Med Co
26041	UH-60A	A/5-158th Avn
26042	UH-60A	A/5-158th Avn
26045	UH-60A	45th Med Co
26050	UH-60A	159th Med Co
26051	UH-60A	A/5-158th Avn
26052	UH-60A	B/5-158th Avn
26053	UH-60A	A/5-158th Avn
26054	UH-60A	236th Med Co
26055	UH-60A	236th Med Co
26056	UH-60A	A/5-158th Avn
26058	UH-60A	159th Med Co
26063	UH-60A	B/5-158th Avn
26067	UH-60A	B/5-158th Avn
26072	UH-60A	236th Med Co
26075	UH-60A	159th Med Co
26077	UH-60A	C/5-158th Avn
26080	UH-60A	159th Med Co
26083	UH-60A	B/5-158th Avn
26085	UH-60A	159th Med Co
26086	UH-60A	159th Med Co
FY89		
26142	UH-60A	B/7-159th AVIM
26145	UH-60A	B/5-158th Avn
26146	UH-60A	159th Med Co
26153	UH-60A	B/5-158th Avn
26164	UH-60A	C/5-158th Avn
26165	UH-60A	214th Avn
FY95		
26621	UH-60L	2-1st Avn
26628	UH-60L	2-1st Avn
26629	UH-60L	2-1st Avn
26630	UH-60L	2-1st Avn
26631	UH-60L	2-1st Avn
26632	UH-60L	2-1st Avn
26633	UH-60L	2-1st Avn
26635	UH-60L	2-1st Avn
26636	UH-60L	2-1st Avn
26637	UH-60L	2-1st Avn
26638	UH-60L	2-1st Avn
26639	UH-60L	2-1st Avn

Type		
26640	UH-60L	2-1st Avn
26641	UH-60L	D/3-158th Avn
26642	UH-60L	D/3-158th Avn
26643	UH-60L	D/3-158th Avn
26644	UH-60L	2-1st Avn
26645	UH-60L	D/3-158th Avn
26646	UH-60L	2-1st Avn
26647	UH-60L	2-1st Avn
26648	UH-60L	2-1st Avn
26649	UH-60L	D/3-158th Avn
26650	UH-60L	D/3-158th Avn
26651	UH-60L	C/3-158th Avn
26652	UH-60L	C/3-158th Avn
26653	UH-60L	C/3-158th Avn
26654	UH-60L	C/3-158th Avn
26655	UH-60L	C/3-158th Avn
FY96		
26674	UH-60L	D/3-158th Avn
26675	UH-60L	D/3-158th Avn
26676	UH-60L	D/3-158th Avn
26677	UH-60L	D/3-158th Avn
26678	UH-60L	D/3-158th Avn
26679	UH-60L	D/3-158th Avn
26680	UH-60L	D/3-158th Avn
26681	UH-60L	D/3-158th Avn
26682	UH-60L	D/3-158th Avn
26683	UH-60L	C/3-158th Avn
26684	UH-60L	C/3-158th Avn
26685	UH-60L	C/3-158th Avn
26686	UH-60L	C/3-158th Avn
26687	UH-60L	C/3-158th Avn
26688	UH-60L	C/3-158th Avn
26689	UH-60L	C/3-158th Avn
26690	UH-60L	C/3-158th Avn
26691	UH-60L	C/3-158th Avn
26692	UH-60L	C/3-158th Avn
FY97		
26762	UH-60L	2-501st Avn
26763	UH-60L	2-501st Avn
26764	UH-60L	2-501st Avn
26765	UH-60L	2-501st Avn
26766	UH-60L	2-501st Avn
26767	UH-60L	2-501st Avn
FY98		
26795	UH-60L	2-501st Avn
26796	UH-60L	2-501st Avn
26797	UH-60L	2-501st Avn
26798	UH-60L	2-501st Avn
26799	UH-60L	2-501st Avn
26800	UH-60L	2-501st Avn
26801	UH-60L	2-501st Avn
26802	UH-60L	2-501st Avn
26813	UH-60L	2-501st Avn
26814	UH-60L	2-501st Avn
FY00		
26884	UH-60L	D/3-158th Avn
FY01		
26885	UH-60L	D/3-158th Avn
26886	UH-60L	D/3-158th Avn
26889	UH-60L	D/3-158th Avn

MDH AH-64 Apache
1st Btn, 1st Avn Reg't, Ansbach;
127th ASB, Hanau;
1st Btn, 501st Avn Reg't, Hanau;
2nd Btn, 6th Cavalry Reg't, Illesheim;
6th Btn, 6th Cavalry Reg't, Illesheim;
'A' Co, 7th Btn, 159th Avn Reg't,
  Illesheim
AH-64A

FY86		
68940		2-6th Cav
68942		2-6th Cav

Type		Notes	Type		Notes
68943	2-6th Cav		70455	1-501st Avn	
68946	2-6th Cav		70457	1-1st Avn	
68948	2-6th Cav		70470	1-1st Avn	
68951	2-6th Cav		70471	1-1st Avn	
68952	2-6th Cav		70474	1-1st Avn	
68955	2-6th Cav		70475	1-1st Avn	
68956	2-6th Cav		70476	1-1st Avn	
68957	2-6th Cav		70477	1-1st Avn	
68959	2-6th Cav		70478	1-1st Avn	
68960	2-6th Cav		70481	1-1st Avn	
68961	2-6th Cav		70487	1-501st Avn	
68981	2-6th Cav		70496	1-501st Avn	
69011	2-6th Cav		70503	A/7-159th Avn	
69026	2-6th Cav		70504	1-501st Avn	
69030	2-6th Cav		70505	1-501st Avn	
69032	2-6th Cav		70506	1-501st Avn	
69037	2-6th Cav		*FY88*		
69041	1-501st Avn		80197	1-501st Avn	
69048	2-6th Cav		80198	1-501st Avn	
FY87			**AH-64D**		
70409	1-1st Avn		*FY00*		
70410	1-501st Avn		05175	6-6th Cav	
70412	1-1st Avn		05199	6-6th Cav	
70413	1-1st Avn		05200	6-6th Cav	
70415	1-501st Avn		05204	6-6th Cav	
70417	1-1st Avn		05205	6-6th Cav	
70418	1-501st Avn		05206	6-6th Cav	
70420	1-1st Avn		05207	6-6th Cav	
70428	1-1st Avn		05208	6-6th Cav	
70432	1-1st Avn		05209	6-6th Cav	
70436	1-1st Avn		05210	6-6th Cav	
70437	1-1st Avn		05211	6-6th Cav	
70438	1-501st Avn		05212	6-6th Cav	
70439	1-1st Avn		05213	6-6th Cav	
70440	1-501st Avn		05214	6-6th Cav	
70442	1-1st Avn		05215	6-6th Cav	
70443	2-6th Cav		05217	6-6th Cav	
70444	1-501st Avn		05218	6-6th Cav	
70445	1-501st Avn		05220	6-6th Cav	
70446	1-501st Avn		05225	6-6th Cav	
70447	1-501st Avn		05226	6-6th Cav	
70449	1-501st Avn		05231	6-6th Cav	
70451	1-501st Avn		05232	6-6th Cav	
70454	1-501st Avn				

US-based USAF Aircraft

The following aircraft are normally based in the USA but are likely to be seen visiting the UK from time to time. The presentation is in numerical order of the type, commencing with the B-1B and concluding with the C-141. The aircraft are listed in numerical progression by the serial actually carried externally. Fiscal year information is provided, together with details of mark variations and in some cases operating units. Where base-code letter information is carried on the aircrafts' tails, this is detailed with the squadron/base data; for example the 7th Wing's B-1B 60105 carries the letters DY on its tail, thus identifying the Wing's home base as Dyess AFB, Texas.

Notes	Type			Notes	Type		
	Rockwell B-1B Lancer				60109	7th BW	*bl/w*
	7th BW, Dyess AFB, Texas [DY]:				60110	7th BW	*bl/w*
	9th BS (*bk*), 13th BS (*r*)				60111	28th BW	*bk/or*
	& 28th BS (*bl/w*);				60112	7th BW	*bk*
	28th BW, Ellsworth AFB,				60113	28th BW	*bk/y*
	South Dakota [EL]:				60114	28th BW	*bk/or*
	13th BS (*bl/br*), 37th BS (*bk/y*)				60115	28th BW	*bk/or*
	& 77th BS (*bk/or*);				60116		
	419th FLTS/412th TW, Edwards AFB,				60117	7th BW	*bl/w*
	California [ED]				60118		
	FY84				60119	7th BW	*bl/w*
	40049	412th TW			60120	7th BW	*bk*
	40053	7th BW			60121	28th BW	*bk/y*
	FY85				60122	7th BW	*r*
	50059				60123	7th BW	*bl/w*
	50060	7th BW	*bk*		60124	7th BW	
	50061				60125	28th BW	*bk/or*
	50065	7th BW	*bl/w*		60126	7th BW	*bl/w*
	50066	28th BW	*bk/or*		60127		
	50067	7th BW	*bl/w*		60128	28th BW	*bk/or*
	50068	412th TW			60129	28th BW	*bk/or*
	50069				60130	7th BW	*bl/w*
	50072	28th BW	*bk*		60132	7th BW	*bl/w*
	50073	7th BW	*bk*		60133		
	50074	7th BW	*r*		60134		
	50075	28th BW	*bk/or*		60135	7th BW	*bk*
	50077	28th BW	*bk/or*		60136		
	50079	28th BW	*bk/or*		60137	7th BW	*r*
	50080				60138	28th BW	*bk/y*
	50081				60139	28th BW	*bk/y*
	50082	412th TW			60140	7th BW	*bk*
	50083	28th BW	*bk/y*				
	50084	28th BW	*bk/or*		**Northrop B-2 Spirit**		
	50085	28th BW	*bk/y*		419th FLTS/412th TW, Edwards AFB,		
	50087	28th BW	*bk/or*		California [ED];		
	50088				509th BW, Whiteman AFB,		
	50089				Missouri [WM]:		
	50090	28th BW	*bk/or*		325th BS, 393rd BS & 715th BS		
	50091	28th BW	*bk/y*		(Names are given where known.		
	FY86				Each begins *Spirit of ...*)		
	60093	28th BW	*bk/or*		*FY90*		
	60094	28th BW	*bk/or*		00040	509th BW	*Alaska*
	60095				00041	509th BW	*Hawaii*
	60096	28th BW	*bk/y*		*FY92*		
	60097	28th BW	*bk/or*		20700	509th BW	*Florida*
	60098				*FY82*		
	60099	28th BW	*bk/or*		21066	509th BW	*America*
	60100	7th BW	*r*		21067	509th BW	*Arizona*
	60101	7th BW	*bl/w*		21068	412th TW	*New York*
	60102	28th BW	*bk/or*		21069	509th BW	*Indiana*
	60103	7th BW	*bk*		21070	Northrop	*Ohio*
	60104	28th BW	*bk/y*		21071	509th BW	*Mississippi*
	60105	7th BW	*bl/w*		*FY93*		
	60107				31085	509th BW	*Oklahoma*
	60108	7th BW	*bl/w*		31086	509th BW	*Kitty Hawk*

Type			Notes	Type				Notes
31087	509th BW	Pennsylvania		40787	(FY74)			
31088	509th BW	Louisiana		50125	(FY75)			
FY88								
80328	509th BW	Texas		**Lockheed C-5 Galaxy**				
80329	509th BW	Missouri		60th AMW, Travis AFB, California:				
80330	509th BW	California		21st AS (bk/gd) & 22nd AS (bk/bl);				
80331	509th BW	South Carolina		56th AS/97th AMW, Altus AFB,				
80332	509th BW	Washington		Oklahoma (r/y);				
FY89				137th AS/105th AW, Stewart AFB,				
90127	509th BW	Kansas		New York (bl);				
90128	509th BW	Nebraska		68th AS/433rd AW AFRC, Kelly AFB,				
90129	509th BW	Georgia		Texas;				
				436th AW, Dover AFB, Delaware:				
Boeing E-3 Sentry				3rd AS (y/r) & 9th AS (y/bl);				
552nd ACW, Tinker AFB,				337th AS/439th AW AFRC, Westover				
Oklahoma [OK]:				ARB, Massachusetts (bl/r)				
960th AACS (w), 963rd AACS (bk),				FY70				
964th AACS (r), 965th AACS (y)				00445	C-5A	433rd AW		
& 966th AACS (bl);				00446	C-5A	433rd AW		
961st AACS/18th Wg, Kadena AB,				00447	C-5A	436th AW	y	
Japan [ZZ] (or);				00448	C-5A	439th AW	bl/r	
962nd AACS/3rd Wg, Elmendorf AFB,				00449	C-5A	60th AMW	bk/gd	
Alaska [AK] (gn)				00450	C-5A	97th AMW	r/y	
FY80				00451	C-5A	60th AMW		
00137	E-3C	bk		00452	C-5A	97th AMW	r/y	
00138	E-3C	y		00453	C-5A	436th AW	y	
00139	E-3C	bk		00454	C-5A	97th AMW	r/y	
FY81				00455	C-5A	97th AMW	r/y	
10004	E-3C	bk		00456	C-5A	60th AMW	bk/gd	
10005	E-3C	bk		00457	C-5A	60th AMW	bk/gd	
FY71				00458	C-5A	433rd AW		
11407	E-3B	w		00459	C-5A	60th AMW	bk/gd	
11408	E-3B	w		00460	C-5A	105th AW	bl	
FY82				00461	C-5A	436th AW	y	
20006	E-3C	y		00462	C-5A	97th AMW	r/y	
20007	E-3C	m		00463	C-5A	436th AW	y	
FY83				00464	C-5A	60th AMW	bk/bl	
30008	E-3C	gn		00465	C-5A	97th AMW	r/y	
30009	E-3C	bk		00466	C-5A	436th AW		
FY73				00467	C-5A	436th AW	y	
31674	JE-3C	Boeing		FY83				
31675	E-3B	gn		31285	C-5B	436th AW	y/r	
FY75				FY84				
50556	E-3B	w		40059	C-5B	436th AW		
50557	E-3B	w		40060	C-5B	60th AMW	bk/bl	
50558	E-3B	or		40061	C-5B	436th AW	y	
50559	E-3B	bl		40062	C-5B	60th AMW	bk/gd	
50560	E-3B	y		FY85				
FY76				50001	C-5B	436th AW	m	
61604	E-3B	r		50002	C-5B	60th AMW	bk/bl	
61605	E-3B	gn		50003	C-5B	436th AW	y	
61606	E-3B	gn		50004	C-5B	60th AMW	bk/bl	
61607	E-3B	bl		50005	C-5B	436th AW	y	
FY77				50006	C-5B	60th AMW	bk/gd	
70351	E-3B	w		50007	C-5B	436th AW	y/bl	
70352	E-3B	r		50008	C-5B	60th AMW	bk/gd	
70353	E-3B	y		50009	C-5B	436th AW	y	
70355	E-3B	gn		50010	C-5B	60th AMW	bk/gd	
70356	E-3B	y		FY86				
FY78				60011	C-5B	436th AW	y/bl	
80576	E-3B	r		60012	C-5B	60th AMW	bk/bl	
80577	E-3B	r		60013	C-5B	436th AW	y	
80578	E-3B	or		60014	C-5B	60th AMW	bk/bl	
FY79				60015	C-5B	436th AW	y/r	
90001	E-3B	r		60016	C-5B	60th AMW	bk/bl	
90002	E-3B	y		60017	C-5B	436th AW	y	
90003	E-3B	bl		60018	C-5B	60th AMW	bk/gd	
				60019	C-5B	436th AW	y	
Boeing E-4B				60020	C-5B	436th AW	y	
1st ACCS/55th Wg, Offutt AFB,				60021	C-5B	60th AMW	bk/gd	
Nebraska [OF]				60022	C-5B	60th AMW	bk/bl	
31676	(FY73)			60023	C-5B	436th AW	y	
31677	(FY73)			60024	C-5B	60th AMW	bk/bl	

Notes	Type			
	60025	C-5B	436th AW	y
	60026	C-5B	60th AMW	bk/gd
	FY66			
	68304	C-5A	439th AW	bl/r
	68305	C-5A	433rd AW	
	68306	C-5A	433rd AW	
	68307	C-5A	433rd AW	
	FY87			
	70027	C-5B	436th AW	y/bl
	70028	C-5B	60th AMW	bk/bl
	70029	C-5B	436th AW	y
	70030	C-5B	60th AMW	bk/bl
	70031	C-5B	436th AW	y
	70032	C-5B	60th AMW	bk/bl
	70033	C-5B	436th AW	y
	70034	C-5B	60th AMW	bk/gd
	70035	C-5B	436th AW	y
	70036	C-5B	60th AMW	bk/gd
	70037	C-5B	436th AW	y
	70038	C-5B	60th AMW	bk/bl
	70039	C-5B	436th AW	y
	70040	C-5B	60th AMW	bk/gd
	70041	C-5B	436th AW	y
	70042	C-5B	60th AMW	bk/gd
	70043	C-5B	436th AW	y/bl
	70044	C-5B	60th AMW	bk/gd
	70045	C-5B	436th AW	y
	FY67			
	70167	C-5A	439th AW	bl/r
	70168	C-5A	433rd AW	
	70169	C-5A	105th AW	
bl	70170	C-5A	105th AW	bl
	70171	C-5A	433rd AW	
	70173	C-5A	105th AW	bl
	70174	C-5A	105th AW	bl
	FY68			
	80211	C-5A	439th AW	bl/r
	80212	C-5A	105th AW	bl
	80213	C-5C	60th AMW	bk/bl
	80214	C-5A	436th AW	
	80215	C-5A	439th AW	bl/r
	80216	C-5C	60th AMW	bk/gd
	80217	C-5A	97th AMW	r/y
	80219	C-5A	439th AW	bl/r
	80220	C-5A	433rd AW	
	80221	C-5A	433rd AW	
	80222	C-5A	439th AW	bl/r
	80223	C-5A	433rd AW	
	80224	C-5A	105th AW	bl
	80225	C-5A	439th AW	bl/r
	80226	C-5A	105th AW	bl
	FY69			
	90001	C-5A	60th AMW	bk/gd
	90002	C-5A	433rd AW	
	90003	C-5A	439th AW	bl/r
	90004	C-5A	433rd AW	
	90005	C-5A	439th AW	bl/r
	90006	C-5A	433rd AW	
	90007	C-5A	433rd AW	
	90008	C-5A	105th AW	bl
	90009	C-5A	105th AW	bl
	90010	C-5A	60th AMW	bk/bl
	90011	C-5A	439th AW	bl/r
	90012	C-5A	105th AW	bl
	90013	C-5A	439th AW	bl/r
	90014	C-5A	97th AMW	r/y
	90015	C-5A	105th AW	bl
	90016	C-5A	433rd AW	
	90017	C-5A	439th AW	bl/r
	90018	C-5A	97th AMW	r/y
	90019	C-5A	439th AW	bl/r
	90020	C-5A	439th AW	bl/r
	90021	C-5A	105th AW	bl

Notes	Type			
	90022	C-5A	439th AW	bl/r
	90023	C-5A	60th AMW	bk/bl
	90024	C-5A	436th AW	y
	90025	C-5A	97th AMW	r/y
	90026	C-5A	60th AMW	bk/bl
	90027	C-5A	436th AW	y

Boeing E-8 J-STARS

116th ACW, Robins AFB,
  Georgia [WR]:
  12th ACCS (gn), 16th ACCS (r),
  128th ACS/Georgia ANG
  & 330th CTS (y);
Grumman, Melbourne, Florida

	Type			
	FY00			
	02000	E-8C		
	FY90			
	00175	E-8A	Grumman	
	FY92			
	23289	E-8C	116th ACW	m
	23290	E-8C	116th ACW	m
	FY93			
	30597	E-8C	116th ACW	
	31097	E-8C	116th ACW	gn
	FY94			
	40284	E-8C	116th ACW	gn
	40285	E-8C	116th ACW	r
	FY95			
	50121	E-8C	116th ACW	r
	50122	E-8C	116th ACW	
	FY96			
	60042	E-8C	116th ACW	r
	60043	E-8C		
	FY86			
	60416	TE-8A	116th ACW	y
	60417	TE-8A	116th ACW	y
	FY97			
	70100	E-8C	116th ACW	gn
	70200	E-8C	116th ACW	
	70201	E-8C	116th ACW	r
	FY99			
	90006	E-8C	116th ACW	

McDonnell Douglas
C-9 Nightingale

86th AW, Ramstein, Germany:
  75th AS & 76th AS;
99th AS/89th AW, Andrews AFB,
  Maryland;
30th AS/374th AW, Yokota AB, Japan;
11th AS/375th AW, Scott AFB, Illinois

	Type			
	FY71			
	10874	C-9A	374th AW	
	10875	C-9A	374th AW	
	10876	C-9A	76th AS (VIP)	
	10877	C-9A	374th AW	
	10878	C-9A	375th AW	
	10879	C-9A	75th AS	
	10880	C-9A	75th AS	
	10881	C-9A	75th AS	
	10882	C-9A	75th AS	
	FY68			
	10958	C-9A	375th AW	
	10959	C-9A	375th AW	
	10960	C-9A	375th AW	
	10961	C-9A	375th AW	
	FY67			
	22583	C-9A	374th AW	
	22584	C-9A	375th AW	
	22585	C-9A	75th AS	

Type			Notes
FY73			
31681	C-9C	89th AW	
31682	C-9C	89th AW	
31683	C-9C	89th AW	
FY68			
88932	C-9A	375th AW	
88933	C-9A	375th AW	
88934	C-9A	374th AW	
88935	C-9A	375th AW	

McDonnell Douglas
KC-10A Extender
60th AMW, Travis AFB, California:
6th ARS (*bk/bl*) & 9th ARS (*bk/r*);
305th AMW, McGuire AFB,
New Jersey:
2nd ARS (*bl/r*) & 32nd ARS (*bl*)

FY82		
20191	60th AMW	bk/bl
20192	60th AMW	bk/r
20193	60th AMW	bk/bl
FY83		
30075	60th AMW	bk/r
30076	60th AMW	bk/bl
30077	60th AMW	bk/r
30078	60th AMW	bk/bl
30079	305th AMW	bl/r
30080	60th AMW	bk/bl
30081	305th AMW	bl
30082	305th AMW	bl
FY84		
40185	60th AMW	bk/bl
40186	305th AMW	bl/r
40187	60th AMW	bk/bl
40188	305th AMW	bl/r
40189	305th AMW	bl
40190	305th AMW	bl/r
40191	60th AMW	bk/bl
40192	305th AMW	bl/r
FY85		
50027	305th AMW	bl/r
50028	305th AMW	bl/r
50029	60th AMW	bk/r
50030	305th AMW	bl/r
50031	305th AMW	bl/r
50032	305th AMW	bl/r
50033	305th AMW	bl
50034	305th AMW	bl/r
FY86		
60027	305th AMW	bl
60028	305th AMW	bl/r
60029	60th AMW	bk/r
60030	305th AMW	bl/r
60031	60th AMW	bk/r
60032	60th AMW	bk/r
60033	60th AMW	bk/r
60034	60th AMW	bk/r
60035	305th AMW	bl
60036	305th AMW	bl
60037	60th AMW	bk/r
60038	60th AMW	bk/r
FY87		
70117	60th AMW	bk/r
70118	60th AMW	bk/bl
70119	60th AMW	bk/r
70120	305th AMW	bl
70121	305th AMW	bl
70122	305th AMW	bl/r
70123	305th AMW	bl
70124	305th AMW	bl/r
FY79		
90433	305th AMW	bl
90434	305th AMW	bl/r

			Notes
91710	305th AMW	bl/r	
91711	305th AMW	bl	
91712	305th AMW	bl/r	
91713	305th AMW	bl	
91946	60th AMW	bk/bl	
91947	305th AMW	bl	
91948	60th AMW	bk/bl	
91949	305th AMW	bl/r	
91950	60th AMW	bk/bl	
91951	60th AMW	bk/bl	

McDonnell Douglas
C-17 Globemaster III
62nd AW, McChord AFB, Washington:
4th AS, 7th AS & 8th AS;
58th AS/97th AMW, Altus AFB,
Oklahoma (*r/y*);
417th FLTS/412th TW, Edwards AFB,
California [ED];
437th AW, Charleston AFB,
South Carolina (*y/bl*):
14th AS, 15th AS,
16th AS & 17th AS

FY00			
00171	C-17A	62nd AW	
00172	C-17A	62nd AW	
00173	C-17A	62nd AW	
00174	C-17A	62nd AW	
00175	C-17A	62nd AW	
00176	C-17A	437th AW	y/bl
00177	C-17A	437th AW	y/bl
00178	C-17A	62nd AW	
00179	C-17A	62nd AW	
00180	C-17A	62nd AW	
00181	C-17A	62nd AW	
00182	C-17A	62nd AW	
00183	C-17A	62nd AW	
00184	C-17A	62nd AW	
00185	C-17A	62nd AW	
FY90			
00532	C-17A	437th AW	y/bl
00533	C-17A	97th AMW	r/y
00534	C-17A	437th AW	y/bl
00535	C-17A	97th AMW	r/y
FY01			
10186	C-17A	62nd AW	
10187	C-17A	62nd AW	
10188	C-17A	437th AW	y/bl
10189	C-17A	437th AW	y/bl
10190	C-17A	437th AW	y/bl
10191	C-17A	437th AW	y/bl
10192	C-17A	437th AW	y/bl
10193	C-17A	437th AW	y/bl
10194	C-17A	437th AW	y/bl
10195	C-17A	437th AW	y/bl
10196	C-17A	437th AW	y/bl
10197	C-17A	437th AW	y/bl
FY02			
21098	C-17A		
21099	C-17A		
21100	C-17A		
21101	C-17A		
21102	C-17A		
21103	C-17A		
21104	C-17A		
21105	C-17A		
21106	C-17A		
21107	C-17A		
21108	C-17A		
21109	C-17A		
21110	C-17A		
FY92			
23291	C-17A	62nd AW	

Notes	Type				Notes	Type			
	23292	C-17A	437th AW	y/bl		91190	C-17A	437th AW	y/bl
	23293	C-17A	97th AMW	r/y		91191	C-17A	437th AW	y/bl
	23294	C-17A	97th AMW	r/y		91192	C-17A	437th AW	y/bl
	FY93								
	30599	C-17A	97th AMW	r/y		**Boeing TC-18E**			
	30600	C-17A	97th AMW	r/y		552nd ACW, Tinker AFB,			
	30601	C-17A	437th AW	y/bl		Oklahoma [OK]:			
	30602	C-17A	62nd AW			966th AACS (*bl*)			
	30603	C-17A	437th AW	y/bl		*FY81*			
	30604	C-17A	437th AW	y/bl		10893			
	FY94					10898			
	40065	C-17A	437th AW	y/bl					
	40066	C-17A	437th AW	y/bl		**Grumman C-20 Gulfstream III/IV**			
	40067	C-17A	437th AW	y/bl		89th AW, Andrews AFB, Maryland:			
	40068	C-17A	437th AW	y/bl		99th AS;			
	40069	C-17A	437th AW	y/bl		OSAC/PAT, US Army, Andrews AFB,			
	40070	C-17A	437th AW	y/bl		Maryland;			
	FY95					Pacific Flight Detachment,			
	50102	C-17A	437th AW	y/bl		Hickam AFB, Hawaii			
	50103	C-17A	437th AW	y/bl		**C-20A Gulfstream III**			
	50104	C-17A	437th AW	y/bl		*FY83*			
	50105	C-17A	97th AMW	r/y		30500	89th AW		
	50106	C-17A	437th AW	y/bl		30501	89th AW		
	50107	C-17A	437th AW	y/bl		**C-20B Gulfstream III**			
	FY96					*FY86*			
	60001	C-17A	437th AW	y/bl		60201	89th AW		
	60002	C-17A	437th AW	y/bl		60202	89th AW		
	60003	C-17A	437th AW	y/bl		60203	89th AW		
	60004	C-17A	437th AW	y/bl		60204	89th AW		
	60005	C-17A	437th AW	y/bl		60206	89th AW		
	60006	C-17A	437th AW	y/bl		60403	89th AW		
	60007	C-17A	437th AW	y/bl		**C-20C Gulfstream III**			
	60008	C-17A	437th AW	y/bl		*FY85*			
	FY87					50049	89th AW		
	70025	C-17A	412th TW			50050	89th AW		
	FY97					**C-20E Gulfstream III**			
	70041	C-17A	437th AW	y/bl		*FY87*			
	70042	C-17A	97th AMW	r/y		70139	Pacific Flt Det		
	70043	C-17A	437th AW	y/bl		70140	OSAC/PAT		
	70044	C-17A	437th AW	y/bl		**C-20F Gulfstream IV**			
	70045	C-17A	437th AW	y/bl		*FY91*			
	70046	C-17A	437th AW	y/bl		10108	OSAC/PAT		
	70047	C-17A	437th AW	y/bl					
	70048	C-17A	437th AW	y/bl		**Boeing C-22B**			
	FY98					201st AS/113th FW, DC ANG,			
	80049	C-17A	62nd AW			Andrews AFB, Maryland			
	80050	C-17A	62nd AW			*FY83*			
	80051	C-17A	62nd AW			34615			
	80052	C-17A	62nd AW			34616			
	80053	C-17A	62nd AW						
	80054	C-17A	62nd AW			**Boeing VC-25A**			
	80055	C-17A	62nd AW			89th AW, Andrews AFB, Maryland			
	80056	C-17A	62nd AW			*FY82*			
	80057	C-17A	97th AMW	r/y		28000			
	FY88					*FY92*			
	80265	C-17A	437th AW	y/bl		29000			
	80266	C-17A	97th AMW	r/y					
	FY99					**Boeing C-32A**			
	90058	C-17A	62nd AW			1st AS/89th AW, Andrews AFB,			
	90059	C-17A	62nd AW			Maryland			
	90060	C-17A	62nd AW			*FY98*			
	90061	C-17A	62nd AW			80001			
	90062	C-17A	62nd AW			80002			
	90063	C-17A	62nd AW			*FY99*			
	90064	C-17A	62nd AW			90003			
	90165	C-17A	62nd AW			90004			
	90166	C-17A	62nd AW						
	90167	C-17A	62nd AW			**Gulfstream Aerospace C-37A**			
	90168	C-17A	62nd AW			**Gulfstream V**			
	90169	C-17A	62nd AW			6th AMW, MacDill AFB, Florida:			
	90170	C-17A	62nd AW			310th AS;			
	FY89					15th ABW, Hickam AFB, Hawaii:			
	91189	C-17A	437th AW	y/bl		65th AS;			

Type		Notes	Type			Notes
89th AW, Andrews AFB, Maryland:			00002	2nd BW	gd	
99th AS;			00003	93rd BS	y/bl	
OSAC/PAT, US Army, Andrews AFB,			00004	5th BW	r/y	
Maryland			00005	5th BW	r/y	
FY01			00007	5th BW	r/y	
10028	6th AMW		00008	2nd BW	r	
10029	6th AMW		00009	5th BW	r/y	
10030	6th AMW		00010	2nd BW	r	
10065	15th ABW		00011	2nd BW	gd	
FY02			00012	2nd BW	r	
21863			00013	2nd BW	r	
FY97			00014	2nd BW	bl	
70049	OSAC/PAT		00015	5th BW	r/y	
70400	89th AW		00016	2nd BW	r	
70401	89th AW		00017	2nd BW	gd	
FY99			00018	5th BW	r/y	
90402	89th AW		00019	2nd BW	r	
90404	89th AW		00020	2nd BW	bl	
			00022	2nd BW	r	
IAI C-38A Astra			00023	5th BW	r/y	
201st AS/113th FW, DC ANG,			00024	5th BW	r/y	
Andrews AFB, Maryland			00025	2nd BW	bl	
FY94			00026	5th BW	r/y	
41569			00028	2nd BW	r	
41570			00029	5th BW	r/y	
			00030	2nd BW	bl	
Boeing C-40			00031	2nd BW	bl	
15th ABW, Hickam AFB, Hawaii:			00032	2nd BW	gd	
65th AS;			00033	5th BW	r/y	
89th AW, Andrews AFB, Maryland:			00034	5th BW	r/y	
1st AS;			00035	2nd BW	gd	
201st AS/113th FW, DC ANG,			00036	419th FLTS		
Andrews AFB, Maryland			00037	2nd BW	r	
FY01			00038	2nd BW	gd	
10005	C-40B	89th AW	00041	93rd BS	y/bl	
10015	C-40B	15th ABW	00042	93rd BS	y/bl	
FY02			00043	2nd BW	bl	
20201	C-40C	201st AS	00044	5th BW	r/y	
20202	C-40C	201st AS	00045	93rd BS	y/bl	
20203	C-40C		00046	2nd BW	bl	
20204	C-40C		00048	2nd BW	gd	
			00049	2nd BW	bl	
Boeing T-43A			00050	412th TW		
562nd FTS/12th FTW, Randolph			00051	5th BW	r/y	
AFB, Texas [RA] (*bk/y*)			00052	2nd BW	r	
FY71			00053	2nd BW	r	
11403			00054	2nd BW	r	
11404			00055	5th BW	r/y	
11405			00056	5th BW	r/y	
FY72			00057	2nd BW	bl	
20288			00058	2nd BW	gd	
FY73			00059	2nd BW	r	
31150			00060	5th BW	r/y	
31151			00061	2nd BW	gd	
31152			00062	2nd BW	bl	
31153			*FY61*			
31154			10001	5th BW	r/y	
31156			10002	2nd BW	bl	
			10003	2nd BW	gd	
Boeing B-52H Stratofortress			10004	2nd BW	bl	
2nd BW, Barksdale AFB,			10005	5th BW	r/y	
Louisiana [LA]:			10006	2nd BW	gd	
11th BS (*gd*), 20th BS (*bl*)			10007	5th BW	r/y	
& 96th BS (*r*);23rd			10008	93rd BS	y/bl	
BS/5th BW, Minot AFB,			10009	2nd BW	r	
North Dakota [MT] (*r/y*);			10010	2nd BW	bl	
93rd BS/917th Wg AFRC,			10011	2nd BW	gd	
Barksdale AFB,			10012	2nd BW	gd	
Louisiana [BD] (*y/bl*);			10013	2nd BW	r	
419th FLTS/412th TW Edwards AFB,			10014	5th BW	r/y	
California [ED]			10015	2nd BW	gd	
FY60			10016	2nd BW	r	
00001	2nd BW	bl	10017	93rd BS	y/bl	

B-52 – C-130

Notes	Type				Notes	Type			
	10018	5th BW	r/y			86-822	(86-0822)	HO	
	10019	2nd BW	r			86-823	(86-0823)	HO r	
	10020	2nd BW	r			86-837	(86-0837)	HO y	
	10021	93rd BS	y/bl			86-838	(86-0838)	HO y	[8th FS]
	10022	93rd BS	y/bl			86-839	(86-0839)	HO r	
	10023	2nd BW	bl			86-840	(86-0840)	HO r	
	10024	2nd BW	r			88-841	(88-0841)	HO r	[9th FS]
	10027	5th BW	r/y			88-842	(88-0842)	HO y	
	10028	2nd BW	gd			88-843	(88-0843)	HO y	
	10029	93rd BS	y/bl						
	10031	2nd BW	gd						
	10032	93rd BS	y/bl			**Lockheed C-130 Hercules**			
	10034	5th BW	r/y			1st SOS/353rd SOG, Kadena AB,			
	10035	5th BW	r/y			Japan;			
	10036	2nd BW	gd			3rd Wg, Elmendorf AFB, Alaska [AK]:			
	10038	2nd BW	gd			517th AS (w);			
	10039	2nd BW	gd			4th SOS/16th SOW, Hurlburt Field,			
	10040	5th BW	r/y			Florida;			

Lockheed F-117A Nighthawk
49th FW, Holloman AFB,
New Mexico [HO]:
7th FS (si), 8th FS (y) & 9th FS (r);
53rd Wg, Nellis AFB,
Nevada [OT] (gy/w);
445th FLTS/412th TW, Edwards AFB,
California [ED]

79-783	(79-10783)	ED	
79-784	(79-10784)	ED	
80-786	(80-0786)	HO r	
80-787	(80-0787)	HO y	
80-788	(80-0788)	HO si	
80-789	(80-0789)	HO r	
80-790	(80-0790)	HO r	
80-791	(80-0791)	HO y	
81-794	(81-10794)	HO r	
81-795	(81-10795)	HO y	
81-796	(81-10796)	HO si	
81-797	(81-10797)	HO r	
81-798	(81-10798)	HO r	
82-799	(82-0799)	HO y	
82-800	(82-0800)	HO y	[8th FS]
82-801	(82-0801)	HO	
82-802	(82-0802)	HO y	
82-803	(82-0803)	HO y	
82-804	(82-0804)	HO y	
82-805	(82-0805)	HO si	
83-807	(83-0807)	HO r	
83-808	(83-0808)	HO si	
84-809	(84-0809)	HO r	[9th FS]
84-810	(84-0810)	HO r	
84-811	(84-0811)	HO si	
84-812	(84-0812)	HO si	[49th OG]
84-824	(84-0824)	HO r	
84-825	(84-0825)	HO y	
84-826	(84-0826)	HO r	
84-827	(84-0827)	HO y	
84-828	(84-0828)	HO r	
85-813	(85-0813)	HO y	
85-814	(85-0814)	HO y	
85-816	(85-0816)	HO y	[49th FW]
85-817	(85-0817)	HO y	
85-818	(85-0818)	HO y	
85-819	(85-0819)	HO y	[49th FW]
85-820	(85-0820)	HO r	
85-829	(85-0829)	HO y	
85-830	(85-0830)	HO r	
85-831	(85-0831)	ED	
85-832	(85-0832)	HO y	
85-833	(85-0833)	HO si	[49th OG]
85-834	(85-0834)	HO y	
85-835	(85-0835)	OT gy/w	
85-836	(85-0836)	HO y	
86-821	(86-0821)	HO r	

7th SOS/352nd SOG, RAF Mildenhall,
UK;
8th SOS/16th SOW, Duke Field,
Florida;
9th SOS/16th OG, Eglin AFB, Florida;
15th SOS/16th SOW, Hurlburt Field,
Florida;
16th SOS/16th SOW, Hurlburt Field,
Florida;
17th SOS/353rd SOG, Kadena AB,
Japan;
37th AS/86th AW, Ramstein AB,
Germany [RS] (bl/w);
39th RQS/920th RQW AFRC,
Patrick AFB, Florida [FL];
41st ECS/355th Wg, Davis-Monthan
AFB, Arizona [DM] (bl);
43rd AW, Pope AFB,
North Carolina [FT]:
2nd AS (gn/bl) & 41st AS (gn/or);
43rd ECS/355th Wg, Davis-Monthan
AFB, Arizona [DM] (r);
53rd WRS/403rd AW AFRC,
Keesler AFB, Missouri;
58th SOW, Kirtland AFB, New Mexico:
550th SOS;
67th SOS/352nd SOG,
RAF Mildenhall, UK;
71st RQS/347th Wg, Moody AFB,
Georgia [MY] (bl);
95th AS/440th AW AFRC,
General Mitchell ARS,
Wisconsin (w/r);
96th AS/934th AW AFRC,
Minneapolis/St Paul,
Minnesota (pr);
102nd RQS/106th RQW, Suffolk Field,
New York ANG [LI];
105th AS/118th AW, Nashville,
Tennessee ANG (r);
109th AS/133rd AW,
Minneapolis/St Paul,
Minnesota ANG [MN] (gn/bl);
115th AS/146th AW,
Channel Island ANGS,
California ANG [CI] (gn);
122nd FS/159th FW,
NAS New Orleans,
Louisiana [JZ];
129th RQS/129th RQW, Moffet Field,
California ANG [CA] (bl);
130th AS/130th AW, Yeager Int'l
Airport, Charleston
West Virginia ANG [WV] (pr/y);
135th AS/135th AW, Martin State
Airport, Maryland ANG [MD] (bk/y);

Type	Notes
139th AS/109th AW, Schenectady, New York ANG [NY];	
142nd AS/166th AW, New Castle County Airport, Delaware ANG [DE] (*bl*);	
143rd AS/143rd AW, Quonset, Rhode Island ANG [RI] (*r*);	
144th AS/176th CW, Kulis GB Alaska ANG (*bk/y*);	
154th TS/189th AW, Little Rock, Arkansas ANG (*r*);	
156th AS/145th AW, Charlotte, North Carolina ANG [NC] (*bl*);	
157th FS/169th FW, McEntire ANGS, South Carolina ANG [SC];	
158th AS/165th AW, Savannah, Georgia ANG (*r*);	
159th FS/125th FW, Jacksonville, Florida ANG;	
164th AS/179th AW, Mansfield, Ohio ANG [OH] (*bl*);	
165th AS/123rd AW, Standiford Field, Kentucky ANG [KY];	
167th AS/167th AW, Martinsburg, West Virginia ANG [WV] (*r*);	
169th AS/182nd AW, Peoria, Illinois ANG [IL];	
171st AS/191st AW, Selfridge ANGB, Michigan ANG (*y/bk*);	
180th AS/139th AW, Rosencrans Memorial Airport, Missouri ANG [XP] (*y*);	
181st AS/136th AW, NAS Dallas, Texas ANG (*bl/w*);	
185th AS/137th AW, Will Rogers World Airport, Oklahoma ANG [OK] (*bl*);	
187th AS/153rd AW, Cheyenne, Wyoming ANG [WY];	
189th AS/124th Wg, Boise, Idaho ANG [ID];	
192nd AS/152nd AW, Reno, Nevada ANG [NV] (*w*);	
193rd SOS/193rd SOW, Harrisburg, Pennsylvania ANG [PA];	
198th AS/156th AW, San Juan, Puerto Rico ANG;	
204th AS/154th Wg, Hickam AFB, Hawaii ANG [HH];	
210th RQS/176th CW, Kulis ANGB, Alaska ANG [AK];	
303rd RQS/939th RQW AFRC, Portland, Oregon [PD] (*y*);	
314th AW, Little Rock AFB, Arkansas: 53rd AS (*bk*) & 62nd AS (*bl*);	
317th AG, Dyess AFB, Texas: 39th AS (*r*) & 40th AS (*bl*);	
327th AS/913th AW AFRC, NAS Willow Grove, Pennsylvania (*bk*);	
328th AS/914th AW AFRC, Niagara Falls, New York [NF] (*bl*);	
357th AS/908th AW AFRC, Maxwell AFB, Alabama (*bl*);	
374th AW, Yokota AB, Japan [YJ]: 36th AS (*r*);	
412th TW Edwards AFB, California: 452nd FLTS [ED];	
463rd AG Little Rock AFB, Arkansas [LK]: 50th AS (*r*) & 61st AS (*gn*);	
645th Materiel Sqn, Palmdale, California [D4];	

Type		Notes
700th AS/94th AW AFRC, Dobbins ARB, Georgia [DB] (*bl*);		
711th SOS/919th SOW AFRC, Duke Field, Florida;		
731st AS/302nd AW AFRC, Peterson AFB, Colorado (*pr/w*);		
757th AS/910th AW AFRC, Youngstown ARS, Ohio [YO] (*bl*);		
758th AS/911th AW AFRC, Pittsburgh ARS, Pennsylvania (*bk/y*);		
773rd AS/910th AW AFRC, Youngstown ARS, Ohio [YO] (*r*);		
815th AS/403rd AW AFRC, Keesler AFB, Missouri [KT] (*r*);		
LMTAS, Marietta, Georgia		
FY90		
00162	MC-130H	15th SOS
00163	AC-130U	4th SOS
00164	AC-130U	4th SOS
00165	AC-130U	4th SOS
00166	AC-130U	4th SOS
00167	AC-130U	4th SOS
FY80		
00320	C-130H	158th AS	r
00321	C-130H	158th AS	r
00322	C-130H	158th AS	r
00323	C-130H	158th AS	r
00324	C-130H	158th AS	r
00325	C-130H	158th AS	r
00326	C-130H	158th AS	r
00332	C-130H	158th AS	r
FY90		
01057	C-130H	204th AS
01058	C-130H	204th AS
FY70		
01259	C-130E	43rd AW	gn/or
01260	C-130E	37th AS	bl/w
01261	C-130E	43rd AW	gn/or
01262	C-130E	43rd AW	gn/or
01263	C-130E	43rd AW	gn/or
01264	C-130E	37th AS	bl/w
01265	C-130E	43rd AW	gn/bl
01266	C-130E	43rd AW	gn/or
01267	C-130E	43rd AW	gn/or
01268	C-130E	43rd AW	gn/bl
01270	C-130E	43rd AW	gn/bl
01271	C-130E	37th AS	bl/w
01272	C-130E	43rd AW	gn/bl
01273	C-130E	43rd AW	gn/bl
01274	C-130E	37th AS	bl/w
01275	C-130E	43rd AW	gn/bl
01276	C-130E	43rd AW	gn/bl
FY90		
01791	C-130H	164th AS	bl
01792	C-130H	164th AS	bl
01793	C-130H	164th AS	bl
01794	C-130H	164th AS	bl
01795	C-130H	164th AS	bl
01796	C-130H	164th AS	bl
01797	C-130H	164th AS	bl
01798	C-130H	164th AS	bl
FY00		
01934	EC-130J LMTAS	
FY90		
02103	HC-130N	210th RQS
09107	C-130H	757th AS	bl
09108	C-130H	757th AS	bl
FY81		
10626	C-130H	700th AS	bl
10627	C-130H	700th AS	bl
10628	C-130H	700th AS	bl
10629	C-130H	700th AS	bl
10630	C-130H	700th AS	bl

C-130

Notes	Type				Notes	Type			
	10631	C-130H	700th AS	bl		20550	C-130H	463rd AG	r
	FY68					20551	C-130H	463rd AG	r
	10934	C-130E	43rd AW	gn/bl		20552	C-130H	463rd AG	r
	10935	C-130E	37th AS	bl/w		20553	C-130H	463rd AG	r
	10937	C-130E	43rd AW	gn/or		20554	C-130H	463rd AG	r
	10938	C-130E	37th AS	bl/w		21094	LC-130H	139th AS	
	10939	C-130E	43rd AW	gn/bl		21095	LC-130H	139th AS	
	10940	C-130E	43rd AW	gn/or		*FY72*			
	10941	C-130E	43rd AW	gn/bl		21288	C-130E	374th AW	r
	10942	C-130E	43rd AW	gn/bl		21289	C-130E	374th AW	r
	10943	C-130E	37th AS	bl/w		21290	C-130E	374th AW	r
	10947	C-130E	37th AS	bl/w		21291	C-130E	314th AW	bk
	10948	C-130E	463rd AG	gn		21292	C-130E	463rd AG	gn
	FY91					21293	C-130E	463rd AG	gn
	11231	C-130H	165th AS			21294	C-130E	463rd AG	gn
	11232	C-130H	165th AS			21295	C-130E	314th AW	bl
	11233	C-130H	165th AS			21296	C-130E	314th AW	bk
	11234	C-130H	165th AS			21299	C-130E	374th AW	r
	11235	C-130H	165th AS			*FY92*			
	11236	C-130H	165th AS			21451	C-130H	156th AS	bl
	11237	C-130H	165th AS			21452	C-130H	156th AS	bl
	11238	C-130H	165th AS			21453	C-130H	156th AS	bl
	11239	C-130H	165th AS			21454	C-130H	156th AS	bl
	FY01					21531	C-130H	187th AS	
	11461	CC-130J	115th AS	gn		21532	C-130H	187th AS	
	11462	CC-130J	115th AS	gn		21533	C-130H	187th AS	
	FY91					21534	C-130H	187th AS	
	11651	C-130H	165th AS			21535	C-130H	187th AS	
	11652	C-130H	165th AS			21536	C-130H	187th AS	
	11653	C-130H	165th AS			21537	C-130H	187th AS	
	FY61					21538	C-130H	187th AS	
	12358	C-130E	171st AS	y/bk		*FY62*			
	12359	C-130E	115th AS	gn		21784	C-130E	154th TS	r
	12367	C-130E	115th AS	gn		21786	C-130E	189th AS	
	12369	C-130E	198th AS			21787	C-130E	154th TS	r
	12370	C-130E	171st AS	y/bk		21788	C-130E	154th TS	r
	12372	C-130E	115th AS	gn		21789	C-130E	314th AW	bk
	FY64					21791	EC-130E		
	14852	HC-130P	71st RQS	bl		21792	C-130E	463rd AG	gn
	14853	HC-130P	71st RQS	bl		21793	C-130E	115th AS	gn
	14854	MC-130P	9th SOS			21795	C-130E	154th TS	r
	14855	HC-130P	303rd RQS	y		21798	C-130E	314th AW	bk
	14858	MC-130P	58th SOW			21799	C-130E	115th AS	gn
	14859	C-130E	16th SOW			21801	C-130E	115th AS	gn
	14860	HC-130P	303rd RQS	y		21804	C-130E	154th TS	r
	14861	WC-130H	53rd WRS			21806	C-130E	96th AS	pr
	14862	EC-130H	645th MS			21808	C-130E	314th AW	bk
	14863	HC-130P	71st RQS	bl		21810	C-130E	314th AW	bl
	14864	HC-130P	303rd RQS	y		21811	C-130E	115th AS	gn
	14865	HC-130P	71st RQS	bl		21812	C-130E	115th AS	gn
	14866	WC-130H	53rd WRS			21816	C-130E	314th AW	bl
	17680	C-130E	314th AW	bk		21817	C-130E	189th AS	
	17681	C-130E	37th AS	bl/w		21818	EC-130E	355th Wg	
	18240	C-130E	37th AS	bl/w		21820	C-130E	171st AS	y/bk
	FY91					21823	C-130E	96th AS	pr
	19141	C-130H	773rd AS	r		21824	C-130E	154th TS	r
	19142	C-130H	773rd AS	r		21825	EC-130E		
	19143	C-130H	773rd AS	r		21826	C-130E	115th AS	gn
	19144	C-130H	773rd AS	r		21829	C-130E	171st AS	y/bk
	FY82					21832	EC-130E		
	20054	C-130H	144th AS	bk/y		21833	C-130E	115th AS	gn
	20055	C-130H	144th AS	bk/y		21834	C-130E	374th AW	r
	20056	C-130H	144th AS	bk/y		21835	C-130E	96th AS	pr
	20057	C-130H	144th AS	bk/y		21836	EC-130E		
	20058	C-130H	144th AS	bk/y		21837	C-130E	189th AS	
	20059	C-130H	144th AS	bk/y		21839	C-130E	96th AS	pr
	20060	C-130H	144th AS	bk/y		21842	C-130E	171st AS	y/bk
	20061	C-130H	144th AS	bk/y		21843	MC-130E	711th SOS	
	FY92					21844	C-130E	96th AS	pr
	20253	AC-130U	4th SOS			21846	C-130E	189th AS	
	20547	C-130H	463rd AG	r		21847	C-130E	96th AS	pr
	20548	C-130H	463rd AG	r		21848	C-130E	96th AS	pr
	20549	C-130H	463rd AG	r		21849	C-130E	463rd AG	gn

Type			Notes	Type			Notes
21850	C-130E	314th AW	bk	32105	HC-130N	210th RQS	
21851	C-130E	115th AS	gn	32106	HC-130N	210th RQS	
21852	C-130E	96th AS	pr	37311	C-130H	731st AS	pr/w
21855	C-130E	374th AW	r	37312	C-130H	731st AS	pr/w
21856	C-130E	143rd AS	r	37313	C-130H	731st AS	pr/w
21857	EC-130E			37314	C-130H	731st AS	pr/w
21858	C-130E	171st AS	y/bk				
21859	C-130E	122nd FS		*FY63*			
21862	C-130E	115th AS	gn	37764	C-130E	463rd AG	gn
21863	EC-130E			37765	C-130E	314th AW	bl
21864	C-130E	189th AS		37767	C-130E	314th AW	bl
21866	C-130E	314th AW	bk	37768	C-130E	314th AW	bl
FY92				37769	C-130E	327th AS	bk
23021	C-130H	773rd AS	r	37770	C-130E	96th AS	pr
23022	C-130H	773rd AS	r	37773	EC-130E	193rd SOS	
23023	C-130H	773rd AS	r	37776	C-130E	327th AS	bk
23024	C-130H	773rd AS	r	37777	C-130E	198th AS	
23281	C-130H	328th AS	bl	37778	C-130E	314th AW	bk
23282	C-130H	328th AS	bl	37781	C-130E	463rd AG	gn
23283	C-130H	328th AS	bl	37782	C-130E	143rd AS	r
23284	C-130H	328th AS	bl	37783	EC-130E	193rd SOS	
23285	C-130H	328th AS	bl	37784	C-130E	314th AW	bl
23286	C-130H	328th AS	bl	37785	MC-130E	711th SOS	
23287	C-130H	328th AS	bl	37786	C-130E	171st AS	y/bk
23288	C-130H	328th AS	bl	37788	C-130E	143rd AS	r
FY83				37790	C-130E	374th AW	r
30486	C-130H	139th AS		37791	C-130E	314th AW	bl
30487	C-130H	139th AS		37792	C-130E	169th AS	
30488	C-130H	139th AS		37796	C-130E	314th AW	bk
30489	C-130H	139th AS		37799	C-130E	314th AW	bl
30490	LC-130H	139th AS		37800	C-130E	169th AS	
30491	LC-130H	139th AS		37804	C-130E	314th AW	bl
30492	LC-130H	139th AS		37805	C-130E	327th AS	bk
30493	LC-130H	139th AS		37808	C-130E	463rd AG	gn
FY93				37809	C-130E	463rd AG	gn
31036	C-130H	463rd AG	r	37811	C-130E	143rd AS	r
31037	C-130H	463rd AG	r	37812	C-130E	169th AS	
31038	C-130H	463rd AG	r	37814	C-130E	67th SOS	
31039	C-130H	463rd AG	r	37815	C-130E	193rd SOS	
31040	C-130H	463rd AG	r	37816	C-130E	193rd SOS	
31041	C-130H	463rd AG	r	37817	C-130E	463rd AG	gn
31096	LC-130H	139th AS		37818	C-130E	169th AS	
FY83				37819	C-130E	374th AW	r
31212	MC-130H	15th SOS		37821	C-130E	374th AW	r
FY93				37822	C-130E	96th AS	pr
31455	C-130H	156th AS	bl	37823	C-130E	327th AS	bk
31456	C-130H	156th AS	bl	37824	C-130E	143rd AS	r
31457	C-130H	156th AS	bl	37825	C-130E	169th AS	
31458	C-130H	156th AS	bl	37826	C-130E	327th AS	bk
31459	C-130H	156th AS	bl	37828	EC-130E	193rd SOS	
31561	C-130H	156th AS	bl	37829	C-130E	463rd AG	gn
31562	C-130H	156th AS	bl	37830	C-130E	314th AW	bk
31563	C-130H	156th AS	bl	37831	C-130E	115th AS	gn
FY73				37832	C-130E	327th AS	bk
31580	EC-130H	43rd ECS	r	37833	C-130E	327th AS	bk
31581	EC-130H	43rd ECS	r	37834	C-130E	327th AS	bk
31582	C-130H	317th AG	r	37835	C-130E	314th AW	bk
31583	EC-130H	43rd ECS	r	37837	C-130E	374th AW	r
31584	EC-130H	43rd ECS	r	37838	C-130E	314th AW	bl
31585	EC-130H	41st ECS	bl	37839	C-130E	463rd AG	gn
31586	EC-130H	41st ECS	bl	37840	C-130E	143rd AS	r
31587	EC-130H	41st ECS	bl	37841	C-130E	198th AS	
31588	EC-130H	41st ECS	bl	37842	C-130E	303rd RQS	y
31590	EC-130H	43rd ECS	r	37845	C-130E	463rd AG	
31592	EC-130H	41st ECS	bl	37846	C-130E	314th AW	
31594	EC-130H	41st ECS	bl	37847	C-130E	154th TS	r
31595	EC-130H	43rd ECS	r	37848	C-130E	327th AS	bk
31597	C-130H	317th AG	r	37849	C-130E	314th AW	bl
31598	C-130H	317th AG	r	37850	C-130E	374th AW	r
FY93				37851	C-130E	198th AS	
32041	C-130H	204th AS		37852	C-130E	463rd AG	gn
32042	C-130H	204th AS		37853	C-130E	327th AS	bk
32104	HC-130N	210th RQS		37856	C-130E	463rd AG	gn

C-130

Notes	Type				Notes	Type			
	37857	C-130E	463rd AG	gn		40529	C-130E	43rd AW	gn/or
	37858	C-130E	169th AS			40531	C-130E	43rd AW	gn/bl
	37859	C-130E	143rd AS	r		40533	C-130E	37th AS	bl/w
	37860	C-130E	314th AW	bl		40537	C-130E	43rd AW	gn/or
	37861	C-130E	129th RQS	bl		40538	C-130E	314th AW	bk
	37864	C-130E	314th AW	bl		40539	C-130E	43rd AW	gn/or
	37865	C-130E	374th AW	r		40540	C-130E	43rd AW	gn/bl
	37866	C-130E	314th AW	bk		40541	C-130E	314th AW	bk
	37867	C-130E	327th AS	bk		40542	C-130E	314th AW	bk
	37868	C-130E	143rd AS	r		40544	C-130E	198th AS	
	37869	EC-130E	193rd SOS			40550	C-130E	37th AS	bl/w
	37871	C-130E	374th AW	r		40551	MC-130E	711th SOS	
	37872	C-130E	169th AS			40555	MC-130E	711th SOS	
	37874	C-130E	314th AW	bk		40559	MC-130E	8th SOS	
	37876	C-130E	463rd AG	gn		40561	MC-130E	711th SOS	
	37877	C-130E	169th AS			40562	MC-130E	711th SOS	
	37879	C-130E	374th AW	r		40565	MC-130E	711th SOS	
	37880	C-130E	314th AW	bl		40566	MC-130E	8th SOS	
	37882	C-130E	314th AW	bk		40567	MC-130E	8th SOS	
	37883	C-130E	327th AS	bk		40568	MC-130E	8th SOS	
	37884	C-130E	463rd AG	gn		40569	C-130E	314th AW	bl
	37885	C-130E	37th AS	bl/w		40570	C-130E	43rd AW	gn/or
	37887	C-130E	37th AS	bl/w		40571	MC-130E	711th SOS	
	37888	C-130E	463rd AG	gn		40572	MC-130E	8th SOS	
	37889	C-130E	143rd AS	r		*FY74*			
	37890	C-130E	314th AW	bl		41658	C-130H	3rd Wg	w
	37892	C-130E	327th AS	bk		41659	C-130H	3rd Wg	w
	37893	C-130E	314th AW	bk		41660	C-130H	3rd Wg	w
	37894	C-130E	463rd AG	gn		41661	C-130H	3rd Wg	w
	37895	C-130E	171st AS	y/bk		41663	C-130H	317th AG	bl
	37896	C-130E	314th AW	bk		41664	C-130H	3rd Wg	w
	37897	C-130E	169th AS	or		41665	C-130H	317th AG	bl
	37898	C-130E	8th SOS			41666	C-130H	317th AG	bl
	37899	C-130E	314th AW	bl		41667	C-130H	317th AG	r
	39810	C-130E	71st RQS	bl		41668	C-130H	3rd Wg	w
	39812	C-130E	314th AW	bk		41669	C-130H	317th AG	bl
	39813	C-130E	171st AS	y/bk		41670	C-130H	317th AG	r
	39814	C-130E	314th AW	bl		41673	C-130H	317th AG	bl
	39815	C-130E	198th AS			41674	C-130H	317th AG	r
	39816	EC-130E	193rd SOS			41675	C-130H	317th AG	r
	39817	EC-130E	193rd SOS			41676	C-130H	3rd Wg	m
	FY84					41677	C-130H	317th AG	bl
	40204	C-130H	700th AS	bl		41679	C-130H	317th AG	bl
	40205	C-130H	700th AS	bl		41680	C-130H	317th AG	r
	40206	C-130H	142nd AS	bl		41682	C-130H	3rd Wg	w
	40207	C-130H	142nd AS	bl		41684	C-130H	3rd Wg	w
	40208	C-130H	142nd AS	bl		41685	C-130H	3rd Wg	w
	40209	C-130H	142nd AS	bl		41687	C-130H	317th AG	r
	40210	C-130H	142nd AS	bl		41688	C-130H	317th AG	bl
	40211	C-130H	142nd AS	bl		41689	C-130H	317th AG	bl
	40212	C-130H	142nd AS	bl		41690	C-130H	3rd Wg	w
	40213	C-130H	142nd AS	bl		41691	C-130H	317th AG	r
	40476	MC-130H	15th SOS			41692	C-130H	3rd Wg	w
	FY64					42061	C-130H	317th AG	r
	40495	C-130E	43rd AW	gn/or		42062	C-130H	3rd Wg	w
	40496	C-130E	43rd AW	gn/bl		42063	C-130H	317th AG	bl
	40498	C-130E	43rd AW	gn/bl		42065	C-130H	317th AG	bl
	40499	C-130E	43rd AW	gn/bl		42066	C-130H	3rd Wg	w
	40502	C-130E	37th AS	bl/w		42067	C-130H	317th AG	r
	40504	C-130E	43rd AW	gn/bl		42069	C-130H	317th AG	r
	40510	C-130E	198th AS			42070	C-130H	3rd Wg	w
	40512	C-130E	154th TS	r		42071	C-130H	3rd Wg	w
	40514	C-130E	154th TS	r		42072	C-130H	317th AG	bl
	40515	C-130E	198th AS			42130	C-130H	317th AG	r
	40517	C-130E	43rd AW	gn/bl		42131	C-130H	3rd Wg	w
	40518	C-130E	463rd AG	gn		42132	C-130H	317th AG	r
	40519	C-130E	314th AW	bl		42133	C-130H	3rd Wg	w
	40520	C-130E	157th FS			42134	C-130H	317th AG	r
	40521	C-130E	159th FS			*FY94*			
	40523	MC-130E	8th SOS			46701	C-130H	167th AS	r
	40525	C-130E	43rd AW	gn/bl		46702	C-130H	167th AS	r
	40526	C-130E	154th TS	r		46703	C-130H	167th AS	r
	40527	C-130E	37th AS	bl/w					

Type			Notes	Type			Notes
46704	C-130H	167th AS	r	FY66			
46705	C-130H	167th AS	r	60212	HC-130P	129th RQS	bl
46706	C-130H	167th AS	r	60213	MC-130P	9th SOS	
46707	C-130H	167th AS	r	60216	HC-130P	129th RQS	bl
46708	C-130H	167th AS	r	60217	MC-130P	9th SOS	
47310	C-130H	731st AS	pr/w	60219	HC-130P	129th RQS	bl
47315	C-130H	731st AS	pr/w	60220	MC-130P	17th SOS	
47316	C-130H	731st AS	pr/w	60221	HC-130P	129th RQS	bl
47317	C-130H	731st AS	pr/w	60222	HC-130P	102nd RQS	
47318	C-130H	731st AS	pr/w	60223	MC-130P	9th SOS	
47319	C-130H	731st AS	pr/w	60224	HC-130P	39th RQS	
47320	C-130H	731st AS	pr/w	60225	MC-130P	9th SOS	
47321	C-130H	731st AS	pr/w	FY86			
48151	C-130J	815th AS	r	60410	C-130H	758th AS	bk/y
48152	C-130J	815th AS	r	60411	C-130H	758th AS	bk/y
FY85				60412	C-130H	758th AS	bk/y
50011	MC-130H	58th SOW		60413	C-130H	758th AS	bk/y
50012	MC-130H	15th SOS		60414	C-130H	758th AS	bk/y
50035	C-130H	357th AS	bl	60415	C-130H	758th AS	bk/y
50036	C-130H	357th AS	bl	60418	C-130H	758th AS	bk/y
50037	C-130H	357th AS	bl	60419	C-130H	758th AS	bk/y
50038	C-130H	357th AS	bl	FY96			
50039	C-130H	357th AS	bl	61003	C-130H	109th AS	gn/bl
50040	C-130H	357th AS	bl	61004	C-130H	109th AS	gn/bl
50041	C-130H	357th AS	bl	61005	C-130H	109th AS	gn/bl
50042	C-130H	357th AS	bl	61006	C-130H	109th AS	gn/bl
FY65				61007	C-130H	109th AS	gn/bl
50962	EC-130H	43rd ECS	r	61008	C-130H	109th AS	gn/bl
50963	WC-130H	53rd WRS		FY86			
50964	MC-130P			61391	C-130H	180th AS	y
50966	WC-130H	53rd WRS		61392	C-130H	180th AS	y
50967	WC-130H	53rd WRS		61393	C-130H	180th AS	y
50968	WC-130H	53rd WRS		61394	C-130H	180th AS	y
50970	HC-130P	303rd RQS	y	61395	C-130H	180th AS	y
50971	MC-130P	58th SOW		61396	C-130H	180th AS	y
50973	HC-130P	71st RQS	bl	61397	C-130H	180th AS	y
50974	HC-130P	102nd RQS		61398	C-130H	180th AS	y
50975	MC-130P	58th SOW		61699	MC-130H	7th SOS	
50976	HC-130P			FY76			
50977	WC-130H	53rd WRS		63300	LC-130R	139th AS	
50978	HC-130P	102nd RQS		63302	LC-130R	139th AS	
50979	NC-130H	412th TW		FY96			
50980	WC-130H	53rd WRS		65300	WC-130J	53rd WRS	
50981	HC-130P	71st RQS	bl	65301	WC-130J	53rd WRS	
50982	HC-130P	71st RQS	bl	65302	WC-130J	53rd WRS	
50983	HC-130P	71st RQS	bl	67322	C-130H	731st AS	pr/w
50984	WC-130H	53rd WRS		67323	C-130H	731st AS	pr/w
50985	WC-130H	53rd WRS		67324	C-130H	731st AS	pr/w
50986	HC-130P	71st RQS	bl	67325	C-130H	731st AS	pr/w
50987	HC-130P	71st RQS	bl	68153	C-130J	815th AS	r
50988	HC-130P	71st RQS	bl	68154	C-130J	815th AS	r
50989	EC-130H	41st ECS	bl	FY87			
50991	MC-130P	9th SOS		70023	MC-130H		
50992	MC-130P	17th SOS		7th SOS			
50993	MC-130P	17th SOS		70024	MC-130H	15th SOS	
50994	MC-130P	17th SOS		70125	MC-130H	58th SOW	
FY95				70126	MC-130H	58th SOW	
51001	C-130H	109th AS	gn/bl	70127	MC-130H	58th SOW	
51002	C-130H	109th AS	gn/bl	70128	AC-130U		
FY85				4th SOS			
51361	C-130H	181st AS	bl/w	FY97			
51362	C-130H	181st AS	bl/w	71351	C-130J	135th AS	bk/y
51363	C-130H	181st AS	bl/w	71352	C-130J	135th AS	bk/y
51364	C-130H	181st AS	bl/w	71353	C-130J	135th AS	bk/y
51365	C-130H	181st AS	bl/w	71354	C-130J	135th AS	bk/y
51366	C-130H	181st AS	bl/w	71931	EC-130J LMTAS		
51367	C-130H	181st AS	bl/w	75303	WC-130J	53rd WRS	
51368	C-130H	181st AS	bl/w	75304	WC-130J	53rd WRS	
FY95				75305	WC-130J	53rd WRS	
56709	C-130H	167th AS	r	75306	WC-130J	53rd WRS	
56710	C-130H	167th AS	r	FY87			
56711	C-130H	167th AS	r	79281	C-130H	95th AS	w/r
56712	C-130H	167th AS	r	79282	C-130H	95th AS	w/r

C-130 – C135

Notes	Type				Notes	Type			
	79283	C-130H	95th AS	w/r		90514	AC-130U	4th SOS	
	79284	C-130H	700th AS	bl		91051	C-130H	105th AS	r
	79285	C-130H	95th AS	w/r		91052	C-130H	105th AS	r
	79286	C-130H	357th AS	bl		91053	C-130H	105th AS	r
	79287	C-130H	95th AS	w/r		91054	C-130H	105th AS	r
	79288	C-130H	758th AS	bk/y		91055	C-130H	204th AS	
FY88						91056	C-130H	180th AS	y
	80191	MC-130H	1st SOS			91181	C-130H	105th AS	r
	80192	MC-130H	1st SOS			91182	C-130H	105th AS	r
	80193	MC-130H	7th SOS			91183	C-130H	105th AS	r
	80194	MC-130H	7th SOS			91184	C-130H	105th AS	r
	80195	MC-130H	1st SOS			91185	C-130H	105th AS	r
	80264	MC-130H	1st SOS			91186	C-130H	105th AS	r
FY78						91187	C-130H	105th AS	r
	80806	C-130H	185th AS	bl		91188	C-130H	105th AS	r
	80807	C-130H	185th AS	bl	*FY99*				
	80808	C-130H	185th AS	bl		91431	CC-130J	143rd AS	r
	80809	C-130H	185th AS	bl		91432	CC-130J	143rd AS	r
	80810	C-130H	185th AS	bl		91433	CC-130J	143rd AS	r
	80811	C-130H	185th AS	bl		91933	EC-130J	LMTAS	
	80812	C-130H	185th AS	bl		95309	WC-130J	53rd WRS	
	80813	C-130H	185th AS	bl	*FY69*				
FY88						95819	MC-130P	9th SOS	
	81301	C-130H	130th AS	pr/y		95820	MC-130P	9th SOS	
	81302	C-130H	130th AS	pr/y		95821	MC-130P	58th SOW	
	81303	C-130H	130th AS	pr/y		95822	MC-130P	9th SOS	
	81304	C-130H	130th AS	pr/y		95823	MC-130P	67th SOS	
	81305	C-130H	130th AS	pr/y		95825	MC-130P	9th SOS	
	81306	C-130H	130th AS	pr/y		95826	MC-130P	67th SOS	
	81307	C-130H	130th AS	pr/y		95827	MC-130P	9th SOS	
	81308	C-130H	130th AS	pr/y		95828	MC-130P	67th SOS	
FY98						95829	HC-130N	39th RQS	
	81355	C-130J	135th AS	bk/y		95830	HC-130N	39th RQS	
	81356	C-130J	135th AS	bk/y		95831	MC-130P	67th SOS	
	81357	C-130J	135th AS	bk/y		95832	MC-130P	67th SOS	
	81358	C-130J	135th AS	bk/y		95833	HC-130N	39th RQS	
FY88						96566	C-130E	37th AS	bl/w
	81803	MC-130H	1st SOS			96568	AC-130H	16th SOS	
FY98						96569	AC-130H	16th SOS	
	81932	EC-130J	LMTAS			96570	AC-130H	16th SOS	
FY88						96572	AC-130H	16th SOS	
	82101	HC-130N	102nd RQS			96573	AC-130H	16th SOS	
	82102	HC-130N	102nd RQS			96574	AC-130H	16th SOS	
	84401	C-130H	95th AS	w/r		96575	AC-130H	16th SOS	
	84402	C-130H	95th AS	w/r		96577	AC-130H	16th SOS	
	84403	C-130H	95th AS	w/r		96580	C-130E	43rd AW	gn/or
	84404	C-130H	95th AS	w/r		96582	C-130E	37th AS	bl/w
	84405	C-130H	95th AS	w/r		96583	C-130E	37th AS	bl/w
	84406	C-130H	95th AS	w/r	*FY89*				
	84407	C-130H	95th AS	w/r		99101	C-130H	757th AS	bl
FY98						99102	C-130H	757th AS	bl
	85307	WC-130J	53rd WRS			99103	C-130H	757th AS	bl
	85308	WC-130J	53rd WRS			99104	C-130H	757th AS	bl
FY89						99105	C-130H	757th AS	bl
	90280	MC-130H	7th SOS			99106	C-130H	757th AS	bl
	90281	MC-130H	15th SOS						
	90282	MC-130H	15th SOS						
	90283	MC-130H	15th SOS						
FY79									
	90473	C-130H	192nd AS	w					
	90474	C-130H	192nd AS	w					
	90475	C-130H	192nd AS	w					
	90476	C-130H	192nd AS	w					
	90477	C-130H	192nd AS	w					
	90478	C-130H	192nd AS	w					
	90479	C-130H	192nd AS	w					
	90480	C-130H	192nd AS	w					
FY89									
	90509	AC-130U	4th SOS						
	90510	AC-130U	4th SOS						
	90511	AC-130U	4th SOS						
	90512	AC-130U	4th SOS						
	90513	AC-130U	4th SOS						

Boeing C-135/C-137
6th AMW, MacDill AFB, Florida:
  91st ARS (*y/bl*);
15th ABW, Hickam AFB, Hawaii:
  65th AS;
18th Wg, Kadena AB, Japan [ZZ]:
  909th ARS (*w*);
19th ARG, Robins AFB, Georgia:
  99th ARS (*y/bl*);
22nd ARW, McConnell AFB, Kansas:
  344th ARS (*y/bk*), 349th ARS (*y/bl*)
  350th ARS (*y/r*) & 384th ARS (*y/pr*);
55th Wg, Offutt AFB, Nebraska [OF]:
  38th RS (*gn*) & 45th RS (*bk*);
88th ABW, Wright-Patterson AFB,
  Ohio;

Type	Notes	Type	Notes
92nd ARW, Fairchild AFB, Washington: 92nd ARS (*bk*), 93rd ARS (*bl*), 96th ARS (*gn*) & 97th ARS (*y*);		916th ARW AFRC, Seymour Johnson AFB, North Carolina: 77th ARS (*gn*);	
97th AMW, Altus AFB, Oklahoma: 55th ARS (*y/r*);		927th ARW AFRC, Selfridge ANGB, Michigan: 63rd ARS (*pr/w*);	
100th ARW, RAF Mildenhall, UK [D]: 351st ARS (*r/w/bl*);		940th ARW AFRC, McClellan AFB, California: 314th ARS (*or/bk*)	
106th ARS/117th ARW, Birmingham, Alabama ANG (*w/r*);		**FY60**	
108th ARS/126th ARW, Scott AFB, Illinois ANG (*w/bl*);		00313 KC-135R 100th ARW *r/w/bl*	
108th ARW, McGuire AFB, New Jersey ANG: 141st ARS (*bk/y*) & 150th ARS (*bl*);		00314 KC-135R 434th ARW *r/w*	
		00315 KC-135R 126th ARS *w/bl*	
		00316 KC-135E 116th ARS *gn/w*	
116th ARS/141st ARW, Fairchild AFB, Washington ANG (*gn/w*);		00318 KC-135R 203rd ARS *y/bk*	
117th ARS/190th ARW, Forbes Field, Kansas ANG (*bl/y*);		00319 KC-135R 22nd ARW	
		00320 KC-135R 319th ARW *w*	
		00321 KC-135R 97th AMW *y/r*	
121st ARW, Rickenbacker ANGB, Ohio ANG: 145th ARS & 166th ARS (*bl*);		00322 KC-135R 434th ARW *bl*	
		00323 KC-135R 319th ARW *bl*	
		00324 KC-135R 319th ARW	
126th ARS/128th ARW, Mitchell Field, Wisconsin ANG (*w/bl*);		00327 KC-135E 191st ARS *bl/bk*	
		00328 KC-135R 22nd ARW	
127th ARS/184th ARW, McConnell AFB, Kansas ANG;		00329 KC-135R 203rd ARS *y/bk*	
		00331 KC-135R 92nd ARW *bk*	
132nd ARS/101st ARW, Bangor, Maine ANG (*w/gn*);		00332 KC-135R 6th AMW *y/bl*	
		00333 KC-135R 92nd ARW *bk*	
133rd ARS/157th ARW, Pease ANGB New Hampshire ANG (*bl*);		00334 KC-135R 168th ARS *bl/y*	
		00335 KC-135T 22nd ARW *y/bk*	
136th ARS/107th ARW, Niagara Falls, New York ANG (*bl*);		00336 KC-135T 92nd ARW *gn*	
		00337 KC-135T 92nd ARW *m*	
151st ARS/134th ARW, Knoxville, Tennessee ANG (*w/or*);		00339 KC-135T 92nd ARW *bl*	
		00341 KC-135T 121st ARW *bl*	
153rd ARS/186th ARW, Meridian, Mississippi ANG (*bk/gd*);		00342 KC-135T 319th ARW *y*	
		00343 KC-135T 19th ARG *y/bl*	
168th ARS/168th ARW, Eielson AFB, Alaska ANG (*bl/y*);		00344 KC-135T 319th ARW *r*	
		00345 KC-135T 18th Wg *w*	
171st ARW, Greater Pittsburgh Pennsylvania ANG: 146th ARS (*y/bk*) & 147th ARS (*bk/y*);		00346 KC-135T 92nd ARW *bk*	
		00347 KC-135R 121st ARW *bl*	
		00348 KC-135R 319th ARW *r*	
		00349 KC-135R 916th ARW *gn*	
173rd ARS/155th ARW, Lincoln, Nebraska ANG (*r/w*);		00350 KC-135R 97th AMW *y/r*	
		00351 KC-135R 22nd ARW	
191st ARS/151st ARW, Salt Lake City, Utah ANG (*bl/bk*);		00353 KC-135R 22nd ARW	
		00355 KC-135R 319th ARW *y*	
196th ARS/163rd ARW, March ARB, California ANG (*bl/w*);		00356 KC-135R 22nd ARW *y/bl*	
		00357 KC-135R 22nd ARW *y/bk*	
197th ARS/161st ARW, Phoenix, Arizona ANG;		00358 KC-135R 136th ARS *bl*	
		00359 KC-135R 434th ARW *r/w*	
		00360 KC-135R 22nd ARW	
203rd ARS/154th Wg, Hickam AFB, Hawaii ANG [HH] (*y/bk*);		00362 KC-135R 22nd ARW *y/r*	
		00363 KC-135R 434th ARW *bl*	
319th ARW, Grand Forks AFB, North Dakota: 905th ARS (*bl*), 906th ARS (*y*), 911th ARS (*r*) & 912th ARS (*w*);		00364 KC-135R 434th ARW *r/w*	
		00365 KC-135R 127th ARS	
		00366 KC-135R 19th ARG *y/bl*	
		00367 KC-135R 121st ARW *bl*	
366th Wg, Mountain Home AFB, Idaho [MO]: 22nd ARS (*y/gn*);		00372 C-135E 412th TW *bl*	
		FY61	
412th TW, Edwards AFB, California [ED]: 452nd FLTS (*bl*);		10264 KC-135R 121st ARW *bl*	
		10266 KC-135R 173rd ARS *r/w*	
		10267 KC-135R	
434th ARW AFRC, Grissom AFB, Indiana: 72nd ARS (*bl*) & 74th ARS (*r/w*);		10268 KC-135E 940th ARW *or/bk*	
		10270 KC-135R 927th ARW *pr/w*	
		10271 KC-135R 927th ARW *pr/w*	
		10272 KC-135R 434th ARW *r/w*	
452nd AMW AFRC, March ARB, California: 336th ARS (*y*);		10275 KC-135R 319th ARW *bl*	
		10276 KC-135R 173rd ARS *r/w*	
		10277 KC-135R 366th Wg *y/gn*	
507th ARW AFRC, Tinker AFB, Oklahoma: 465th ARS (*bl/y*);		10280 KC-135R 452nd AMW *y*	
		10281 KC-135E 197th ARS	
		10284 KC-135R 319th ARW *bl*	
645th Materiel Sqn, Greenville, Texas;		10288 KC-135R 92nd ARW *bk*	

C-135

Notes	Type				Notes	Type			
	10290	KC-135R	203rd ARS	y/bk		23513	KC-135R	366th Wg	y/gn
	10292	KC-135R	6th AMW	y/bl		23514	KC-135R	203rd ARS	y/bk
	10293	KC-135R	22nd ARW	y/r		23515	KC-135R	133rd ARS	bl
	10294	KC-135R	19th ARG	y/bl		23516	KC-135R	22nd ARW	
	10295	KC-135R	319th ARW	bl		23517	KC-135R	22nd ARW	
	10298	KC-135R	126th ARS	w/bl		23518	KC-135R	434th ARW	bl
	10299	KC-135R	319th ARW	bl		23519	KC-135R	22nd ARW	
	10300	KC-135R	6th AMW	y/bl		23520	KC-135R	319th ARW	y
	10302	KC-135R	100th ARW	r/w/bl		23521	KC-135R	434th ARW	r/w
	10303	KC-135E	452nd AMW	y		23523	KC-135R	19th ARG	y/bl
	10304	KC-135R	92nd ARW	y		23524	KC-135R	106th ARS	w/r
	10305	KC-135R	92nd ARW	bl		23526	KC-135R	173rd ARS	r/w
	10306	KC-135R	319th ARW	bl		23527	KC-135E	108th ARW	bl
	10307	KC-135R	434th ARW	r/w		23528	KC-135R	22nd ARW	
	10308	KC-135R	97th AMW	y/r		23529	KC-135R	319th ARW	w
	10309	KC-135R	126th ARS	w/bl		23530	KC-135R	434th ARW	bl
	10310	KC-135R	133rd ARS	bl		23531	KC-135R	121st ARW	bl
	10311	KC-135R	22nd ARW	y/r		23533	KC-135R	319th ARW	bl
	10312	KC-135R	319th ARW	r		23534	KC-135R	19th ARG	y/bl
	10313	KC-135R	916th ARW	gn		23537	KC-135R	22nd ARW	
	10314	KC-135R	97th AMW	y/r		23538	KC-135R	100th ARW	r/w/bl
	10315	KC-135R	97th AMW	y/r		23540	KC-135R	22nd ARW	
	10317	KC-135R	6th AMW	y/bl		23541	KC-135R	22nd ARW	
	10318	KC-135R	319th ARW	bl		23542	KC-135R	916th ARW	gn
	10320	KC-135R	97th AMW	y/r		23543	KC-135R	434th ARW	bl
	10321	KC-135R	22nd ARW			23544	KC-135R	19th ARG	y/bl
	10323	KC-135R	319th ARW	bl		23545	KC-135R	22nd ARW	
	10324	KC-135R	452nd AMW	y		23546	KC-135R	97th AMW	y/r
	10330	EC-135E	412th TW	bl		23547	KC-135R	133rd ARS	bl
	12662	RC-135S	55th Wg	bk		23548	KC-135R	319th ARW	y
	12663	RC-135S	55th Wg	bk		23549	KC-135R	319th ARW	r
	12666	NC-135W	645th MS			23550	KC-135R	22nd ARW	
	12669	C-135C	412th TW	bl		23551	KC-135R	100th ARW	r/w/bl
	12670	OC-135B	55th Wg			23552	KC-135R	319th ARW	r
	12672	OC-135B	55th Wg			23553	KC-135R	22nd ARW	y/r
	FY64					23554	KC-135R	19th ARG	y/bl
	14828	KC-135R	97th AMW	y/r		23556	KC-135R	916th ARW	gn
	14829	KC-135R	100th ARW	r/w/bl		23557	KC-135R	319th ARW	y
	14830	KC-135R	100th ARW	r/w/bl		23558	KC-135R	22nd ARW	y/bk
	14831	KC-135R	22nd ARW			23559	KC-135R	22nd ARW	y/pr
	14832	KC-135R	203rd ARS	y/bk		23561	KC-135R	92nd ARW	y
	14833	KC-135R	22nd ARW			23562	KC-135R	319th ARW	w
	14834	KC-135R	434th ARW	r/w		23564	KC-135R	22nd ARW	
	14835	KC-135R	100th ARW	r/w/bl		23565	KC-135R	22nd ARW	
	14836	KC-135R	6th AMW	y/bl		23566	KC-135E	153rd ARS	bk/gd
	14837	KC-135R	22nd ARW			23568	KC-135R	319th ARW	w
	14838	KC-135R				23569	KC-135R	19th ARG	y/bl
	14839	KC-135R	136th ARS	bl		23571	KC-135R	168th ARS	bl/y
	14840	KC-135R	121st ARW	bl		23572	KC-135R	366th Wg	y/gn
	14841	RC-135V	55th Wg	gn		23573	KC-135R	92nd ARW	
	14842	RC-135V	55th Wg	gn		23575	KC-135R	22nd ARW	
	14843	RC-135V	55th Wg	gn		23576	KC-135R	133rd ARS	bl
	14844	RC-135V	55th Wg	gn		23577	KC-135R	916th ARW	gn
	14845	RC-135V	55th Wg	gn		23578	KC-135R	22nd ARW	
	14846	RC-135V	55th Wg	gn		23580	KC-135R	22nd ARW	
	14847	RC-135U	55th Wg	gn		23582	WC-135C	55th Wg	bk
	14848	RC-135V	55th Wg	gn		24125	RC-135W	55th Wg	gn
	14849	RC-135U	55th Wg	gn		24126	C-135B	108th ARW	bk/y
	FY62					24127	RC-135W	55th Wg	
	23498	KC-135R	319th ARW	y		24128	RC-135S	55th Wg	
	23499	KC-135R	22nd ARW	y/pr		24129	TC-135W	55th Wg	gn
	23500	KC-135R	126th ARS	w/bl		24130	RC-135W	55th Wg	gn
	23502	KC-135R	18th Wg	w		24131	RC-135W	55th Wg	gn
	23503	KC-135R	18th Wg	w		24132	RC-135W	55th Wg	gn
	23504	KC-135R	319th ARW	y		24133	TC-135S	55th Wg	bk
	23505	KC-135R	22nd ARW			24134	RC-135W	55th Wg	gn
	23506	KC-135R	133rd ARS	bl		24135	RC-135W	55th Wg	gn
	23507	KC-135R	18th Wg	w		24138	RC-135W	55th Wg	gn
	23508	KC-135R	19th ARG	y/bl		24139	RC-135W	55th Wg	gn
	23509	KC-135R	916th ARW	gn		*FY63*			
	23510	KC-135R	434th ARW	r/w		37976	KC-135R	6th AMW	y/bl
	23511	KC-135R	121st ARW	bl		37977	KC-135R	97th AMW	y/r
	23512	KC-135R	126th ARS	w/bl		37978	KC-135R	100th ARW	r/w/bl

Type			Notes	Type			Notes
37979	KC-135R	22nd ARW		38885	KC-135R	18th Wg	w
37980	KC-135R	100th ARW	r/w/bl	38886	KC-135R	319th ARW	w
37981	KC-135R	136th ARS	bl	38887	KC-135R		
37982	KC-135R	22nd ARW		38888	KC-135R	97th AMW	y/r
37984	KC-135R	106th ARS	w/r	39792	RC-135V	55th Wg	gn
37985	KC-135R	507th ARW	bl/y	FY55			
37987	KC-135R	319th ARW	bl	53132	NKC-135E	412th TW	bl
37988	KC-135R	173rd ARS	r/w	53135	NKC-135E	412th TW	bl
37991	KC-135R	173rd ARS	r/w	53141	KC-135E	116th ARS	gn/w
37992	KC-135R	121st ARW	bl	53143	KC-135E	197th ARS	
37993	KC-135R	121st ARW	m	53145	KC-135E	940th ARW	or/bk
37995	KC-135R	22nd ARW	y/bl	53146	KC-135E	108th ARW	bk/y
37996	KC-135R	434th ARW	bl	FY56			
37997	KC-135R	319th ARW	bl	63593	KC-135E	108th ARW	bk/y
37999	KC-135R	97th AMW	y/r	63604	KC-135E	108th ARW	bk/y
38000	KC-135R	22nd ARW		63606	KC-135E	132nd ARS	w/gn
38002	KC-135R	22nd ARW		63607	KC-135E	151st ARS	w/or
38003	KC-135R	18th Wg	w	63609	KC-135E	151st ARS	w/or
38004	KC-135R	127th ARS		63611	KC-135E	171st ARS	y/bk
38006	KC-135R	319th ARW	w	63612	KC-135E	171st ARS	y/bk
38007	KC-135R	106th ARS	w/r	63622	KC-135E	132nd ARS	w/gn
38008	KC-135R	100th ARW	r/w/bl	63626	KC-135E	171st ARS	y/bk
38011	KC-135R	6th AMW	y/bl	63630	KC-135E	171st ARW	y/bk
38012	KC-135R	319th ARW	r	63631	KC-135E	191st ARS	bl/bk
38013	KC-135R	121st ARW	bl	63638	KC-135E	197th ARS	
38014	KC-135R	319th ARW	bl	63640	KC-135E	132nd ARS	w/gn
38015	KC-135R	168th ARS	bl/y	63641	KC-135E	117th ARS	bl/y
38017	KC-135R	92nd ARW	bk	63643	KC-135E	151st ARS	w/or
38018	KC-135R	173rd ARS	r/w	63648	KC-135E	171st ARW	y/bk
38019	KC-135R	22nd ARW	y/pr	63650	KC-135E	116th ARS	gn/w
38020	KC-135R	97th AMW	y/r	63654	KC-135E	132nd ARS	w/gn
38021	KC-135R	18th Wg	w	FY57			
38022	KC-135R	22nd ARW	m	71418	KC-135R	153rd ARS	bk/gd
38023	KC-135R	97th AMW	y/r	71419	KC-135R	19th ARG	y/bl
38024	KC-135R	452nd AMW	y	71421	KC-135E	116th ARS	gn/w
38025	KC-135R	100th ARW	r/w/bl	71422	KC-135R	927th ARW	pr/w
38026	KC-135R	319th ARW	y	71423	KC-135E	171st ARW	bk/y
38027	KC-135R	92nd ARW	gn	71425	KC-135E	151st ARS	w/or
38028	KC-135R	168th ARS	bl/y	71426	KC-135E	197th ARS	
38029	KC-135R	126th ARS	w/bl	71427	KC-135R	121st ARW	bl
38030	KC-135R	203rd ARS	y/bk	71428	KC-135E	196th ARS	bl/w
38031	KC-135R	92nd ARW	y	71429	KC-135E	117th ARS	bl/y
38032	KC-135R	434th ARW	bl	71430	KC-135E	133rd ARS	bl
38033	KC-135R	92nd ARW	bl	71431	KC-135E	108th ARW	bk/y
38034	KC-135R	97th AMW	y/r	71432	KC-135R	106th ARS	w/r
38035	KC-135R	106th ARS	w/r	71433	KC-135E	197th ARS	
38036	KC-135R	136th ARS	bl	71434	KC-135E	116th ARS	gn/w
38037	KC-135R	97th AMW	y/r	71435	KC-135R	18th Wg	w
38038	KC-135R	133rd ARS	bl	71436	KC-135R	196th ARS	bl/w
38039	KC-135R	507th ARW	bl/y	71437	KC-135R	916th ARW	gn
38040	KC-135R	6th AMW	y/bl	71438	KC-135E	927th ARW	pr/w
38041	KC-135R	434th ARW	bl	71439	KC-135R	6th AMW	y/bl
38043	KC-135R	168th ARS	bl/y	71440	KC-135R	319th ARW	r
38044	KC-135R	18th Wg	w	71441	KC-135E	108th ARS	w/bl
38045	KC-135R	319th ARW		71443	KC-135E	132nd ARS	w/gn
38050	NKC-135B	412th TW	bl	71445	KC-135E	108th ARW	bk/y
38058	KC-135D	117th ARS	bl/y	71447	KC-135E	171st ARW	y/bk
38059	KC-135D	117th ARS	bl/y	71448	KC-135E	132nd ARS	w/gn
38060	KC-135D	117th ARS	bl/y	71450	KC-135E	132nd ARS	w/gn
38061	KC-135D	117th ARS	bl/y	71451	KC-135E	196th ARS	bl/w
38871	KC-135R	319th ARW	y	71452	KC-135E	197th ARS	
38872	KC-135R	136th ARS	bl	71453	KC-135R	106th ARS	w/r
38873	KC-135R	319th ARW	y	71454	KC-135R	6th AMW	y/bl
38874	KC-135R	22nd ARW		71455	KC-135E	151st ARS	w/or
38875	KC-135R	127th ARS		71456	KC-135R	319th ARW	y
38876	KC-135R	168th ARS	bl/y	71458	KC-135E	108th ARS	w/bl
38877	KC-135R	97th AMW	y/r	71459	KC-135R	196th ARS	bl/w
38878	KC-135R	97th AMW	y/r	71460	KC-135E	117th ARS	bl/y
38879	KC-135R	100th ARW	r/w/bl	71461	KC-135E	173rd ARS	r/w
38880	KC-135R	507th ARW	bl/y	71462	KC-135R	121st ARW	bl
38881	KC-135R	97th AMW	y/r	71463	KC-135E	117th ARS	bl/y
38883	KC-135R	319th ARW	w	71464	KC-135E	108th ARW	bk/y
38884	KC-135R	100th ARW	r/w/bl	71465	KC-135E	151st ARS	w/or

Notes	Type			
	71468	KC-135E	452nd AMW	y
	71469	KC-135R	121st ARW	bl
	71471	KC-135R	132nd ARS	w/gn
	71472	KC-135R	434th ARW	bl
	71473	KC-135R	19th ARG	y/bl
	71474	KC-135R	319th ARW	bl
	71475	KC-135E	197th ARS	
	71479	KC-135E	452nd AMW	y
	71480	KC-135E	108th ARS	w/bl
	71482	KC-135E	108th ARS	w/bl
	71483	KC-135R	319th ARW	bl
	71484	KC-135E	197th ARS	
	71485	KC-135E	151st ARS	w/or
	71486	KC-135R	18th Wg	w
	71487	KC-135R	434th ARW	bl
	71488	KC-135R	97th AMW	y/r
	71491	KC-135E	132nd ARS	w/gn
	71492	KC-135E	151st ARS	w/or
	71493	KC-135E	97th AMW	y/r
	71494	KC-135E	108th ARS	w/bl
	71495	KC-135E	197th ARS	
	71496	KC-135E	197th ARS	
	71497	KC-135E	191st ARS	bl/bk
	71499	KC-135R	18th Wg	w
	71501	KC-135E	116th ARS	gn/w
	71502	KC-135R	97th AMW	y/r
	71503	KC-135E	151st ARS	w/or
	71504	KC-135E	927th ARW	pr/w
	71505	KC-135E	132nd ARS	w/gn
	71506	KC-135R	6th AMW	y/bl
	71507	KC-135E	108th ARS	bk/y
	71508	KC-135R	203rd ARS	y/bk
	71509	KC-135E	171st ARW	bk/y
	71510	KC-135E	191st ARS	bl/bk
	71511	KC-135E	940th ARW	or/bk
	71512	KC-135R	452nd AMW	y
	71514	KC-135R	126th ARS	w/bl
	72589	KC-135E	412th TW	bl
	72593	KC-135R	121st ARW	bl
	72594	KC-135E	108th ARS	w/bl
	72595	KC-135E	171st ARW	bk/y
	72597	KC-135R	153rd ARS	bk/gd
	72598	KC-135R	452nd AMW	y
	72599	KC-135R	916th ARW	gn
	72600	KC-135E	116th ARS	gn/w
	72601	KC-135E	151st ARS	w/or
	72602	KC-135E	108th ARS	bl
	72603	KC-135R	452nd AMW	y
	72604	KC-135E	171st ARW	y/bk
	72605	KC-135R	100th ARW	r/w/bl
	72606	KC-135E	108th ARS	bl
	72607	KC-135E	171st ARW	bk/y
	72608	KC-135E	171st ARW	bk/y
	FY58			
	80001	KC-135R	319th ARW	w
	80003	KC-135E	108th ARS	w/bl
	80004	KC-135R	153rd ARS	bk/gd
	80005	KC-135E	117th ARS	bl/y
	80006	KC-135R	191st ARS	bl/bk
	80008	KC-135R	133rd ARS	bl
	80009	KC-135R	126th ARS	w/bl
	80010	KC-135R	153rd ARS	bk/gd
	80011	KC-135R	22nd ARW	y/bl
	80012	KC-135E	191st ARS	bl/bk
	80013	KC-135E	927th ARW	pr/w
	80014	KC-135E	117th ARS	bl/y
	80015	KC-135R	434th ARW	r/w
	80016	KC-135R	92nd ARW	y
	80017	KC-135E	171st ARW	y/bk
	80018	KC-135R	22nd ARW	y/pr
	80020	KC-135E	116th ARS	gn/w
	80021	KC-135R	126th ARS	w/bl
	80023	KC-135R	136th ARS	bl
	80024	KC-135E	171st ARW	y/bk
	80027	KC-135R	319th ARW	y
	80030	KC-135R	106th ARS	w/r
	80032	KC-135E	108th ARW	bl
	80034	KC-135R	6th AMW	y/bl
	80035	KC-135R	22nd ARW	y/bl
	80036	KC-135R	319th ARW	
	80037	KC-135E	171st ARW	bk/y
	80038	KC-135R	916th ARW	gn
	80040	KC-135E	108th ARW	bl
	80041	KC-135E	927th ARW	pr/w
	80042	KC-135T	22nd ARW	
	80043	KC-135E	191st ARS	bl/bk
	80044	KC-135E	108th ARW	bk/y
	80045	KC-135T	92nd ARW	bl
	80046	KC-135T	92nd ARW	bl
	80047	KC-135T	19th ARG	y/bl
	80049	KC-135T	92nd ARW	y
	80050	KC-135T	92nd ARW	bk
	80051	KC-135R	507th ARW	bl/y
	80052	KC-135R	452nd AMW	y
	80053	KC-135E	927th ARW	pr/w
	80054	KC-135T	18th Wg	w
	80055	KC-135T	92nd ARW	bk
	80056	KC-135R	153rd ARS	bk/gd
	80057	KC-135E	108th ARS	w/bl
	80058	KC-135R	507th ARW	bl/y
	80059	KC-135R	153rd ARS	bk/gd
	80060	KC-135T	92nd ARW	gn
	80061	KC-135T	319th ARW	r
	80062	KC-135T	18th Wg	w
	80063	KC-135R	507th ARW	bl/y
	80064	KC-135E	940th ARW	or/bk
	80065	KC-135T	22nd ARW	
	80066	KC-135R	507th ARW	bl/y
	80067	KC-135E	108th ARS	w/bl
	80068	KC-135E	108th ARS	w/bl
	80069	KC-135T	92nd ARW	bk
	80071	KC-135T	22nd ARW	y/bk
	80072	KC-135T	92nd ARW	gn
	80073	KC-135R	106th ARS	w
	80074	KC-135T	18th Wg	w
	80075	KC-135R	434th ARW	bl
	80076	KC-135R	434th ARW	r/w
	80077	KC-135T	92nd ARW	bk
	80078	KC-135E	108th ARW	bl
	80079	KC-135R	507th ARW	bl/y
	80080	KC-135E	191st ARS	bl/bk
	80082	KC-135E	116th ARS	gn/w
	80083	KC-135R	121st ARW	bl
	80084	KC-135T	92nd ARW	bl
	80085	KC-135E	452nd AMW	y
	80086	KC-135T	92nd ARW	gn
	80087	KC-135E	108th ARW	bl
	80088	KC-135T	22nd ARW	y/bk
	80089	KC-135T	319th ARW	w
	80090	KC-135E	940th ARW	or/bk
	80092	KC-135R	133rd ARS	bl
	80093	KC-135R	319th ARW	r
	80094	KC-135T	92nd ARW	bk
	80095	KC-135T	319th ARW	w
	80096	KC-135E	940th ARW	or/bk
	80098	KC-135R	133rd ARS	bl
	80099	KC-135T	92nd ARW	bl
	80100	KC-135R	18th Wg	w
	80102	KC-135R	434th ARW	r/w
	80103	KC-135T	92nd ARW	gn
	80104	KC-135R	136th ARS	bl
	80106	KC-135R	106th ARS	w/r
	80107	KC-135E	191st ARS	bl/bk
	80108	KC-135E	940th ARW	or/bk
	80109	KC-135R	153rd ARS	bk/gd
	80111	KC-135E	108th ARW	bk/y

Type			Notes	Type			Notes
80112	KC-135T	92nd ARW	bl	91502	KC-135R		
80113	KC-135R	97th AMW	y/r	91503	KC-135E	108th ARW	bk/y
80114	KC-135R	92nd ARW	bl	91504	KC-135T	92nd ARW	bk
80115	KC-135E	108th ARW	bl	91505	KC-135R	196th ARS	bl/w
80116	KC-135R	197th ARS		91506	KC-135E	171st ARW	bk/y
80117	KC-135T	92nd ARW	bl	91507	KC-135R	19th ARG	y/bl
80118	KC-135R			91508	KC-135R	92nd ARW	y
80119	KC-135R	18th Wg	w	91509	KC-135E	196th ARS	bl/w
80120	KC-135R	319th ARW	y	91510	KC-135T	319th ARW	r
80121	KC-135R	507th ARW	bl/y	91511	KC-135R	22nd ARW	
80122	KC-135R	168th ARS	bl/y	91512	KC-135T	18th Wg	w
80123	KC-135R	18th Wg	w	91513	KC-135T	92nd ARW	bl
80124	KC-135R	22nd ARW	y/bl	91515	KC-135T	319th ARW	r
80125	KC-135T	92nd ARW	bl	91516	KC-135R	196th ARS	bl/w
80126	KC-135R	22nd ARW	y/bl	91517	KC-135E	97th AMW	y/r
80128	KC-135R	6th AMW	y/bl	91518	C-135K	15th ABW	
80129	KC-135R	92nd ARW	bl	91519	KC-135E	171st ARW	y/bk
80130	KC-135R	126th ARS	w/bl	91520	KC-135T	92nd ARW	bl
FY88				91521	KC-135R	168th ARS	bl/y
86005	EC-137D	88th ABW		91522	KC-135R	136th ARS	bl
86008	EC-137D	88th ABW		91523	KC-135T	92nd ARW	bk
FY59							
91444	KC-135R	121st ARW	bl	**Lockheed C-141 Starlifter**			
91445	KC-135R	116th ARS	gn/w	164th AW, Memphis, Tennessee ANG:			
91446	KC-135R	153rd ARS	bk/gd	155th AS (*r*);			
91447	KC-135E	927th ARW	pr/w	172nd AW, Jackson Int'l Airport,			
91448	KC-135R	196th ARS	bl/w	Mississippi ANG:			
91449	KC-135R	196th ARS	bl/w	183rd AS (*bl/gd*);			
91451	KC-135E	927th ARW	pr/w	305th AMW, McGuire AFB,			
91453	KC-135R	121st ARW	bl	New Jersey (*bl*):			
91455	KC-135R	153rd ARS	bk/gd	6th AS, 13th AS & 18th AS;			
91456	KC-135E	108th ARW	bk/y	445th AW AFRC, Wright-Patterson			
91457	KC-135E	171st ARW	bk/y	AFB, Ohio (*si*):			
91458	KC-135R	121st ARW	bl	89th AS & 356th AS;			
91459	KC-135R	100th ARW	r/w/bl	452nd AMW AFRC, March ARB,			
91460	KC-135T	92nd ARW	gn	California (*or/y*):			
91461	KC-135R	168th ARS	bl/y	729th AS & 730th AS;			
91462	KC-135T	319th ARW	bl	459th AW, AFRC, Andrews AFB,			
91463	KC-135R	173rd ARS	r/w	Maryland:			
91464	KC-135T	92nd ARW	bk	756th AS (*y/bk*)			
91466	KC-135R	136th ARS	bl	**C-141B/C-141C***			
91467	KC-135T	92nd ARW	bl	*FY63*			
91468	KC-135T	92nd ARW	bl	38076	305th AMW	bl	
91469	KC-135R	916th ARW	gn	38080*	164th AW	r	
91470	KC-135T	92nd ARW	y	38082			
91471	KC-135T	92nd ARW	y	38084*	452nd AMW	or/y	
91472	KC-135R	203rd ARS	y/bk	38085*	452nd AMW	or/y	
91473	KC-135E	191st ARS	bl/bk	*FY64*			
91474	KC-135T	92nd ARW	bk	40611			
91475	KC-135R	97th AMW	y/r	40614*	172nd AW	bl/gd	
91476	KC-135R	319th ARW	r	40619	305th AMW	bl	
91477	KC-135R	927th ARW	pr/w	40620*	459th AW	y/bk	
91478	KC-135R	153rd ARS	bk/gd	40622*	172nd AW	bl/gd	
91479	KC-135E	171st ARW	y/bk	40627*	164th AW	r	
91480	KC-135T	92nd ARW	bl	40632*	172nd AW	bl/gd	
91482	KC-135R	18th Wg	w	40633			
91483	KC-135R	121st ARW	bl	40637*	459th AW	y/bk	
91484	KC-135E	171st ARW	bk/y	40640*	172nd AW	bl/gd	
91485	KC-135E	108th ARW	bl	40645*	459th AW	y/bk	
91486	KC-135R	22nd ARW	y/bl	*FY65*			
91487	KC-135R	108th ARS	w/bl	50216*	459th AW	y/bk	
91488	KC-135R	18th Wg	w	50222*	164th AW	r	
91489	KC-135R	191st ARS	bl/bk	50225*	452nd AMW	or/y	
91490	KC-135T	92nd ARW	bk	50226*	459th AW	y/bk	
91492	KC-135R	97th AMW	y/r	50229*	452nd AMW	or/y	
91493	KC-135R	132nd ARS	w/gn	50232*	445th AW	si	
91495	KC-135E	173rd ARS	r/w	50237*	445th AW	si	
91496	KC-135E	171st ARW	y/bk	50245*	452nd AMW	or/y	
91497	KC-135E	108th ARW	bl	50248*	452nd AMW	or/y	
91498	KC-135R	366th Wg	y/gn	50249*	445th AW	si	
91499	KC-135R	196th ARS	bl/w	50250*	445th AW	si	
91500	KC-135R	18th Wg	w	50256*	445th AW	si	
91501	KC-135R	319th ARW		50258*	445th AW	si	

Notes	Type		
	50261*	445th AW	si
	50271*	459th AW	y/bk
	59409*	445th AW	si
	59412*	445th AW	si
	59414*	452nd AMW	or/y
	FY66		
	60130*	172nd AW	bl/gd
	60132*	445th AW	si
	60133		
	60134*	445th AW	si
	60136*	452nd AMW	or/y
	60139*	164th AW	r
	60147	305th AMW	bl
	60148*	445th AW	si
	60151*	452nd AMW	or/y
	60152*	452nd AMW	or/y
	60157*	164th AW	r
	60160	305th AMW	bl
	60164*	172nd AW	bl/gd
	60167*	452nd AMW	or/y
	60168	305th AMW	bl
	60169	305th AMW	bl
	60174*	459th AW	y/bk
	60177*	445th AW	si
	60181*	452nd AMW	or/y
	60182*	452nd AMW	or/y
	60183	305th AMW	bl
	60185*	172nd AW	bl/gd

Notes	Type		
	60190*	172nd AW	bl/gd
	60191*	172nd AW	bl/gd
	60193*	445th AW	si
	60201*	452nd AMW	or/y
	67944	305th AMW	bl
	67947	305th AMW	bl
	67948		
	67950*	445th AW	si
	67952*	452nd AMW	or/y
	67953*	445th AW	si
	67954*	445th AW	si
	67955	305th AMW	bl
	67957*	445th AW	si
	67959*	445th AW	si
	FY67		
	70003	305th AMW	bl
	70004	305th AMW	bl
	70011	305th AMW	bl
	70012	305th AMW	bl
	70015*	452nd AMW	or/y
	70019	305th AMW	bl
	70021*	164th AW	r
	70024*	164th AW	r
	70027*	459th AW	y/bk
	70029*	164th AW	r
	70031*	445th AW	si
	70166*	445th AW	si

Lakenheath-based F-15C Eagle 86-0178 of the 48th Fighter Wing. *Daniel J March*

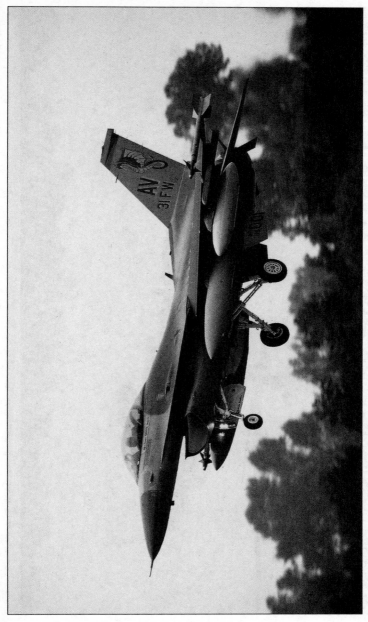

Clearly displaying its Wing markings (31 FW) and serial (89-2001), this USAFE F-16C flies from Aviano, Italy. *PRM*

One of the US Army AH-64 Apaches flown by the 6th Cavalry Regiment at Illesheim, Germany. *PRM*

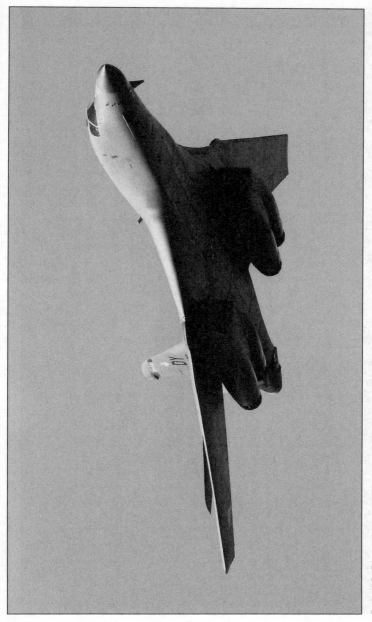

Rockwell B-1B Lancer from the 7th Bomb Wing at Dyess AFB, Texas. *PRM*

509th BW's B-2 Spirit 21067 *Spirit of Arizona* is based at Whiteman AFB, Missouri. *PRM*

US-based USN/USMC Aircraft

Lockheed P-3 Orion
CinCLANT/VP-30, NAS Jacksonville, Florida;
CinCPAC/ETD, MCBH Kaneohe Bay, Hawaii;
CinCUSNFE, NAF Sigonella, Italy;
CNO/VP-30, NAS Jacksonville, Florida;
NAF Keflavik, Iceland;
NASC-FS, Point Mugu, California;
Navy Research Lab, Patuxent River, Maryland;
USNTPS, NAS Point Mugu, California;
VP-1, NAS Whidbey Island, Washington [YB];
VP-4, MCBH Kaneohe Bay, Hawaii [YD];
VP-5, NAS Jacksonville, Florida [LA];
VP-8, NAS Brunswick, Maine [LC];
VP-9, MCBH Kaneohe Bay, Hawaii [PD];
VP-10, NAS Brunswick, Maine [LD];
VP-16, NAS Jacksonville, Florida [LF];
VP-26, NAS Brunswick, Maine [LK];
VP-30, NAS Jacksonville, Florida [LL];
VP-40, NAS Whidbey Island, Washington [QE];
VP-45, NAS Jacksonville, Florida [LN];
VP-46, NAS Whidbey Island, Washington [RC];
VP-47, MCBH Kaneohe Bay, Hawaii [RD];
VP-62, NAS Jacksonville, Florida [LT];
VP-64, NAS Willow Grove, Pennsylvania [LU];
VP-65, NAS Point Mugu, California [PG];
VP-66, NAS Willow Grove, Pennsylvania [LV];
VP-69, NAS Whidbey Island, Washington [PJ];
VP-92, NAS Brunswick, Maine [LY];
VP-94, NAS New Orleans, Louisiana [PZ];
VPU-1, NAS Brunswick, Maine;
VPU-2, MCBH Kaneohe Bay, Hawaii;
VQ-1, NAS Whidbey Island, Washington [PR];
VQ-2, NAF Rota, Spain;
VX-1, NAS Patuxent River, Maryland;
VX-20, Patuxent River, Maryland;
VX-30, NAS Point Mugu, California

Serial	Code	Type	Unit
148889		UP-3A	VX-20
149674	[674]	NP-3D	NRL
149675		VP-3A	CinCPAC
149676		VP-3A	CNO
150495		UP-3A	NAF Keflavik
150496		VP-3A	CinCUSNFE
150499	[337]	NP-3D	VX-30
150511		VP-3A	
150515		VP-3A	VP-30
150521	[341]	NP-3D	VX-30
150522	[340]	NP-3D	VX-30
150524	[335]	NP-3D	VX-30
150526		UP-3A	VQ-1
152141	[408]	P-3A	VP-1
152150	[150]	NP-3D	VX-20
152165	[404]	P-3A	VP-1
152739		NP-3B	LMAS
153442	[442]	NP-3D	NRL
153443	[443]	NP-3D	USNTPS
153450	[227]	P-3B	VPU-1
154577	[336]	P-3B	VPU-1
154587	[587]	NP-3D	NRL
154589	[589]	NP-3D	NRL
156507	[PR-31]	EP-3E	VQ-1
156509	[LC-509]	P-3C	VP-8
156510	[LL-510]	P-3C	VP-30
156514	[PR-33]	EP-3E	VQ-1
156515	[LY-515]	P-3C	VP-92
156516		P-3C	VP-5
156517	[PR-34]	EP-3E	VQ-1
156518	[LL-518]	P-3C	VP-30
156519	[21]	EP-3E	VQ-2
156520	[10]	P-3C	VP-5
156521	[PG-521]	P-3C	VP-65
156522	[LL-522]	P-3C	VP-30
156523	[LL-523]	P-3C	VP-30
156525	[11]	P-3C	VQ-2
156527	[PG-527]	P-3C	VP-65
156528	[PR-36]	EP-3E	VQ-1
156529	[24]	EP-3E	VQ-2
156530	[LL-530]	P-3C	VP-30
157310	[LA-310]	P-3C	VP-5
157311	[LN-311]	P-3C	VP-45
157312	[PG-312]	P-3C	VP-65
157313	[LN-313]	P-3C	VP-45
157314	[314]	P-3C	VP-8
157315	[LC-315]	P-3C	VP-8
157316	[23]	EP-3E	VQ-2
157317		P-3C	VP-92
157318	[PR-318]	EP-3E	VQ-1
157319	[LD-319]	P-3C	VP-10
157321	[LK-321]	P-3C	VP-26
157322	[322]	P-3C	VP-46
157323	[PG-323]	P-3C	VP-65
157324	[PD-324]	P-3C	VP-9
157325	[25]	EP-3E	VQ-2
157326	[22]	EP-3E	VQ-2
157327	[LD-327]	P-3C	VP-10
157328	[LL-328]	P-3C	VP-30
157329	[329]	P-3C	VP-47
157330	[RC-330]	P-3C	VP-46
157331	[LL-331]	P-3C	VP-30
158204	[204]	P-3C	VX-20
158205	[YB-205]	P-3C	VP-1
158206		P-3C	VPU-1
158207	[LD-207]	P-3C	VP-10
158208	[YD-208]	P-3C	VP-4
158209	[YD-209]	P-3C	VP-4
158210		P-3C	VP-5
158211	[211]	P-3C	VP-40
158212	[212]	P-3C	VP-9
158214	[LL-214]	P-3C	VP-30
158215	[YD-215]	P-3C	VP-4
158216	[216]	P-3C	VP-46
158218	[RD-218]	P-3C	VP-47
158219	[LN-219]	P-3C	VP-45
158220	[YD-220]	P-3C	VP-4
158221	[221]	P-3C	VP-40
158222	[222]	P-3C	VP-9
158223	[223]	P-3C	VP-9
158224	[LD-224]	P-3C	VP-10
158225	[225]	P-3C	VP-47
158226	[PJ-226]	P-3C	VP-69
158227	[227]	NP-3D	NRL
158563	[LL-563]	P-3C	VP-30
158564	[564]	P-3C	VP-16
158565	[LD-565]	P-3C	VP-10
158566	[LA-566]	P-3C	VP-5
158567	[567]	P-3C	VP-16
158568	[568]	P-3C	VP-10
158569	[569]	P-3C	VP-8
158570	[JA]	P-3C	VX-1
158571	[LC-571]	P-3C	VP-8
158572	[LA-572]	P-3C	VP-5
158573	[LC-573]	P-3C	VP-8
158574		P-3C	NASC-FS
158912	[912]	P-3C	VX-20
158913	[913]	P-3C	VP-40
158914	[914]	P-3C	VP-46
158915	[915]	P-3C	VP-46
158916	[LL-916]	P-3C	VP-30
158917	[LC-917]	P-3C	VP-8
158918	[RD-918]	P-3C	VP-47
158919	[LN-919]	P-3C	VP-45

Serial	Code	Type	Unit
158920		P-3C	VP-45
158921		P-3C	VP-47
158922	[PD-922]	P-3C	VP-9
158923	[923]	P-3C	VP-4
158924	[LN-924]	P-3C	VP-45
158925	[LK-925]	P-3C	VP-46
158926	[LD-926]	P-3C	VP-10
158927	[927]	P-3C	VP-16
158929	[LC-929]	P-3C	VP-8
158931		P-3C	VP-5
158932	[LF-932]	P-3C	VP-16
158933	[LF-933]	P-3C	VP-16
158934	[YB-934]	P-3C	VP-1
158935	[LL-935]	P-3C	VP-30
159318	[LA-318]	P-3C	VP-5
159319	[RD-319]	P-3C	VP-47
159320	[LD-320]	P-3C	VP-10
159321	[QE-321]	P-3C	VP-40
159322	[322]	P-3C	VP-26
159323	[RC-323]	P-3C	VP-46
159324	[YB-324]	P-3C	VP-1
159326	[326]	P-3C	VP-9
159327	[YD-327]	P-3C	VP-4
159328	[YB-328]	P-3C	VP-1
159329	[RD-329]	P-3C	VP-47
159503	[LN-503]	P-3C	VP-45
159504		P-3C	VPU-2
159506	[568]	P-3C	VPU-1
159507	[RD-507]	P-3C	VP-47
159512	[512]	P-3C	VP-5
159513	[LL-513]	P-3C	VP-30
159514	[LL-514]	P-3C	VP-30
159884	[LD-884]	P-3C	VP-10
159885	[PD-885]	P-3C	VP-9
159886	[09]	P-3C	VQ-2
159887		P-3C	NASC-FS
159889	[04]	P-3C	VX-1
159891	[LN-891]	P-3C	VP-45
159894	[LL-894]	P-3C	VP-30
160283	[RD-283]	P-3C	VP-47
160284	[LL-284]	P-3C	VP-30
160286	[LD-286]	P-3C	VP-10
160287	[LC-287]	P-3C	VP-8
160288		P-3C	NASC-FS
160290	[JA-04]	P-3C	VX-1
160291	[JA-05]	P-3C	VX-1
160292	[292]	P-3C	VPU-2
160293		P-3C	VP-4
160610	[RC-610]	P-3C	VP-46
160611	[LU-611]	P-3C	VP-64
160612	[YB-612]	P-3C	VP-1
160761	[RD-761]	P-3C	VP-47
160762		P-3C	VPU-2
160763	[LT-763]	P-3C	VP-62
160764	[764]	P-3C	NRL
160765	[765]	P-3C	VP-10
160766	[766]	P-3C	VPU-2
160767	[LV-767]	P-3C	VP-66
160768	[PR-51]	P-3C	VQ-1
160769	[LD-769]	P-3C	VP-10
160770	[770]	P-3C	VP-10
160999	[LL-999]	P-3C	VP-30
161000	[000]	P-3C	VQ-2
161001	[LU-001]	P-3C	VP-64
161002	[LF-002]	P-3C	VP-16
161003	[PD-003]	P-3C	VP-9
161004	[LK-004]	P-3C	VP-26
161005	[JA-07]	P-3C	VX-1
161006	[LD-006]	P-3C	VP-10
161007	[PZ-007]	P-3C	VP-94
161008	[LL-008]	P-3C	VP-30
161009		P-3C	VP-5
161010	[LL-010]	P-3C	VP-30
161011	[LK-011]	P-3C	VP-26
161012	[YD-012]	P-3C	VP-4
161013	[LT-013]	P-3C	VP-62
161014	[LV-014]	P-3C	VP-66
161121		P-3C	VP-5
161122	[226]	P-3C	VPU-1
161123	[LU-123]	P-3C	VP-64
161124	[LF-124]	P-3C	VP-16
161125	[LV-125]	P-3C	VP-66
161126	[PR-50]	P-3C	VQ-1
161127	[LU-127]	P-3C	VP-64
161128	[128]	P-3C	VP-5
161129	[LV-129]	P-3C	VP-66
161130	[PR-52]	P-3C	VQ-1
161131	[LU-131]	P-3C	VP-64
161132	[PD-132]	P-3C	VP-9
161329	[LU-329]	P-3C	VP-64
161330	[030]	P-3C	VP-46
161331	[LY-331]	P-3C	VP-92
161332	[PG-332]	P-3C	VP-65
161333	[PZ-333]	P-3C	VP-94
161334	[PZ-334]	P-3C	VP-94
161335	[PZ-335]	P-3C	VP-94
161336	[LY-336]	P-3C	VP-92
161337	[PZ-337]	P-3C	VP-94
161338	[338]	P-3C	VP-5
161339	[YD-339]	P-3C	VP-4
161340	[LF-340]	P-3C	VP-16
161404	[LL-404]	P-3C	VP-30
161405	[405]	P-3C	VP-40
161406		P-3C	VP-40
161407	[PG-407]	P-3C	VP-65
161408	[LV-408]	P-3C	VP-66
161409	[LV-409]	P-3C	VP-66
161411	[LL-411]	P-3C	VP-30
161412	[LU-412]	P-3C	VP-64
161413	[LL-413]	P-3C	VP-30
161414	[LA-414]	P-3C	VP-5
161415	[LL-415]	P-3C	VP-30
161585	[585]	P-3C	VPU-1
161586	[LL-586]	P-3C	VP-30
161587	[YD-587]	P-3C	VP-4
161588	[LL-588]	P-3C	VP-30
161589	[589]	P-3C	VP-9
161590	[LL-590]	P-3C	VP-30
161591	[PZ-591]	P-3C	VP-94
161592	[PZ-592]	P-3C	VP-94
161593	[LL-593]	P-3C	VP-30
161594	[LL-594]	P-3C	VP-30
161595	[LV-595]	P-3C	VP-66
161596	[LL-596]	P-3C	VP-30
161763	[763]	P-3C	VP-47
161764	[YD-764]	P-3C	VP-4
161765	[PG-765]	P-3C	VP-65
161766	[PJ-766]	P-3C	VP-69
161767	[LV-767]	P-3C	VP-66
162314	[LY-314]	P-3C	VP-92
162315	[YB-315]	P-3C	VP-1
162316		P-3C	VP-45
162317	[YB-317]	P-3C	VP-1
162318	[PJ-318]	P-3C	VP-69
162770	[PJ-770]	P-3C	VP-69
162771	[YD-771]	P-3C	VP-4
162772	[YB-772]	P-3C	VP-1
162773	[773]	P-3C	VP-40
162774	[774]	P-3C	VX-20
162775	[775]	P-3C	VP-40
162776	[LA-776]	P-3C	VP-5
162777	[777]	P-3C	VP-9
162778	[LD-778]	P-3C	VP-10
162998	[RD-998]	P-3C	VP-47
162999	[PJ-999]	P-3C	VP-69
163000	[000]	P-3C	VP-45

163001	[LT-001]	P-3C	VP-62
163002	[LT-002]	P-3C	VP-62
163003	[PJ-003]	P-3C	VP-69
163004	[PG-004]	P-3C	VP-65
163005	[LT-005]	P-3C	VP-62
163006	[006]	P-3C	VP-45
163289	[LT-289]	P-3C	VP-62
163290	[PJ-290]	P-3C	VP-69
163291	[PG-291]	P-3C	VP-65
163292	[LF-292]	P-3C	VP-16
163293	[LF-293]	P-3C	VP-16
163294	[LY-294]	P-3C	VP-92
163295	[LY-295]	P-3C	VP-92

Boeing E-6 Mercury
Boeing, McConnell AFB, Kansas;
VQ-3 & VQ-4, SCW-1, Tinker AFB, Oklahoma

162782	E-6B	VQ-3
162783	E-6B	VQ-3
162784	E-6B	VQ-3
163918	E-6B	VQ-3
163919	E-6B	VQ-3
163920	E-6B	VQ-3
164386	E-6A	VQ-3
164387	E-6B	VQ-3
164388	E-6A	VQ-4
164404	E-6B	VQ-4
164405	E-6A	VQ-4
164406	E-6B	VQ-3
164407	E-6A	VQ-4
164408	E-6B	VQ-4
164409	E-6B	VQ-4
164410	E-6A	VQ-4

McDonnell Douglas C-9B Skytrain II/DC-9-32*
VMR-1, Cherry Point MCAS, North Carolina;
VR-46, Atlanta, Georgia [JS];
VR-52, Willow Grove NAS, Pennsylvania [JT];
VR-56, Norfolk NAS, Virginia [JU];
VR-57, North Island NAS, California [RX];
VR-61, Whidbey Island NAS, Washington [RS];

159113	[RX]	VR-57
159114	[RX]	VR-57
159115	[RX]	VR-57
159116	[RX]	VR-57
159117	[JU]	VR-56
159118	[JU]	VR-56
159119	[JU]	VR-56
159120	[JU]	VR-56
160046		VMR-1
160047		VMR-1
160048	[JT]	VR-52
160049	[JT]	VR-52
160050	[JT]	VR-52
160051	[JT]	VR-52
161266	[JS]	VR-46
161529	[JS]	VR-46
161530	[JS]	VR-46
162753	[JT]	VR-52
162754	[RS]	VR-61
163036*	[JS]	VR-46
163513*	[JU]	VR-56
164605*	[RS]	VR-61
164606*	[RS]	VR-61
164607*	[RS]	VR-61
164608*	[RS]	VR-61

Grumman C-20D Gulfstream III/
C-20G Gulfstream IV*
VR-1, NAF Washington, Maryland;
VR-48, NAF Washington, Maryland [JR];
VR-51, MCBH Kaneohe Bay, Hawaii [RG]

163691		VR-1
163692		VR-1
165093*	[JR]	VR-48
165094*	[JR]	VR-48
165151*	[RG]	VR-51
165152*	[RG]	VR-51
165153*		VR-1

Gulfstream Aerospace C-37A Gulfstream V
VR-1, NAF Washington, Maryland;

166375		VR-1
166376		
166377		
166378		
166379		

Boeing C-40A Clipper
VR-58, Jacksonville NAS, Florida [JV];
VR-59, NAS Fort Worth JRB, Texas [RY]

165829	[JV]	VR-58
165830	[RY]	VR-59
165831	[RY]	VR-59
165832	[JV]	VR-58
165833	[RY]	VR-59
165834	[JV]	VR-58
165835		Boeing
165836		Boeing

Lockheed C-130 Hercules
NAWC-AD, NAS Patuxent River, Maryland;
VR-53, NAF Washington, Maryland [AX];
VR-54, New Orleans, Louisiana [CW];
VR-55, NAS Point Mugu, California [RU];
VR-62, Brunswick NAS, Maine [JW];
VMGR-152, Futenma MCAS, Japan [QD];
VMGR-234, NAS Fort Worth, Texas [QH];
VMGR-252, Cherry Point MCAS,
   North Carolina [BH];
VMGRT-253, Cherry Point MCAS,
   North Carolina [GR];
VMGR-352, MCAS Miramar, California [QB];
VMGR-452, Stewart Field, New York [NY]

147572	[QB]	KC-130F	VMGR-352
147573	[QD]	KC-130F	VMGR-152
148246	[GR]	KC-130F	VMGRT-253
148247	[QD]	KC-130F	VMGR-152
148248	[QD]	KC-130F	VMGR-152
148249	[GR]	KC-130F	VMGRT-253
148891	[BH]	KC-130F	VMGR-252
148893	[QD]	KC-130F	VMGR-152
148894	[GR]	KC-130F	VMGRT-253
148896	[BH]	KC-130F	VMGR-252
148897	[BH]	KC-130F	VMGR-252
148898	[BH]	KC-130F	VMGR-252
148899	[BH]	KC-130F	VMGR-252
149788	[BH]	KC-130F	VMGR-252
149789	[BH]	KC-130F	VMGR-252
149791	[QB]	KC-130F	VMGR-352
149792	[QB]	KC-130F	VMGR-352
149795	[QB]	KC-130F	VMGR-352
149796	[QB]	KC-130F	VMGR-352
149798	[QB]	KC-130F	VMGR-352
149799	[QD]	KC-130F	VMGR-152
149800	[QB]	KC-130F	VMGR-352
149803	[GR]	KC-130F	VMGRT-253
149806		KC-130F	NAWC-AD
149807	[QD]	KC-130F	VMGR-152
149808	[BH]	KC-130F	VMGR-252
149811	[BH]	KC-130F	VMGR-252
149812	[QD]	KC-130F	VMGR-152
149815	[QB]	KC-130F	VMGR-352
149816	[QD]	KC-130F	VMGR-152
150684	[GR]	KC-130F	VMGRT-253
150686	[BH]	KC-130F	VMGR-252

USN/USMC

150688	[GR]	KC-130F	VMGRT-253		164763		C-130T	*Blue Angels*
150689	[QB]	KC-130F	VMGR-352		164993	[CW]	C-130T	VR-54
150690	[QD]	KC-130F	VMGR-152		164994	[WV]	C-130T	VR-53
160013	[QD]	KC-130R	VMGR-152		164995	[CW]	C-130T	VR-54
160014	[QD]	KC-130R	VMGR-152		164996	[WV]	C-130T	VR-53
160015	[QB]	KC-130R	VMGR-352		164997	[WV]	C-130T	VR-53
160016	[QB]	KC-130R	VMGR-352		164998	[WV]	C-130T	VR-53
160017	[QB]	KC-130R	VMGR-352		164999	[QH]	KC-130T	VMGR-234
160018	[QD]	KC-130R	VMGR-152		165000	[QH]	KC-130T	VMGR-234
160019	[QD]	KC-130R	VMGR-152		165158	[CW]	C-130T	VR-54
160020	[QD]	KC-130R	VMGR-152		165159	[CW]	C-130T	VR-54
160022	[QB]	KC-130R	VMGR-352		165160	[CW]	C-130T	VR-54
160240	[QB]	KC-130R	VMGR-352		165161	[RU]	C-130T	VR-55
160625	[BH]	KC-130R	VMGR-252		165162	[QH]	KC-130T	VMGR-234
160626	[BH]	KC-130R	VMGR-252		165163	[QH]	KC-130T	VMGR-234
160627	[BH]	KC-130R	VMGR-252		165313	[JW]	C-130T	VR-62
160628	[BH]	KC-130R	VMGR-252		165314	[JW]	C-130T	VR-62
162308	[QH]	KC-130T	VMGR-234		165315	[NY]	KC-130T	VMGR-452
162309	[QH]	KC-130T	VMGR-234		165316	[NY]	KC-130T	VMGR-452
162310	[QH]	KC-130T	VMGR-234		165348	[JW]	C-130T	VR-62
162311	[QH]	KC-130T	VMGR-234		165349	[JW]	C-130T	VR-62
162785	[QH]	KC-130T	VMGR-234		165350	[RU]	C-130T	VR-55
162786	[QH]	KC-130T	VMGR-234		165351	[RU]	C-130T	VR-55
163022	[QH]	KC-130T	VMGR-234		165352	[NY]	KC-130T	VMGR-452
163023	[QH]	KC-130T	VMGR-234		165353	[NY]	KC-130T	VMGR-452
163310	[QH]	KC-130T	VMGR-234		165378	[RU]	C-130T	VR-55
163311	[NY]	KC-130T	VMGR-452		165379	[RU]	C-130T	VR-55
163591	[NY]	KC-130T	VMGR-452		165735	[BH]	KC-130J	VMGR-252
163592	[NY]	KC-130T	VMGR-452		165736	[BH]	KC-130J	VMGR-252
164105	[NY]	KC-130T	VMGR-452		165737	[GR]	KC-130J	VMGRT-253
164106	[NY]	KC-130T	VMGR-452		165738	[BH]	KC-130J	VMGR-252
164180	[NY]	KC-130T	VMGR-452		165739	[BH]	KC-130J	VMGR-252
164181	[NY]	KC-130T	VMGR-452		165809	[BH]	KC-130J	VMGR-252
164441	[NY]	KC-130T	VMGR-452		165810	[BH]	KC-130J	VMGR-252
164442	[NY]	KC-130T	VMGR-452		165957	[BH]	KC-130J	VMGR-252
164597	[NY]	KC-130T-30	VMGR-452		166380	[BH]	KC-130J	VMGR-252
164598	[QH]	KC-130T-30	VMGR-234		166381		KC-130J	
164762		C-130T	NAWC-AD		166382		KC-130J	

US-based US Coast Guard Aircraft

Gulfstream Aerospace C-37A Gulfstream V
USCG, Washington DC
01

Grumman Gulfstream IV
USCG, Washington DC
02

Lockheed HC-130H Hercules
USCGS Barbers Point, Hawaii;
USCGS Clearwater, Florida;
USCGS Elizabeth City, North Carolina;
USCGS Kodiak, Alaska;
USCGS Sacramento, California

1500	Elizabeth City
1501	Elizabeth City
1502	Clearwater
1503	Elizabeth City
1504	Elizabeth City
1603	Elizabeth City
1700	Sacramento
1701	Clearwater
1702	Kodiak
1703	Barbers Point
1704	Sacramento
1705	Barbers Point
1706	Clearwater
1707	Kodiak
1708	Clearwater
1709	Kodiak
1710	Kodiak
1711	Clearwater
1712	Elizabeth City
1713	Clearwater
1714	Barbers Point
1715	Kodiak
1716	Sacramento
1717	Kodiak
1718	Clearwater
1719	Clearwater
1720	Clearwater
1790	Sacramento

Aircraft in US Government or Military Services with Civil Registrations

BAe 125-800A (C-29A)
Federal Aviation Administration, Oklahoma
N94	(88-0269)
N95	(88-0270)
N96	(88-0271)
N97	(88-0272)
N98	(88-0273)
N99	(88-0274)

Gates LearJet 35A
Phoenix Aviation/Flight International/
US Navy, Naples
N20DK
N50FN
N88JA
N118FN
N710GS

Military Aviation Sites on the Internet

The list below is not intended to be a complete list of military aviation sites on the Internet. The sites listed cover Museums, Locations, Air Forces, Companies and Organisations that are mentioned elsewhere in 'Military Aircraft Markings'. Sites listed are in English or contain sufficient English to be reasonably easily understood. Each site address is believed to be correct at the time of going to press. Additions are welcome, via the usual address found at the front of the book, or via e-mail to hjcurtis@ntlworld.com.

Name of site	Internet Dial (all prefixed 'http://')
No 2 Sqn	www.rafmarham.co.uk/organisation/2squadron/2squadron.htm
No 4 Regiment Army Air Corps	www.4regimentaac.co.uk/
No 5 Sqn	www.5squadron.fsnet.co.uk/
No 6 Flt	www.shawbury.raf.mod.uk/6fltaac.htm
No 6 Sqn	www.raf.mod.uk/rafcoltishall/squadrons/6Sqn.htm
No 8 Sqn	www.users.globalnet.co.uk/~8sqnwad/
No 9 Sqn	www.rafmarham.co.uk/organisation/9squadron/9sqn_front.htm
No 13 Sqn	www.rafmarham.co.uk/organisation/13squadron/13squadron.htm
No 15 Sqn	www.xvsquadron.co.uk/
No 16(R) Sqn	www.raf.mod.uk/rafcoltishall/squadrons/16Sqn.htm
No 20(R) Sqn	www.raf.mod.uk/rafwittering/sqn20.htm
No 23 Sqn	www.users.globalnet.co.uk/~23sqnwad/
No 31 Sqn	www.rafmarham.co.uk/organisation/31squadron/31sqn.htm
No 39(1 PRU) Sqn	www.rafmarham.co.uk/organisation/39squadron/39squadron2.htm
No 41 Sqn	www.raf.mod.uk/rafcoltishall/squadrons/41Sqn.htm
No 42(R) Sqn	www.kinloss.raf.mod.uk/opswing/ops42r.htm
No 45(R) Sqn	www.cranwell.raf.mod.uk/3fts/45sqn/45sqn.htm
No 54 Sqn	www.raf.mod.uk/rafcoltishall/squadrons/54Sqn.htm
No 55(R) Sqn	www.cranwell.raf.mod.uk/3fts/55sqn/55sqn.htm
No 56 Sqn	www.56firebirds.raf.mod.uk/
No 120 Sqn	www.kinloss.raf.mod.uk/opswing/ops120.htm
No 201 Sqn	www.kinloss.raf.mod.uk/opswing/ops201.htm
No 206 Sqn	www.kinloss.raf.mod.uk/opswing/ops206.htm
Aberdeen, Dundee and St Andrews UAS	dialspace.dial.pipex.com/town/way/gba87/adstauas/
The Army Air Corps	www.army.mod.uk/armyaircorps/index.htm
Blue Eagles Home Page	www.deltaweb.co.uk/eagles/
Defence Helicopter Flying School	www.shawbury.raf.mod.uk/dhfs.htm
Liverpool University Air Squadron	www.sn63.dial.pipex.com/
Manchester & Salford Universities Air Sqn	www.masuas.dial.pipex.com/
Ministry of Defence	www.mod.uk/
Oxford University Air Sqn	users.ox.ac.uk/~ouairsqn/
QinetiQ	www.qinetiq.com/
RAF Benson	www.raf.mod.uk/rafbenson/index.htm
RAF Church Fenton (unofficial)	www.rafchurchfenton.org.uk/
RAF College Cranwell	www.cranwell.raf.mod.uk/
RAF Cosford	www.raf.mod.uk/cosford/
RAF Kinloss	www.kinloss.raf.mod.uk/
RAF Leuchars	www.leuchars.raf.mod.uk/
RAF Lossiemouth	www.raf.mod.uk/raflossiemouth/
RAF Lyneham	www.lyneham.raf.mod.uk/
RAF Marham	www.rafmarham.co.uk/
RAF Northolt	www.northolt.com/
RAF Northolt (unofficial)	www.fly.to/Northolt/
RAF Odiham	www.rafodiham.co.uk/
RAF St Athan	ourworld.compuserve.com/homepages/st_athan/
RAF Shawbury	www.shawbury.raf.mod.uk/
RAF Valley	www.rafvalley.org/
RAF Waddington	www.raf-waddington.com/
RAF Wittering	www.raf.mod.uk/rafwittering/
Red Arrows	www.raf.mod.uk/reds/redhome.html
Royal Air Force	www.raf.mod.uk/
Royal Auxiliary Air Force	www.rauxaf.mod.uk/
SAOEU	www.saoeu.org/
Universities of Glasgow & Strathclyde Air Squadron	www.ugsas.fsnet.co.uk/

Military Aviation Internet

Name of site	Internet Dial (all prefixed 'http://')
The University of Birmingham Air Squadron	www.sn61.dial.pipex.com/
University of London Air Sqn	www.raf.mod.uk/ulas

MILITARY SITES – US

Air Combat Command	www.acc.af.mil/
Air Force Flight Test Center (Edwards AFB)	www.edwards.af.mil/
Air Force Reserve Command	www.afrc.af.mil/
Air National Guard	www.ang.af.mil/
AMARC – up to date list of aircraft	www.dm.af.mil/amarc/inventory.htm
Aviano Air Base	www.aviano.af.mil/
Holloman Air Force Base	www.holloman.af.mil/
Hurricane Hunters Home Page (53rd WRS)	www.hurricanehunters.com/
Liberty Wing Home Page (48th FW)	www.lakenheath.af.mil/
NASA	www.nasa.gov/
Nellis Air Force Base	www.nellis.af.mil/
Spangdahlem Air Base	www.spangdahlem.af.mil/
Travis Air Force Base	www.travis.af.mil/
The Thunderbirds	www.nellis.af.mil/thunderbirds/
USAF	www.af.mil/
USAF Europe	www.usafe.af.mil/
USAF World Wide Web Sites	www.af.mil/sites/
US Army	www.army.mil/
US Marine Corps	www.usmc.mil/
US Navy	www.navy.mil/
US Navy Patrol Squadrons (unofficial)	www.vpnavy.com/
Whiteman Air Force Base	www.whiteman.af.mil/

MILITARY SITES – ELSEWHERE

301 Sqn KLu	www.301sqn.com/
315 Sqn KLu	www.315sqn.nl/
322 Sqn KLu	www.322squadron.nl/
323 Sqn KLu	www.323squadron.nl/
334 Sqn KLu	www.334squadron.nl/
Armée de l'Air	www.defense.gouv.fr/air/
Armée de l'Air (unofficial)	www.mygale.org/06/airmil/index.shtml
Aeronautica Militare	www.aeronautica.difesa.it
Austrian Armed Forces (in German)	www.bmlv.gv.at/
Belgian Air Force	www.mil.be/baf/eng/index_e.htm
East European Air Forces (unofficial)	mm.iit.uni-miskolc.hu/Data/Winx/
Finnish Defence Force	www.mil.fi/english/
Forca Aerea Portuguesa	www.emfa.pt/
Frecce Tricolori	users.iol.it/gromeo/
German Marine	www.bundeswehr.de/bundeswehr/marine/index.html
Indian Air Force	www.bharat-rakshak.com/IAF/
Israeli Defence Force/Air Force	www.idf.il/
Japan Air Self Defence Force	www.jda.go.jp/jasdf/indexe.htm
Luftforsvaret	www.mil.no/luftforsvaret/
Luftwaffe	www.bundeswehr.de/bundeswehr/luftwaffe/index.html
NATO	www.nato.int/
Royal Australian Air Force	www.adfa.oz.au/DOD/RAAF/
Royal Danish Air Force (in Danish)	www.ftk.dk/
Royal Netherlands AF	www.mindef.nl/english/rnlaf1.htm
Royal New Zealand AF	www.airforce.mil.nz/
Royal Thai Air Force	www.rtaf.mi.th
Singapore Air Force	www.mindef.gov.sg/rsaf/
South African AF Site (unofficial)	www.geocities.com/dwingrin/saaf.htm
Spanish Air Force	www.aire.org/
Swedish Air Force	www2.mil.se/
Swedish Military Aviation (unofficial)	www.canit.se/%7Egriffon/aviation/
Swiss Armed Forces	www.vbs.admin.ch/internet/e/armee/
Turkish General Staff (Armed Forces)	www.tsk.mil.tr/

AIRCRAFT & AERO ENGINE MANUFACTURERS

BAE Systems	www.baesystems.com/
Bell Helicopter Textron	www.bellhelicopter.textron.com/index.html
Boeing	www.boeing.com/
Bombardier	www.bombardier.com/
Britten-Norman	www.britten-norman.com/
CFM International	www.cfm56.com/
Dassault	www.dassault-aviation.com/
EADS	www.eads.net/
Embraer	www.embraer.com/

Name of site	Internet Dial (all prefixed 'http://')
Fairchild Dornier	www.fairchilddornier.com/
Fokker	www.fokker.com/
General Electric	www.ge.com/
Gulfstream Aerospace	www.gulfstream.com/
Kaman Aerospace	www.kaman.com/
LET	www.let.cz/
Lockheed Martin	www.lockheedmartin.com/
Lockheed Martin Aeronautics	www.lmaeronautics.com/palmdale/index.html
Raytheon	www.raytheon.com/rac/
Rolls-Royce	www.rolls-royce.com/
SAAB	www.saab.se/
Sikorsky	www.sikorsky.com/
Westland	www.gkn-whl.co.uk/

UK AVIATION MUSEUMS

Aviation Museums in Great Britain	www.rdg.ac.uk/AcaDepts/sn/wsn1/dept/av/gb.html
Bournemouth Aviation Museum	www.aviation-museum.co.uk/
Brooklands Museum	www.motor-software.co.uk/brooklands/
City of Norwich Aviation Museum	www.cnam.co.uk/
de Havilland Aircraft Heritage Centre	www.hertsmuseums.org.uk/dehavilland/index.htm
Flambards Village Theme Park	www.flambards.co.uk/
Gatwick Aviation Museum	www.gatwick-aviation-museum.co.uk/
The Helicopter Museum	www.helicoptermuseum.co.uk/
Imperial War Museum, Duxford	www.iwm.org.uk/duxford/
Imperial War Museum, Duxford (unofficial)	dspace.dial.pipex.com/town/square/rcy85/
The Jet Age Museum	www.jetagemuseum.org/
Lincs Aviation Heritage Centre	freespace.virgin.net/nick.tasker/ekirkby.htm
Midland Air Museum	www.midlandairmuseum.org.uk/
Museum of Berkshire Aviation	fly.to/MuseumofBerkshireAviation/
Museum of Flight, East Fortune	www.nms.ac.uk/flight/main.htm
Museum of Science & Industry, Manchester	www.msim.org.uk/
Newark Air Museum	www.newarkairmuseum.co.uk/
North East Aircraft Museum	members.tripod.com/~BDaugherty/neam.html
RAF Manston Spitfire & Hurricane Memorial	www.spitfire-museum.com/
RAF Museum, Hendon	www.rafmuseum.org.uk/
Science Museum, South Kensington	www.sciencemuseum.org.uk/
Yorkshire Air Museum, Elvington	www.yorkshireairmuseum.co.uk

AVIATION SOCIETIES

Air Britain	www.air-britain.com/
Air North	www.airnorth.demon.co.uk/
Cleveland Aviation Society	homepage.ntlworld.com/phillip.charlton/cashome.html
East London Aviation Society	www.westrowops.co.uk/newsletter/elas.htm
Friends of Leeming Aviation Group	www.crakehal.demon.co.uk/aviation/flag.htm
Gilze-Rijen Aviation Society	www.gras-spotters.nl/
Royal Aeronautical Society	www.raes.org.uk/
St Athan Aviation Group	www.westrowops.co.uk/newsletter/stamu.htm
Scramble (Dutch Aviation Society)	www.scramble.nl/
Solent Aviation Society	www.solent-aviation-society.co.uk/
Spitfire Society	www.spitfiresociety.demon.co.uk/
Ulster Aviation Society	www.d-n-a.net/users/dnetrAzQ/

OPERATORS OF HISTORIC AIRCRAFT

Battle of Britain Memorial Flight	www.bbmf.co.uk/
Catalina Online	www.catalina.org.uk/
Delta Jets	www.deltajets.ik.com/
Hunter Flying Club	www.hunterflyingclub.co.uk/
Kennet Aircraft	www.airplane.demon.co.uk/
Old Flying Machine Company	www.ofmc.co.uk/
The Fighter Collection	www.fighter-collection.com/
The Real Aeroplane Company	www.realaero.com/
The Vulcan Operating Company	www.tvoc.co.uk/

SITES RELATING TO SPECIFIC TYPES OF MILITARY AIRCRAFT

The 655 Maintenance & Preservation Society	www.jetman.dircon.co.uk/xm655/
The Avro Shackleton Page	www.home.aone.net.au/shack_one/
B-24 Liberator	www.b24bestweb.com/
Buccaneer Supporter's Club	www.buccaneerclub.co.uk/
EE Canberra	www.netcomuk.co.uk/~lesb/canberra.html
English Electric Lightning - Vertical Reality	www.aviation-picture-hangar.co.uk/Lightning.html
The Eurofighter site	www.eurofighter.org/

Military Aviation Internet

Name of site	Internet Dial (all prefixed 'http://')
The ex FRADU Canberra Site	www.fradu-hunters.co.uk/canberra/
The ex FRADU Hunter Site	www.fradu-hunters.co.uk/
F-4 Phantom II Society	www.f4phantom.org/
F-16: The Complete Reference	www.f-16.net/
F-86 Web Page	f-86.tripod.com/
F-105 Thunderchief	www.geocities.com/Pentagon/7002/
The Gripen	www.gripen.com/
International F-104 Society	home.hetnet.nl/~hluijkx/ifs/ifs.html
K5083 – Home Page (Hawker Hurricane)	www3.mistral.co.uk/k5083/
Lockheed C-130 Hercules	hometown.aol.com/SamC130/
Lockheed SR-71 Blackbird	www.wvi.com/~lelandh/sr-71~1.htm
The MiG-21 Page	www.topedge.com/panels/aircraft/sites/kraft/mig.htm
P-3 Orion Research Group	home.wxs.nl/~p3orin/
P-51 Mustang	www.p51mustang.com/
Scramble on the Web – SAAB Viggen Database	www.scramble.nl/viggen.htm
Swiss F-18 Hornet site (unofficial)	www.geocities.com/CapeCanaveral/Lab/6063/
Thunder & Lightnings (Postwar British Aircraft)	www.thunder-and-lightnings.co.uk/
Vulcan 558 Club	www.vulcan558club.demon.co.uk/
Vulcan Restoration Trust	www.XL426.com

MISCELLANEOUS

Aerodata	dspace.dial.pipex.com/aerodata/
Aeroflight	www.netlink.co.uk/users/aeroflt/
The 'AirNet' Web Site	fly.to/AirNet/
Air-Scene UK	www.f4aviation.co.uk
AirSpeed	www.netmontage.co.uk/airspeed/
Chinese Military Aviation	www.concentric.net/~Jetflight/
David Hastings' Military Aviation Page	users.ox.ac.uk/~daveh/Military/
Dutch Spotters On-line	www.dutchspotters.com/
Military Aircraft Database	www.csd.uwo.ca/~pettypi/elevon/gustin_military/
Military Aviation	www.crakehal.demon.co.uk/aviation/aviation.htm
Military Aviation Review/MAP	www.mar.co.uk/
Polish Aviation Site	aviation.pol.pl/
Russian Aviation Page	aeroweb.lucia.it/~agretch/RAP.html
Scramble on the Web – Air Show Reports	www.scramble.nl/airshows.htm
The Spotter's Nest	www.spotters.it/
UK Military Aircraft Serials Resource Centre	www.serials.uk.com/
UK Military Spotting	www.thunder-and-lightnings.co.uk/spotting

C-5A Galaxy 90010 flown by the 60th AMW at Travis AFB, California. *PRM*